CALCULUS
of
VECTOR FUNCTIONS

by R. H. CROWELL
and R. E. WILLIAMSON

WRITTEN with clarity and mathematical precision this book presents an introduction to the calculus of functions of several variables from the viewpoint of linear algebra.

The study permits a unification of techniques and formulas by treating the functions of several variables as vector-valued functions of a vector variable. It avoids duplication by dealing simultaneously with topics using the same ideas.

Successfully tested for two years at Dartmouth College, this volume:

- stresses geometric intuition in the analysis as well as the examples

- provides proofs of all the main theorems

- presents concepts through examples and exercises so that proofs may be skipped without loss of understanding

- defines the differential of a vector function at a point as the best approximating linear transformation at that point

- requires no particular style of calculus preparation and can be used to follow any standard course in one-variable calculus

- includes appendices giving proofs of the deeper calculus theorems and a

(Continued on back flap)

CALCULUS

OF

VECTOR FUNCTIONS

Calculus

of

Vector Functions

by

R. H. CROWELL *and* R. E. WILLIAMSON

Dartmouth College

with the assistance of
H. MIRKIL
Dartmouth College

Prentice-Hall, Inc., *Englewood Cliffs, N.J.*

Second printing...... June, 1965

Library of Congress Catalog Number 62–10553

Printed in the United States of America

11230C

Preface

This textbook was written to be used in teaching some topics in the theory of functions of several variables from the point of view of linear algebra. The first chapter, on vector geometry and linear algebra, is intended to be an introduction to those subjects as well as a preparation for the calculus chapters. Section 12 of Chapter 1 is not needed for the rest of the book. It is also possible to omit sections in the later chapters. For example, the section on quadratic polynomials can be left out. Altogether there is enough material in the book for a one-year course.

Prerequisite for the use of the book is the traditional content of a year's course in one-variable calculus. This material need not be covered in any particular way.

We are very grateful to Professors Kemeny, Mirkil, Snell and Thompson, the authors of *Finite Mathematical Structures*, as well as to the publishers, Prentice-Hall, Incorporated, for permission to use in our book their chapter on linear algebra. The calculus part of the present book has been used at Dartmouth College, in mimeographed form, following a course in which *Finite Mathematical Structures* was used as a text. Thus it was possible to make the algebra chapter and the rest of the book fit well together. We are particularly indebted to Hazleton Mirkil for his help in the revision of Chapter 1 and in writing the appendix on determinants.

We were fortunate in having the very able assistance of Mr. Chin-Yeang Lim in the final preparation of the manuscript. The book has been considerably improved by his suggestions as well as by those of many others of our colleagues and students, in particular, Mr. J. C. Owings, Jr. Mrs. Margaret P. Andrews and Mrs. Helen A. Hanchett typed the manuscript, and we thank them very much.

R.H.C.
R.E.W.

vii

Contents

CALCULUS

OF

VECTOR FUNCTIONS

1

Linear Algebra

1. MATRICES, COLUMN VECTORS, ROW VECTORS

A **matrix** is a rectangular array of numbers, such as

$$\begin{pmatrix} 0 & 5 \\ -1 & \frac{1}{2} \\ 0 & 4 \end{pmatrix}, \quad \begin{pmatrix} 1 & .7 & 3 \\ .9 & 0 & 2.8 \end{pmatrix}, \quad \begin{pmatrix} 1 & 0 \\ 0 & -1 \end{pmatrix}, \quad (\tfrac{1}{2} \ \ \tfrac{1}{3} \ \ \tfrac{1}{4}), \quad \begin{pmatrix} 2 \\ 1 \\ 5 \\ -9 \end{pmatrix}.$$

The horizontal lines of numbers in a matrix are called **rows** and the vertical lines of numbers are called **columns**. For instance, the first matrix

1

above has three rows, of which the first is $(0 \quad 5)$. And it has two columns, of which the first is

$$\begin{pmatrix} 0 \\ -1 \\ 0 \end{pmatrix}.$$

We say that this matrix is a "3-by-2" matrix, *always writing the number of rows before the number of columns*. The 1-by-n matrices are called n-**dimensional row vectors**, and the n-by-1 matrices are called n-**dimensional column vectors**. For instance, the fourth matrix above is a 3-dimensional row vector and the fifth matrix is a 4-dimensional column vector. An n-by-n matrix is said to be a **square** matrix. A 1-by-1 matrix is simply a number.

The number that appears in the ith row and jth column of a given matrix is called the ijth **component** (or **coordinate**) of that matrix. When we use letters to stand for the numbers in the matrix we will often use one fixed letter with appropriate numerical subscripts. Thus we write

$$A = \begin{pmatrix} a_{11} & a_{12} & a_{13} & a_{14} \\ a_{21} & a_{22} & a_{23} & a_{24} \\ a_{31} & a_{32} & a_{33} & a_{34} \end{pmatrix}, \text{ or } A = (a_{ij}) \text{ where } \begin{aligned} i &= 1, 2, 3, \\ j &= 1, 2, 3, 4. \end{aligned}$$

Observe that the first subscript is the row index and the second is the column index.

In general we will use capital letters A or B or C for matrices, with corresponding small letters a_{ij} or b_{ij} or c_{ij} for their respective components. For row vectors, however, we will use E or F or G or H and corresponding small letters e_i or f_i or g_i or h_i for their respective components. For instance,

$$F = (f_1 \quad f_2 \quad f_3).$$

And for column vectors we will use W or X or Y or Z. For instance,

$$X = \begin{pmatrix} x_1 \\ x_2 \\ x_3 \\ x_4 \end{pmatrix}.$$

We write $A = B$ only when the matrices have the same shape (i.e., if A is m-by-n, then so is B) and when corresponding components are identical (i.e., $a_{ij} = b_{ij}$ for each possible i, j).

When A and B have the same shape, we can form a new matrix $A + B$

by adding **corresponding components**. For instance,

$$\begin{pmatrix} 2 & 3 \\ -2 & \frac{1}{2} \\ 0 & 4 \end{pmatrix} + \begin{pmatrix} 1 & -1 \\ 2 & \frac{3}{2} \\ 0 & 0 \end{pmatrix} = \begin{pmatrix} 3 & 2 \\ 0 & 2 \\ 0 & 4 \end{pmatrix}.$$

When A and B do not have the same shape, the operation of addition is not defined. In particular, the sum of two row vectors (or of two column vectors) is defined only when they have the same dimension.

When c is a number and A is a matrix we define a new matrix cA, called a **numerical multiple** of A, whose shape is the same as that of A and each of whose components is c times the corresponding component of A. For instance,

$$2 \begin{pmatrix} 3 & 4 \\ 5 & 6 \end{pmatrix} = \begin{pmatrix} 6 & 8 \\ 10 & 12 \end{pmatrix}$$

$$-3 \begin{pmatrix} -1 \\ 0 \end{pmatrix} = \begin{pmatrix} 3 \\ 0 \end{pmatrix}$$

And we use the notation $-A$ as an abbreviation for $(-1)A$. For instance,

$$-\begin{pmatrix} -1 \\ 0 \\ \frac{3}{2} \end{pmatrix} = \begin{pmatrix} 1 \\ 0 \\ -\frac{3}{2} \end{pmatrix}$$

$$-\begin{pmatrix} 1 & 2 \\ 3 & 4 \end{pmatrix} = \begin{pmatrix} -1 & -2 \\ -3 & -4 \end{pmatrix}.$$

We shall often use the symbol O for a matrix all of whose components are zeros, though in a context in which the meaning is quite clear we shall sometimes just use the symbol 0 for such a matrix. To be completely clear we should perhaps append a subscript to specify the shape of the matrix. For instance,

$$O_{2\times3} = \begin{pmatrix} 0 & 0 & 0 \\ 0 & 0 & 0 \end{pmatrix} \qquad O_{1\times3} = (0 \ \ 0 \ \ 0) \qquad O_{3\times1} = \begin{pmatrix} 0 \\ 0 \\ 0 \end{pmatrix}.$$

But in actual computation no confusion results from using the same symbol O for all of these, since we can tell from context which particular shape the matrix must have.

The first obvious advantage of the matrix notation is that we can manipulate a whole collection of numbers as if it were a single mathematical quantity, and hence can state complicated relationships in a simple manner. The second major reason for introducing vectors is that they have an important geometric interpretation. From analytic geometry you are familiar with the fact that points in the plane can be represented as number-couples, and hence, if we wish, as 2-dimensional column vectors. This representation is usually carried out by means of a **cartesian coordinate system**, that is, by drawing a horizontal axis and a perpendicular axis, and choosing the same unit of length on each. We assign to each point X the column vector

$$\begin{pmatrix} x_1 \\ x_2 \end{pmatrix}$$

whose first component x_1 is the perpendicular distance of X from the vertical axis (or the negative of that distance if X lies to the left of the vertical axis), and whose second component x_2 is the perpendicular distance of X from the horizontal axis (or the negative of that distance if X lies below the horizontal axis).

Thus, for instance, to find the first coordinate of the point X pictured in Figure 1 we draw a horizontal line segment from X to the vertical axis

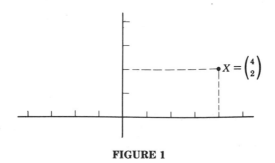

FIGURE 1

and measure the length of this segment. Although the segment is drawn *perpendicular* to the vertical axis, it is also drawn *parallel* to the horizontal axis; and we will see below that the latter way of looking at it is in general more useful.

Let us now describe a more general kind of coordinate system, called an **oblique coordinate system**. To set up such a system we draw any two intersecting lines as axes, labeling one the "first axis" and the other the "second axis," and choose perhaps different units on them. In choosing the units on a given axis we choose one end of the axis as the plus end and the other end as the minus end. Now given a point X, we draw line segments from X parallel to each axis, and then measure the length of each segment in the appropriate scale, prefixing a minus sign to that length when it is appropriate. The 2-dimensional column vector corresponding to the point X has, for instance, as its first component the length (plus or minus) that was measured parallel to the first axis. See Figures 2 and 3.

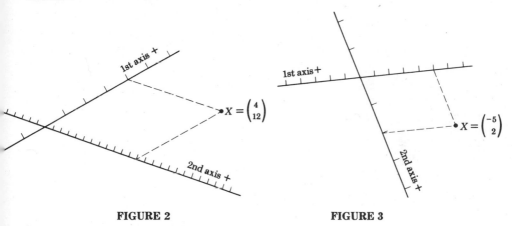

FIGURE 2   **FIGURE 3**

Standard graph paper, which covers the plane with squares, is meant to be used for a cartesian coordinate system. The appropriate graph paper for an oblique coordinate system covers the plane with parallelograms. See Figure 4.

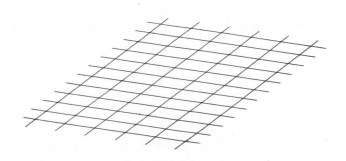

FIGURE 4

It is often useful to think of a geometric vector as not simply a point $\begin{pmatrix} x_1 \\ x_2 \end{pmatrix}$ in the plane but rather as an arrow from the origin $\begin{pmatrix} 0 \\ 0 \end{pmatrix}$ to the point $\begin{pmatrix} x_1 \\ x_2 \end{pmatrix}$. The most important fact about geometric vectors, a fact we will explain and verify in later sections of this chapter, is that addition and numerical multiplication have a direct geometric interpretation, independent of the coordinate system. If you have taken a course in physics, you are already familiar with this interpretation. Otherwise you may infer the geometric interpretation by looking closely at Exercises 27–31.

We will now define a multiplication for vectors and matrices. Let F be a row vector and X a column vector *of the same dimension*. Then we define the **inner product** FX to be $f_1x_1 + f_2x_2 + \ldots + f_nx_n$. Notice that we always write the row vector on the left and the column vector on the right. And notice that the result is not a vector but an ordinary number. Here are some numerical examples.

$$(1 \quad 2) \begin{pmatrix} -4 \\ 2 \end{pmatrix} = 1 \cdot (-4) + 2 \cdot 2 = 0$$

$$(1 \quad 2 \quad 3 \quad 4 \quad 5) \begin{pmatrix} \frac{1}{5} \\ \frac{1}{5} \\ \frac{1}{5} \\ \frac{1}{5} \\ \frac{1}{5} \end{pmatrix} = 1 \cdot \frac{1}{5} + 2 \cdot \frac{1}{5} + 3 \cdot \frac{1}{5} + 4 \cdot \frac{1}{5} + 5 \cdot \frac{1}{5} = 3.$$

The first product shows that it is possible for FX to be 0 even though $F \neq O$ and $X \neq O$.

By using inner products of rows and columns we can define a useful notion of multiplication of matrices. The product AB is defined only when there are exactly as many columns in A as there are rows in B, in other words, only when the dimension of each row in A equals the dimension of each column in B. Thus, if A is m-by-k, then B must be k-by-n. (It may well happen that AB makes sense and yet BA does not make sense; for instance when A is a 2-by-2 matrix, and X is a 2-dimensional column vector, then AX always is defined, and XA never.) The result of the multiplication AB is defined to be a certain m-by-n matrix C, whose ijth component c_{ij} is the inner product of the ith row of A by the jth column of B. Here is a numerical example:

$$\begin{pmatrix} 3 & 1 & 4 \\ 2 & 0 & 5 \end{pmatrix} \begin{pmatrix} 1 & 3 & 0 & 0 \\ 1 & 1 & 0 & 0 \\ 0 & 0 & 1 & 1 \end{pmatrix}$$

$$= \begin{pmatrix} 3\cdot1+1\cdot1+4\cdot0 & 3\cdot3+1\cdot1+4\cdot0 & 3\cdot0+1\cdot0+4\cdot1 & 3\cdot0+1\cdot0+4\cdot1 \\ 2\cdot1+0\cdot1+5\cdot0 & 2\cdot3+0\cdot1+5\cdot0 & 2\cdot0+0\cdot0+5\cdot1 & 2\cdot0+0\cdot0+5\cdot1 \end{pmatrix}$$

$$= \begin{pmatrix} 4 & 10 & 4 & 4 \\ 2 & 6 & 5 & 5 \end{pmatrix}$$

Notice the following two special cases: m-dimensional row vector times m-by-n matrix:

$$(3 \quad 2 \quad -1) \begin{pmatrix} 0 & 1 \\ 1 & 0 \\ 1 & 1 \end{pmatrix} = (3\cdot0 + 2\cdot1 - 1\cdot1 \quad 3\cdot1 + 2\cdot0 - 1\cdot1)$$

$$= (1 \quad 2);$$

m-by-n matrix times n-dimensional column vector:

$$\begin{pmatrix} 0 & 1 \\ 1 & 0 \\ 1 & 1 \end{pmatrix} \begin{pmatrix} 3 \\ -3 \end{pmatrix} = \begin{pmatrix} 0\cdot3 + 1\cdot(-3) \\ 1\cdot3 + 0\cdot(-3) \\ 1\cdot3 + 1\cdot(-3) \end{pmatrix} = \begin{pmatrix} -3 \\ 3 \\ 0 \end{pmatrix}.$$

Notice also that an inner product FX itself can be looked at as the matrix product of a 1-by-n matrix with an n-by-1 matrix.

The n-by-n matrix

$$I = \begin{pmatrix} 1 & 0 & \ldots & 0 & 0 \\ 0 & 1 & \ldots & 0 & 0 \\ & & \ldots & & \\ 0 & 0 & \ldots & 0 & 1 \end{pmatrix},$$

which has 1's for its "main diagonal" components a_{ii}, and 0's elsewhere, has the property that

$$IA = A \text{ for every } n\text{-by-}m \text{ matrix } A$$

and $\qquad\qquad AI = A \text{ for every } m\text{-by-}n \text{ matrix } A.$

In particular $AI = IA = A$ for every n-by-n matrix A, and $FI = F$ for every n-dimensional row vector F, and $IX = X$ for every n-dimensional column vector X. Thus I behaves for products of matrices the way 1 behaves for products of numbers. We call I the **identity matrix**.

Similarly the (not necessarily square) matrix O which has all components 0 has the property that $AO = O$ or $OA = O$ or both whenever the products make sense. For instance, when A is 2-by-3 and O the 3-by-4 zero matrix, then AO is the 2-by-4 zero matrix.

Under the operations of addition, multiplication, and numerical multiplication, matrices and vectors act in much the same way as ordinary numbers do. In fact *matrix operations obey the following laws.* (We assume that the shapes of the matrices are such that the sums and products are defined.)

Distributive Laws:

$$\begin{cases} (A + B)C = AC + BC \\[2mm] A(B + C) = AB + AC \end{cases}$$

Associative Laws:

$$\begin{cases} (cA)B = c(AB) = A(cB) \\[2mm] A(BC) = (AB)C \end{cases}$$

In order to prove the first distributive law, let

$$A = (a_{ij}) \quad \text{and} \quad B = (b_{ij}), \qquad i = 1, \ldots, m, \, j = 1, \ldots, n.$$

$$C = (b_{kl}), \qquad\qquad\qquad k = 1, \ldots, n, \, l = 1, \ldots, r.$$

Then $(A + B)C$ is defined by

$$\sum_{j=1}^{n} (a_{ij} + b_{ij})c_{jl},$$

and $AC + BC$ is defined by

$$\left(\sum_{j=1}^{n} a_{ij}c_{jl} \right) + \left(\sum_{j=1}^{n} b_{ij}c_{jl} \right).$$

The distributive law for matrices then follows from the distributive law and commutative law of addition for real numbers. We have

$$\sum_{j=1}^{n} (a_{ij} + b_{ij})c_{jl} = \sum_{j=1}^{n} (a_{ij}c_{jl} + b_{ij}c_{jl})$$

$$= \sum_{j=1}^{n} a_{ij}c_{jl} + \sum_{j=1}^{n} b_{ij}c_{jl}.$$

The other laws can be proved in the same way, and we omit the details. A more natural method of verification is possible once we have identified matrices and linear transformations.

EXAMPLE 1. The quantity $Y = AX$, where A is a square matrix and X is a vector, always has a geometric interpretation that will be explained in detail in later sections of this chapter. We give here one specific example. Suppose that the plane has the usual euclidean coordinate system, and let X be the point in the plane whose coordinates are $\begin{pmatrix} x_1 \\ x_2 \end{pmatrix}$. Suppose that we rotate the plane (but not the coordinate axes) through an angle of 30° counterclockwise, with the origin of coordinates as the center of rotation. Then X will move to a new point $Y = \begin{pmatrix} y_1 \\ y_2 \end{pmatrix}$. How are the coordinates of Y related to those of X? In Figure 5 we have drawn the points X and Y. If d is the distance from X to the origin (which may be found using the Pythagorean formula) and θ is the angle indicated, then it is easy to see that

$$y_1 = d \cos (\theta + 30°)$$

$$= d \cos \theta \cos 30° - d \sin \theta \sin 30°$$

$$= \frac{\sqrt{3}}{2} x_1 - \frac{1}{2} x_2$$

$$y_2 = d \sin (\theta + 30°)$$

$$= d \cos \theta \sin 30° + d \sin \theta \cos 30°$$

$$= \frac{1}{2} x_1 + \frac{\sqrt{3}}{2} x_2.$$

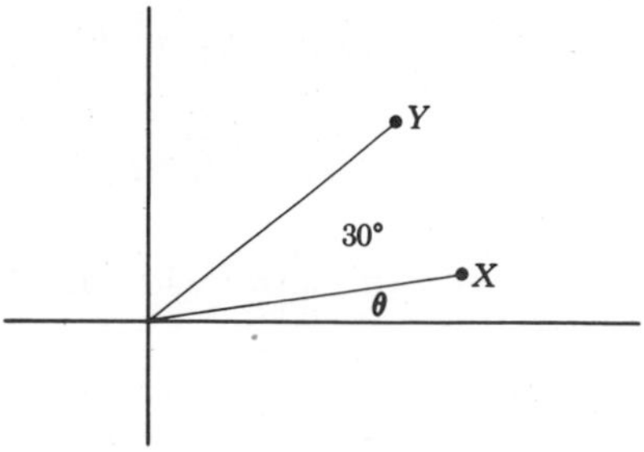

FIGURE 5

But now we see that we can write these two equations as a single matrix equation as follows:

$$\begin{pmatrix} y_1 \\ y_2 \end{pmatrix} = \begin{pmatrix} \sqrt{3}/2 & -\frac{1}{2} \\ \frac{1}{2} & \sqrt{3}/2 \end{pmatrix} \begin{pmatrix} x_1 \\ x_2 \end{pmatrix}.$$

Or, if we call the matrix

$$A = \begin{pmatrix} \sqrt{3}/2 & -\frac{1}{2} \\ \frac{1}{2} & \sqrt{3}/2 \end{pmatrix},$$

we can simply write this equation as $Y = AX$.

In general, if we rotate the plane through α degrees counterclockwise, then the coordinates of the new point Y are related to the coordinates of the old point X by the formula $Y = AX$, where

$$A = \begin{pmatrix} \cos \alpha & -\sin \alpha \\ \sin \alpha & \cos \alpha \end{pmatrix}.$$

EXAMPLE 2. Consider the system of first-degree equations

$$y_k = \sum_{l=1}^{n} b_{kl} x_l, \qquad k = 1, \ldots, m.$$

If we are given another system

$$z_j = \sum_{k=1}^{m} a_{jk} y_k, \qquad j = 1, \ldots, p,$$

we can eliminate the variables $y_1, \ldots, y_m$ by substitution. We get

$$z_j = \sum_{k=1}^{m} a_{jk} \sum_{l=1}^{n} b_{kl} x_l = \sum_{l=1}^{n} \left(\sum_{k=1}^{m} a_{jk} b_{kl} \right) x_l.$$

But the p-by-n matrix with entries

$$c_{jl} = \sum_{k=1}^{m} a_{jk} b_{kl}$$

is just the product AB of the p-by-m matrix $A = (a_{jk})$ and the m-by-n matrix $B = (b_{kl})$. Thus to compute the result of the above substitution it is enough to make a routine computation of the product of two matrices.

EXERCISES

1. Under the operations of addition and numerical multiplication, matrices and vectors act in very much the same way as ordinary numbers do. We list below seven important algebraic rules that they obey. In each rule, of course, we assume that all the matrices involved have the same shape.

(1) $(A + B) + C = A + (B + C)$ (associate law for addition).

(2) $0 + A = A$.

(3) $-A + A = 0$.

(4) $A + B = B + A$ (commutative law for addition).

(5) $(ab) C = a(bC)$.

(6) $(a + b) C = aC + bC$.

(7) $a(B + C) = aB + aC$.

Illustrate each of these rules with the specific 3-by-2 matrices A, B, and C of Exercise 2 and the numbers $a = \frac{1}{2}$, $b = -3$.

2. Given the 3-by-2 matrices

$$A = \begin{pmatrix} 1 & 2 \\ 3 & 4 \\ 5 & 6 \end{pmatrix}, \qquad B = \begin{pmatrix} 0 & 3 \\ -1 & 1 \\ 1 & -1 \end{pmatrix}, \qquad C = \begin{pmatrix} 0 & 0 \\ 0 & 0 \\ 0 & 0 \end{pmatrix},$$

compute each of the following:

(a) $2A$.

$$Ans. \begin{pmatrix} 2 & 4 \\ 6 & 8 \\ 10 & 12 \end{pmatrix}.$$

(b) $-B$.

(c) $2A - B$.

(d) $B + C$.

(e) $2A - 3B - C$.

$$Ans. \begin{pmatrix} 2 & -5 \\ 9 & 5 \\ 7 & 15 \end{pmatrix}.$$

3. Given 3-dimensional row vectors

$$F = (7 \quad 0 \quad -3), \qquad G = (2 \quad 1 \quad -5), \qquad H = (1 \quad -1 \quad 0),$$

compute each of the following:

(a) $-G.$

(b) $2F - G.$

(c) $F + G - H.$

(d) $2F - 3G - H.$

4. Given the 3-dimensional column vectors

$$X = \begin{pmatrix} 3 \\ 1 \\ 2 \end{pmatrix}, \qquad Y = \begin{pmatrix} -2 \\ 3 \\ 0 \end{pmatrix}, \qquad Z = \begin{pmatrix} -1 \\ -1 \\ 1 \end{pmatrix},$$

compute each of the following:

(a) $2X - Y.$

(b) $X + Y + Z.$

(c) $2X - 3Y - Z.$ $\quad\left[Ans. \begin{pmatrix} 13 \\ -6 \\ 3 \end{pmatrix} \right].$

5. If A, B, C, F, G, H, X, Y, Z are as in Exercises 2, 3, 4, what are the following components: a_{12}, b_{31}, c_{22}, f_2, g_1, h_3, x_2, y_1, z_3?

6. Show that $OA = O$ for any matrix A. And show also that $aO = O$ for any number a. These two rules show the similarity between the ordinary number 0 and the matrix O.

7. If $\begin{pmatrix} 1 \\ 1 \\ 2 \end{pmatrix} + 2 \begin{pmatrix} x_1 \\ x_2 \\ x_3 \end{pmatrix} = \begin{pmatrix} 1 \\ -1 \\ 0 \end{pmatrix}$, find $\begin{pmatrix} x_1 \\ x_2 \\ x_3 \end{pmatrix}$. $\quad\left[Ans. \begin{pmatrix} 0 \\ -1 \\ -1 \end{pmatrix} \right].$

8. Let $F = (1\ {-1}\ \ 4)$

$G = (0\ \ 1\ \ 2)$

$$X = \begin{pmatrix} 5 \\ 0 \\ 1 \end{pmatrix}, \qquad Y = \begin{pmatrix} -1 \\ -1 \\ 2 \end{pmatrix}.$$

Compute the following:

(a) $FX + GY$.   [*Ans.* 12.]

(b) $(-F + 5G)(3X - 2Y)$.

(c) $2(F - G)(X + Y)$.   [*Ans.* 24.]

9. Perform the following multiplications:

(a) $\begin{pmatrix} 1 & -1 \\ -2 & 2 \end{pmatrix}\begin{pmatrix} 7 \\ 2 \end{pmatrix} = ?$

(b) $(3\ {-4}) \begin{pmatrix} 1 & -1 \\ -2 & 2 \end{pmatrix} = ?$ [*Ans.* (11 -11).]

(c) $\begin{vmatrix} 1 & 3 & 0 \\ 7 & -1 & 3 \\ -8 & 14 & -5 \\ 9 & 2 & 7 \\ 10 & -6 & 0 \end{vmatrix} \begin{pmatrix} 3 \\ -1 \\ 1 \end{pmatrix} = ?$

(d) $(2\ \ 2) \begin{pmatrix} 1 & -1 \\ -1 & 1 \end{pmatrix} = ?$ [*Ans.* (0 0).]

(e) $\begin{pmatrix} 1 & -1 \\ -1 & 1 \end{pmatrix}\begin{pmatrix} 5 \\ 5 \end{pmatrix} = ?$

(f) $(0\ \ 2\ \ {-3}) \begin{pmatrix} 1 & 7 & -8 & 9 & 10 \\ 3 & -1 & 14 & 2 & -6 \\ 0 & 3 & -5 & 7 & 0 \end{pmatrix} = ?$

(g) $\begin{pmatrix} 6 & 1 \\ 0 & -3 \end{pmatrix}\begin{pmatrix} 4 & 0 & -4 \\ 2 & 1 & -1 \end{pmatrix} = ?$

(h) $\begin{pmatrix} 6 & 0 & -1 \\ 1 & -3 & 2 \end{pmatrix}\begin{pmatrix} 4 & 2 \\ 0 & 1 \\ -5 & -1 \end{pmatrix} = ?$ $\left[Ans. \begin{pmatrix} 29 & 13 \\ -6 & -3 \end{pmatrix}. \right]$

(i) $\begin{pmatrix} 1 & -1 \\ -1 & 1 \end{pmatrix}\begin{pmatrix} 1 & -1 \\ -1 & 1 \end{pmatrix} = ?$

(j) $\begin{pmatrix} 4 & 1 & 4 \\ -1 & -2 & -1 \\ 2 & -1 & -2 \end{pmatrix}\begin{pmatrix} 3 & 0 & 1 \\ -1 & 2 & 0 \\ 0 & 0 & 2 \end{pmatrix} = ?$

$\left[Ans. \begin{pmatrix} 11 & 2 & 12 \\ -1 & -4 & -3 \\ 7 & -2 & -2 \end{pmatrix}. \right]$

(k) $\begin{vmatrix} 1 & -2 \\ 0 & 0 \\ 7 & 5 \\ -4 & 8 \\ 0 & -2 \end{vmatrix}\begin{pmatrix} -7 & 9 & -5 & 6 & 0 \\ -1 & 0 & 3 & -4 & 1 \end{pmatrix} = ?$

10. Consider the matrices

$$A = \begin{pmatrix} 1 & 0 & 1 \\ -1 & 17 & 57 \end{pmatrix}, \quad B = \begin{pmatrix} 1 & 1 & 1 \\ 2 & 2 & 2 \\ 3 & 3 & 3 \\ 0 & 0 & 0 \end{pmatrix},$$

$$C = \begin{pmatrix} 1 & 0 & -1 \\ 0 & -1 & 1 \\ -1 & 1 & 0 \end{pmatrix}, \quad D = \begin{pmatrix} -1 & -1 \\ 2 & 2 \\ 1 & 1 \end{pmatrix}.$$

The shapes of these are 2-by-3, 4-by-3, 3-by-3, and 3-by-2 respectively. What is the shape of

(a) AC.
(b) DA.
(c) AD.
(d) BC.
(e) CD.
(f) DAC.
(g) $BCDA$.   [*Ans.* 4-by-3.]

11. In Exercise 10 find:
    (a) The component in the second row and second column of AC.
                                                [*Ans.* 40.]
    (b) The component in the fourth row and first column of BC.
    (c) The component in the last row and last column of DA.
                                                [*Ans.* 58.]
    (d) The component in the first row and first column of $BCDA$.

12. Prove that $IA = AI = A$ for the 3-by-3 identity matrix I and all 3-by-3 matrices A.

13. Find a 3-by-3 matrix C such that for every 3-by-3 matrix A we have $CA = 3A$.

14. Prove that $IX = X$ for the 3-by-3 identity matrix I and all 3-dimensional column vectors X.

15. Prove that $FI = F$ for the 3-by-3 identity matrix I and all 3-dimensional row vectors F.

16. Prove that $OA = AO = O$ for the 3-by-3 zero matrix O and all 3-by-3 matrices A.

17. Prove that

$$\begin{pmatrix} 0 & 0 & 0 \\ 0 & 0 & 0 \\ 0 & 0 & 0 \end{pmatrix} X = \begin{pmatrix} 0 \\ 0 \\ 0 \end{pmatrix}$$

for all 3-dimensional column vectors X.

18. (a) Show that $AB = O$ where

$$A = \begin{pmatrix} 1 & 0 \\ 0 & 0 \end{pmatrix}, \quad B = \begin{pmatrix} 0 & 0 \\ 1 & 1 \end{pmatrix}.$$

(b) Find another example of two matrices A and B such that $A \neq O$ and $B \neq O$ but $AB = O$.

19. (a) Show that $BA \neq O$ for the matrices of Exercise 18(a).

(b) Find another example of two matrices A and B such that $AB = O$ but $BA \neq O$.

20. (a) Show that $AB \neq BA$ and neither product is the zero matrix where

$$A = \begin{pmatrix} 1 & 0 \\ 1 & 0 \end{pmatrix}, \qquad B = \begin{pmatrix} 0 & 1 \\ 0 & 1 \end{pmatrix}.$$

(b) Find another example of matrices A and B such that $AB \neq BA$ and neither product is the zero matrix.

21. Prove that if one row of the 2-by-2 matrix A is a numerical multiple of the other row, then there exists a 2-by-2 matrix $B \neq O$ such that $AB = O$.

22. Prove the converse of Exercise 21.

23. Prove that if one row of the 2-by-2 matrix A is a numerical multiple of the other row, then the same fact is true for the columns.

24. If A is a square matrix, it can be multiplied by itself; hence we can define (using the associative law)

$$A^2 = A \cdot A$$

$$A^3 = A^2 \cdot A = A \cdot A \cdot A$$

$$\cdots$$

$$A^n = A^{n-1} \cdot A = A \cdot A \cdot \ldots A \ (n \text{ factors})$$

These are naturally called "powers" of a matrix—the first one being called the square; the second, the cube; etc. Compute the indicated powers of the following matrices.

(a) If $A = \begin{pmatrix} 1 & 0 \\ 3 & 4 \end{pmatrix}$, find A^2, A^3, and A^4.

$$\left[Ans. \ \begin{pmatrix} 1 & 0 \\ 15 & 16 \end{pmatrix}; \begin{pmatrix} 1 & 0 \\ 63 & 64 \end{pmatrix}; \begin{pmatrix} 1 & 0 \\ 255 & 256 \end{pmatrix}. \right]$$

(b) If I and O are the identity and zero matrices, respectively, find I^2, I^3, I^n, O^2, O^3, and O^n.

(c) If $A = \begin{pmatrix} 0 & 0 & 0 \\ 1 & 0 & 0 \\ 2 & -1 & 0 \end{pmatrix}$, find A^2, A^3, and A^n.

(d) If $A = \begin{pmatrix} 1 & 1 \\ 1 & 1 \end{pmatrix}$, find A^n.

25. What are the column vectors $\begin{pmatrix} x_1 \\ x_2 \end{pmatrix}$ and $\begin{pmatrix} y_1 \\ y_2 \end{pmatrix}$ corresponding to the points

X and Y in the oblique coordinate system pictured in Figure 6?

$$\left[Ans. \; X = \begin{pmatrix} -2 \\ 5 \end{pmatrix}, \; Y = \begin{pmatrix} -3 \\ -2 \end{pmatrix}. \right]$$

26. What are the column vectors $\begin{pmatrix} x_1 \\ x_2 \end{pmatrix}$ and $\begin{pmatrix} y_1 \\ y_2 \end{pmatrix}$ corresponding to the points

X and Y in the oblique coordinate system pictured in Figure 7?

27. Draw the vectors $2X$, $-\frac{3}{4}X$, and $-5X$ on a coordinate system with axes like those of Figure 6.

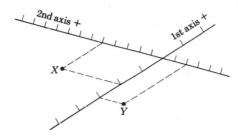

FIGURE 6

28. Draw the vectors $2X$, $-\frac{3}{4}X$, and $-5X$ on a coordinate system like that in Figure 7.

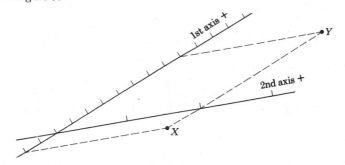

FIGURE 7

29. Draw the vectors $X + Y$, $-2X + 3Y$, $2X + 3Y$ on a coordinate system like that of Figure 6.

30. Draw the vectors $X + Y$, $-2X + 3Y$, $2X + 3Y$ on a coordinate system like that of Figure 7.

31. Consider an oblique coordinate system such as that of Figure 6 or Figure 7. Discuss the general problem of how to construct the vector kX for k a positive or negative number or zero. Discuss the problem of how to construct the vector $hX + kY$ for h and k positive or negative numbers or zero. Do your constructions hold good in case the axes are perpendicular?

2. SYSTEMS OF LINEAR EQUATIONS

By a **system of linear equations** we mean a finite set of equations

$$a_{11}x_1 + \ldots + a_{1n}x_n = b_1$$

$$\cdot \qquad\qquad \cdot \qquad\quad \cdot$$

$$a_{m1}x_1 + \ldots + a_{mn}x_n = b_m$$

with the a's and b's given and the x's unknown. Notice that m, the number of equations, does not have to be the same as n, the number of unknowns. The whole system can be written in matrix form as $AX = B$, where A stands for the **matrix of coefficients**, B stands for a known m-dimensional column vector (called the right-hand side), and X stands for an unknown n-dimensional column vector. Thus,

$$\begin{pmatrix} a_{11} & \cdots & a_{1n} \\ \cdot & & \cdot \\ \cdot & & \cdot \\ \cdot & & \cdot \\ a_{m1} & \cdots & a_{mn} \end{pmatrix} \begin{pmatrix} x_1 \\ \cdot \\ \cdot \\ \cdot \\ x_n \end{pmatrix} = \begin{pmatrix} b_1 \\ \cdot \\ \cdot \\ \cdot \\ b_m \end{pmatrix}.$$

By a **solution of the system** we mean any particular n-dimensional column vector

$$C = \begin{pmatrix} c_1 \\ \cdot \\ \cdot \\ \cdot \\ c_n \end{pmatrix}$$

such that $AC = B$. We sometimes say that

$$\begin{pmatrix} c_1 \\ \cdot \\ \cdot \\ \cdot \\ c_n \end{pmatrix}$$

is a "simultaneous solution" of all the individual equations

$$a_{i1}x_1 + \ldots + a_{in}x_n = b_i, \qquad i = 1, 2, \ldots, m.$$

For a nice system of equations there is exactly one solution

$$\begin{pmatrix} c_1 \\ \cdot \\ \cdot \\ \cdot \\ c_n \end{pmatrix}$$

But it is possible for a system to have infinitely many different solutions, and it is possible for a system to have no solutions at all. In the present section we develop an effective method for deciding whether a given system has at least one solution, and for surveying all its solutions. The method consists in replacing the given system by an equivalent system whose solutions are obvious. This replacement is carried out in steps. At each step we alter the system slightly, but in such a way that every solution to the new system is a solution to the old and vice versa.

We shall introduce the method by three examples. Example 1 has exactly one solution, Example 3 has infinitely many, Example 4 has none.

EXAMPLE 1.

$$3x + 12y + 9z = 3$$

$$2x + 5y + 4z = 4$$

$$-x + 3y + 2z = -5.$$

By numerical multiplications, make x have coefficient 1 in each equation (i.e. multiply the top equation—on both sides—by 1/3, the middle equation by 1/2, the bottom equation by -1).

$$x + 4y + 3z = 1$$

$$x + \tfrac{5}{2}y + 2z = 2$$

$$x - 3y - 2z = 5.$$

Subtract the top equation from each of the others (keeping the top equation itself unchanged).

$$x + 4y + 3z = 1$$

$$-\tfrac{3}{2}y - z = 1$$

$$-7y - 5z = 4.$$

By numerical multiplications, make y have coefficient 1 in each equation.

$$\frac{1}{4}x + y + \frac{3}{4}z = \frac{1}{4}$$
$$y + \frac{2}{3}z = -\frac{2}{3}$$
$$y + \frac{5}{7}z = -\frac{4}{7}.$$

Subtract the middle equation from each of the others.

$$\frac{1}{4}x \quad + \frac{1}{12}z = \frac{11}{12}$$
$$y + \frac{2}{3}z = -\frac{2}{3}$$
$$\frac{1}{21}z = \frac{2}{21}.$$

By numerical multiplications, make z have coefficient 1 in each equation.

$$3x \quad + z = 11$$
$$\frac{3}{2}y + z = -1$$
$$z = 2.$$

Subtract the bottom equation from each of the others.

$$3x \quad = 9$$
$$\frac{3}{2}y \quad = -3$$
$$z = 2.$$

Finally, make every coefficient 1.

$$x \quad = 3$$
$$y \quad = -2$$
$$z = 2.$$

Hence there is exactly one solution, namely

$$X = \begin{pmatrix} x \\ y \\ z \end{pmatrix} = \begin{pmatrix} 3 \\ -2 \\ 2 \end{pmatrix}.$$

The above computations are considerably more transparent in matrix notation:

$$\begin{pmatrix} 3 & 12 & 9 \\ 2 & 5 & 4 \\ -1 & 3 & 2 \end{pmatrix} X = \begin{pmatrix} 3 \\ 4 \\ -5 \end{pmatrix},$$

$$\begin{pmatrix} 1 & 4 & 3 \\ 1 & \frac{5}{2} & 2 \\ 1 & -3 & -2 \end{pmatrix} X = \begin{pmatrix} 1 \\ 2 \\ 5 \end{pmatrix}$$

$$\begin{pmatrix} 1 & 4 & 3 \\ 0 & -\frac{3}{2} & -1 \\ 0 & -7 & -5 \end{pmatrix} X = \begin{pmatrix} 1 \\ 1 \\ 4 \end{pmatrix},$$

$$\begin{pmatrix} \frac{1}{4} & 1 & \frac{3}{4} \\ 0 & 1 & \frac{2}{3} \\ 0 & 1 & \frac{5}{7} \end{pmatrix} X = \begin{pmatrix} \frac{1}{4} \\ -\frac{2}{3} \\ -\frac{4}{7} \end{pmatrix}$$

$$\begin{pmatrix} \frac{1}{4} & 0 & \frac{1}{12} \\ 0 & 1 & \frac{2}{3} \\ 0 & 0 & \frac{1}{21} \end{pmatrix} X = \begin{pmatrix} \frac{11}{12} \\ -\frac{2}{3} \\ \frac{2}{21} \end{pmatrix},$$

$$\begin{pmatrix} 3 & 0 & 1 \\ 0 & \frac{3}{2} & 1 \\ 0 & 0 & 1 \end{pmatrix} X = \begin{pmatrix} 11 \\ -1 \\ 2 \end{pmatrix}$$

$$\begin{pmatrix} 3 & 0 & 0 \\ 0 & \frac{3}{2} & 0 \\ 0 & 0 & 1 \end{pmatrix} X = \begin{pmatrix} 9 \\ -3 \\ 2 \end{pmatrix},$$

$$\begin{pmatrix} 1 & 0 & 0 \\ 0 & 1 & 0 \\ 0 & 0 & 1 \end{pmatrix} X = \begin{pmatrix} 3 \\ -2 \\ 2 \end{pmatrix}.$$

The operations used in solving the above system have been **elementary operations** of the following two types:

Elementary numerical multiplication. Erase one of the equations

$$a_{i1}x_1 + \ldots + a_{in}x_n = b_i,$$

and replace it by

$$ca_{i1}x_1 + \ldots + ca_{in}x_n = cb_i,$$

for some $c \neq 0$.

Elementary addition. Erase one of the equations

$$a_{k1}x_1 + \ldots + a_{kn}x_n = b_k,$$

and replace it by

$$(a_{i1} + a_{k1})x_1 + \ldots + (a_{in} + a_{kn})x_n = b_i + b_k,$$

where

$$a_{i1}x_1 + \ldots + a_{in}x_n = b_i$$

is some *other* equation in the system. (But do not alter this other equation.)

More briefly, writing A_i for the ith row of coefficients, we have

Elementary numerical multiplication:

Before	After
.	.
.	.
.	.
$A_iX = b_i$	$cA_iX = cb_i$ (with $c \neq 0$)
.	.
.	.
.	.

Elementary addition:

Before	After
.	.
.	.
$A_iX = b_i$	$A_iX = b_i$
.	.
.	.
$A_kX = b_k$	$(A_i + A_k)X = b_i + b_k$
.	.
.	.

In the above operation, we say that $A_iX = b_i$ is the **active** equation. Notice that we use the active equation to alter other equations in the system, while the active equation itself stays untouched.

In solving the system of equations in Example 1, we seemingly used not elementary addition, but **elementary subtraction**. That is, the active equation $A_iX = b_i$ was subtracted from $A_kX = b_k$. But we can regard this as first multiplying $A_iX = b_i$ by -1, then adding $-A_iX = -b_i$ to $A_kX = b_k$, and finally multiplying $-A_iX = -b_i$ by -1. In developing the abstract theory of systems of equations, we shall continue to make statements about elementary addition, because it is a more fundamental operation than subtraction.

Let us now show that neither of the elementary operations changes the set of solutions of a system. For elementary numerical multiplication, it is immediate that $A_iX = b_i$ if and only if $cA_iX = cb_i$, since we have $c \neq 0$. For elementary addition, suppose $A_iX = b_i$ and $A_kX = b_k$. Then clearly $A_iX + A_kX = b_i + b_k$. Suppose conversely that $(A_i + A_k)X = b_i + b_k$, and also that $A_iX = b_i$ (because we did not alter the active equation). Then

$$(A_i + A_k)X - A_iX = (b_i + b_k) - b_i, \quad \text{or} \quad A_kX = b_k.$$

Notice that an elementary subtraction undoes the effect of an elementary addition, and vice versa.

Let us sum up the arguments of the last few paragraphs.

2.1 Theorem. Elementary operations on a system of equations do not change the set of solutions of the system.

We pause to observe that an elementary operation on a matrix A can always be accomplished by multiplying it on the left by a suitable matrix P, called the **elementary matrix** associated with the operation.

2.2 Theorem. Apply a certain elementary operation (addition or numerical multiplication) to an m-by-n matrix A, getting a new matrix B. Apply the same elementary operation to the m-by-m identity matrix I, getting a new matrix P. Then

$$B = PA.$$

Proof. There are three possibilities for the ith row B_i of the matrix B.
(0) B_i is exactly the same as the ith row A_i of the matrix A, in which case $P_i = I_i$.
(1) $B_i = cA_i$ for some $c \neq 0$, in which case $P_i = cI_i$.
(2) $B_i = A_i + A_k$ for some $k \neq i$, in which case $P_i = I_i + I_k$.
It is a fundamental fact of matrix multiplication that, for any matrices A and Q, we have the ith row of QA equal to Q_iA, where Q_i is the ith

row of Q. Hence, to get the theorem we apply associative and distributive laws (see Theorem 1.1). In case (0),

$$B_i = A_i = I_iA = P_iA = (PA)_i.$$

In case (1),

$$B_i = cA_i = c(I_iA) = (cI_i)A = P_iA = (PA)_i.$$

In case (2),

$$B_i = A_i + A_k = I_iA + I_kA = (I_i + I_k)A = P_iA = (PA)_i.$$

Then $B_i = (PA)_i$ for each row, so $B = PA$.

EXAMPLE 2. We compute the elementary matrix for multiplication of a 3-rowed matrix in its middle row by the number 2. It is obtained by multiplying the middle row of the 3-by-3 identity matrix by 2. We get the elementary matrix

$$P = \begin{pmatrix} 1 & 0 & 0 \\ 0 & 2 & 0 \\ 0 & 0 & 1 \end{pmatrix}.$$

Thus,

$$\begin{pmatrix} 1 & 0 & 0 \\ 0 & 2 & 0 \\ 0 & 0 & 1 \end{pmatrix} \begin{pmatrix} a_{11} & a_{12} & a_{13} & a_{14} \\ a_{21} & a_{22} & a_{23} & a_{24} \\ a_{31} & a_{32} & a_{33} & a_{34} \end{pmatrix} = \begin{pmatrix} a_{11} & a_{12} & a_{13} & a_{14} \\ 2a_{21} & 2a_{22} & 2a_{23} & 2a_{24} \\ a_{31} & a_{32} & a_{33} & a_{34} \end{pmatrix},$$

which effects the required elementary operation on a 3-by-4 matrix. The elementary matrix for addition of the bottom row of a 3-rowed matrix to the top row is got by performing the corresponding operation on the 3-by-3 identity matrix. Thus we get

$$P = \begin{pmatrix} 1 & 0 & 1 \\ 0 & 1 & 0 \\ 0 & 0 & 1 \end{pmatrix}.$$

EXAMPLE 3. We now return to the business of solving systems with concrete numerical coefficients, this time exhibiting a system that has infinitely many solutions.

$$x - 2y - 3z = 2$$
$$\tfrac{1}{2}x - 2y - \tfrac{13}{2}z = 7$$
$$-3x + 5y + 4z = 0.$$

In matrix form,

$$\begin{pmatrix} 1 & -2 & -3 \\ \tfrac{1}{2} & -2 & -\tfrac{13}{2} \\ -3 & 5 & 4 \end{pmatrix} X = \begin{pmatrix} 2 \\ 7 \\ 0 \end{pmatrix}.$$

Perform elementary numerical multiplications, to make the left-hand column all 1's.

$$\begin{pmatrix} 1 & -2 & -3 \\ 1 & -4 & -13 \\ 1 & -\tfrac{5}{3} & -\tfrac{4}{3} \end{pmatrix} X = \begin{pmatrix} 2 \\ 14 \\ 0 \end{pmatrix}.$$

Perform elementary subtractions, with the top equation active.

$$\begin{pmatrix} 1 & -2 & -3 \\ 0 & -2 & -10 \\ 0 & \tfrac{1}{3} & \tfrac{5}{3} \end{pmatrix} X = \begin{pmatrix} 2 \\ 12 \\ -2 \end{pmatrix}.$$

Perform elementary numerical multiplications, to make the middle column all 1's.

$$\begin{pmatrix} -\tfrac{1}{2} & 1 & \tfrac{3}{2} \\ 0 & 1 & 5 \\ 0 & 1 & 5 \end{pmatrix} X = \begin{pmatrix} -1 \\ -6 \\ -6 \end{pmatrix}.$$

Perform elementary subtractions, with the middle row active.

$$\begin{pmatrix} -\tfrac{1}{2} & 0 & -\tfrac{7}{2} \\ 0 & 1 & 5 \\ 0 & 0 & 0 \end{pmatrix} X = \begin{pmatrix} 5 \\ -6 \\ 0 \end{pmatrix}.$$

Finally, perform numerical multiplications, to make each row have 1 as its extreme left nonzero component.

$$\begin{pmatrix} 1 & 0 & 7 \\ 0 & 1 & 5 \\ 0 & 0 & 0 \end{pmatrix} X = \begin{pmatrix} -10 \\ -6 \\ 0 \end{pmatrix}.$$

In other words,

$$x + 0y + 7z = -10$$

$$0x + y + 5z = -6$$

$$0x + 0y + 0z = 0.$$

Every $\begin{pmatrix} x \\ y \\ z \end{pmatrix}$ is a solution to the bottom equation, hence we need only consider the other two equations. We transpose terms involving z to the other sides of the equations

$$x = -7z - 10$$

$$y = -5z - 6.$$

Then we can assign any value whatever to z, and produce a corresponding solution

$$\begin{pmatrix} x \\ y \\ z \end{pmatrix} = \begin{pmatrix} -7z & -10 \\ -5z & -6 \\ z & \end{pmatrix}.$$

Equivalently, the set of solutions consists of all vectors

$$X = t \begin{pmatrix} -7 \\ -5 \\ 1 \end{pmatrix} + \begin{pmatrix} -10 \\ -6 \\ 0 \end{pmatrix},$$

where t is any real number. Later we shall see that this infinite set of solutions can be interpreted as a certain line in 3-dimensional space.

EXAMPLE 4. We take a system whose matrix of coefficients is the same as in Example 3, but with a different column given on the right-hand side of the equals sign. This time we shall see that no solution exists.

$$
\begin{pmatrix}
1 & -2 & -3 \\
\frac{1}{2} & -2 & -\frac{13}{2} \\
-3 & 5 & 4
\end{pmatrix} X =
\begin{pmatrix}
2 \\
7 \\
2
\end{pmatrix}
$$

Perform exactly the same sequence of operations as in Example 3. To the left of the equals sign, each step will look the same as in Example 3. But the right-hand side will be different, and we finally arrive at

$$
\begin{pmatrix}
1 & 0 & 7 \\
0 & 1 & 5 \\
0 & 0 & 0
\end{pmatrix} X =
\begin{pmatrix}
-10 \\
-6 \\
2
\end{pmatrix},
$$

or

$$
\begin{aligned}
x + 0y + 7z &= -10 \\
0x + y + 5z &= -6 \\
0x + 0y + 0z &= 2.
\end{aligned}
$$

Clearly there is no

$$
X = \begin{pmatrix}
x \\
y \\
z
\end{pmatrix}
$$

satisfying the bottom equation. Hence this system has no solution.

In each of the above examples we manipulated the given system of equations to get it into a certain standard final form. Let us spell out this form more explicitly. If we write R_i for the ith row of the final coefficient matrix R, then the m final equations can be written

$$
R_1 X = c_1
$$

$$
\cdot
$$

$$
\cdot
$$

$$
\cdot
$$

$$
R_r X = c_r
$$

$$
OX = c_{r+1}
$$

$$
\cdot
$$

$$
\cdot
$$

$$
\cdot
$$

$$
OX = c_m.
$$

Now let us describe the coefficient rows R_i. Any nonzero row is said to **begin** at its left-hand-most nonzero component. For instance

$$(0 \quad \tfrac{1}{2} \quad 3 \quad -1)$$

begins at its second component. In our standard form the nonzero coefficient rows have two simple properties:

2.3 Noninterference property. Each row has 0's at all the components where other rows begin.

2.4 Monic property. Each nonzero row has 1 at the component where this row begins.

Such a set of rows is called a **reduced set**. To avoid complicating our terminology, we shall sometimes also call the whole set of m equations a reduced set. The noninterference property is very much more important than the monic property. For instance, from the former we immediately deduce that *each row begins at a different component*.

Although we have just been talking about the reduced form R of a matrix A, this concept is not really well defined until we specify the arrangement of the rows R_i. Henceforth, whenever we are concerned with the actual matrix R, and not simply with the (unordered) set of its rows R_i, we shall require another property. Like the monic property, it is mainly for neatness and can often be disregarded.

2.5 Echelon property. Row R_1 begins before row R_2, row R_2 begins before row R_3, and so on.

In working toward the echelon property it is useful to be able to shuffle rows at will. We could introduce this shuffling as a third type of elementary operation. But in fact, the following is true.

2.6 One can interchange the ith and jth rows of a matrix A by a sequence of elementary numerical multiplications and elementary additions.

Proof. The following sequence of elementary operations will accomplish the interchange.

$$
\begin{pmatrix} \cdot \\ \cdot \\ \cdot \\ A_i \\ \cdot \\ \cdot \\ A_j \\ \cdot \\ \cdot \end{pmatrix}
\rightarrow
\begin{pmatrix} \cdot \\ \cdot \\ \cdot \\ A_i \\ \cdot \\ \cdot \\ A_i + A_j \\ \cdot \\ \cdot \end{pmatrix}
\rightarrow
\begin{pmatrix} \cdot \\ \cdot \\ \cdot \\ -A_j \\ \cdot \\ \cdot \\ A_i + A_j \\ \cdot \\ \cdot \end{pmatrix}
\rightarrow
\begin{pmatrix} \cdot \\ \cdot \\ \cdot \\ -A_j \\ \cdot \\ \cdot \\ A_i \\ \cdot \\ \cdot \end{pmatrix}
\rightarrow
\begin{pmatrix} \cdot \\ \cdot \\ \cdot \\ A_j \\ \cdot \\ \cdot \\ A_i \\ \cdot \\ \cdot \end{pmatrix}.
$$

Each of the above steps, except the last numerical multiplication, is either an addition or a subtraction, and we have seen that subtractions can be manufactured out of additions and numerical multiplications.

EXAMPLE 5. Suppose that after suitable row operations we arrive at the reduced form

$$x_1 \qquad + 2x_4 - x_5 = 0$$
$$x_2 - x_4 + x_5 = 0$$
$$x_3 + 3x_4 + 6x_5 = 0.$$

Then we can transpose the nonbeginner variables x_4 and x_5 to the right-hand side and let these two variables take on arbitrary numerical values independently. The set of solutions consists of all vectors of the form

$$\begin{pmatrix} x_1 \\ x_2 \\ x_3 \\ x_4 \\ x_5 \end{pmatrix} = \begin{pmatrix} -2x_4 + x_5 \\ x_4 - x_5 \\ -3x_4 - 6x_5 \\ x_4 \\ x_5 \end{pmatrix} .$$

Equivalently, the set of solutions consists of all vectors that can be written as sums of numerical multiples of the two special vectors

$$\begin{pmatrix} -2 \\ 1 \\ -3 \\ 1 \\ 0 \end{pmatrix} \quad \text{and} \quad \begin{pmatrix} 1 \\ -1 \\ -6 \\ 0 \\ 1 \end{pmatrix} .$$

A system of linear equations with all 0's on the right-hand side, like the one at the beginning of Example 5, is called a **homogeneous system**.

EXAMPLE 6. Suppose that our reduced form has left-hand sides exactly like those of Example 5, but with the right-hand side different.

$$x_1 \qquad + 2x_4 - x_5 = 1$$
$$x_2 - x_4 + x_5 = 2$$
$$x_3 + 3x_4 + 6x_5 = 3.$$

Transposing x_4 and x_5, and letting them take arbitrary values independently, the most general solution is

$$\begin{pmatrix} 1 - 2x_4 + x_5 \\ 2 + x_4 - x_5 \\ 3 - 3x_4 - 6x_5 \\ x_4 \\ x_5 \end{pmatrix}.$$

Equivalently, the most general solution X can be written

$$X = \begin{pmatrix} 1 \\ 2 \\ 3 \\ 0 \\ 0 \end{pmatrix} + X_0$$

where X_0 is the most general solution to the homogeneous system of equations in Example 5.

EXAMPLE 7. Suppose that our reduced form is

$$x_1 + 2x_2 + x_4 - x_5 = 7$$

$$x_3 + 3x_4 + x_5 = 9.$$

Then we transpose the variables x_2, x_4, x_5. And the most general solution is

$$\begin{pmatrix} x_1 \\ x_2 \\ x_3 \\ x_4 \\ x_5 \end{pmatrix} = \begin{pmatrix} 7 - 2x_2 - x_4 + x_5 \\ x_2 \\ 9 - 3x_4 - x_5 \\ x_4 \\ x_5 \end{pmatrix}$$

where x_2, x_4, x_5 are arbitrary. Equivalently the most general solution can be written

$$X = u \begin{pmatrix} -2 \\ 1 \\ 0 \\ 0 \\ 0 \end{pmatrix} + v \begin{pmatrix} -1 \\ 0 \\ -3 \\ 1 \\ 0 \end{pmatrix} + w \begin{pmatrix} 1 \\ 0 \\ -1 \\ 0 \\ 1 \end{pmatrix} + \begin{pmatrix} 7 \\ 0 \\ 9 \\ 0 \\ 0 \end{pmatrix},$$

where u, v, w are arbitrary.

We have seen in Example 4 that a set of equations in reduced form has no solution if and only if at least one of the zero equations $OX = b_i$ has its right-hand side b_i not equal to zero. Now if we consider only consistent reduced sets of equations and ignore all the zero equations, then there will be exactly one solution when each variable occurs at the beginning of some row. Then the equations have as matrix of coefficients the identity matrix. Thus we have the

Theorem. If a system of equations has a unique solution then in the reduced form $RX = D$, with zero equations deleted, the matrix R is the identity matrix.

EXAMPLE 8. Let us make a survey of all possible reduced forms that can arise, for example, from three equations in four unknowns. If we consider *only the coefficient matrix*, and *only the positions of the beginner components* in this matrix, then there are 14 possibilities for the coefficient matrix. We list eight of these below, using the symbol ? for the components that are not required to be 0 or 1.

$$\begin{pmatrix} 1 & 0 & 0 & ? \\ 0 & 1 & 0 & ? \\ 0 & 0 & 1 & ? \end{pmatrix} \qquad \begin{pmatrix} 1 & 0 & ? & 0 \\ 0 & 1 & ? & 0 \\ 0 & 0 & 0 & 1 \end{pmatrix}$$

$$\begin{pmatrix} 1 & 0 & ? & ? \\ 0 & 1 & ? & ? \\ 0 & 0 & 0 & 0 \end{pmatrix} \qquad \begin{pmatrix} 1 & ? & 0 & 0 \\ 0 & 0 & 1 & 0 \\ 0 & 0 & 0 & 1 \end{pmatrix}$$

$$\begin{pmatrix} 1 & ? & 0 & ? \\ 0 & 0 & 1 & ? \\ 0 & 0 & 0 & 0 \end{pmatrix} \qquad \begin{pmatrix} 1 & ? & ? & 0 \\ 0 & 0 & 0 & 1 \\ 0 & 0 & 0 & 0 \end{pmatrix}$$

$$\begin{pmatrix} 1 & ? & ? & ? \\ 0 & 0 & 0 & 0 \\ 0 & 0 & 0 & 0 \end{pmatrix} \qquad \begin{pmatrix} 0 & 1 & 0 & 0 \\ 0 & 0 & 1 & 0 \\ 0 & 0 & 0 & 1 \end{pmatrix}$$

You may feel that, for instance, the last possibility listed above is somewhat artificial, since it could only arise when each equation in the original system looked like

$$0x + a_2y + a_3z + a_4w = b_1,$$

in which case we could ignore x from the outset and call this a system of equations in *three* unknowns y, z, w. But in listing all the possibilities for the coefficient matrix it is technically simpler to allow columns of 0's on the left-hand side. You should try your hand at listing the other possibilities for the 3-by-4 coefficient matrix.

EXERCISES

1. Find all the solutions of the following systems.

(a) $4x_1 + 5x_3 = \quad 6$

$\quad\quad x_2 - 6x_3 = -2$

$\quad 3x_1 + 4x_3 = \quad 3.$ $[Ans.\ x_1 = 9,\ x_2 = -38,\ x_3 = -6.]$

(b) $3x_1 - \quad x_2 - 2x_3 = \quad 2$

$\quad\quad\quad 2x_2 - \quad x_3 = -1$

$\quad 3x_1 - 5x_2 \quad\quad\quad = \quad 3.$ $[Ans.\ \text{No solution.}]$

(c) $\quad -x_1 + 2x_2 + \quad 3x_3 = 0$

$\quad\quad\quad x_1 - 4x_2 - 13x_3 = 0$

$\quad -3x_1 + 5x_2 + \quad 4x_3 = 0.$

$[Ans.\ x_1 = -7x_3,\ x_2 = -5x_3,\ x_3\ \text{arbitrary}.]$

2. Find all the solutions of the following systems.

(a) $x_1 + x_2 + x_3 = 0$

  $2x_1 + 4x_2 + 3x_3 = 0$

    $4x_2 + 4x_3 = 0.$

(b) $x_1 + x_2 + x_3 = -2$

  $2x_1 + 4x_2 + 3x_3 = 3$

    $4x_2 + 2x_3 = 2.$

(c) $4x_1 + 4x_3 = 8$

    $x_2 - 6x_3 = -3$

  $3x_1 + x_2 - 3x_3 = 3.$

3. Find all solutions of the following systems.

(a) $5x_1 - 3x_2 = -7$

   $-2x_1 + 9x_2 = 4$

   $2x_1 + 4x_2 = -2.$ $[Ans.\ x_1 = -\frac{17}{13}; x_2 = \frac{2}{13}.]$

(b) $x_1 + 2x_2 = 1$

   $-3x_1 + 2x_2 = -2$

   $2x_1 + 3x_2 = 1.$ $[Ans.\ \text{No solution.}]$

(c) $5x_1 - 3x_2 - 7x_3 + x_4 = 10$

  $-x_1 + 2x_2 + 6x_3 - 3x_4 = -3$

  $x_1 + x_2 + 4x_3 - 5x_4 = 0.$

4. Find all solutions of:

$$x_1 + 2x_2 + 3x_3 + 4x_4 = 10$$
$$2x_1 - x_2 + x_3 - x_4 = 1$$
$$3x_1 + x_2 + 4x_3 + 3x_4 = 11$$
$$-2x_1 + 6x_2 + 4x_3 + 10x_4 = 18.$$

$[Ans.\ x_1 = \frac{12}{5} - x_3 - \frac{2}{5}x_4; x_2 = \frac{19}{5} - x_3 - \frac{9}{5}x_4, x_3$ and x_4 arbitrary.$]$

5. (a) Let $H = (h_1 \quad h_2)$ and $A = \begin{pmatrix} 3 & -4 \\ 2 & -6 \end{pmatrix}$. Find all solutions of the equa-

  tion $HA = H$. $[Ans.\ H = (0 \quad 0).]$

(b) Let $H = (h_1 \quad h_2)$ and $A = \begin{pmatrix} 3 & 6 \\ -2 & -5 \end{pmatrix}$. Find all solutions of the

  equation $HA = H$. $[Ans.\ H = (k \quad k)\ \text{for any number } k.]$

6. Let $H = (h_1 \quad h_2)$ and $P = \begin{pmatrix} \frac{1}{3} & \frac{2}{3} \\ \frac{4}{5} & \frac{1}{5} \end{pmatrix}$.

    (a) Find all solutions of the equation $HP = H$.

    (b) Choose the solution for which $h_1 + h_2 = 1$.

7. If $H = (h_1 \quad h_2 \quad h_3)$ and $A = \begin{pmatrix} 1 & -2 & 0 \\ 0 & 5 & 4 \\ 0 & -6 & -4 \end{pmatrix}$, find all solutions of the

equation $HA = H$. $[Ans.\ H = (-k/2 \quad 5k/4 \quad k)$ for any number $k.]$

8. If $H = (h_1 \quad h_2 \quad h_3)$ and $P = \begin{pmatrix} 0 & \frac{1}{2} & \frac{1}{2} \\ \frac{1}{3} & \frac{1}{3} & \frac{1}{3} \\ \frac{1}{5} & 0 & \frac{4}{5} \end{pmatrix}$, find all solutions of the equa-

tion $HP = H$. Select the unique solution for which $h_1 + h_2 + h_3 = 1$.

9. Find all column vectors $\begin{pmatrix} x_1 \\ x_2 \\ x_3 \end{pmatrix}$ such that

$$\begin{pmatrix} -1 & 1 & 2 \\ 3 & 0 & 4 \end{pmatrix} \begin{pmatrix} x_1 \\ x_2 \\ x_3 \end{pmatrix} = \begin{pmatrix} 1 \\ 1 \end{pmatrix}$$

$$\left[Ans.\ X = \begin{pmatrix} \frac{1}{3} - \frac{4}{3}x_3 \\ \frac{4}{3} - \frac{10}{3}x_3 \\ x_3 \end{pmatrix} . \right]$$

10. Find all column vectors $\begin{pmatrix} x_1 \\ x_2 \end{pmatrix}$ such that

$$\begin{pmatrix} 1 & 2 \\ 3 & 4 \\ 5 & 6 \end{pmatrix} \begin{pmatrix} x_1 \\ x_2 \end{pmatrix} = \begin{pmatrix} 1 \\ -1 \\ 0 \end{pmatrix} .$$

11. Find all possible ways of writing $\begin{pmatrix} 1 \\ 2 \end{pmatrix}$ as a sum of numerical multiples of

$\begin{pmatrix} 1 \\ -1 \end{pmatrix}$ and $\begin{pmatrix} 3 \\ -2 \end{pmatrix}$ and $\begin{pmatrix} 0 \\ 1 \end{pmatrix}$.

12. Consider three homogeneous equations in four unknowns. Write all possible forms that the reduced set of equations equivalent to the original equations can take. Show that for each such form there is at least one non-beginner variable and hence an infinite number of solutions. [*Hint.* Eight of these forms were found in Example 8.]

13. (a) Compute the elementary 3-by-3 matrix for addition of a first row to a third row, and verify that multiplication by this matrix on the left has the effect of adding the first row of a matrix to its third row.

(b) Describe two kinds of matrix such that multiplication by them has the effect respectively of multiplying a column by a number and adding one column to another.

3. LINEAR EQUATIONS (CONTINUED)

We have seen in Examples 1, 3, and 4 of the previous section that there exists a cut-and-dried process for bringing an arbitrary system of equations into reduced form. At each successive stage of this process, we choose a column of the coefficient matrix that contains at least two nonzero entries. Call this the **active column.** By elementary numerical multiplications, we make all the components of the active column 1 or 0. Next choose a row of the matrix, called the **active row,** which intersects the active column in a 1. Perform elementary subtractions to make the active column have all components 0 except for the 1 at its intersection with the active row. At the next stage of the process, we choose a new active column, reduce it to 1's and 0's, and perform subtractions with a new active row. We continue in this way, at each stage choosing a new active column and active row that have never before been chosen. Eventually no more new choices of active column and row are available. This stage is reached when and only when the rows satisfy the noninterference condition (2.3). More numerical multiplications may be needed to make the matrix satisfy the monic condition (2.4). Finally some shuffling of rows may be required to get the echelon condition (2.5).

If we want to prescribe rigidly the sequence of choices of active column, we can simply choose in turn the first column, second column, and so forth, skipping over any column that is identically zero. For the active row, we cannot in general proceed from first row to second row to third row, and so forth. (Give an example.) But if we want a rigid prescription for choosing the active row, assuming the active column of that stage has already been chosen, we can always choose it to be the topmost among those previously unchosen rows having nonzero intersection with the active column.

From the above discussion we conclude that at each stage of the reduction either there is an active column available, in which case the next step can be carried out, or else the reduction is in fact already complete, except for possible elementary numerical multiplications and reshuffling. Thus we have proved the following theorem.

3.1 Theorem. Every set of equations can be brought into reduced form by repeated use of elementary numerical multiplications and elementary subtractions.

In particular examples you may be tempted to depart from the rigid sequence of operations prescribed above. This is fine. We have shown (see Theorem 2.1) that elementary operations do not change the set of solutions to a system of linear equations. Hence, if you are careful to use only elementary multiplications and subtractions, you will never get into trouble. For instance, you may want at each stage to reshuffle the rows so as to put on top those that begin early. And you may want to perform certain elementary additions before the component at which the active row begins has been made equal to 1.

We conclude this section with some theorems that give a qualitative description of the sets of solutions that can occur when a system of linear equations fails to have a unique solution.

3.2 Theorem. A reduced set of equations has no solution if and only if the set contains a zero equation $OX = b$ with $b \neq 0$, that is, if and only if one of the equations of the reduced set has no solution.

Proof. Let S be the set of solution vectors X for the nonzero equations

$$R_1 X = d_1$$
$$\cdot$$
$$\cdot$$
$$\cdot$$
$$R_r X = d_r.$$

and let T be the set of solutions for the zero equations

$$OX = d_{r+1}$$
$$\cdot$$
$$\cdot$$
$$\cdot$$
$$OX = d_m.$$

The solution set to all m equations is the intersection of S and T, that is, the set of vectors that are in both S and T. From the reduced form it is clear that S is nonempty. For instance, in each nonzero equation one can set all variables except the one at which the row begins equal to zero, and then the solution is displayed. Looking at the zero equations we see that if all the b_i, $i = r + 1, \ldots, m$, are zero then T consists of *all* vectors X. If this happens, the intersection of S and T equals S and is therefore not empty. So the only way to get an empty solution set is to have some equation of the form $OX = d_i \neq 0$ in the reduced set.

The next theorem and its corollary give information about the set of solutions when there are more unknowns than equations.

3.3 Theorem. Consider a set of equations of the form

$$A_1X = b_1$$
$$\cdot$$
$$\cdot$$
$$\cdot$$
$$A_mX = b_m$$

where X is an n-dimensional column vector. If $n > m$ then either these equations have no solution or else they have infinitely many solutions.

Proof. When the equations are put into reduced form, either (a) one of them will be of the form $OX = b_i \neq 0$ or (b) none of them will have this form.

In case (a), the equations have no solution.

In case (b), by the previous theorem, there will be at least one solution. Now in the process of putting the equations into reduced form not every variable can be one at which a row begins, because there are more variables than rows. Hence there is at least one variable not at the beginning of a row. This variable can be transferred to the right-hand side and allowed to assume any value. Thus, as in Examples 5, 6, and 7 of Section 2, there will be infinitely many solutions.

We recall that a homogeneous system of equations is one of the form $AX = 0$.

Corollary. A set of homogeneous equations (see Example 5 of Section 2)

$$A_1X = 0$$

$$A_2X = 0$$

$$\cdot$$
$$\cdot$$
$$\cdot$$

$$A_mX = 0,$$

where X is an n-component column vector and $n > m$ always has infinitely many solutions.

Proof. One obvious solution to these equations is

$$X = \begin{pmatrix} 0 \\ 0 \\ \cdot \\ \cdot \\ \cdot \\ 0 \end{pmatrix}.$$

Since the equations have one solution, by the above theorem they have infinitely many.

By the **homogeneous system associated with a system** $AX = B$, we mean the system $AY = 0$ (using Y for the unknown column vector).

3.4 Theorem. Let X_0 be one solution for $AX = B$. Let Y range over all solutions to the associated homogeneous system. Then $X = Y + X_0$ ranges over all solutions to $AX = B$.

Proof. Given two solutions X_0 and X_1 for $AX = B$, their difference $X_1 - X_0$ is a solution Y for $AX = 0$, so $X_0 + Y = X_1$. Conversely, it is obvious that any vector $Y + X_0$ is a solution.

EXAMPLE. The system of equations

$$\begin{pmatrix} 1 & -2 & -3 \\ 1 & -4 & -13 \\ -3 & 5 & 4 \end{pmatrix} X = \begin{pmatrix} 2 \\ 14 \\ 0 \end{pmatrix}$$

has reduced form

$$\begin{pmatrix} 1 & 0 & 7 \\ 0 & 1 & 5 \\ 0 & 0 & 0 \end{pmatrix} X = \begin{pmatrix} -10 \\ -6 \\ 0 \end{pmatrix},$$

and

$$X_0 = \begin{pmatrix} -10 \\ -6 \\ 0 \end{pmatrix}$$

is easily seen to be one solution. The associated homogeneous system has reduced form

$$\begin{pmatrix} 1 & 0 & 7 \\ 0 & 1 & 5 \\ 0 & 0 & 0 \end{pmatrix} X = \begin{pmatrix} 0 \\ 0 \\ 0 \end{pmatrix}.$$

Letting

$$X = \begin{pmatrix} x_1 \\ x_2 \\ x_3 \end{pmatrix},$$

we transpose x_3 in the above equations to the right-hand side and get

$$\begin{pmatrix} x_1 \\ x_2 \\ x_3 \end{pmatrix} = \begin{pmatrix} -7x_3 \\ -5x_3 \\ x_3 \end{pmatrix}.$$

The solutions to the associated homogeneous system are therefore of the form

$$t \begin{pmatrix} -7 \\ -5 \\ 1 \end{pmatrix}, \qquad -\infty < t < \infty.$$

Hence the solution to the original system consists of all vectors

$$X = t \begin{pmatrix} -7 \\ -5 \\ 1 \end{pmatrix} + \begin{pmatrix} -10 \\ -6 \\ 0 \end{pmatrix}, \quad -\infty < t < \infty.$$

EXERCISES

1. (a) Show that the following system of two equations in three unknowns has no solution:

$$x_1 + 2x_2 + 3x_3 = -7$$
$$x_1 + 2x_2 + 3x_3 = 3.$$

   (b) Construct another example that shows that it is *not* true in the inhomogeneous case that if there are more unknowns than equations then there always is a solution.

2. Consider three homogeneous equations in three unknowns. Show by examples that there may be either a unique solution or infinitely many solutions.

3. Consider the following three equations:

$$x_1 + x_2 + x_3 + 4x_4 + 6x_5 = w_1$$
$$x_1 - x_2 - x_3 - 8x_5 = w_2$$
$$x_1 - x_2 + x_3 + 6x_4 + 4x_5 = w_3.$$

   Choose values for w_1, w_2, w_3 so that these equations reduce to

$$x_1 + 2x_4 - x_5 = 1$$
$$ x_2 - x_4 + x_5 = 2$$
$$x_3 + 3x_4 + 6x_5 = 3.$$

4. Show that, if two nonzero equations have the same set of solutions, then each is a nonzero numerical multiple of the other.

5. The following set of equations has a unique solution. Determine which of the equations could be thrown away without altering the solution.

$$x_1 + x_2 = 5$$
$$-x_1 + 3x_3 = 2$$
$$x_1 + 2x_2 + x_3 = 1$$
$$ x_2 + x_3 = -4.$$

6. Consider a set of three nonhomogeneous equations in two unknowns. Show that, if there is a solution, then at least one of the equations is superfluous and may be omitted. Show that, if there are infinitely many solutions, then two equations are superfluous and may be omitted.

7. Show that the equations

$$-4x_1 + 3x_2 + ax_3 = c$$

$$5x_1 - 4x_2 + bx_3 = d$$

always have a solution for all values of a, b, c, and d.

8. Find conditions on a, b, and c in order that the equations

$$-4x_1 + 3x_2 = a$$

$$5x_1 - 4x_2 = b$$

$$-3x_1 + 2x_2 = c$$

have a solution. $[Ans.\ 2a + b = c.]$

9. (a) Show that the simultaneous linear equations

$$x_1 + x_2 + x_3 = 1$$

$$x_1 + 2x_2 + 3x_3 = 0$$

can be interpreted as a single matrix-times-column-vector equation of the form

$$\begin{pmatrix} 1 & 1 & 1 \\ 1 & 2 & 3 \end{pmatrix} \begin{pmatrix} x_1 \\ x_2 \\ x_3 \end{pmatrix} = \begin{pmatrix} 1 \\ 0 \end{pmatrix}.$$

(b) Show that *any* set of simultaneous linear equations may be interpreted as a matrix equation of the form $AX = B$, where A is an m-by-n matrix, X is an n-component column vector, and B is an m-component column vector.

10. (a) Show that the equations of Exercise 9(a) can be interpreted as a row-vector-times-matrix equation of the form

$$(x_1 \quad x_2 \quad x_3) \begin{pmatrix} 1 & 1 \\ 1 & 2 \\ 1 & 3 \end{pmatrix} = (1 \quad 0).$$

(b) Show that *any* set of simultaneous linear equations may be interpreted as a matrix equation of the form $XA = B$, where A is an m-by-n matrix, X is an m-component row vector, and B is an n-component row vector.

11. (a) Show that the simultaneous linear equations of Exercise 9(a) can be interpreted as asking for all possible ways of expressing the column vector $\begin{pmatrix} 1 \\ 0 \end{pmatrix}$ in terms of the column vectors $\begin{pmatrix} 1 \\ 1 \end{pmatrix}$, $\begin{pmatrix} 1 \\ 2 \end{pmatrix}$, and $\begin{pmatrix} 1 \\ 3 \end{pmatrix}$.

(b) Show that *any* set of linear equations may be interpreted as asking for all possible ways of expressing a column vector in terms of given column vectors.

4. THE INVERSE OF A SQUARE MATRIX

If A and B are square matrices of the same size and such that $AB = BA = I$ (where I is the identity matrix) then we say that A and B are **inverse** to each other and we use the notations $B = A^{-1}$ and $A = B^{-1}$. Here is a numerical example.

$$A = \begin{pmatrix} 4 & 0 & 5 \\ 0 & 1 & -6 \\ 3 & 0 & 4 \end{pmatrix}, \qquad A^{-1} = \begin{pmatrix} 4 & 0 & -5 \\ -18 & 1 & 24 \\ -3 & 0 & 4 \end{pmatrix}.$$

You should verify the fact that the product in both orders gives

$$I = \begin{pmatrix} 1 & 0 & 0 \\ 0 & 1 & 0 \\ 0 & 0 & 1 \end{pmatrix}.$$

No matrix has more than one inverse. For if A has the inverse A^{-1}, and if B is another matrix such that $AB = I$, then

$$B = IB = (A^{-1}A)B = A^{-1}(AB) = A^{-1}I = A^{-1}.$$

A matrix that has an inverse is said to be **invertible**. Often the words **nonsingular** and **singular** are used to mean **invertible** and **noninvertible** respectively.

The notation A^{-1} suggests that the inverse of a matrix might behave much like the reciprocal of a number. But the analogy cannot be pushed too far. Though there is only one number without a reciprocal, namely 0, there are many matrices without inverses. In fact, whenever nonzero matrices A and B are such that their product AB is equal to O – as in

Exercise 18 of Section 1 – then neither A nor B can have an inverse. For if say A^{-1} did exist, then

$$B = IB = (A^{-1}A)B = A^{-1}(AB) = A^{-1}O = O,$$

contradicting the fact that $B \neq O$. It can be proved that the above situation is typical, in the sense that whenever A fails to have an inverse then there exist (infinitely many) nonzero matrices B such that $AB = O$.

In Exercises 9 and 10 you are asked to prove that $(A^{-1})^{-1} = A$, and that $(AB)^{-1} = B^{-1}A^{-1}$.

If you are confronted with a simultaneous set of linear equations involving exactly as many unknowns as there are equations, it makes good sense to ask whether the matrix of coefficients is invertible. If so, there is exactly one solution. For if the column vector X satisfies $AX = W$, then necessarily $X = A^{-1}W$. And on the other hand, this choice of X always works. Hence when we apply our equation-solving process to a set of equations $AX = W$ with invertible coefficient matrix A we must reduce to an equivalent set of equations $IX = W^*$ in which the coefficient matrix is the identity matrix, and in which the right-hand coincides with the unique column-vector solution (see the last theorem of Section 2).

From the above remarks we can develop a general method for computing the inverse of a matrix. Let us begin, however, by considering a more general situation. Suppose we have several sets of equations to solve, but that these sets differ from one another only on their right-hand sides. Writing the coefficients as a matrix A, we have

$$AX_1 = W_1, \quad AX_2 = W_2, \ldots, AX_n = W_n.$$

Then we need to reduce the left-hand side only once, applying the same sequence of row operations simultaneously to each of the right-hand sides. If we line up the column vectors $W_1, W_2, \ldots, W_n$ side by side to form a matrix C, then we are really solving a matrix equation $AB = C$, where A and C are known matrices and we are asked to find all possible matrices B. These B's are formed by lining up the various column-vector solutions $X_1, X_2, \ldots, X_n$.

EXAMPLE 1. Let us illustrate this method by solving the following system of two equations for three different right-hand sides, (a), (b), (c).

$$\text{(a) \quad (b) \quad (c)}$$

$$x_1 + 2x_2 = \quad 1 \quad\quad 1 \quad\quad 0$$

$$2x_1 + 3x_2 = \quad 1 \quad -3 \quad\quad 0.$$

Subtracting twice the first equation from the second one,

$$x_1 + 2x_2 = \quad 1 \quad\quad 1 \quad\quad 0$$

$$- \ x_2 = -1 \quad -5 \quad\quad 0.$$

Multiplying the second equation by -1 and subtracting twice the result from the first equation,

$$x_1 \quad\quad = -1 \quad -9 \quad\quad 0$$

$$x_2 = \quad 1 \quad\quad 5 \quad\quad 0,$$

we find that the solution for (a) is $\begin{pmatrix} -1 \\ 1 \end{pmatrix}$, for (b) it is $\begin{pmatrix} -9 \\ 5 \end{pmatrix}$, and for (c)

we get $\begin{pmatrix} 0 \\ 0 \end{pmatrix}$.

Let us now consider the particular case in which the matrix of coefficients A is n-by-n and invertible. And let us have n different right-hand sides $W_1, W_2, \ldots, W_n$, corresponding to the various columns of the identity matrix I. In other words W_j, for $j = 1, 2, \ldots, n$, is the column vector that has 1 at the jth component and 0's elsewhere. Then the column-vector solution X_j to the equation $AX_j = W_j$ must be the jth column of A^{-1}. Hence we have the following rule for computing the inverse of an invertible matrix A. *Perform a sequence of row operations on A that reduce it to the identity matrix I. Then the result of performing the same sequence of row operations on the matrix I will be the matrix A^{-1}.*

EXAMPLE 2. For a numerical example let us again take

$$A = \begin{pmatrix} 4 & 0 & 5 \\ 0 & 1 & -6 \\ 3 & 0 & 4 \end{pmatrix}, \quad I = \begin{pmatrix} 1 & 0 & 0 \\ 0 & 1 & 0 \\ 0 & 0 & 1 \end{pmatrix}.$$

Subtract third row from first row:

$$\begin{pmatrix} 1 & 0 & 1 \\ 0 & 1 & -6 \\ 3 & 0 & 4 \end{pmatrix}, \quad \begin{pmatrix} 1 & 0 & -1 \\ 0 & 1 & 0 \\ 0 & 0 & 1 \end{pmatrix}.$$

Subtract three times first row from third row:

$$
\begin{pmatrix} 1 & 0 & 1 \\ 0 & 1 & -6 \\ 0 & 0 & 1 \end{pmatrix}, \qquad
\begin{pmatrix} 1 & 0 & -1 \\ 0 & 1 & 0 \\ -3 & 0 & 4 \end{pmatrix}.
$$

Subtract third row from first row:

$$
\begin{pmatrix} 1 & 0 & 0 \\ 0 & 1 & -6 \\ 0 & 0 & 1 \end{pmatrix}, \qquad
\begin{pmatrix} 4 & 0 & -5 \\ 0 & 1 & 0 \\ -3 & 0 & 4 \end{pmatrix}.
$$

Add six times the third row to the second row:

$$
I = \begin{pmatrix} 1 & 0 & 0 \\ 0 & 1 & 0 \\ 0 & 0 & 1 \end{pmatrix}, \qquad
A^{-1} = \begin{pmatrix} 4 & 0 & -5 \\ -18 & 1 & 24 \\ -3 & 0 & 4 \end{pmatrix}.
$$

And this last matrix agrees with what we already know A^{-1} to be. Notice that it is only twice as hard to compute A^{-1} as it is to solve a set of simultaneous equations that has A as coefficient matrix, although naively we might expect it to be n times as hard in view of the fact that we are solving n sets of equations, one for each column W_k of the identity matrix I.

We have insisted above that, in order to apply the given technique for finding A^{-1}, you must first know that A^{-1} exists. Actually you can attempt to apply the technique without this knowledge. If you are successful (that is, if it is possible to reduce A to the identity matrix I) then you know that A^{-1} does exist.

Since each elementary operation on a matrix A can be accomplished by multiplying A on the left by an elementary matrix P (see Theorem 2.2), then, when A is invertible, we have

$$
P_s \dots P_1 A = I, \quad \text{and so} \quad A = P_1^{-1} \dots P_s^{-1}.
$$

If we note that the inverse of an elementary matrix is again elementary, we have proved

4.1 Theorem. Every invertible matrix can be expressed as a product of elementary matrices.

EXERCISES

1. Compute the inverse of each of the following matrices:

$$A = \begin{pmatrix} 1 & 0 & 0 \\ 3 & 1 & 5 \\ -2 & 0 & 1 \end{pmatrix}, \qquad B = \begin{pmatrix} 4 & 3 & 2 \\ 0 & 1 & -1 \\ 0 & 0 & 7 \end{pmatrix},$$

$$C = \begin{pmatrix} 9 & -1 & 0 & 0 \\ 0 & 8 & -2 & 0 \\ 0 & 0 & 7 & -3 \\ 0 & 0 & 0 & 6 \end{pmatrix}, \qquad D = \begin{pmatrix} 1 & 0 & 0 \\ \frac{1}{3} & 4 & 0 \\ \frac{1}{2} & 3 & 2 \end{pmatrix}.$$

2. Show that each of the following matrices fails to have an inverse.

$$A = \begin{pmatrix} 1 & 2 & 3 \\ -1 & 1 & 0 \\ 0 & 3 & 3 \end{pmatrix}, \qquad B = \begin{pmatrix} 1 & 1 & 0 \\ 2 & 0 & 5 \\ -1 & 1 & -5 \end{pmatrix},$$

$$C = \begin{pmatrix} 1 & 1 & 2 & 3 \\ 0 & 5 & 4 & 2 \\ -1 & -3 & 1 & 0 \\ 0 & 3 & 7 & 5 \end{pmatrix}, \qquad D = \begin{pmatrix} 1 & 1 & 1 \\ 1 & 1 & 1 \\ 1 & 1 & 1 \end{pmatrix}.$$

3. Solve the following four systems whose right-hand sides are listed under (a), (b), (c) and (d) below.

$$\begin{array}{ccccccc}
& & & (a) & (b) & (c) & (d) \\
4x_1 & + 5x_3 & = & 1 & 1 & 0 & 0 \\
x_2 & - 6x_3 & = & 2 & 0 & 0 & 1 \\
3x_1 & + 4x_3 & = & 3 & 0 & 1 & 0.
\end{array}$$

$$[\textit{Ans.} \ (a) \ x_1 = -11, \ x_2 = 56, \ x_3 = 9.]$$

4. Solve the following four systems, which differ only in their right-hand sides.

$$
\begin{array}{cccc}
 & \text{(a)} & \text{(b)} & \text{(c)} & \text{(d)} \\
x_1 + x_2 + \ x_3 = & 3 & 0 & 12 & 0 \\
x_1 - x_2 + 2x_3 = & 2 & -1 & 7 & 0 \\
2x_1 + x_2 - \ x_3 = & 2 & 3 & 11 & 0.
\end{array}
$$

5. Show that the following systems have different kinds of solution sets for the different right-hand sides.

$$
\begin{array}{ccc}
 & \text{(a)} & \text{(b)} & \text{(c)} \\
x_1 + x_2 + \ x_3 = & 1 & 2 & 0 \\
x_1 - x_2 + 2x_3 = & -2 & 2 & 0 \\
3x_1 - x_2 + 5x_3 = & -3 & 2 & 0.
\end{array}
$$

6. Solve the following problem by first inverting the matrix. (Assume $ad \neq bc$.) If a Holstein cow is fed x units of grain and y units of hay per day, then she will produce $ax + by$ pounds of skim milk and $cx + dy$ pounds of butterfat per day. In other words her production vector is

$$
\begin{pmatrix} a & b \\ c & d \end{pmatrix}\begin{pmatrix} x \\ y \end{pmatrix}.
$$

What must you feed her to get 40 lb of milk and $\frac{1}{2}$ lb of butterfat? In order to get 60 lb of milk and 1 lb of butterfat?

7. For each of the matrices A and D in Exercise 2 find a nonzero vector whose product with the given matrix is O.

8. Show that if A has no inverse, then neither does any of its positive powders A^k.

9. The formula $(A^{-1})^{-1} = A$ really states that if A has an inverse A^{-1}, then A^{-1} itself has an inverse, and this inverse is A. Prove both parts of this statement.

10. Expand the formula $(AB)^{-1} = B^{-1}A^{-1}$ into a two-part statement analogous to the one in the exercise above. Then prove both parts of your statement.

11. (a) Show that $(AB)^{-1} \neq A^{-1}B^{-1}$ for the matrices $A = \begin{pmatrix} 1 & 1 \\ 0 & 1 \end{pmatrix}$ and $B = \begin{pmatrix} 1 & 0 \\ 2 & 1 \end{pmatrix}.$

(b) Find $(AB)^{-1}$ in two different ways. [*Hint.* Use Exercise 10.]

12. Give a criterion for deciding whether the 2-by-2 matrix $\begin{pmatrix} a & b \\ c & d \end{pmatrix}$ has an

inverse. $\left[Ans.\ ad \neq bc. \right]$

13. Give a formula for $\begin{pmatrix} a & b \\ c & d \end{pmatrix}^{-1}$, when it exists.

14. If $\begin{pmatrix} a & b \\ c & d \end{pmatrix}$ is invertible and has integer components, what condition must

it fulfill in order that $\begin{pmatrix} a & b \\ c & d \end{pmatrix}^{-1}$ have integer components?

15. Prove the identity

$$I + B(I - AB)^{-1}A = (I - BA)^{-1}.$$

5. GEOMETRIC VECTORS

In Section 1 we saw that 2-dimensional column vectors could be interpreted as points in the plane. Let us now see what happens geometrically when we perform the algebraic operations of addition and numerical multiplication. Suppose we are given the origin O and the points X and Y as in Figure 8. Where is the point $X + Y$? So far we know how to add directly only column (or row) vectors, hence to add X and Y we must pick a coordinate system. The simplest choice makes the axes run through X and Y, respectively, with scales such that

$$X = \begin{pmatrix} 1 \\ 0 \end{pmatrix} \quad \text{and} \quad Y = \begin{pmatrix} 0 \\ 1 \end{pmatrix}$$

(see Figure 9). Then

$$X + Y = \begin{pmatrix} 1 \\ 1 \end{pmatrix},$$

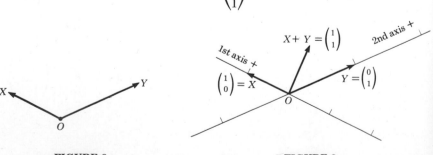

FIGURE 8   FIGURE 9

which can be described (without talking about the coordinate system) as
the fourth vertex of a parallelogram whose other three vertices are O and
X and Y.

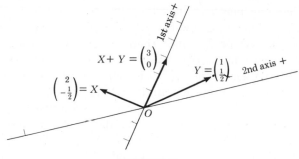

FIGURE 10

Let us try another coordinate system, for instance the one pictured in
Figure 10. Here we manipulate completely different numbers:

$$X = \begin{pmatrix} 2 \\ -\frac{1}{2} \end{pmatrix}, \qquad Y = \begin{pmatrix} 1 \\ \frac{1}{2} \end{pmatrix}, \qquad X + Y = \begin{pmatrix} 3 \\ 0 \end{pmatrix}.$$

But the net geometric result is the same: $X + Y$ is again the fourth
vertex of a parallelogram whose other three vertices are O and X and Y.

Numerical multiplication has an even simpler geometric interpretation.
Figures 11 and 12 each illustrate $-2X$ in different coordinate systems. In
both cases this vector can be described in coordinate-free language as a
point on the line through O and X, but on the opposite side of O and twice
as far from O as X.

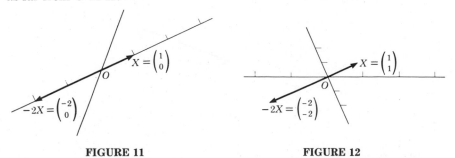

FIGURE 11   **FIGURE 12**

From the above examples it would seem that addition and numerical
multiplication of vectors have purely geometric interpretations that do
not depend on the particular coordinate system. Let us then proceed

to define **geometric vectors**, and the operations on them, without using co-ordinates.

First we must choose one fixed point as **origin**. This point we call the vector O. The other points in the plane are the nonzero vectors. Often it is convenient to draw an arrow from O to a given point X and think of this arrow as the vector X. Since there is an obvious one-to-one corre-spondence between points other than O and arrows issuing from O, the distinction between points and arrows is unimportant. When it is necessary to emphasize one interpretation and exclude the other, we will write "point" or "arrow." Otherwise we will usually write "vector."

To add X and Y we complete the parallelogram, as described above. In case this is impossible, i.e., when O and X and Y lie on one line, then we have special rules, as follows. If X and Y are on the same side of O, then $X + Y$ is also on that side and the length of the arrow $X + Y$ is the sum of the lengths of the arrows X and Y. If X and Y are on opposite sides of O and have different lengths, then the arrow $X + Y$ is on the side of the longer arrow and has length equal to the difference of the lengths of X and Y. If the arrows X and Y have the same length but opposite directions, then $X + Y$ is O. These three degenerate cases are illustrated in Figures 13, 14, and 15. We define $O + X = X + O = X$ for each vector X.

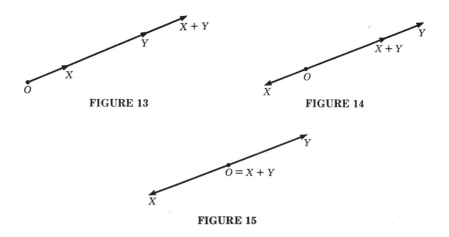

FIGURE 13   FIGURE 14

FIGURE 15

To multiply the vector X by a positive number c, we draw an arrow pointing in the same direction as X, but having length c times the length of X. To multiply X by a negative number $-c$ we draw an arrow c times the length of X but pointing in the opposite direction. And we define $0X = O$ for any vector X.

We will also have occasion to "subtract" vectors. We do this by defining $X - Y$ to be the same as $X + (-Y)$.

Which notions from high school geometry have we used in defining geometric vectors? Essentially only four:

1. We can recognize certain special subsets of the plane, called **lines**.
2. We know when two lines are **parallel**.
3. Given two points on a line we can recognize the **segment** of points that lies between them.
4. We can **compare the lengths** of **parallel** segments.

(And, as a matter of fact, only these four notions were used in Section 1 to construct oblique coordinate systems.) Never in the present section (and never in constructing an oblique coordinate system) do we need to compare the lengths of nonparallel segments, and we do not ever consider the angle between intersecting lines. On the other hand, we made use of both these ideas in constructing a cartesian coordinate system.

The notion of angle and the unrestricted notion of length are commonly felt to be part of the structure of the ordinary space we live in. Yet it is easy to invent practical examples in which these two notions must be ignored.

EXAMPLE 1. Suppose, for instance, that a reconnaissance plane brings back a photograph of enemy fortifications that looks like Figure 16. In the figure, the points labeled X, Y, Z, and W are pillboxes and the lines connecting them are trenches. Assume that the camera is so crude that it shows only a bare ground plan; and assume that we do not know the position from which the picture was taken. Then we can be sure of the following facts: (1) all the trenches are laid out in straight lines, (2) the trench joining pillboxes W and X is parallel to the trench joining pillboxes Y and Z, (3) there is a break in the trench between X and Y, (4) the distance between W and X is twice the distance between Y and Z.

Later, having captured the fortifications, we may discover that they really look like Figure 17. In particular, (5) all angles are right angles,

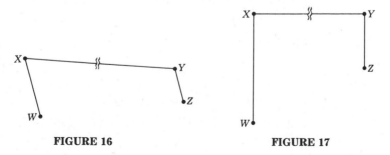

FIGURE 16   FIGURE 17

(6) X is equidistant from W and Y. But there is no hope of deducing these last two facts from the aerial photograph alone.

It is, of course, also possible to define *three*-dimensional geometric vectors. We choose one particular point in 3-dimensional space as the origin O, and we define the nonzero vectors to be the other points (or arrows issuing from O). Then the definitions of addition and numerical multiplication are exactly what they were for 2-dimensional geometric vectors. In fact we scarcely need to think 3-dimensionally at all. For in adding vectors X and Y not collinear with O we restrict our attention to the plane determined by O and X and Y, and complete the parallelogram in this plane. Similarly, in numerical multiplication, or in the degenerate cases of addition illustrated in Figures 13, 14, and 15, we restrict our attention to a certain line.

EXERCISES

1. Draw a figure like Figure 18 and construct the following vectors.
   (a) $X + Y$.
   (b) $X + Z$.
   (c) $Y + Z$.
   (d) $Z + X$.

2. Draw a figure like that of Figure 18 and construct the vectors
   (a) $(X + Y) + Z$
   (b) $X + (Y + Z)$
   and compare your results.

3. In a figure like Figure 18, find
   (a) $3X$.
   (b) $\frac{1}{2}Y$.
   (c) $-Z$.
   (d) $X - Y$.
   (e) $3X - Z$.

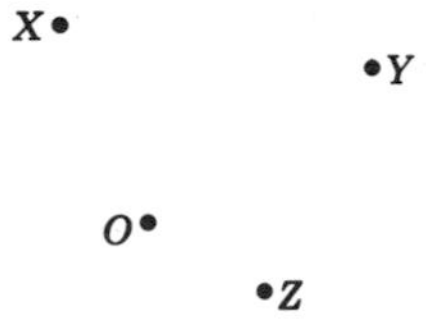

$X\bullet$

$\bullet Y$

$O\bullet$

$\bullet Z$

FIGURE 18

4. Prove for any vector X and any pair of numbers c_1, c_2 that $c_2(c_1X) = (c_2c_1)X$. [*Hint.* Divide the problem into cases that depend on the signs of c_1 and c_2.]

5. In a figure like Figure 18, choose a coordinate system whose axes run through X and Z.
   (a) Express X and Y in this coordinate system.
   (b) Express $X + Y$, as found in Exercise 1(a), in this coordinate system.
   (c) Check your answer by numerical vector addition.

6. In a figure like Figure 18 find $3(X + Y)$ and $3X + 3Y$. Present a geometrical argument to prove that these two vectors are the same.

7. In a figure like Figure 18 choose a convenient coordinate system, and use it to prove the result of Exercise 6 numerically.

8. In a figure like Figure 19 find

    (a) $X + Y$.

    (b) $X - Y$.

    (c) $2X + 3Y$.

FIGURE 19

9. In a figure like Figure 19 find $3(X + Y)$ and $3X + 3Y$. Present a geometric argument to prove that the two resulting vectors are the same.

10. In a figure like Figure 19 determine c_1, c_2 so that $O = c_1X + c_2Y$, and $c_1 + c_2 = 1$.

6. ABSTRACT VECTOR SPACES

You may be inclined to ask at this point whether vectors are "really" columns and rows of numbers, or geometrical objects? And what right has a physicist to speak of velocities and forces as vectors? Mathematicians dodge such questions by refusing to consider the nature of the individual vectors and instead concentrating their attention upon how the totality of vectors in a given problem acts with respect to addition and numerical multiplication. The best way to do this is to write down a reasonable set of axioms for an abstract mathematical structure, called a **vector space**, that has all the important algebraic properties common to the various concrete collections of vectors (numerical, geometrical, physical) that we have mentioned.

A **vector space** is any set of objects X, Y, Z, ... called **vectors** that can be "added" to each other and "multiplied" by real numbers a, b, c, ... – the resulting sums and products being again vectors in the vector space – provided that these abstract operations of addition and multiplication obey certain of the laws of ordinary arithmetic, to wit:

1. Triple sums can be computed from the left or from the right. That is, $(X + Y) + Z = X + (Y + Z)$.
2. There is a special vector called O with the property that $O + X = X$, for every vector X.
3. The numerical multiple $(-1)X$ acts like the "negative" of X. That is, $(-1)X + X = O$. And hence we usually write $(-1)X = -X$.
4. Sums can be computed in either order. That is, $X + Y = Y + X$.
5. Repeated numerical multiples can be computed from the left or from the right. That is, $a(bX) = (ab)X$. Notice the resemblance of this rule to rule (1).

6. The multiple of a vector by a sum of numbers acts like ordinary multiplication. That is, $(a + b)X = aX + bX$.

7. The multiple of a sum of vectors by a number acts like ordinary multiplication. That is, $a(X + Y) = aX + aY$.

Other important rules can be derived from the rules 1 through 7. For instance, $-(-X) = X$. For by rule 3, $-(-X) + (-X) = 0$. Hence, adding X to both sides,

$$(-(-X) + (-X)) + X = X.$$

Now by rule 1 the left-hand side of this last expression equals $-(-X) + ((-X) + X)$, which by rule 3 equals $-(-X) + O$, and then by rules 2 and 4 equals $-(-X)$.

Let us also prove the fact that the number 1 behaves well as a multiplier, i.e., $1X = X$. It is enough to prove that $((-1)(-1))X = X$. By rule 5, the left-hand side equals $(-1)((-1)X)$, which we have agreed in rule 3 to write $-(-X)$. And we have just proved this last equal to X. To summarize this proof we restate the steps thus:

$$1X = ((-1)(-1))X = (-1)((-1)X) = -(-X) = X.$$

EXAMPLE 1. The space $\mathfrak{R}^n$ of n-dimensional column vectors. The seven axioms are identical with the seven rules listed in Exercise 1 of Section 1. The proof that column vectors obey these rules is done in two steps: first, the operations of addition and numerical multiplication of column vectors are both performed component by component; second, an individual component is simply a number, and numbers are well known to obey the seven rules.

EXAMPLE 2. The space of plane geometrical vectors. Before verifying the seven axioms it will be useful to mention a method equivalent to the one discussed in Section 5 for adding Y to X. We draw an auxiliary arrow having the same length and direction as Y but issuing from the tip of X. Then $X + Y$ is the arrow from the origin to the tip of this auxiliary arrow. In Figure 20 we have not drawn Y itself, but instead have attached the label Y to the auxiliary arrow.

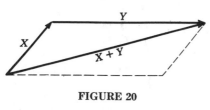

FIGURE 20

It is obvious that this method of addition gives the same result as the method discussed in Section 5 because if we complete the parallelogram (see the dotted lines in Figure 20) then the arrow $X + Y$ *is* the diagonal of the parallelogram.

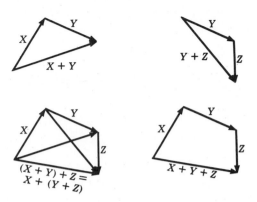

FIGURE 21

Axiom 1 is now verified in Figure 21. Again, we have attached the labels Y and Z to appropriate auxiliary arrows. Once this axiom is verified we can write $X + Y + Z$ without parentheses. This triple sum has the direct geometrical interpretation pictured in Figure 21.

Axiom 2 is true because we have defined $O + X = X + O = X$.

Axiom 3 is a consequence of our definition of $-1X$ (namely, as a vector having the same length as X but pointing in the opposite direction) and of our definition of addition in the degenerate cases where the two vectors do not form a true parallelogram. This axiom states informally that if we walk from one end of a line segment to the other, and then walk back again, the net result is the same as if we had not moved at all.

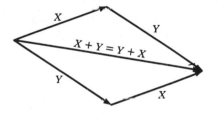

FIGURE 22

Axiom 4 corresponds to the situation pictured in Figure 22, and its validity is a consequence of well-known facts about parallelograms.

To check Axiom 5 we must check that $a(bX)$ has the same length and direction as $(ab)X$. The directions are the same because they are either both in the same direction as X (in the case when a and b have like sign, i.e., both positive or both negative) or else both in the direction opposite to that of X (in the case where a and b have unlike sign). The lengths, moreover, are both equal to ab times the length of X (when $ab > 0$) or else to $-ab$ times the length of X (when $ab < 0$).

Axiom 6 operates in terms of multiples of one vector X, hence its validity depends on the fact that $(a + b)c = ac + bc$ is true for ordinary numbers, c being interpreted here as the length of X.

Axiom 7 is verified by considering the similar triangles in Figure 23.

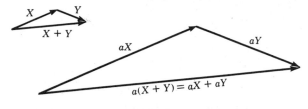

FIGURE 23

In verifying each of the seven axioms, we should also consider the cases where some or all of the vectors and numbers are zero. These cases are hard to picture geometrically, but it is easy to see that none of them disturbs the validity of the axioms. For instance, in Axiom 5, if either a or b is 0 or if X is O, then both $a(bX)$ and $(ab)X$ are O.

EXAMPLE 3. Let $\mathcal{U}$ be a finite set, and let $\mathcal{X}$ be all numerical functions that have $\mathcal{U}$ as domain. Define the sum of two functions $f + g$ and the numerical product cf by $f + g(u) = f(u) + g(u)$ and $cf(u) = c(f(u))$ respectively. With these two definitions the set $\mathcal{X}$ becomes a vector space. It is easy to verify the seven axioms directly. But it is even easier to observe that when $\mathcal{U}$ contains n points there is a natural one-one correspondence between numerical functions f on $\mathcal{U}$ and n-dimensional column vectors. If f is defined by the table

u	$f(u)$
u_1	a_1
u_2	a_2
.	.
.	.
.	.
u_n	a_n

then we make correspond to f the column vector

$$\begin{pmatrix} a_1 \\ a_2 \\ \cdot \\ \cdot \\ \cdot \\ a_n \end{pmatrix}.$$

From the definition of addition of numerical functions it is clear that if the column vector

$$\begin{pmatrix} a_1 \\ a_2 \\ \cdot \\ \cdot \\ \cdot \\ a_n \end{pmatrix}$$

corresponds to the function f and if the column vector

$$\begin{pmatrix} b_1 \\ b_2 \\ \cdot \\ \cdot \\ \cdot \\ b_n \end{pmatrix}$$

corresponds to the function g, then the column vector

$$\begin{pmatrix} a_1 + b_1 \\ \cdot \\ \cdot \\ \cdot \\ a_n + b_n \end{pmatrix}$$

corresponds to the function $f + g$.

Similarly

$$\begin{pmatrix} ca_1 \\ \cdot \\ \cdot \\ \cdot \\ ca_n \end{pmatrix}$$

corresponds to cf. And since we already know that the set of n-dimensional column vectors satisfies the axioms, then so must the set of numerical functions on $\mathfrak{U}$.

EXERCISES

1. Is the following a vector space? Let $\mathfrak{X}$ be the set of all positive numbers. Define the abstract "addition" to be the same as ordinary multiplication. And if c is a number and X a "vector," define the abstract numerical product to be the same as the ordinary number X to the cth power.

[*Ans.* Yes.]

2. Verify informally that the space of 3-dimensional geometrical vectors obeys the vector space axioms.

3. Show that the vector O described in Axiom 2 is unique. That is, no abstract vector space possess two different vectors O_1 and O_2 fulfilling the requirements of Axiom 2.

4. Show by using Axiom 6 that $0X = O$.

5. Show by using Axiom 7 that $cO = O$.

6. Show that if $cX = O$, then either $c = 0$ or else $X = O$.

7. Show that the set of ordinary real numbers forms a vector space.

8. Is it possible for a vector space to contain only finitely many vectors, but more than one?   [*Ans.* No.]

9. Let $\mathfrak{X}$ be any one-element set. Show how to define addition and numerical multiplication in such a way that $\mathfrak{X}$ becomes a vector space.

10. In Example 3 let us restrict our functions to those having nonnegative values. Is the resulting space a vector space?   [*Ans.* No.]

11. Let $\mathfrak{X}$ be the space of all 3-by-2 matrices, with addition and numerical multiplication defined as usual. Is $\mathfrak{X}$ a vector space?

12. Let $\mathfrak{X}$ consist of that subset of $\mathfrak{R}^3$ in which each column vector has the second component equal to 0. Show that $\mathfrak{X}$ is a vector space.

13. Let $\mathfrak{X}$ consist of that subset of $\mathfrak{R}^3$ in which each column vector has second component equal to 1. Show that $\mathfrak{X}$ is *not* a vector space.

7. LINEAR TRANSFORMATIONS

A function f whose domain is a vector space and whose range is a subset of a vector space is **linear** if it satisfies the following two axioms:

(1) $f(X + Y) = f(X) + f(Y)$, for every X and Y in the domain.
(2) $f(cX) = cf(X)$, for every X in the domain and every number c.

In the rest of this book we shall call a linear function a **linear transformation**. For the special case of a numerical valued linear function we shall use the word **functional**. We shall often use the letters **A, B, C** for transformations and the letters **F, G, H** for functionals. The choice of these letters is dictated by the fact (proved later) that every transformation on a space of column vectors can be defined by a matrix, and every functional by a row vector.

For the value of the transformation **A** at the vector X we will write **A**X instead of the usual function notation **A**(X). Similarly **F**X. We will often write $\mathfrak{X} \xrightarrow{A} \mathfrak{Y}$ for the transformation **A** whose domain is equal to the vector space $\mathfrak{X}$ and whose range is a subset of the vector space $\mathfrak{Y}$. If it happens that the range of **A** is all of $\mathfrak{Y}$, then **A** is said to be a transformation **onto** $\mathfrak{Y}$.

EXAMPLE 1. The following rule defines a linear transformation **A** whose domain is the space $\Re^3$ of 3-dimensional column vectors and whose range is the space $\Re^2$ of 2-dimensional column vectors.

$$\mathbf{A}\begin{pmatrix} x_1 \\ x_2 \\ x_3 \end{pmatrix} = \begin{pmatrix} x_1 - x_3 \\ 3x_1 + 2x_2 + x_3 \end{pmatrix}.$$

It is easy to see that

$$\mathbf{A}\begin{pmatrix} x_1 + y_1 \\ x_2 + y_2 \\ x_3 + y_3 \end{pmatrix} = \mathbf{A}\begin{pmatrix} x_1 \\ x_2 \\ x_3 \end{pmatrix} + \mathbf{A}\begin{pmatrix} y_1 \\ y_2 \\ y_3 \end{pmatrix}.$$

And it is easy to see that

$$\mathbf{A}\begin{pmatrix} cx_1 \\ cx_2 \\ cx_3 \end{pmatrix} = c\mathbf{A}\begin{pmatrix} x_1 \\ x_2 \\ x_3 \end{pmatrix}.$$

The fact that **A** has as range the whole space of 2-dimensional column vectors is equivalent to the fact that the simultaneous equations

$$x_1 \quad\quad - x_3 = c_1$$
$$3x_1 + 2x_2 + x_3 = c_2$$

have a solution for every choice of numbers c_1 and c_2 on the right-hand side.

Notice that the transformation **A** can be defined by means of the matrix

$$A = \begin{pmatrix} 1 & 0 & -1 \\ 3 & 2 & 1 \end{pmatrix}$$

That is, when $X = \begin{pmatrix} x_1 \\ x_2 \\ x_3 \end{pmatrix}$, then

$$AX = \begin{pmatrix} 1 & 0 & -1 \\ 3 & 2 & 1 \end{pmatrix}\begin{pmatrix} x_1 \\ x_2 \\ x_3 \end{pmatrix}.$$

EXAMPLE 2. Let $\mathfrak{X}$ be the vector space of vectors in the plane. Let $\mathcal{L}$ be a fixed line through the origin. Define $\mathbf{A}$ to be the **reflection** of $\mathfrak{X}$ across the line $\mathcal{L}$. That is, the point X and the image point $\mathbf{A}X$ are the same distance from $\mathcal{L}$ but on opposite sides, and the line segment joining X and $\mathbf{A}X$ is perpendicular to $\mathcal{L}$. See Figure 24.

The fact that $\mathbf{A}(X + Y) = \mathbf{A}X + \mathbf{A}Y$ is illustrated in Figure 25.

And the fact that $\mathbf{A}(cX) = c\mathbf{A}X$ is illustrated in Figure 26.

The above example disobeys the strictures against angle and length that we imposed in Section 5. In order to give interesting geometric examples of transformations we are in fact forced to recognize properties of the plane that cannot be stated in pure vector-space terms. It is correct for us to use the nonvector-space properties in giving examples of transformations, but it would not be correct to use them for proving theorems about transformations.

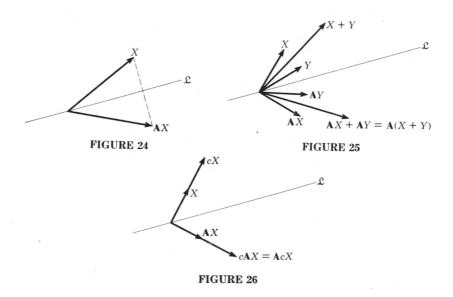

FIGURE 24

FIGURE 25

FIGURE 26

A function that never takes on the same value twice is known as a **one-one function** because it matches uniquely one element of the domain with one of the range. To put it negatively, a function f is *not* one-one if and only if

$$f(X_1) = f(X_2), \qquad \text{for some } X_1 \neq X_2$$
$$\text{in the domain of } f.$$

When a linear transformation $\mathbf{A}$ with domain $\mathfrak{X}$ and range $\mathfrak{Y}$ is one-one, then it makes the space $\mathfrak{X}$ and the space $\mathfrak{Y}$ abstractly identical as vector spaces. Each element X of $\mathfrak{X}$ corresponds to a unique element Y of $\mathfrak{Y}$, and vice versa. And both of the abstract algebraic operations, vector addition and numerical multiplication, are preserved by this correspondence. Hence any statement about vectors in $\mathfrak{X}$, provided this statement uses only pure vector space terms, is equivalent, in the obvious way, to a certain statement about vectors in $\mathfrak{Y}$.

EXAMPLE 3. The outstanding example of an abstract identification of two vector spaces is given by the transformation that sends each 2-dimensional column vector $\begin{pmatrix} x \\ y \end{pmatrix}$ onto the point in the plane that has these two numbers as its x and y coordinates. The fact that this identification of number-couples with geometric points is very familiar to you should not obscure the fact that two quite different things are being identified.

Another example of abstract identification of vector spaces is the correspondence between functions and column vectors explained in Example 3 of the previous section.

If $\mathfrak{X} \xrightarrow{A} \mathfrak{Y}$ is a transformation between a space $\mathfrak{X}$ and a space $\mathfrak{Y}$ then the **kernel** of the transformation is the set of all vectors X in $\mathfrak{X}$ such that $AX = O$. The kernel of any transformation always contains the vector O and hence is nonempty.

The kernel of A is itself a vector space (see Exercise 19 of Section 8). If the transformation A is one-one its kernel consists of the vector O only (see Exercise 2).

EXAMPLE 4. Let the transformation $\mathfrak{R}^2 \xrightarrow{A} \mathfrak{R}$ be defined by

$$A \begin{pmatrix} a \\ b \end{pmatrix} = a + b.$$

The kernel of this transformation is the set of all vectors of the form $\begin{pmatrix} a \\ -a \end{pmatrix}$ and it is easy to see that this is a vector space.

EXERCISES

1. Show that for any transformation A, $A(X - Y) = AX - AY$.

2. Show that A is one-one if and only if the kernel of A consists of the vector O alone.

3. Give a necessary and sufficient condition for a 2-by-2 matrix $\begin{pmatrix} a & b \\ c & d \end{pmatrix}$ to have a nonzero vector in its kernel.   [*Ans.* $ad = bc$.]

4. Consider the set of real numbers $\mathfrak{R}$ as a vector space. Among the various numerical functions with domain $\mathfrak{R}$ that are familiar to you from calculus, which ones are linear transformations? In particular, what constant functions are linear? (*Warning*: the usual calculus definition of "linear function" is different from ours.)   [*Ans.* $f(x) = ax$; 0.]

5. Show that the identity function **I**, such that $\mathbf{I}X = X$ for each vector X in a given space $\mathfrak{X}$, is a linear transformation.

6. Let **A** be a transformation of ordinary plane vectors. Suppose that there are vectors X and Y such that $\mathbf{A}X = X$ and $\mathbf{A}Y = Y$. And suppose that the line through (the tips of) X and Y does not pass through O. What can we say about the transformation **A**?

                    [*Ans.* **A** is the identity transformation.]

7. Let **A** and **B** be transformations each with domain the space $\mathfrak{R}^3$ of 3-dimensional column vectors. Let

$$E_1 = \begin{pmatrix} 1 \\ 0 \\ 0 \end{pmatrix}, \quad E_2 = \begin{pmatrix} 0 \\ 1 \\ 0 \end{pmatrix}, \quad E_3 = \begin{pmatrix} 0 \\ 0 \\ 1 \end{pmatrix}.$$

Suppose that $\mathbf{A}E_1 = \mathbf{B}E_1$, $\mathbf{A}E_2 = \mathbf{B}E_2$, $\mathbf{A}E_3 = \mathbf{B}E_3$. Show that then $\mathbf{A} = \mathbf{B}$.

8. Let $\mathfrak{X}$ be the set of 2-dimensional column vectors. Show that numerical multiplication by a fixed number $c \neq 0$ is a transformation of $\mathfrak{X}$ into itself.

9. Consider the following transformation **T** with domain and range 2-dimensional column vectors:

$$\mathbf{T}\begin{pmatrix} x_1 \\ x_2 \end{pmatrix} = \begin{pmatrix} x_2 \\ -x_1 \end{pmatrix}.$$

When the column vectors are interpreted as points in the plane, what geometric effect does the transformation have?

10. Show that the rotation of the plane defined in Example 1 of Section 1 is a linear transformation.

11. Given a one-one transformation **A** of a space $\mathfrak{X}$ onto a space $\mathfrak{Y}$ let us define the following function **B** with domain $\mathfrak{Y}$ and range $\mathfrak{X}$. Since the range of **A** is all of $\mathfrak{Y}$, then each Y in $\mathfrak{Y}$ can be written $Y = \mathbf{A}X$ for some

X in $\mathfrak{X}$. And since $\mathbf{A}$ is one-one, then Y can be written $\mathbf{A}X$ for only one X. We now define $\mathbf{B}(Y) = X$. Prove that this function is a linear transformation from $\mathfrak{Y}$ onto $\mathfrak{X}$. (We call the transformations $\mathbf{A}$ and $\mathbf{B}$ **inverse** to each other.)

12. Show that if A is an invertible n-by-n matrix, then A defines a one-one transformation with domain and range the space of n-dimensional column vectors.

13. In Exercise 12, show that the matrices A and A^{-1} define transformations inverse to each other.

14. Let $\mathfrak{R}^3$ be the set of all 3-dimensional column vectors and $\mathfrak{R}^2$ be the set of all 2-dimensional column vectors. Find the kernels of the following transformations.

(a)
$$A \begin{pmatrix} x_1 \\ x_2 \\ x_3 \end{pmatrix} = \begin{pmatrix} x_1 + x_3 \\ x_2 - x_3 \end{pmatrix}.$$

$$\left[\textit{Ans.} \text{ The set of vectors of the form } \begin{pmatrix} -a \\ a \\ a \end{pmatrix}. \right]$$

(b)
$$A \begin{pmatrix} x_1 \\ x_2 \\ x_3 \end{pmatrix} = \begin{pmatrix} 3x_1 + 7x_2 \\ x_3 \end{pmatrix}.$$

(c)
$$A \begin{pmatrix} x_1 \\ x_2 \\ x_3 \end{pmatrix} = \begin{pmatrix} x_2 \\ x_3 \end{pmatrix}.$$

$$\left[\textit{Ans.} \text{ The set of vectors of the form } \begin{pmatrix} a \\ 0 \\ 0 \end{pmatrix}. \right]$$

(d)
$$A \begin{pmatrix} x_1 \\ x_2 \\ x_3 \end{pmatrix} = \begin{pmatrix} 0 \\ 0 \end{pmatrix}.$$

8. MORE EXAMPLES OF VECTOR SPACES AND TRANSFORMATIONS

Once you understand the notion of an abstract vector space, you will discover in mathematics many examples of this structure.

EXAMPLE 1. The set of all real numbers is itself a vector space. In checking the axioms we must not be confused by the fact that each real number now plays two roles. Let us write each number in **boldface** when it plays the role of a vector. Then the axioms simply coincide with certain familiar rules of elementary arithmetic.

$$(\mathbf{x} + \mathbf{y}) + \mathbf{z} = \mathbf{x} + (\mathbf{y} + \mathbf{z})$$

$$0 + \mathbf{x} = \mathbf{x}$$

$$-\mathbf{x} + \mathbf{x} = 0$$

$$\mathbf{x} + \mathbf{y} = \mathbf{y} + \mathbf{x}$$

$$a(b\mathbf{x}) = (ab)\mathbf{x}$$

$$(a + b)\mathbf{x} = a\mathbf{x} + b\mathbf{x}$$

$$a(\mathbf{x} + \mathbf{y}) = a\mathbf{x} + a\mathbf{y}.$$

EXAMPLE 2. For fixed m and n, say $m = 3$ and $n = 7$, the set of all m-by-n matrices constitutes a vector space. In checking the axioms we consider only addition and numerical multiplication, and ignore matrix multiplication.

EXAMPLE 3. In Example 3 of Section 6 we took the set $\mathfrak{U}$ to be finite. Actually this example is valid for an infinite set $\mathfrak{U}$; for instance, suppose that $\mathfrak{U}$ is the "unit interval" of all real numbers between 0 and 1. We again take $\mathfrak{X}$ to be the set of all numerical functions with domain $\mathfrak{U}$, defining addition and numerical multiplication as usual. There is now, of course, no question of making a column vector correspond to each function unless we are willing to contemplate an infinite-dimensional column vector that has a "component" for each real number between 0 and 1.

When a subset $\mathfrak{Y}$ of a vector space $\mathfrak{X}$ is itself a vector space, then $\mathfrak{Y}$ is called a **subspace** of $\mathfrak{X}$. It is understood that the operations of addition and numerical multiplication for vectors in $\mathfrak{Y}$ are identical with the operations already defined for vectors in $\mathfrak{X}$.

Theorem. In order that a subset $\mathcal{Y}$ of a vector space $\mathcal{X}$ be a subspace it is necessary and sufficient that $\mathcal{Y}$ have the following two properties:

(1) if X and Y belong to $\mathcal{Y}$, then so does $X + Y$;

(2) if X belongs to $\mathcal{Y}$, then so do all numerical multiples cX.

Proof. Suppose $\mathcal{Y}$ is a subspace. Then it is a vector space. Hence when X and Y belong to $\mathcal{Y}$, then $X + Y$ and cX are defined and belong to $\mathcal{Y}$. But these operations in $\mathcal{Y}$ are assumed to be the same as those defined for the vector space $\mathcal{X}$. Hence $\mathcal{Y}$ has properties (1) and (2). Conversely, suppose that the subset $\mathcal{Y}$ has the properties (1) and (2). Then for each pair of vectors X and Y in $\mathcal{Y}$ we have an operation of addition already defined, and $X + Y$ is in $\mathcal{Y}$. Similarly for numerical multiplication. And these two operations, looked at as operations on $\mathcal{Y}$, surely satisfy the axioms for a vector space, since the axioms are satisfied on $\mathcal{X}$.

EXAMPLE 4. Every vector space $\mathcal{X}$ has two trivial subspaces: the space $\mathcal{X}$ itself, and the space consisting of the vector O alone.

EXAMPLE 5. Let $\mathcal{Y}$ be a subspace of the space $\mathcal{X}$ of 2-dimensional geometrical vectors, not one of the two trivial subspaces mentioned in Example 4. Then $\mathcal{Y}$ must be a line through the origin. For, because $\mathcal{Y}$ does not consist of O alone, it must contain some nonzero vector Y. Because Y is a subspace it must then contain all numerical multiples of Y. These form a line through the origin. If $\mathcal{Y}$ contains no other vectors, well and good. If $\mathcal{Y}$ contains some Z that is not a numerical multiple of Y, then it is not hard to prove that every vector X in $\mathcal{X}$ can be written as a sum of numerical multiples of Y and Z, and hence that $\mathcal{Y}$ would then be the same as the whole space $\mathcal{X}$. The details of the last assertion will be verified in Section 9.

EXAMPLE 6. Let $\mathcal{U}$ be the unit interval and let $\mathcal{Y}$ be the set of all numerical functions with domain $\mathcal{U}$ that are defined by polynomial formulas. Then $\mathcal{Y}$ is the subspace of the space $\mathcal{X}$ of all numerical functions with domain $\mathcal{U}$. For instance, if **X** has the polynomial formula

$$\mathbf{X}(t) = 5 - 2t + 3t^2$$

and **Y** has the formula

$$\mathbf{Y}(t) = 1 + 2t - t^2 + t^3,$$

then $\mathbf{X} + \mathbf{Y}$ has the formula

$$(\mathbf{X} + \mathbf{Y})(t) = 6 + 2t^2 + t^3.$$

EXAMPLE 7. Let $\mathfrak{U}$ and $\mathfrak{X}$ be as in Example 6 and let $\mathfrak{Y}$ be the set of all functions with domain $\mathfrak{U}$ that are solutions of the homogeneous differential equation

$$\mathbf{X}'''' - 5\mathbf{X}''' + 5\mathbf{X}'' + 5\mathbf{X}' - 6\mathbf{X} = 0.$$

Then $\mathfrak{Y}$ is a subspace of $\mathfrak{X}$. For instance, if the functions $\mathbf{W}(t) = e^{-t}$ and $\mathbf{Y}(t) = e^{3t}$ are solutions (and they are), then the function $\mathbf{Z}(t) = e^{-t} + e^{3t}$ must be a solution, since $\mathbf{Z}(t) = \mathbf{W}(t) + \mathbf{Y}(t)$, $\mathbf{Z}'(t) = \mathbf{W}'(t) + \mathbf{Y}'(t)$, $\mathbf{Z}''(t) = \mathbf{W}''(t) + \mathbf{Y}''(t)$, etc. Hence substitution of $\mathbf{Z}$ in the differential equation yields $0 + 0 = 0$.

With the above additions to our vector space repertory it is possible to give new interesting examples of transformations.

EXAMPLE 8. Let $\mathfrak{X}$ be the vector space of all polynomials in one variable. We denote a typical element in this space by

$$X = a_0 + a_1 t + a_2 t^2 + a_3 t^3 + \ldots + a_n t^n.$$

(This notation is less formal than that used above where $\mathbf{X}$ denoted a function and $\mathbf{X}(t)$ its value at t.) Let $\mathbf{A}X$ be the derivative

$$\mathbf{A}X = a_1 + 2a_2 t + 3a_3 t^2 + 4a_4 t^3 + \ldots + na_n t^{n-1}.$$

Then it is easy to show that $\mathbf{A}$ is a linear transformation.

EXAMPLE 9. Let $\mathfrak{X}$ be the vector space of polynomials, let X be a polynomial in $\mathfrak{X}$, and let $\mathbf{A}X$ be the result of substituting $t + 1$ for t in X. For instance, if $X = 3 + t - 2t^2$, then

$$\mathbf{A}X = 3 + (t + 1) - 2(t + 1)^2 = 2 - 3t - 2t^2.$$

EXAMPLE 10. If $\mathfrak{X}$ is the space of 3-by-7 matrices, and A is some fixed 2-by-3 matrix, and B is some fixed 7-by-5 matrix, then the following transformation $\mathbf{T}$ has domain $\mathfrak{X}$ and range some subspace of the vector space of 2-by-5 matrices.

$$\mathbf{T}C = ACB.$$

EXAMPLE 11. Let $X_1, \ldots, X_n$ be vectors in an abstract vector space

$\mathfrak{X}$. Define a transformation **A** from column vectors onto a subspace of $\mathfrak{X}$ by the rule

$$\mathbf{A}\begin{pmatrix} c_1 \\ \cdot \\ \cdot \\ \cdot \\ c_n \end{pmatrix} = c_1 X_1 + \ldots + c_n X_n.$$

EXAMPLE 12. Let $\mathbf{F}_1, \ldots, \mathbf{F}_n$ be functionals on an abstract space $\mathfrak{X}$. Define a transformation **A** from $\mathfrak{X}$ onto a subspace of column vectors by the rule

$$\mathbf{A}X = \begin{pmatrix} \mathbf{F}_1 X \\ \cdot \\ \cdot \\ \cdot \\ \mathbf{F}_n X \end{pmatrix}.$$

We also include below two new examples of transformations on the space $\mathfrak{X}$ of plane geometric vectors. In defining these we again take the point of view that in this illustration it is legitimate to use all the familiar notions of elementary geometry even though some of these notions make no sense in an abstract vector space.

EXAMPLE 13. Let $\mathfrak{X}$ be provided with cartesian horizontal and vertical axes. Let **A** send every point into the point on the x-axis that is directly above it or directly below it. This kind of transformation is called a **projection**.

EXAMPLE 14. Let **A** move each point in the upper half-plane horizontally to the right, and in the lower half-plane horizontally to the left, a distance equal to the distance of the point from the x-axis. This kind of transformation is called a **shear**.

EXERCISES

1. If $\mathfrak{X} \xrightarrow{A} \mathcal{Y}$ is a linear transformation, prove that the range of **A** is a subspace of the vector space $\mathcal{Y}$.

2. Describe geometrically all the subspaces of the space of 3-dimensional geometric vectors. [*Hint.* There are four types of subspaces.]

3. (a) Verify that the transformation in Example 8 is really a linear function.
   (b) Verify that the transformation in Example 10 is really a linear function.

4. Verify geometrically that the transformations in Examples 13 and 14 are really linear functions.

5. Let $\mathfrak{U}$ be the unit interval, that is, the set of real numbers between 0 and 1, and let $\mathfrak{X}$ be the vector space of all numerical functions with domain $\mathfrak{U}$. Verify that each of the following sets of functions is a subspace of $\mathfrak{X}$.
   (a) All continuous numerical functions with domain $\mathfrak{U}$.
   (b) All differentiable functions with domain $\mathfrak{U}$.
   (c) All numerical functions **X** on $\mathfrak{U}$ such that

$$\int_0^1 \mathbf{X}(t) \, dt = 0.$$

   (d) All differentiable functions **X** with domain $\mathfrak{U}$ that have $\mathbf{X}'(0) = \mathbf{X}'(1) = 0$.
   (e) All numerical functions on $\mathfrak{U}$ that have straight-line graphs. (These are called "linear" functions in elementary calculus, but not in this book.)

   [*Hint.* Use the theorem of this section.]

6. Prove that the set of polynomials of degree ≤ 5 constitutes a subspace of the vector space of all polynomials. Prove also that the set of polynomials of degree exactly 5 does not constitute a subspace.

7. Prove that the set of functions that are solutions to the nonhomogeneous linear differential equation

$$\mathbf{X}''''(t) - 5\mathbf{X}'''(t) + 5\mathbf{X}''(t) + 5\mathbf{X}'(t) - 6\mathbf{X}(t) = e^t$$

   does *not* form a vector space.

8. Which of the following are subspaces of the space $\mathfrak{R}^4$ of 4-dimensional column vectors?

   (a) All $X = \begin{pmatrix} x_1 \\ x_2 \\ x_3 \\ x_4 \end{pmatrix}$ such that $x_4 = 2x_1$.

   (b) All numerical multiples of $\begin{pmatrix} 1 \\ -1 \\ 0 \\ 2 \end{pmatrix}$.

(c) All X that have all components positive.

(d) The vector $\begin{pmatrix} 0 \\ 0 \\ 0 \\ 0 \end{pmatrix}$ alone.

(e) All sums of numerical multiples of $\begin{pmatrix} 1 \\ -1 \\ 0 \\ 2 \end{pmatrix}$ and $\begin{pmatrix} 1 \\ 2 \\ 3 \\ 4 \end{pmatrix}$.

(f) All numerical multiples of the sum of $\begin{pmatrix} 1 \\ -1 \\ 0 \\ 2 \end{pmatrix}$ and $\begin{pmatrix} 1 \\ 2 \\ 3 \\ 4 \end{pmatrix}$.

(g) All X such that $x_1 = 0$.

(h) All X such that $x_1 \geq x_2$.

(i) All X such that $x_2 = 1$.

(j) All X such that $FX = 0$, where $F = (1 \quad -1 \quad 2 \quad 3)$.

[*Ans.* (a), (b), (d), (e), (f), (g), (j) are subspaces.]

9. Show that the set of solutions to a set of simultaneous *homogeneous* equations in variables $x_1, \ldots, x_n$ constitutes a subspace of the space $\mathcal{R}^n$ of n-dimensional column vectors. Show also that if one or more of the equations were nonhomogeneous, then the set of solutions would not be a subspace.

10. In Example 1 consider the integers (positive and negative) as a subset of all real numbers. Show that if Y_1 and Y_2 are in this subset, then $Y_1 - Y_2$ is also in the subset. Show also that the set of integers does not form a subspace of the vector space of real numbers.

11. In Example 9, what is the relationship between the graph of the function $3 + t - 2t^2$ and the graph of the function $3 + (t + 1) - 2(t^2 + 2t + 1)$?

12. A vector X such that $AX = X$ is called a "fixed point" of the transformation A. The vector O is always a fixed point. In which of the Examples 8–14 of this section do there exist nonzero fixed points?

[*Ans.* 9, 13, 14]

13. Show that the set of solutions to equations

$$F_1 X = w_1$$
$$\cdot$$
$$\cdot$$
$$\cdot$$
$$F_m X = w_m$$

can be expressed as follows: Let $\mathfrak{X}_0$ be the subspace of solutions to

$$F_1 X = 0$$
$$\cdot$$
$$\cdot$$
$$\cdot$$
$$F_m X = 0$$

and $Z = \begin{pmatrix} z_1 \\ \cdot \\ \cdot \\ \cdot \\ z_m \end{pmatrix}$ be any one fixed solution to the original set of equa-

tions. Then the set of all solutions to the original equations is the set of all $Z + X_0$, with X_0 in $\mathfrak{X}_0$.

14. In which of the examples of transformations in this section is it true that $\mathbf{A}^2 = \mathbf{A}$, i.e., that the result of transforming X into $\mathbf{A}(\mathbf{A}X)$ is the same as that of transforming X into $\mathbf{A}X$?   [*Ans.* Example 13.]

15. Show that the intersection of subspaces is a subspace.

16. Show that the complement of a subspace is never a subspace.

17. Show that the union of two subspaces is never a subspace unless one is contained in the other.

18. Prove that the kernels of the transformations given in Exercise 14 of the preceding section are subspaces of $\mathfrak{X}$.

19. If $\mathbf{A}$ is a transformation of a space $\mathfrak{X}$ into a space $\mathfrak{Y}$ show that the kernel of $\mathbf{A}$ is a subspace of $\mathfrak{X}$.

9. LINEAR INDEPENDENCE AND BASES

Let $\mathfrak{X}$ be a vector space and let $X_1, \ldots, X_n$ be vectors in $\mathfrak{X}$. What vectors do we get when we perform additions and numerical multiplications using only these vectors? First of all, for each X_i we get all its (infinitely many) multiples cX_i. And then taking sums of such, we get expressions of the form

$$c_1X_1 + c_2X_2 + \ldots + c_nX_n.$$

For instance,

$$\pi X_1 - 1X_2 + 1X_3 - 1X_4 \quad \text{or} \quad 1X_1 + 0X_2 + 0X_3 + 1X_4$$

or for that matter

$$0X_1 + 0X_2 + 0X_3 + 0X_4.$$

Such an expression is called a **linear combination** of $X_1, \ldots, X_n$. Sums and numerical multiples can themselves be looked at as linear combinations. For instance,

$$X_1 + X_3 = 1X_1 + 0X_2 + 1X_3 + 0X_4$$

and

$$-5X_2 = 0X_1 - 5X_2 + 0X_3 + 0X_4.$$

Furthermore, sums and numerical multiples of linear combinations are again linear combinations. For instance

$$(2X_1 - 1X_2 + 1X_3 - 3X_4) + (-2X_1 + 2X_2 - 3X_3 - 1X_4)$$

$$= 0X_1 + 1X_2 - 2X_3 - 4X_4$$

and

$$3(2X_1 - 1X_2 + 1X_3 - 3X_4) = 6X_1 - 3X_2 + 3X_3 - 9X_4.$$

Hence when we perform additions and numerical multiplications starting with $X_1, \ldots, X_n$ we get all linear combinations $c_1X_1 + \ldots + c_nX_n$, and we get nothing else.

> **Definition.** The set of all linear combinations of $X_1, \ldots, X_n$, which is clearly a subspace of $\mathfrak{X}$, is called the **subspace spanned** by $X_1, \ldots, X_n$.

Any subspace of $\mathfrak{X}$ that contains $X_1, \ldots, X_n$ must contain all linear combinations of them. Hence the subspace of $\mathfrak{X}$ spanned by $X_1, \ldots, X_n$ is the *smallest subspace of $\mathfrak{X}$ that contains them all*.

Note that it is perfectly possible for two different linear combinations of $X_1, \ldots, X_n$ to represent the same vector X. For instance if we know that X_2 is really the same as $\frac{1}{3}X_1$, then the linear combination $-1X_1 + 3X_2$ represents the same vector as the linear combination $0X_1 + 0X_2$. However, there exist sets of vectors $X_1, \ldots, X_n$ having the agreeable property that $a_1X_1 + \ldots + a_nX_n$ never equals $b_1X_1 + \ldots + b_nX_n$ unless $a_1 = b_1$ and $a_2 = b_2$ and $\ldots$ and $a_n = b_n$. Such a set of vectors $X_1, \ldots, X_n$ is called linearly independent.

To check that $X_1, \ldots, X_n$ are linearly independent we need only check to see that O cannot be written as a linear combination $c_1X_1 + \ldots + c_nX_n$ except in the trivial way $0X_1 + \ldots + 0X_n$. We can prove this condition for linear independence as follows: Suppose two different linear combinations $a_1X_1 + \ldots + a_nX_n$ and $b_1X_1 + \ldots + b_nX_n$ were both equal to the same vector X. Then the vector O could be written as the linear combination $(a_1 - b_1)X_1 + \ldots + (a_n - b_n)X_n$. And since at least one a_k is different from the corresponding b_k, then this last linear combination is not the same as $0X_1 + \ldots + 0X_n$. Conversely, if $X_1, \ldots, X_n$ are linearly independent, then O can only be written in the trivial way $O = 0X_1 + \ldots + 0X_n$.

The last result gives an equivalent definition of linear independence which we shall take as the formal definition for this concept.

Definition. The vectors $X_1, \ldots, X_n$ are said to be **linearly independent** if a relation of the form

$$a_1X_1 + \ldots + a_nX_n = O$$

can hold only when $a_1 = \ldots = a_n = 0$. Vectors that are not independent are said to be **dependent**.

It is easy to show that if a set of vectors is linearly dependent then some one of them is a linear combination of the others, and conversely (see Exercise 6).

Let us illustrate these notions with vectors from the space $\mathcal{R}^4$ of 4-dimensional column vectors.

EXAMPLE 1. The following three vectors

$$X_1 = \begin{pmatrix} 1 \\ 1 \\ 1 \\ 1 \end{pmatrix}, \qquad X_2 = \begin{pmatrix} 0 \\ 1 \\ 1 \\ 1 \end{pmatrix}, \qquad X_3 = \begin{pmatrix} 0 \\ 0 \\ 1 \\ 1 \end{pmatrix}$$

are linearly independent. We must show that

$$y_1 \begin{pmatrix} 1 \\ 1 \\ 1 \\ 1 \end{pmatrix} + y_2 \begin{pmatrix} 0 \\ 1 \\ 1 \\ 1 \end{pmatrix} + y_3 \begin{pmatrix} 0 \\ 0 \\ 1 \\ 1 \end{pmatrix} = \begin{pmatrix} 0 \\ 0 \\ 0 \\ 0 \end{pmatrix}$$

only if

$$\begin{pmatrix} y_1 \\ y_2 \\ y_3 \end{pmatrix} = \begin{pmatrix} 0 \\ 0 \\ 0 \end{pmatrix}.$$

In other words, that

$$(1 \quad 0 \quad 0)\,Y = 0$$

$$(1 \quad 1 \quad 0)\,Y = 0$$

$$(1 \quad 1 \quad 1)\,Y = 0$$

$$(1 \quad 1 \quad 1)\,Y = 0$$

only if $Y = O$, a fact that is true if this set of equations has a unique solution. And uniqueness can be established by our standard equation-solving techniques, for the reduced form of these equations is

$$(1 \quad 0 \quad 0)\,Y = 0$$

$$(0 \quad 1 \quad 0)\,Y = 0$$

$$(0 \quad 0 \quad 1)\,Y = 0$$

$$(0 \quad 0 \quad 0)\,Y = 0.$$

EXAMPLE 2. The vectors X_1, X_2, X_3 above, together with

$$X_4 = \begin{pmatrix} 0 \\ 0 \\ 0 \\ 1 \end{pmatrix}, \qquad X_5 = \begin{pmatrix} 1 \\ 1 \\ 0 \\ 0 \end{pmatrix},$$

span the space $\mathfrak{R}^4$ of 4-dimensional column vectors. To see this we must show that for any vector

$$\begin{pmatrix} w_1 \\ w_2 \\ w_3 \\ w_4 \end{pmatrix} = W$$

the following equations can be solved.

$$y_1 \begin{pmatrix} 1 \\ 1 \\ 1 \\ 1 \end{pmatrix} + y_2 \begin{pmatrix} 0 \\ 1 \\ 1 \\ 1 \end{pmatrix} + y_3 \begin{pmatrix} 0 \\ 0 \\ 1 \\ 1 \end{pmatrix} + y_4 \begin{pmatrix} 0 \\ 0 \\ 0 \\ 1 \end{pmatrix} + y_5 \begin{pmatrix} 1 \\ 1 \\ 0 \\ 0 \end{pmatrix} = \begin{pmatrix} w_1 \\ w_2 \\ w_3 \\ w_4 \end{pmatrix}.$$

Written in row vector form, the equations are

$$(1 \quad 0 \quad 0 \quad 0 \quad 1) \, Y = w_1$$

$$(1 \quad 1 \quad 0 \quad 0 \quad 1) \, Y = w_2$$

$$(1 \quad 1 \quad 1 \quad 0 \quad 0) \, Y = w_3$$

$$(1 \quad 1 \quad 1 \quad 1 \quad 0) \, Y = w_4.$$

If we put these equations in reduced form we have

$$(1 \quad 0 \quad 0 \quad 0 \quad\quad 1) \, Y = w_1$$

$$(0 \quad 1 \quad 0 \quad 0 \quad\quad 0) \, Y = w_2 - w_1$$

$$(0 \quad 0 \quad 1 \quad 0 \quad -1) \, Y = w_3 - w_2$$

$$(0 \quad 0 \quad 0 \quad 1 \quad\quad 0) \, Y = w_4 - w_3.$$

We see that y_5 is a nonbeginner variable so that there are an infinite number of solutions to this set of equations.

If we choose the solution for which $y_5 = 0$ we obtain

$$y_1 = w_1$$

$$y_2 = w_2 - w_1$$

$$y_3 = w_3 - w_2$$

$$y_4 = w_4 - w_3$$

$$y_5 = 0$$

as suitable components for the vector Y. Other solutions of these equations are asked for in Exercise 4.

Definition. If the vectors $X_1, \ldots, X_n$ span the whole space $\mathfrak{X}$ and are also linearly independent, they are said to form a **basis** for the space $\mathfrak{X}$.

It follows from the definitions of spanning and linear independence that if $X_1, \ldots, X_n$ are a basis for $\mathfrak{X}$ then each vector X in $\mathfrak{X}$ can be written in exactly one way as a linear combination $X = c_1 X_1 + \ldots + c_n X_n$.

Once we have a basis, the transformation

$$\begin{pmatrix} c_1 \\ \cdot \\ \cdot \\ \cdot \\ c_n \end{pmatrix} \longrightarrow c_1 X_1 + \ldots + c_n X_n$$

completely identifies the space $\mathcal{R}^n$ of column vectors with the abstract space $\mathcal{X}$. Thus every problem concerning the vectors in $\mathcal{X}$ becomes a problem concerning n-dimensional column vectors. We call the numbers $c_1, \ldots, c_n$ the **components** (or **coordinates**) **of** X **with respect to the basis** $X_1, \ldots, X_n$.

EXAMPLE 3. The vectors X_1, X_2, X_3, X_4 in Examples 1 and 2 constitute a basis for the space of 4-dimensional column vectors. To show this, one must check that they are linearly independent, and that they span the whole space.

EXAMPLE 4. The most obvious basis for the space $\mathcal{R}^n$ of n-dimensional column vectors consists of

$$E_1 = \begin{pmatrix} 1 \\ 0 \\ \cdot \\ \cdot \\ 0 \\ 0 \end{pmatrix}, \quad E_2 = \begin{pmatrix} 0 \\ 1 \\ \cdot \\ \cdot \\ 0 \\ 0 \end{pmatrix}, \quad \ldots, \quad E_n = \begin{pmatrix} 0 \\ 0 \\ \cdot \\ \cdot \\ 0 \\ 1 \end{pmatrix}.$$

These are in fact the columns of the n-by-n identity matrix. We will call this the **natural basis** for the space $\mathcal{R}^n$. Obviously there is a similar natural basis for the space of n-dimensional row vectors.

EXAMPLE 5. Let $\mathcal{X}$ be the geometrical plane. Then the vectors in Figure 27 constitute a basis for $\mathcal{X}$. It is important to establish this fact geometrically, without using coordinates. For we can identify the plane with the space of number-couples only after we know that X_1, X_2 constitute a basis. The linear independence of X_1 and X_2 amounts to the assertion that if you first walk a certain distance east (or a distance west) and then walk a distance northeast (or a distance southwest) you will certainly not find yourself at the origin O unless both distances were zero. The fact that X_1 and X_2 span the plane amounts to the assertion that every point in the plane can be reached by first walking a certain distance (possibly 0) east or west, and then walking a distance northeast or southwest.

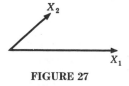

FIGURE 27

EXAMPLE 6. We have seen in Exercise 9 of Section 8 that the set of solutions to a set of simultaneous homogeneous equations constitutes a subspace of the space of column vectors. From the reduced form of the equations it is possible to write down a basis for the solution space in a mechanical way. For instance in Example 5 of Section 2 the basis for the solution subspace consists of the vectors

$$\begin{pmatrix} -2 \\ 1 \\ -3 \\ 1 \\ 0 \end{pmatrix} \quad \text{and} \quad \begin{pmatrix} 1 \\ -1 \\ -6 \\ 0 \\ 1 \end{pmatrix}.$$

We now want to introduce some useful notation. We have just seen that if an abstract vector space $\mathfrak{X}$ possesses a basis we can identify $\mathfrak{X}$ with some space $\mathfrak{R}^n$ of column vectors. The particular way in which we identify the abstract vector space $\mathfrak{X}$ with the column-vector space $\mathfrak{R}^n$ depends on the particular basis we choose for $\mathfrak{X}$ It will be convenient to let a single capital Greek letter Γ or Δ or Ω stand for a basis. Suppose that the basis $\Gamma = \{X_1, X_2, X_3, X_4\}$ is chosen, and $X = 3X_1 + X_3 - X_4$. Then the abstract vector X is expressed by a column vector with respect to the basis Γ, and for this we write

$$\begin{pmatrix} X \\ \Gamma \end{pmatrix} = \begin{pmatrix} 3 \\ 0 \\ 1 \\ -1 \end{pmatrix}.$$

This notation emphasizes the fact that the abstract vector X can be identified with a column vector only after a basis for the abstract space $\mathfrak{X}$ has been chosen. In terms of this notation the one-one transformation of the "abstract" space $\mathfrak{X}$ onto the "concrete" space $\mathfrak{R}^n$ can be written

$$X \longrightarrow \begin{pmatrix} X \\ \Gamma \end{pmatrix}.$$

EXAMPLE 7. Let Γ be the basis for the geometrical plane illustrated in Example 5. Given an arbitrary point X in the plane, here is a general procedure for writing down $\begin{pmatrix} X \\ \Gamma \end{pmatrix}$. We first draw the subspaces spanned by X_1 and X_2. These are lines through O. Then we draw lines parallel to these subspaces through (the tip of) X. Now X will be one vertex of a parallelogram whose diagonally opposite vertex is O. The sides of this parallelogram adjacent to the vertex O are (positive or negative) numerical multiples of X_1 and X_2. In Figure 28, for instance, we might estimate these sides to be

$\frac{3}{2}X_1$ and $-3X_2$, respectively. And then $X = \frac{3}{2}X_1 - 3X_2$, so that

$$\begin{pmatrix} X \\ \Gamma \end{pmatrix} = \begin{pmatrix} \frac{3}{2} \\ -3 \end{pmatrix}.$$

It is clear then that the *basis* X_1, X_2 serves the same purpose as the *oblique coordinate system* introduced in Section 1.

If we are given the coordinate system directly we can easily discover the relevant basis. Simply choose vectors X_1 and X_2 pointing in the positive direction on the first and second axes, respectively, and each having length 1 relative to the scale of its own axis.

We say that a vector space $\mathfrak{X}$ is the **direct sum** of two of its subspaces $\mathcal{Y}$ and $\mathcal{Z}$ if every vector X in $\mathfrak{X}$ can be written in exactly one way as a sum

$$X = Y + Z,$$

where Y is in $\mathcal{Y}$ and Z is $\mathcal{Z}$.

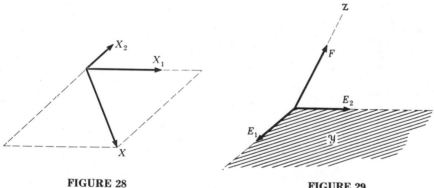

FIGURE 28   **FIGURE 29**

EXAMPLE 8. Consider in $\mathcal{R}^3$ the 2-dimensional subspace $\mathcal{Y}$ spanned by the vectors

$$E_1 = \begin{pmatrix} 1 \\ 0 \\ 0 \end{pmatrix} \quad \text{and} \quad E_2 = \begin{pmatrix} 0 \\ 1 \\ 0 \end{pmatrix}.$$

Consider also the 1-dimensional subspace $\mathcal{Z}$ spanned by

$$F = \begin{pmatrix} 1 \\ 1 \\ 1 \end{pmatrix}.$$

Since these three vectors form a basis for $\mathcal{R}^3$, every vector X in $\mathcal{R}^3$ can be written uniquely as a linear combination

$$X = aE_1 + bE_2 + cF.$$

We can set $Y = aE_1 + bE_2$ and $Z = cF$. Then, because the basis representation is unique, Y and Z are the only vectors in $\mathcal{Y}$ and $\mathcal{Z}$ respectively such that $X = Y + Z$. Hence $\mathcal{R}^3$ is the direct sum of $\mathcal{Y}$ and $\mathcal{Z}$. (See Figure 29.)

A vector space $\mathcal{X}$ that possesses a basis is called **finite-dimensional**. In this book we restrict our attention almost exclusively to finite-dimensional spaces. All the vector spaces in Sections 6 and 8 are finite-dimensional except for those spaces which are defined in Examples 3 and 4 of Section 8. In Section 10 we will prove that if $X_1, \ldots, X_n$ is a basis for $\mathcal{X}$, then *every* basis for $\mathcal{X}$ contains exactly n vectors. This integer n is called the **dimension** of $\mathcal{X}$. Each abstract finite-dimensional vector space can be identified with exactly one of the column vector spaces $\mathcal{R}^n$, namely the one having the right dimension.

EXERCISES

1. In $\mathcal{R}^n$ show that none of the following sets of vectors is linearly independent.

(a) $\begin{pmatrix} 2 \\ 6 \end{pmatrix}, \begin{pmatrix} 3 \\ 9 \end{pmatrix}.$
   (b) $\begin{pmatrix} 1 \\ 2 \end{pmatrix}, \begin{pmatrix} 2 \\ 3 \end{pmatrix}, \begin{pmatrix} 3 \\ 4 \end{pmatrix}.$

(c) $\begin{pmatrix} 1 \\ 2 \end{pmatrix}, \begin{pmatrix} 2 \\ 1 \end{pmatrix}, \begin{pmatrix} 5 \\ 5 \end{pmatrix}.$
   (d) $\begin{pmatrix} 0 \\ 0 \end{pmatrix}, \begin{pmatrix} 6 \\ 11 \end{pmatrix}.$

2. We choose ordinary (cartesian) coordinates in 3-dimensional space. Describe geometrically the subspaces spanned by the following sets of vectors.

(a) $\begin{pmatrix} 1 \\ 0 \\ 0 \end{pmatrix}, \begin{pmatrix} 0 \\ 1 \\ 0 \end{pmatrix}.$
   (b) $\begin{pmatrix} 1 \\ 1 \\ 1 \end{pmatrix}, \begin{pmatrix} 3 \\ 3 \\ 3 \end{pmatrix}.$

(c) $\begin{pmatrix} 1 \\ 2 \\ 3 \end{pmatrix}, \begin{pmatrix} 2 \\ 5 \\ 7 \end{pmatrix}.$
   (d) $\begin{pmatrix} 1 \\ 1 \\ 1 \end{pmatrix}, \begin{pmatrix} 1 \\ 2 \\ 3 \end{pmatrix}, \begin{pmatrix} 0 \\ 0 \\ 1 \end{pmatrix}.$

3. Let $\mathfrak{X}$ be the vector space of polynomials whose degree is at most 2.

Let $X = 3x^2 - 2x + 7$. Write $\begin{pmatrix} X \\ \Gamma \end{pmatrix}$ where Γ is

(a) $x^2, x, 1$.

(b) $x^2 - x, x - 1, 1$.

$Ans.$ (b) $\begin{bmatrix} \begin{pmatrix} 3 \\ 1 \\ 8 \end{pmatrix} \end{bmatrix}$.

(c) $(x - 2)^2, (x - 2)^1, (x - 2)^0$.

4. In Example 2 show that the reduced set of equations is correct. Then find solutions of the equations corresponding to $y_5 = 3$ and to $y_5 = -5$.

5. Show that the vectors X_1, X_2, X_3, X_4, X_5 of Example 2 are *not* linearly independent.

6. Show that a set of vectors is linearly independent if and only if no one of them is in the subspace spanned by the others.

7. Verify that the vectors

$$X_1 = \begin{pmatrix} 1 \\ 1 \\ 1 \end{pmatrix}, \qquad X_2 = \begin{pmatrix} 1 \\ 2 \\ 3 \end{pmatrix}, \qquad X_3 = \begin{pmatrix} 0 \\ 1 \\ 0 \end{pmatrix}$$

form a basis for $\mathfrak{R}^3$.

8. Express each of the following vectors in terms of the basis in Exercise 7.

(a) $\begin{pmatrix} 3 \\ 2 \\ 1 \end{pmatrix}$

$[Ans.\ 4X_1 - X_2.]$

(b) $\begin{pmatrix} -1 \\ -2 \\ -3 \end{pmatrix}$

(c) $\begin{pmatrix} -3 \\ 2 \\ 5 \end{pmatrix}$

9. Show that the three vectors in Exercise 8 span $\mathcal{R}^3$ by expressing the vectors of Exercise 7 in terms of them. Is this spanning set a basis?

10. Show that the effect of a transformation $\mathbf{A}$ on a space $\mathcal{X}$ is completely determined by what it does to the vectors $X_1, \ldots, X_n$ of a basis.

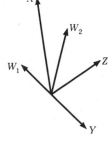

11. For the basis $\{W_1, W_2\} = \Gamma$ pictured in Figure 30, and the vectors X and Y and Z, write (approximately) the corresponding column vectors

$$\begin{pmatrix} X \\ \Gamma \end{pmatrix} \quad \text{and} \quad \begin{pmatrix} Y \\ \Gamma \end{pmatrix} \quad \text{and} \quad \begin{pmatrix} Z \\ \Gamma \end{pmatrix}.$$

FIGURE 30

12. Let $\mathcal{U}$ be the interval $0 \le t \le 2$. Let $\mathcal{X}$ be the vector space of functions on $\mathcal{U}$ spanned by the functions $\mathbf{X}_1(t) \equiv 1$, $\mathbf{X}_2(t) = \sin t$, $\mathbf{X}_3(t) = \sin 2t$. Prove that these functions are linearly independent and hence form a basis for $\mathcal{X}$.

13. Prove that the function $\mathbf{Y}(t) = (\sin t + \cos t)^2$ belongs to the space $\mathcal{X}$ of Exercise 12 and find $\begin{pmatrix} \mathbf{Y} \\ \Gamma \end{pmatrix}$, Γ being the basis $\mathbf{X}_1, \mathbf{X}_2, \mathbf{X}_3$ of Exercise 12.

$$\left[Ans. \begin{pmatrix} 1 \\ 0 \\ 1 \end{pmatrix} \right].$$

14. Show that the vector space $\mathcal{X}$ of polynomials of degree ≤ 5 has a basis consisting of the six "monomials" $X_1 = 1$, $X_2 = t$, $X_3 = t^2$, $X_4 = t^3$, $X_5 = t^4$, $X_6 = t^5$.

15. Prove that three fixed vectors X_1, X_2, X_2 constitute a basis for ordinary 3-dimensional space if no single plane through the origin contains all three.

16. Show that the set of all linear combinations of vectors $X_1, \ldots, X_n$ in $\mathcal{X}$ does constitute a subspace of $\mathcal{X}$.

17. Show that the vector O can never belong to a linearly independent set of vectors.

18. Show that any subset of a linearly independent set of vectors is still linearly independent.

19. Show that any set containing a set of vectors that spans $\mathcal{X}$ still spans $\mathcal{X}$.

20. Verify the 'fact that if $\mathbf{A}$ is a one-one transformation of $\mathcal{R}^n$ onto $\mathcal{X}$, and $W_1, \ldots, W_n$ is a basis for $\mathcal{R}^n$, then $\mathbf{A}W_1, \ldots, \mathbf{A}W_n$ is a basis for $\mathcal{X}$.

21. Let $\mathfrak{X}$ be the vector space of all polynomials. Show that no finite set of polynomials $X_1, \ldots, X_n$ can be a basis for $\mathfrak{X}$. (In other words, $\mathfrak{X}$ is not finite-dimensional.)

22. Show that if a finite set S of vectors span the vector space $\mathfrak{X}$, then some subset of S is a basis for $\mathfrak{X}$.

23. If $X_1, \ldots, X_n$ is a basis Γ for the space $\mathfrak{X}$, and if $E_1, \ldots, E_n$ is the natural basis for n-dimensional column vectors, show that $\begin{pmatrix} X_j \\ \Gamma \end{pmatrix} = E_j$.

10. THEOREMS ON DIMENSION

Suppose the abstract vector space $\mathfrak{X}$ is finite-dimensional. By definition this means that $\mathfrak{X}$ contains at least one finite subset of vectors $W_1, \ldots, W_n$ that span all of $\mathfrak{X}$ and are at the same time linearly independent. One object of this section is to prove that then $\mathfrak{X}$ cannot contain another spanning and independent set $X_1, \ldots, X_r$ with $r \neq n$. In addition, we shall give the following description of the action of a linear transformation **A**. The domain of **A** splits into two subspaces: K, the kernel of **A**, and C, a complementary subspace. The domain of **A** is the direct sum of K and C. Furthermore, **A** is one-one from C onto the range of **A**, and, by definition, **A** is identically zero on K. For a detailed discussion of these ideas, see Theorems 10.6 and 10.7.

10.1 Theorem. If the vector space $\mathfrak{X}$ has a basis of n vectors, then no set of more than n vectors can be linearly independent.

Proof. We consider first the case where $n = 3$, that is, where $\mathfrak{X}$ has a basis consisting of three vectors, say W_1, W_2, and W_3. We can identify $\mathfrak{X}$ with the column vector space $\mathfrak{R}^3$ and carry out our argument with 3-dimensional column vectors. We want to prove that every set of four 3-dimensional column vectors, say X_1, X_2, X_3 and X_4, is linearly dependent. Suppose the components of the vectors X_i are

$$X_1 = \begin{pmatrix} a_{11} \\ a_{21} \\ a_{31} \end{pmatrix}, \quad X_2 = \begin{pmatrix} a_{12} \\ a_{22} \\ a_{32} \end{pmatrix}, \quad X_3 = \begin{pmatrix} a_{13} \\ a_{23} \\ a_{33} \end{pmatrix}, \quad \text{and} \quad X_4 = \begin{pmatrix} a_{14} \\ a_{24} \\ a_{34} \end{pmatrix}.$$

In order to show that these vectors are linearly dependent we must find numbers y_1, y_2, y_3, y_4, not all 0, such that

$$y_1 X_1 + y_2 X_2 + y_3 X_3 + y_4 X_4 = 0.$$

In other words we must find a nonzero solution

$$\begin{pmatrix} y_1 \\ y_2 \\ y_3 \\ y_4 \end{pmatrix}$$

to the simultaneous homogeneous equations

$$a_{11}y_1 + a_{12}y_2 + a_{13}y_3 + a_{14}y_4 = 0$$

$$a_{21}y_1 + a_{22}y_2 + a_{23}y_3 + a_{24}y_4 = 0$$

$$a_{31}y_1 + a_{32}y_2 + a_{33}y_3 + a_{34}y_4 = 0$$

And we have seen in Section 3 that a homogeneous system with more unknowns than equations has infinitely many solutions. Hence the theorem is proved, at least for the case $n = 3$ and for any four vectors X_1, X_2, X_3, X_4.

The proof that any set of $n + k$ vectors is linearly dependent when the space $\mathfrak{X}$ has a basis consisting of n vectors follows the same pattern as the special case $(n = 3)$ treated above.

As a corollary we can now state the main theorem about finite-dimensional vector spaces. It is this theorem that allows us to attach a unique dimension to each finite-dimensional space.

10.2 Theorem. If $\mathfrak{X}$ is finite-dimensional and one of its bases contains exactly n vectors, then each of its bases contains exactly n vectors.

Proof. Suppose $\{W_1, \ldots, W_n\}$ and $\{X_1, \ldots, X_r\}$ are two bases for $\mathfrak{X}$. By Theorem 10.1, we conclude that both inequalities $r \leq n$ and $n \leq r$ hold. Hence $n = r$.

We should mention at this point that a vector space containing only the vector O is, by definition, said to have dimension 0 (see Exercise 5).

A theorem that complements Theorem 10.1 is the following.

10.3 Theorem. If $\mathfrak{X}$ has a basis of n vectors, then no set of fewer than n vectors can span $\mathfrak{X}$.

Proof. Suppose a set of r vectors spans $\mathfrak{X}$. It may happen that certain subsets of this set also span $\mathfrak{X}$. Let us take the smallest such subset.

This subset S cannot be linearly dependent. If it were, there would exist a linear combination of its vectors,

$$O = c_1 X_1 + \ldots + c_{r'} X_{r'}, \qquad r' \le r,$$

with, let us say, c_i different from zero. Then

$$X_i = -\sum_{\substack{k=1 \\ k \ne i}}^{r'} \left(\frac{c_k}{c_i}\right) X_k,$$

and so S with X_i deleted would also span $\mathfrak{X}$. This would contradict the fact that S has been chosen as small as possible. Thus S is a basis and must contain exactly n elements. Hence,

$$n = r' \le r.$$

In the course of proving 10.3 we have also proved another result.

10.4 Theorem. If the set $X_1, \ldots, X_r$ spans $\mathfrak{X}$ then some subset of this set is a basis for $\mathfrak{X}$.

As a parallel fact we have

10.5 Theorem. If the set $X_1, \ldots, X_r$ is linearly independent but not a basis for $\mathfrak{X}$, then some larger set $X_1, \ldots, X_r, X_{r+1}, \ldots, X_n$ is a basis for $\mathfrak{X}$ (provided that $\mathfrak{X}$ possesses a finite basis).

Proof. The set $X_1, \ldots, X_r$, being linearly independent, must fail to span $\mathfrak{X}$. Hence, there is some vector in $\mathfrak{X}$, call it X_{r+1}, which can *not* be expressed as a linear combination of $X_1, \ldots, X_r$. This fact implies that the set $X_1, \ldots, X_r, X_{r+1}$ is linearly independent. If $X_1, \ldots, X_r, X_{r+1}$ span $\mathfrak{X}$, we have a basis. If not, we repeat the process. Since $\mathfrak{X}$ is assumed to have a finite basis, the process eventually terminates.

10.6 Theorem. If $\mathbf{A}$ is a linear transformation with n-dimensional domain, r-dimensional range, and k-dimensional kernel, then $r + k = n$.

Proof. Let $X_1, \ldots, X_k$ be a basis for the kernel of $\mathbf{A}$. If the kernel of $\mathbf{A}$ is not all of the domain, use Theorem 10.5 to adjoin vectors $X_{k+1}, \ldots, X_n$ so that $X_1, \ldots, X_n$ form a basis for the domain of $\mathbf{A}$. Then we will prove that the $n - k$ vectors $\mathbf{A}X_{k+1}, \ldots, \mathbf{A}X_n$ form a basis for the range of $\mathbf{A}$, which will prove the theorem, since $(n - k) + k = n$.

First: $\mathbf{A}X_{k+1}, \ldots, \mathbf{A}X_n$ span the range. For let Y belong to the range. Then $Y = \mathbf{A}X$ for some X in the domain. And X is some linear combination of the basis vectors $X_1, \ldots, X_n$. That is,

$$X = c_1 X_1 + \ldots + c_k X_k + c_{k+1} X_{k+1} + \ldots + c_n X_n.$$

Hence

$$Y = \mathbf{A}X = \mathbf{A}(c_1 X_1 + \ldots + c_k X_k) + \mathbf{A}(c_{k+1} X_{k+1} + \ldots + c_n X_n).$$

The first summand is O, because $c_1X_1 + \ldots + c_kX_k$ belongs to the kernel of $\mathbf{A}$. And the second summand is a linear combination

$$c_{k+1}(\mathbf{A}X_{k+1}) + \ldots + c_n(\mathbf{A}X_n).$$

Second: $\mathbf{A}X_{k+1}, \ldots, \mathbf{A}X_n$ are linearly independent. For suppose

$$z_{k+1}(\mathbf{A}X_{k+1}) + \ldots + z_n(\mathbf{A}X_n) = 0.$$

Then

$$\mathbf{A}(z_{k+1}X_{k+1} + \ldots + z_nX_n) = 0,$$

that is,

$$Z = z_{k+1}X_{k+1} + \ldots + z_nX_n$$

belongs to the kernel of $\mathbf{A}$. But then Z is also some linear combination $z_1X_1 + \ldots + z_kX_k$. And we have

$$z_1X_1 + \ldots + z_kX_k - z_{k+1}X_{k+1} - \ldots - z_nX_n = 0.$$

Since the X's are independent we are forced to conclude that

$$z_1 = \ldots = z_k = z_{k+1} = \ldots = z_n = 0.$$

A geometric complement to Theorem 10.6 is as follows.

10.7 Theorem. Let $\mathbf{A}$ be a linear transformation. The domain of $\mathbf{A}$ is the direct sum of the kernel K of $\mathbf{A}$ and of a complementary subspace C. Restricted to C, $\mathbf{A}$ becomes one-one.

Proof. Let $X_1, \ldots, X_k$ be a basis for K, and let

$$X_1, \ldots, X_k, X_{k+1}, \ldots, X_n$$

be an extension to a basis for the domain of $\mathbf{A}$. Then $X_{k+1}, \ldots, X_n$ span a subspace C, and the domain of $\mathbf{A}$ is the direct sum of C and K. To see that $\mathbf{A}$ is one-one on C, let Y_1 be a nonzero vector in C. Since Y_1 is not in K, we must have $\mathbf{A}Y_1 \neq 0$. A linear transformation whose kernel consists of only the zero vector is one-one (see Exercise 2 of Section 7). We therefore conclude that $\mathbf{A}$ restricted to C is one-one.

A corollary of Theorem 10.6 is

10.8 Theorem. Let $\mathbf{A}$ be a transformation whose range is a subspace of its domain. Then $\mathbf{A}$ is one-one if and only if its range is all of its domain.

Proof. Let the domain $\mathfrak{X}$ have dimension n, and suppose that $\mathbf{A}$ is one-one. Then the dimension of its kernel is 0, and by Theorem 10.6 the dimension of its range is then n. In Exercise 4 of this section you will prove that $\mathfrak{X}$ contains no n-dimensional proper subspace. Hence the range of $\mathbf{A}$ must be all of $\mathfrak{X}$.

Conversely suppose that **A** has range of all of $\mathfrak{X}$. Then again by Theorem 10.6, the dimension of its kernel is 0, that is, its kernel is the 1-element subspace consisting of O alone. By Exercise 2 of Section 7 it follows that **A** is one-one.

EXERCISES

1. Suppose that $X_1, \ldots, X_n$ are linearly independent, but that it is impossible to choose any vector X_{n+1} in $\mathfrak{X}$ such that $X_1, \ldots, X_n, X_{n+1}$ are linearly independent. Prove that then $X_1, \ldots, X_n$ form a basis for $\mathfrak{X}$.

2. Suppose that $X_1, \ldots, X_n$ span the vector space $\mathfrak{X}$ but that if any X_i is deleted from this set, then $X_1, \ldots, X_{i-1}, X_{i+1}, \ldots, X_n$ fail to span $\mathfrak{X}$. Prove that then $X_1, \ldots, X_n$ form a basis for $\mathfrak{X}$.

3. Let $\mathfrak{X}$ be n-dimensional. Show that any linearly independent set of n vectors forms a basis. Show that any set of n vectors that span $\mathfrak{X}$ forms a basis.

4. Show that if $\mathfrak{X}$ is n-dimensional and $\mathfrak{Y}$ is a subspace of $\mathfrak{X}$ not equal to $\mathfrak{X}$ then $\mathfrak{Y}$ is finite-dimensional of dimension $r < n$.

5. Prove that the set of vectors consisting of the zero vector alone is not linearly independent. Use this result to motivate the dimensionality of a vector space consisting of a single vector.

6. Use Theorem 10.8 to decide which of the following transformations are one-one.
   (a) Section 7, Example 2.   [*Ans.* One-one.]
   (b) Section 7, Exercise 9.
   (c) Section 7, Exercise 10.
   (d) The transformation on 3-dimensional vectors that projects them on a given plane.
   (e) The transformation on 3-dimensional vectors that transforms every vector into the O vector.

7. For the transformations in Exercise 6 that where not one-one find the dimension of the range and of the kernel, and check your results by Theorem 10.6.

8. For the transformation in Example 13 of Section 8 find the dimension of the range and of the kernel. Check your answers by means of Theorem 10.6.

9. Prove that the transformation in Example 14 of Section 8 is one-one, using the theorems of this section.

10. Consider the vector space $\mathfrak{X}$ of all polynomials $X = a_0 + a_1 t + \ldots + a_n t^n + \ldots$. (This is not a finite-dimensional space.) Let **A** be the transformation that sends X onto its derivative X'. Show that **A** has as range all of $\mathfrak{X}$ but still has a kernel that contains more than one element. Find the kernel.

11. Let $\mathfrak{X}$ be the vector space of all polynomials of degree at most 5, and let $\mathbf{A}$ be the transformation that sends X onto X'. Show that $\mathbf{A}$ maps $\mathfrak{X}$ onto a proper subspace of itself and find the kernel of $\mathbf{A}$.

12. Use Theorem 10.6 to show that if $\mathbf{A}$ is a transformation with domain a vector space $\mathfrak{X}$ and range the same space $\mathfrak{X}$, and if $\mathbf{A}$ has a kernel containing at least two distinct elements, then $\mathfrak{X}$ cannot be a finite-dimensional space. [*Hint.* Use Exercises 10 and 11 as a guide.]

13. Prove that if $m \neq n$ then there is no one-one transformation of $\mathfrak{R}^n$ onto $\mathfrak{R}^m$.

14. Show that the kernel of a nonzero functional is a subspace of $\mathfrak{X}$ of dimension $n - 1$ (assuming that $\mathfrak{X}$ has dimension n).

11. THE MATRIX OF A TRANSFORMATION

Suppose that $\mathbf{A}$ is a transformation with domain the column-vector space $\mathfrak{R}^3$ and range the column-vector space $\mathfrak{R}^2$ (or possibly some subspace of $\mathfrak{R}^2$). Apply the transformation $\mathbf{A}$ to each of the natural basis vectors

$$E_1 = \begin{pmatrix} 1 \\ 0 \\ 0 \end{pmatrix}, \qquad E_2 = \begin{pmatrix} 0 \\ 1 \\ 0 \end{pmatrix}, \qquad E_3 = \begin{pmatrix} 0 \\ 0 \\ 1 \end{pmatrix},$$

and line up the resulting 2-dimensional column vectors

$$\mathbf{A}E_1 = \begin{pmatrix} a_{11} \\ a_{21} \end{pmatrix}, \qquad \mathbf{A}E_2 = \begin{pmatrix} a_{12} \\ a_{22} \end{pmatrix}, \qquad \mathbf{A}E_3 = \begin{pmatrix} a_{13} \\ a_{23} \end{pmatrix}$$

in a matrix

$$\begin{pmatrix} a_{11} & a_{12} & a_{13} \\ a_{21} & a_{22} & a_{23} \end{pmatrix}.$$

Call this matrix A. The result of multiplying

$$A \text{ times} \begin{pmatrix} 1 \\ 0 \\ 0 \end{pmatrix} \text{ is } \begin{pmatrix} a_{11} \\ a_{21} \end{pmatrix};$$

the result of multiplying

$$A \text{ times} \begin{pmatrix} 0 \\ 1 \\ 0 \end{pmatrix} \text{ is } \begin{pmatrix} a_{12} \\ a_{22} \end{pmatrix};$$

and the result of multiplying

$$A \text{ times} \begin{pmatrix} 0 \\ 0 \\ 1 \end{pmatrix} \text{ is } \begin{pmatrix} a_{13} \\ a_{23} \end{pmatrix}.$$

Hence the transformation **A** has the same effect as the matrix A on the three basis vectors E_1, E_2, E_3. Then **A** and A must agree on every X, because a linear transformation is completely determined by what it does to a basis (see Exercise 7 of Section 7). We have just proved a special case of the following important theorem.

11.1 Theorem. Every linear transformation with domain $\Re^n$ and with range some subspace of $\Re^r$ can be defined by an r-by-n matrix.

The above theorem is applicable, of course, to any transformation with finite-dimensional domain and range. For suppose that **A** is a transformation with domain an n-dimensional abstract vector space $\mathfrak{X}$ and with range some subspace of an r-dimensional abstract vector space $\mathfrak{Y}$. Let $\Gamma = \{X_1, \ldots, X_n\}$ be a basis for $\mathfrak{X}$, and let $\Delta = \{Y_1, \ldots, Y_r\}$ be a basis for $\mathfrak{Y}$. Then if we identify each vector X with its corresponding column vector

$$\begin{pmatrix} X \\ \Gamma \end{pmatrix}$$

and each vector Y with its corresponding column vector

$$\begin{pmatrix} Y \\ \Delta \end{pmatrix},$$

A becomes a transformation from $\Re^n$ onto a subspace of $\Re^r$. Let us write

$$\begin{pmatrix} \mathbf{A} \\ \Delta\Gamma \end{pmatrix}$$

for the matrix corresponding to this transformation. Notice that the domain basis Γ is written to the right of the range basis Δ.

To compute the matrix $\begin{pmatrix} \mathbf{A} \\ \Delta\Gamma \end{pmatrix}$ we proceed as follows:

1. Apply $\mathbf{A}$ to each of the vectors $X_1, \ldots, X_n$ in the domain basis Γ. We then have produced n vectors $\mathbf{A}X_1, \ldots, \mathbf{A}X_n$ in the range.

2. Compute the components of $\mathbf{A}X_1$ with respect to the range basis Δ; that is, express $\mathbf{A}X_1$ as a linear combination of $Y_1, \ldots, Y_r$, and write the numerical coefficients as an r-dimensional column vector. According to the notation introduced in Section 9, this column vector is called

$$\begin{pmatrix} \mathbf{A}X_1 \\ \Delta \end{pmatrix}.$$

Do the same for $\mathbf{A}X_2$, for $\mathbf{A}X_3$, etc.

3. Line up the above n columns to form an r-by-n matrix.

To sum up the process briefly: If Γ is the domain basis and Δ is the range basis, then the jth column of

$$\begin{pmatrix} \mathbf{A} \\ \Delta\Gamma \end{pmatrix} \quad \text{is} \quad \begin{pmatrix} \mathbf{A}X_j \\ \Delta \end{pmatrix},$$

X_j being the jth vector of the domain basis Γ.

When the range $\mathcal{Y}$ of the transformation $\mathbf{A}$ happens to be a subspace of the domain $\mathcal{X}$ it is often natural to use the same basis for the domain and range. But in some situations, particularly when $\mathbf{A}$ is the identity transformation, it is useful to take different domain and range bases even in the same vector space.

Let us make a list of matrices corresponding to some of the examples of transformations in Sections 7 and 8.

EXAMPLE 1. Let $\mathbf{A}$ be the transformation defined in Example 1 of Section 7. If Γ is the natural basis in $\mathcal{R}^3$ consisting of the vectors

$$\begin{pmatrix} 1 \\ 0 \\ 0 \end{pmatrix}, \quad \begin{pmatrix} 0 \\ 1 \\ 0 \end{pmatrix}, \quad \begin{pmatrix} 0 \\ 0 \\ 1 \end{pmatrix},$$

and if Δ is the natural basis

$$\begin{pmatrix} 1 \\ 0 \end{pmatrix}, \quad \begin{pmatrix} 0 \\ 1 \end{pmatrix}$$

in $\mathfrak{R}^2$, then we can compute $\begin{pmatrix} \mathbf{A} \\ \Delta\Gamma \end{pmatrix}$, as follows:

$$\mathbf{A}\begin{pmatrix} 1 \\ 0 \\ 0 \end{pmatrix} = \begin{pmatrix} 1 \\ 3 \end{pmatrix}, \quad \mathbf{A}\begin{pmatrix} 0 \\ 1 \\ 0 \end{pmatrix} = \begin{pmatrix} 0 \\ 2 \end{pmatrix}, \quad \mathbf{A}\begin{pmatrix} 0 \\ 0 \\ 1 \end{pmatrix} = \begin{pmatrix} -1 \\ 1 \end{pmatrix}.$$

The results of these computations are already expressed with respect to the natural basis in $\mathfrak{R}^2$, so that we need only line up the results to obtain the desired matrix. It is

$$\begin{pmatrix} \mathbf{A} \\ \Delta\Gamma \end{pmatrix} = \begin{pmatrix} 1 & 0 & -1 \\ 3 & 2 & 1 \end{pmatrix}.$$

EXAMPLE 2. Let $\mathbf{A}$ be the reflection transformation defined in Example 2 of Section 7, and let Γ be the two vectors X_1 and X_2 in Figure 31. Then, since $\mathbf{A}$ is the reflection transformation, we have $\mathbf{A}X_1 = X_1$ and $\mathbf{A}X_2 = -X_2$. Since the components of X_1, X_2, and $-X_2$ are

$$\begin{pmatrix} 1 \\ 0 \end{pmatrix}, \quad \begin{pmatrix} 0 \\ 1 \end{pmatrix}, \quad \text{and} \quad \begin{pmatrix} 0 \\ -1 \end{pmatrix}$$

respectively, we see that

$$\begin{pmatrix} \mathbf{A} \\ \Gamma\Gamma \end{pmatrix} = \begin{pmatrix} 1 & 0 \\ 0 & -1 \end{pmatrix}.$$

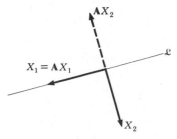

FIGURE 31

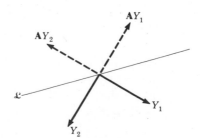

FIGURE 32

On the other hand, let Δ be the basis consisting of the vectors $\dot{Y}_1$ and Y_2 in Figure 32. In that figure each of these vectors makes an angle of 45° with line $\mathcal{L}$. In Figure 32 we have drawn the vectors $\mathbf{A}Y_1$ and $\mathbf{A}Y_2$. Then, if each of the vectors X_1, X_2, Y_1, and Y_2 has unit length, we can easily compute that

$$\begin{pmatrix} \mathbf{A}Y_1 \\ \Gamma \end{pmatrix} = \begin{pmatrix} -\dfrac{1}{\sqrt{2}} \\ -\dfrac{1}{\sqrt{2}} \end{pmatrix} \quad \text{and} \quad \begin{pmatrix} \mathbf{A}Y_2 \\ \Gamma \end{pmatrix} = \begin{pmatrix} \dfrac{1}{\sqrt{2}} \\ -\dfrac{1}{\sqrt{2}} \end{pmatrix}.$$

Lining these vectors up side by side, we obtain

$$\begin{pmatrix} \mathbf{A} \\ \Gamma\Delta \end{pmatrix} = \begin{pmatrix} -\dfrac{1}{\sqrt{2}} & \dfrac{1}{\sqrt{2}} \\ -\dfrac{1}{\sqrt{2}} & -\dfrac{1}{\sqrt{2}} \end{pmatrix}.$$

Similarly, we can compute that

$$\begin{pmatrix} \mathbf{A}X_1 \\ \Delta \end{pmatrix} = \begin{pmatrix} -\dfrac{1}{\sqrt{2}} \\ \dfrac{1}{\sqrt{2}} \end{pmatrix} \quad \text{and} \quad \begin{pmatrix} \mathbf{A}X_2 \\ \Delta \end{pmatrix} = \begin{pmatrix} -\dfrac{1}{\sqrt{2}} \\ -\dfrac{1}{\sqrt{2}} \end{pmatrix}.$$

And by lining up these vectors, we obtain

$$\begin{pmatrix} \mathbf{A} \\ \Delta\Gamma \end{pmatrix} = \begin{pmatrix} -\dfrac{1}{\sqrt{2}} & -\dfrac{1}{\sqrt{2}} \\ \dfrac{1}{\sqrt{2}} & -\dfrac{1}{\sqrt{2}} \end{pmatrix}.$$

In each of these cases the basic transformation is the same; but the matrix that gives the transformation changes as the bases are changed.

EXAMPLE 3. Let $\mathbf{A}$ be the *projection* transformation defined in Example 13 of Section 8. And let Γ consist of a vector X_1 along the x-axis and a vector X_2 along the y-axis. Then

$$\begin{pmatrix} \mathbf{A} \\ \Gamma\Gamma \end{pmatrix} = \begin{pmatrix} 1 & 0 \\ 0 & 0 \end{pmatrix}.$$

EXAMPLE 4. Let **A** be the *shear* transformation defined in Example 14 of Section 8. And let Γ be a basis like that in Example 3, but with both vectors of length 1. Then

$$\binom{A}{\Gamma\Gamma} = \begin{pmatrix} 1 & 1 \\ 0 & 1 \end{pmatrix}.$$

In calculating with the notations defined above, the following two rules are fundamental.

Rule 1.
$$\binom{A}{\Delta\Gamma}\binom{X}{\Gamma} = \binom{AX}{\Delta};$$

Rule 2.
$$\binom{B}{\Omega\Delta}\binom{A}{\Delta\Gamma} = \binom{BA}{\Omega\Gamma}.$$

Notice that in each rule, adjacent basis symbols (Γ in Rule 1, Δ in Rule 2) must be the same.

To establish the validity of Rule 1 we first try it for X equal to one of the basis vectors, say X_2. Then

$$\binom{X_2}{\Gamma} = \begin{pmatrix} 0 \\ 1 \\ 0 \\ \cdot \\ \cdot \\ \cdot \\ 0 \end{pmatrix}.$$

The reader should show that the result of multiplying this column vector by any matrix A is simply the second column of A. Hence in particular $\binom{A}{\Delta\Gamma}\binom{X_2}{\Gamma}$ is the second column of $\binom{A}{\Delta\Gamma}$, which we know to be $\binom{AX_2}{\Delta}$. Hence our rule works for $X = X_2$; and parallel reasoning shows that it works for each of the other basis vectors. Since a transformation is completely determined by its effect on basis vectors (see Exercise 10 of Section 9), Rule 1 follows.

Rule 2 asserts that if **BA** is the *composite* transformation resulting from performing first **A** then **B**, then the matrix $\binom{BA}{\Omega\Gamma}$ is the product of $\binom{B}{\Omega\Delta}$.

and $\begin{pmatrix} \mathbf{A} \\ \Delta\Gamma \end{pmatrix}$ in that order. It is enough to check the equality

$$\begin{pmatrix} \mathbf{BA} \\ \Omega\Gamma \end{pmatrix} W = \begin{pmatrix} \mathbf{B} \\ \Omega\Delta \end{pmatrix}\begin{pmatrix} \mathbf{A} \\ \Delta\Gamma \end{pmatrix} W$$

for each n-dimensional column vector W, since W could be any one of the basis vectors in Γ, and a transformation is completely determined by its effect on the basis vectors. We know that any such W can be written $\begin{pmatrix} X \\ \Gamma \end{pmatrix}$ for some uniquely determined vector X in $\mathfrak{X}$. Hence we must verify that

$$\begin{pmatrix} \mathbf{BA} \\ \Omega\Gamma \end{pmatrix}\begin{pmatrix} X \\ \Gamma \end{pmatrix} = \begin{pmatrix} \mathbf{B} \\ \Omega\Delta \end{pmatrix}\begin{pmatrix} \mathbf{A} \\ \Delta\Gamma \end{pmatrix}\begin{pmatrix} X \\ \Gamma \end{pmatrix}.$$

But by applying Rule 1 to each side we can simplify the above equality to read

$$\begin{pmatrix} \mathbf{BA}X \\ \Omega \end{pmatrix} = \begin{pmatrix} \mathbf{B} \\ \Omega\Delta \end{pmatrix}\begin{pmatrix} \mathbf{A}X \\ \Delta \end{pmatrix}.$$

This equation follows from Rule 1. Hence Rule 2 is proved.

Rule 2 is most often applied to the case where all three spaces and all three bases are the same. In other words,

$$\begin{pmatrix} \mathbf{B} \\ \Gamma\Gamma \end{pmatrix}\begin{pmatrix} \mathbf{A} \\ \Gamma\Gamma \end{pmatrix} = \begin{pmatrix} \mathbf{BA} \\ \Gamma\Gamma \end{pmatrix}.$$

This says that, if we have fixed our basis once and for all, then we can obtain the matrix of the composite of several transformations by multiplying together their respective matrices.

You will recall (Exercise 11 of Section 7) that a one-one transformation $\mathbf{A}$ of a vector space $\mathfrak{X}$ onto itself always possesses a unique inverse transformation $\mathbf{A}^{-1}$ with the property that $\mathbf{AA}^{-1} = \mathbf{A}^{-1}\mathbf{A} =$ the identity transformation. The following theorem tells us that the matrix for the inverse transformation coincides with the inverse of the matrix for the original transformation $\mathbf{A}$.

Theorem. If A is an invertible transformation with domain and range equal to $\mathfrak{X}$, and if Γ is a basis for $\mathfrak{X}$, then

$$\begin{pmatrix} A^{-1} \\ \Gamma\Gamma \end{pmatrix} = \begin{pmatrix} A \\ \Gamma\Gamma \end{pmatrix}^{-1}.$$

Proof. To show that the matrix $\begin{pmatrix} A^{-1} \\ \Gamma\Gamma \end{pmatrix}$ is the inverse of the matrix $\begin{pmatrix} A \\ \Gamma\Gamma \end{pmatrix}$ we multiply them together, hoping to get the identity matrix. And we do, since by Rule 2

$$\begin{pmatrix} A^{-1} \\ \Gamma\Gamma \end{pmatrix}\begin{pmatrix} A \\ \Gamma\Gamma \end{pmatrix} = \begin{pmatrix} A^{-1}A \\ \Gamma\Gamma \end{pmatrix} = \begin{pmatrix} I \\ \Gamma\Gamma \end{pmatrix} = I.$$

The opposite order of multiplication, of course, gives the same answer. The first I in the formula above stands for the identity transformation and the second I stands for the identity matrix.

Corollary. If A and B are square matrices such that $BA = I$ then $AB = I$ also.

Proof. A and B both define linear transformations with domain $\mathfrak{R}^n$ and range some subspace of $\mathfrak{R}^n$. The fact that $BA = I$ shows that A has only O in its kernel; for if $AX = O$, then $BAX = IX = X = O$. Hence A is one-one, and by Theorem 10.8 has range all of $\mathfrak{R}^n$. Hence as a transformation A possesses an inverse, which must be defined by the matrix A^{-1}, and $AA^{-1} = I$. But we have seen in the second paragraph of Section 4 that if the matrix A^{-1} exists then B coincides with A^{-1}. Hence $AB = I$.

It is this result that entitles us to speak of "the inverse" of a matrix, rather than just a "right inverse" or a "left inverse."

When I is the identity transformation (that is, the transformation that does not move any vector X in $\mathfrak{X}$), then for every basis Γ we have $\begin{pmatrix} I \\ \Gamma\Gamma \end{pmatrix}$ equal to the identity matrix I. For different bases Γ and Δ, $\begin{pmatrix} I \\ \Delta\Gamma \end{pmatrix}$ will never be the identity matrix. But it is at least an invertible matrix, and its inverse is $\begin{pmatrix} I \\ \Gamma\Delta \end{pmatrix}$. To see this, we compute by Rule 2,

$$\begin{pmatrix} I \\ \Delta\Gamma \end{pmatrix}\begin{pmatrix} I \\ \Gamma\Delta \end{pmatrix} = \begin{pmatrix} I \\ \Delta\Delta \end{pmatrix} = \text{identity matrix,}$$

and

$$\begin{pmatrix} I \\ \Gamma\Delta \end{pmatrix}\begin{pmatrix} I \\ \Delta\Gamma \end{pmatrix} = \begin{pmatrix} I \\ \Gamma\Gamma \end{pmatrix} = \text{identity matrix.}$$

A matrix like $\begin{pmatrix} I \\ \Delta\Gamma \end{pmatrix}$ is useful for "change of basis." If we know the column-vector that corresponds to a vector X with respect to a basis Γ, then we can find the column-vector that corresponds to X with respect to Δ by multiplying

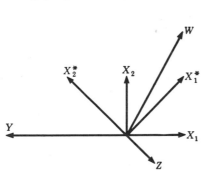

FIGURE 33

$$\begin{pmatrix} X \\ \Gamma \end{pmatrix} \text{ by } \begin{pmatrix} I \\ \Delta\Gamma \end{pmatrix}.$$

For in fact by Rule 1

$$\begin{pmatrix} I \\ \Delta\Gamma \end{pmatrix}\begin{pmatrix} X \\ \Gamma \end{pmatrix} = \begin{pmatrix} IX \\ \Delta \end{pmatrix} = \begin{pmatrix} X \\ \Delta \end{pmatrix}.$$

EXAMPLE 5. Suppose that Γ consists of the vectors X_1 and X_2 in Figure 33. Then with respect to this basis the geometric vectors W and Y and Z determine the column vectors

$$\begin{pmatrix} 1 \\ 2 \end{pmatrix} \text{ and } \begin{pmatrix} -2 \\ 0 \end{pmatrix} \text{ and } \begin{pmatrix} \frac{1}{2} \\ -\frac{1}{2} \end{pmatrix}.$$

But what column vectors do they determine if we use instead a new basis Δ consisting of the vectors X_1^* and X_2^*? To answer this question we first compute the matrix

$$\begin{pmatrix} I \\ \Delta\Gamma \end{pmatrix} = \begin{pmatrix} \frac{1}{2} & \frac{1}{2} \\ -\frac{1}{2} & \frac{1}{2} \end{pmatrix}.$$

Then we multiply this matrix

$$\text{times} \quad \begin{pmatrix} 1 \\ 2 \end{pmatrix} \quad \text{and times} \quad \begin{pmatrix} -2 \\ 0 \end{pmatrix} \quad \text{and times} \quad \begin{pmatrix} \frac{1}{2} \\ -\frac{1}{2} \end{pmatrix}.$$

You should check to see that the answers

$$\begin{pmatrix} \frac{3}{2} \\ \frac{1}{2} \end{pmatrix} \quad \text{and} \quad \begin{pmatrix} -1 \\ 1 \end{pmatrix} \quad \text{and} \quad \begin{pmatrix} 0 \\ -\frac{1}{2} \end{pmatrix}$$

are the same as you would obtain by computing

$$\begin{pmatrix} W \\ \Delta \end{pmatrix} \quad \text{and} \quad \begin{pmatrix} Y \\ \Delta \end{pmatrix} \quad \text{and} \quad \begin{pmatrix} Z \\ \Delta \end{pmatrix} \text{ directly.}$$

Finally, let us note that all the formulas of the present section can be rephrased in terms of simultaneous linear equations. For concreteness, suppose we have the pair of equations

$$y_1 = x_1 - 2x_2, \qquad y_2 = x_1 + x_2.$$

Then these equations have two distinct geometric interpretations. Under the first interpretation they describe a transformation **A** that distorts the plane in a certain way: it moves the vector $\rightarrow$ into the vector $\nearrow$, it moves the vector $\uparrow$ into the vector $\nwarrow$, and in general moves

$$\text{a vector} \quad \begin{pmatrix} x_1 \\ x_2 \end{pmatrix} \quad \text{into a vector} \quad \begin{pmatrix} x_1 - 2x_2 \\ x_1 + x_2 \end{pmatrix}.$$

Under the second interpretation, nothing moves at all: all the points in the plane are simply given new names according to a certain system described by the equations; for instance, if a vector has the old name $\begin{pmatrix} 2 \\ 1 \end{pmatrix}$ then it has the new name $\begin{pmatrix} 0 \\ 3 \end{pmatrix}$. One well-known textbook on modern algebra uses the felicitous adjectives *alibi* and *alias* to describe the first and second interpretations respectively. It is important to notice that every set of simultaneous equations has an alibi interpretation; but the alias interpretation is possible only when (1) there are exactly as many unknowns as equations and (2) the matrix formed from the coefficients is invertible.

EXERCISES

1. Let Γ be a basis for the abstract vector space $\mathfrak{X}$, and let the transformation $\mathbf{A}$ simply multiply each vector X by the number $\frac{3}{2}$. What is $\begin{pmatrix} \mathbf{A} \\ \Gamma\Gamma \end{pmatrix}$?

$$[Ans.\ \tfrac{3}{2}I.]$$

2. Let Γ be the natural cartesian basis for the space of plane geometrical fixed vectors. Let $\mathbf{A}$ be rotation counterclockwise through $45°$, and let $\mathbf{B}$ be rotation clockwise through $30°$. Compute $\begin{pmatrix} \mathbf{A} \\ \Gamma\Gamma \end{pmatrix}$ and $\begin{pmatrix} \mathbf{B} \\ \Gamma\Gamma \end{pmatrix}$.

3. By multiplying the matrices in Exercise 2 compute the matrix with respect to Γ of rotation counterclockwise through $15°$.

4. Let $\mathfrak{X}$ be the (4-dimensional) space of polynomials of degree ≤ 3. Let $\mathbf{A}$ be the transformation defined by differentiation. (See Example 8 of Section 8.) Let Γ be the basis consisting of 1, t, t^2, t^3. (See Exercise 14 of Section 9.) What is $\begin{pmatrix} \mathbf{A} \\ \Gamma\Gamma \end{pmatrix}$?

$$Ans.\ \begin{pmatrix} 0 & 1 & 0 & 0 \\ 0 & 0 & 2 & 0 \\ 0 & 0 & 0 & 3 \\ 0 & 0 & 0 & 0 \end{pmatrix}.$$

5. In Exercise 4 compute $\begin{pmatrix} \mathbf{A} \\ \Gamma\Gamma \end{pmatrix}^2$, and interpret it.

6. Let $\mathfrak{X}$ and Γ be as in Exercise 4 above and let $\mathbf{A}$ be the transformation defined by the translation $t \rightarrow t + 1$, as in Example 9 of Section 8. What is $\begin{pmatrix} \mathbf{A} \\ \Gamma\Gamma \end{pmatrix}$?

7. Prove that a square matrix A is invertible if and only if its columns are linearly independent. [*Hint.* A defines a linear transformation on the space of column vectors.]

8. Prove that a square matrix A is invertible if and only if its rows are linearly independent.

In the remaining exercises $\mathfrak{X}$ will be the space of plane geometric vectors. X, Y, Z are as in Figure 34. Γ consists of X, Y; Δ of Y, X; and Ω of X, Z.

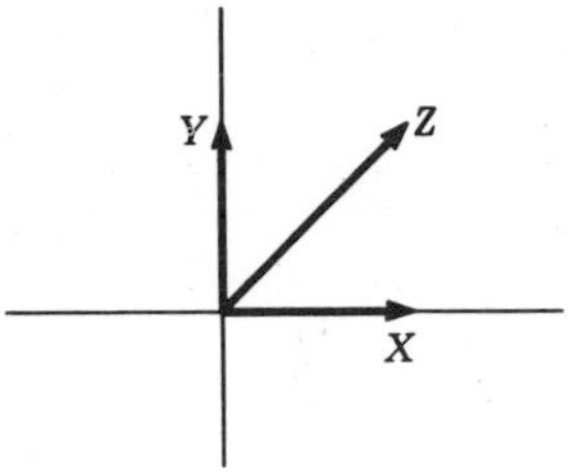

9. Find $\begin{pmatrix} I \\ \Delta\Gamma \end{pmatrix}$. $\left[Ans.\ \begin{pmatrix} 0 & 1 \\ 1 & 0 \end{pmatrix}. \right]$

10. Find $\begin{pmatrix} I \\ \Omega\Delta \end{pmatrix}$.

11. Find $\begin{pmatrix} I \\ \Omega\Gamma \end{pmatrix}$ both from its definition and from Exercises 9 and 10.

FIGURE 34

$\left[Ans.\ \begin{pmatrix} 1 & -1 \\ 0 & 1 \end{pmatrix}. \right]$

12. Find $\begin{pmatrix} Z \\ \Gamma \end{pmatrix}$. Use the results of Exercises 9 and 11 to find $\begin{pmatrix} Z \\ \Delta \end{pmatrix}$ and $\begin{pmatrix} Z \\ \Omega \end{pmatrix}$. Verify your answers geometrically.

13. Let **B** be a rotation clockwise through $30°$. Find

$$\begin{pmatrix} B \\ \Delta\Gamma \end{pmatrix},\quad \begin{pmatrix} B \\ \Omega\Delta \end{pmatrix},\quad \begin{pmatrix} B \\ \Omega\Gamma \end{pmatrix},\quad \begin{pmatrix} B \\ \Gamma\Delta \end{pmatrix}.$$

14. Find $\begin{pmatrix} I \\ \Gamma\Delta \end{pmatrix}$. What is the relation of this matrix to the matrix of Exercise 9?

15. Find $\begin{pmatrix} X - 2Y \\ \Delta \end{pmatrix}$. Use the results of Exercises 10 and 14 to express $X - 2Y$

with respect to the bases Γ and Ω. $\left[Ans.\ \begin{pmatrix} -2 \\ 1 \end{pmatrix}, \begin{pmatrix} 1 \\ -2 \end{pmatrix}, \begin{pmatrix} 3 \\ -2 \end{pmatrix}. \right]$

16. Let **A** be the transformation of Example 13 in Section 8. Find $\begin{pmatrix} A \\ \Delta\Gamma \end{pmatrix}$ and

$\begin{pmatrix} A \\ \Omega\Delta \end{pmatrix}$. $\left[Ans.\ \begin{pmatrix} 0 & 0 \\ 1 & 0 \end{pmatrix}, \begin{pmatrix} 0 & 1 \\ 0 & 0 \end{pmatrix}. \right]$

17. If **A** and **B** are as in Exercises 13 and 16, compute

$$\begin{pmatrix} BA \\ \Omega\Gamma \end{pmatrix} \quad \text{and} \quad \begin{pmatrix} AB \\ \Omega\Gamma \end{pmatrix}.$$

What is the geometric significance of the fact that these two matrices differ?

18. From Exercise 13 find

$$\begin{pmatrix} B \\ \Gamma\Gamma \end{pmatrix} \quad \text{and} \quad \begin{pmatrix} B \\ \Delta\Delta \end{pmatrix}.$$

$$\left[Ans. \begin{pmatrix} \sqrt{3}/2 & \frac{1}{2} \\ -\frac{1}{2} & \sqrt{3}/2 \end{pmatrix}, \begin{pmatrix} \sqrt{3}/2 & -\frac{1}{2} \\ \frac{1}{2} & \sqrt{3}/2 \end{pmatrix}. \right]$$

19. Suppose that

$$\begin{pmatrix} C \\ \Delta\Gamma \end{pmatrix} = \begin{pmatrix} 1 & 0 \\ 0 & 1 \end{pmatrix}.$$

Interpret **C** geometrically.

20. Prove that if **A** is a one-one transformation of $\mathfrak{X}$ onto $\mathfrak{Y}$ then we can find a basis Γ' such that $\begin{pmatrix} A \\ \Gamma'\Gamma \end{pmatrix} = \begin{pmatrix} 1 & 0 \\ 0 & 1 \end{pmatrix}.$

21. Let **A** be a linear transformation with p-by-q matrix A. Suppose that the number of linearly independent columns in A is exactly r.
(a) Prove that the dimension of the range of **A** is r.
(b) Prove that the dimension of the kernel of **A** is $q - r$.

12. APPLICATION OF VECTOR SPACE IDEAS TO DIFFERENTIAL EQUATIONS

One useful application of vector space ideas arises in the theory of linear differential equations. We shall discuss here the simplest case: to wit, the nth-order linear homogeneous differential equation with constant coefficients. The general form of this equation may be written (using the letter **D** to indicate differentiation with respect to the variable t) as follows:

$$(1) \qquad D^n Y + a_1 D^{n-1} Y + \ldots + a_{n-1} DY + a_n Y = 0.$$

In Equation (1) the quantities a_i are numbers and **Y** is the unknown function of t that we want to find. Frequently **initial conditions** are also specified with the problem. These are commonly given by specifying the value of Y and its first $n - 1$ derivatives at a point. For example,

$$(2) \qquad Y = b_1, \quad DY = b_2, \quad \ldots, \quad D^{n-1}Y = b_n, \qquad \text{when } t = 0,$$

is a suitable set of initial conditions.

We first observe that the set of all solutions to Equation (1) forms a vector space. To see this we observe that if Y is a solution then by direct substitution into (1), the function kY is also a solution for any number k; and if Y_1 and Y_2 are two different solutions to (1), then the function $Y = Y_1 + Y_2$ is also a solution, as can be seen by direct substitution. This proves that the solutions to (1) form a vector space, since they constitute a subspace of the space of all numerical functions of t.

Knowing that we have a vector space, we can immediately ask two important questions: (i) What is its dimension? and (ii) What is a convenient basis for it? We shall give the answers to these questions and prove the validity of the answers under certain assumptions concerning the coefficients of (1).

Suppose we try as a solution to (1) the function e^{rt}, where r is a constant to be determined. Using the rule $D^m e^{rt} = r^m e^{rt}$, we have

$$(3) \qquad [r^n + a_1 r^{n-1} + \ldots + a_{n-1} r + a_n] e^{rt} = 0.$$

Since the exponential function e^{rt} is never zero, the product in Equation (3) is zero only if the factor in brackets is zero, that is,

$$(4) \qquad r^n + a_1 r^{n-1} + \ldots + a_{n-1} r + a_n = 0.$$

Equation (4) is sometimes called the **characteristic equation** of the differential equation (1). Equation (4) is an nth-degree polynomial in r and, by a well-known theorem, has n roots (if both real and complex roots are counted, and multiple roots are counted according to their multiplicity). In order to simplify the discussion we shall assume that (4) has n *distinct* *real* roots.

Let $r_1, r_2, \ldots, r_n$ be the n distinct real roots of Equation (4) and consider the functions $e^{r_1 t}, e^{r_2 t}, \ldots, e^{r_n t}$. Our first assertion is that these functions are linearly independent; for suppose the roots are written in ascending order of size (by relabeling, if necessary) so that $r_1 < r_2 < \ldots < r_n$, and suppose that we have a linear relation of the form

$$(5) \qquad c_1 e^{r_1 t} + c_2 e^{r_2 t} + \ldots + c_k e^{r_k t} = 0 \quad \text{and} \quad c_k \neq 0,$$

for all values of t. We have selected our notation here so that k is the largest index of the nonzero coefficients. Now divide Equation (5) by $e^{r_k t}$ and let $t \to \infty$. Since e^{-t} tends to 0 as $t \to \infty$ we obtain $c_k = 0$, contrary to assumption. Hence the functions are linearly independent and the dimension of the vector space of solutions is at least n.

To show that the dimension of the vector space of solutions to Equation (1) is exactly n we must show that the functions $e^{r_1 t}, e^{r_2 t}, \ldots, e^{r_n t}$ span the space. This will then prove that the "most general solution" is

(6) $$\mathbf{Y} = c_1 e^{r_1 t} + c_2 e^{r_2 t} + \ldots + c_n e^{r_n t}.$$

Theorem. Consider a differential equation of the form (1) such that the characteristic equation has n distinct real roots $r_1, r_2, \ldots, r_n$. Then any solution $\mathbf{Y}$ of the equation is a linear combination of the solutions $e^{r_1 t}, e^{r_2 t}, \ldots, e^{r_n t}$.

Proof. We shall give the proof only for the case of a second-degree equation. The general proof is similar. Let the roots of the characteristic equation be r and s, and the differential equation itself be

$$\mathbf{Y}'' + a\mathbf{Y}' + b\mathbf{Y} = 0.$$

Let $\mathbf{Y}$ be any solution of this equation. We define two new functions c and d by the equations

(7) $$\mathbf{Y}(t) = c(t)e^{rt} + d(t)e^{st}$$

(8) $$\mathbf{Y}'(t) = c(t)re^{rt} + d(t)se^{st}.$$

For every value of t, these equations are linear in the unknowns $c(t)$ and $d(t)$, and our equation-solving procedure yields a unique solution. These solutions define differentiable functions c and d. We would like to prove that these are, in fact, constant functions. If we differentiate Equation (7) we obtain

$$\mathbf{Y}'(t) = c'(t)e^{rt} + c(t)re^{rt} + d'(t)e^{st} + d(t)se^{st}.$$

Combining this equation with (8) gives

(9) $$0 = c'(t)e^{rt} + d'(t)e^{st}.$$

Differentiating (8), we have

(10) $$\mathbf{Y}''(t) = c'(t)re^{rt} + c(t)r^2 e^{rt} + d'(t)se^{st} + d(t)s^2 e^{st}.$$

Multiplying (7) by b, (8) by a, and adding the results to (10) gives

$$\mathbf{Y}''(t) + a\mathbf{Y}'(t) + b\mathbf{Y}(t) = c(t)e^{rt}(r^2 + ar + b)$$
$$+ d(t)e^{st}(s^2 + as + b) + c'(t)re^{rt} + d'(t)se^{st}.$$

Making use of the fact that $\mathbf{Y}$ satisfies the differential equation and that r and s satisfy the characteristic equation, we have

(11) $$0 = c'(t)re^{rt} + d'(t)se^{st}.$$

Multiplying (9) by r and subtracting the result from (11) gives

$$0 = d'(t)\,(s - r)e^{st}.$$

Since $s \neq r$ and e^{st} is never zero, we must have $d'(t) = 0$ for every t. Hence d is a constant function. But then from (11) we also have that $c'(t)$ must be zero. Hence c is also a constant function, completing the proof.

EXAMPLE 1. Consider the differential equation

$$\mathbf{D}^2\mathbf{Y} - 3\mathbf{D}\mathbf{Y} + 2\mathbf{Y} = 0.$$

Its characteristic equation is $r^2 - 3r + 2 = 0$, which has roots $r_1 = 1$ and $r_2 = 2$. Hence the most general solution is $\mathbf{Y}(t) = c_1e^t + c_2e^{2t}$. The reader may verify that this function is a solution to the equation by taking its first and second derivatives and substituting them into the equation.

Next we shall prove that given an equation of the form (1) whose characteristic equation has n distinct real roots, there is one and only one solution of (1) that satisfies initial conditions of the form (2). Consider the following transformation $\mathbf{A}$ that has as domain the space $\mathcal{Y}$ of all solutions $\mathbf{Y}$ to the homogeneous differential equation (1) and range contained in the space $\mathcal{R}^n$ of n-dimensional column vectors.

$$(12) \qquad \mathbf{Y} \xrightarrow{\mathbf{A}} \begin{pmatrix} \mathbf{Y}(0) \\ \mathbf{Y}'(0) \\ \cdot \\ \cdot \\ \cdot \\ \mathbf{Y}^{(n-1)}(0) \end{pmatrix}.$$

What we want to prove about the existence and uniqueness of solutions to (1) amounts to proving that the transformation $\mathbf{A}$ is one-one.

If we let Γ be the basis $e^{r_1t}, \ldots, e^{r_nt}$ for $\mathcal{Y}$ and Δ the natural basis for $\mathcal{R}^n$, then

$$(13) \qquad \begin{pmatrix} \mathbf{A} \\ \Delta\Gamma \end{pmatrix} = \begin{pmatrix} 1 & 1 & \ldots & 1 \\ r_1 & r_2 & \ldots & r_n \\ r_1^2 & r_2^2 & \ldots & r_n^2 \\ \cdot & \cdot & \ldots & \cdot \\ r_1^{n-1} & r_2^{n-1} & \ldots & r_n^{n-1} \end{pmatrix}.$$

We must prove that this matrix is invertible. It will be so unless (say) the rows are linearly dependent. Hence suppose there exist n numbers $c_0, \ldots, c_{n-1}$ such that

$$c_0(1 \quad 1 \quad \ldots \quad 1) + c_1(r_1 \quad r_2 \quad \ldots \quad r_n) + \ldots$$
$$+ c_{n-1}(r_1^{n-1} \quad r_2^{n-1} \quad \ldots \quad r_n^{n-1}) = 0.$$

We have then really n simultaneous equations

$$c_0 + c_1 r_1 + \ldots + c_{n-1} r_1^{n-1} = 0$$
$$c_0 + c_1 r_2 + \ldots + c_{n-1} r_2^{n-1} = 0$$
$$\ldots$$
$$c_0 + c_1 r_n + \ldots + c_{n-1} r_n^{n-1} = 0.$$

Or equivalently we have n distinct "roots" of the polynomial

$$c_0 + c_1 x + \ldots + c_{n-1} x^{n-1}.$$

But you are familiar with the fact that a polynomial of degree $n - 1$ cannot have n different roots. Hence our supposition that the rows of the matrix were dependent is impossible, and we have the following theorem.

Theorem. Suppose that the polynomial $a_n + a_{n-1}x + \ldots + a_1 x^{n-1} + x^n$ has n distinct real roots. Then the vector space $\mathcal{Y}$ of solutions $\mathbf{Y}$ to the homogeneous differential equation

$$(\mathbf{D}^n + a_1\mathbf{D}^{n-1} + \ldots + a_{n-1}\mathbf{D} + a_n)\mathbf{Y} = 0$$

is n-dimensional. And the transformation

$$\mathbf{Y} \longrightarrow \begin{pmatrix} \mathbf{Y}(0) \\ \mathbf{Y}'(0) \\ \cdot \\ \cdot \\ \cdot \\ \mathbf{Y}^{(n-1)}(0) \end{pmatrix}$$

is one-one.

EXAMPLE 1 (continued). For the differential equation of Example 1 suppose that the following initial conditions have been specified:

$$\mathbf{Y} = -2 \quad \text{and} \quad \mathbf{DY} = 3 \qquad \text{when } t = 0.$$

Then we must solve the equations

$$c_1 + c_2 = -2, \qquad c_1 + 2c_2 = 3.$$

The matrix of coefficients and its inverse are

$$M = \begin{pmatrix} 1 & 1 \\ 1 & 2 \end{pmatrix} \quad \text{and} \quad M^{-1} = \begin{pmatrix} 2 & -1 \\ -1 & 1 \end{pmatrix}.$$

Hence we have

$$\begin{pmatrix} c_1 \\ c_2 \end{pmatrix} = \begin{pmatrix} 2 & -1 \\ -1 & 1 \end{pmatrix} \begin{pmatrix} -2 \\ 3 \end{pmatrix} = \begin{pmatrix} -7 \\ 5 \end{pmatrix}.$$

The reader may easily check that the solution $Y(t) = -7e^t + 5e^{2t}$ does solve the differential equation and also satisfies the initial conditions.

EXERCISES

Find the general solutions to the following differential equations:

1. $D^2Y - DY - 6Y = 0.$

2. $D^3Y - 5D^2Y - 2DY + 24Y = 0.$

$$\left[Ans. \ Y(t) = a_1 e^{3t} + a_2 e^{4t} + a_3 e^{-2t}. \right]$$

3. $2D^2Y + 13DY + 6Y = 0.$

4. For the differential equation in Exercise 1 find the particular solution Y such that

$$Y(0) = 1, \qquad Y'(0) = 2.$$

5. For the differential equation in Exercise 2 find the particular solution Y such that

$$Y(0) = 0, \qquad Y'(0) = 1, \qquad Y''(0) = -1.$$

$$\left[Ans. \ a_1 = \tfrac{3}{5}, \ a_2 = -\tfrac{1}{3}, \ a_3 = -\tfrac{4}{15}. \right]$$

6. For the differential equation in Exercise 3 find the particular solution Y such that

$$Y(0) = -2, \qquad Y'(0) = 3.$$

7. If A is the transformation in (12) show that $\begin{pmatrix} A \\ \Delta\Gamma \end{pmatrix}$ has the form shown in (13), when Γ consists of the functions $e^{r_1 t}, \ldots, e^{r_n t}$ and Δ is the natural basis in $\mathcal{R}^n$.

8. Given initial conditions (2) and the general solution to the nth-order equation (1), use the theorem of this section to show that a particular solution can always be found that satisfies these initial conditions.

9. A differential equation of the form

$$(*) \qquad D^nY + a_1 D^{n-1}Y + \ldots + a_{n-1}DY + a_nY = W,$$

where W is a given function and Y is the unknown function, is called

nonhomogeneous. Show that if Y_1 and Y_2 are solutions to this equation, then the function $Y_1 - Y_2$ is a solution to the homogeneous equation

$$(**) \qquad D^n Y + a_1 D^{n-1} Y + \ldots + a_{n-1} DY + a_n Y = 0.$$

10. Show that if Y_0 is one solution to the nonhomogeneous differential equation $(*)$ of Exercise 9, then the general solution to this nonhomogeneous equation is of the form $Y + Y_0$, where Y is the general solution to the homogeneous equation $(**)$.

11. Solve Equations (7) and (8) for $c(t)$ and $d(t)$. Show that the resulting functions are differentiable.

13. THREE-DIMENSIONAL VECTOR GEOMETRY

The concepts of ordinary 2- and 3-dimensional geometry can be divided into two main types. The first type contains such concepts as point, plane, between, parallel, and parallel comparative length. Only these concepts of the first type were used in Section 1 for defining (oblique) coordinate systems and in Section 5 for defining geometric vectors. The second type contains angle, distance, perpendicular, and cartesian coordinate system. The significant difference between the two types is that concepts in the first type can be explained purely in terms of vectors, while the second type requires something additional. We will discuss the pure vector concepts in this section and the next section, and will take up concepts of the second type in Section 15. Our discussion will focus at first on three-dimensional space, but we will eventually point out the generalization of our methods to fewer and more dimensions.

It will be convenient to adopt a conventional notation for variables and for constants. In analytic geometry it is customary to use (x, y, z) as the coordinates of a variable point, while subscripts are added if we think of the point as fixed. Similarly in the geometry sections of the present chapter we will write X, F, t for variable vectors, functionals, and numbers, respectively, while X_1, F_1, and t_1 will be thought of as fixed.

As our first problem we consider the vector representation of a line in three dimensions. If the line $\mathcal{L}$ passes through the origin, then it forms a 1-dimensional subspace, and hence must consist of all multiples of some given vector. Hence a line through the origin may be written in the form

$$(1) \qquad\qquad t X_1, \qquad X_1 \neq 0,$$

where t may take on any real number as a value. This is known as a **parametric representation** of $\mathcal{L}$, and t is called a **parameter**. Suppose that we now add the vector X_2 to every point on $\mathcal{L}$. Then the resulting set of points

$$(2) \qquad\qquad t X_1 + X_2, \qquad X_1 \neq 0,$$

will be a line $\mathcal{L}'$ parallel to $\mathcal{L}$ (see Figure 35). We also say that $\mathcal{L}'$ results from $\mathcal{L}$ through **translation** by X_2. (And more generally we say that any subset $\mathcal{S}_1$ of a vector space is a **translate** of some other subset $\mathcal{S}$ if there is some fixed vector Y such that when we add Y to each of the points in $\mathcal{S}$ we obtain precisely the points in $\mathcal{S}_1$.)

But given any line $\mathcal{L}'$ in 3-dimensional space, it always is parallel to some line $\mathcal{L}$ through the origin, and can be obtained from $\mathcal{L}$ through translation. Hence any line can be represented parametrically in the form (2), as all points of the form $tX_1 + X_2$, where t is any real number.

If in (2) we set t equal to 0, we note that X_2 is a point on our line. And conversely, it is easily seen that X_2 may be chosen as any point on the line (see Exercise 1).

From Figure 35 we see that the vector X_1 may be thought of as determining the "direction" of the line. Since X_1 and kX_1 are in the same direction for $k \neq 0$, we may choose any nonzero multiple of X_1 (see Exercise 2), in place of X_1.

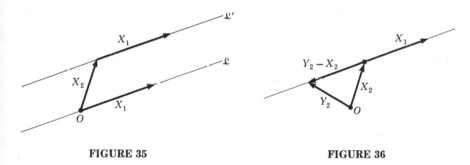

FIGURE 35   FIGURE 36

Thus we see that while any line may be represented parametrically in the form (2), this representation is not unique. The vector X_1 may be replaced by a nonzero multiple, and X_2 may be any point on the line. This representation of a line may be thought of as corresponding to the determination of a line in two dimensions by specifying a point on it and the slope of the line.

EXAMPLE 1. The expression

$$t \begin{pmatrix} 1 \\ 0 \\ 2 \end{pmatrix}$$

is a parametric representation of a line $\mathcal{L}$ through the origin. This line contains all points of the form

$$\begin{pmatrix} t \\ 0 \\ 2t \end{pmatrix}.$$

The line $\mathcal{L}'$ represented by

$$t\begin{pmatrix} 1 \\ 0 \\ 2 \end{pmatrix} + \begin{pmatrix} -1 \\ 5 \\ 3 \end{pmatrix}$$

results from the former by translation, and hence it is a parallel line, through

$$\begin{pmatrix} -1 \\ 5 \\ 3 \end{pmatrix}.$$

It contains all points of the form

$$\begin{pmatrix} t - 1 \\ 5 \\ 2t + 3 \end{pmatrix}.$$

The numerical vectors that appear in the above example, and in subsequent examples, should be interpreted geometrically. They can be interpreted relative to an *oblique* coordinate system, since perpendicularity of the axes plays no role in Sections 13 and 14.

Suppose that we are given a line $tX_1 + X_2$, and a point Y_2. We are asked to determine whether Y_2 lies on the given line. This means that for some value of the parameter, $tX_1 + X_2 = Y_2$, or $tX_1 = Y_2 - X_2$. Hence we have to test only whether $Y_2 - X_2$ is a multiple of X_1. This can also be seen easily from Figure 36.

EXAMPLE 2. Let us ask whether

$$Y_2 = \begin{pmatrix} 2 \\ 5 \\ 9 \end{pmatrix}$$

lies on either line in Example 1. For $\mathcal{L}$ we have $X_2 = 0$, and hence Y_2 itself would have to be a multiple of

$$X_1 = \begin{pmatrix} 1 \\ 0 \\ 2 \end{pmatrix}.$$

But since Y_2 does not have 0 as its second component, this is clearly not so. For $\mathcal{L}'$,

$$Y_2 - X_2 = \begin{pmatrix} 3 \\ 0 \\ 6 \end{pmatrix} = 3X_1.$$

Hence Y_2 lies on $\mathcal{L}'$ and corresponds to the parameter value $t = 3$.

Two lines $tX_1 + X_2$ and $tY_1 + Y_2$ are parallel if and only if they are translated from the same line through the origin. This would be the case if $X_1 = Y_1$. But since we may replace X_1 by any nonzero multiple, the two lines will be parallel if and only if $Y_1 = kX_1$.

EXAMPLE 3. Let us find a line parallel to

$$t \begin{pmatrix} 1 \\ 2 \\ 3 \end{pmatrix} + \begin{pmatrix} 1 \\ 1 \\ 1 \end{pmatrix}$$

which goes through the point

$$\begin{pmatrix} 1 \\ 0 \\ -1 \end{pmatrix}.$$

Obviously, the line

$$t \begin{pmatrix} 1 \\ 2 \\ 3 \end{pmatrix} + \begin{pmatrix} 1 \\ 0 \\ -1 \end{pmatrix}$$

will have both of these properties.

Let us now turn to planes in three dimensions. A **plane** $\mathcal{P}$ through the origin is a 2-dimensional subspace of 3-dimensional space, and hence it must be the kernel of some functional. For let X_1 and X_2 be basis vectors for $\mathcal{P}$, and include a third vector X_3 so that X_1, X_2, and X_3 form a basis for the 3-dimensional space. If we define $\mathbf{F}_1$ by $\mathbf{F}_1(aX_1 + bX_2 + cX_3) = c$, then $\mathbf{F}_1$ is the required functional. Hence the plane is the set of all X satisfying

(3) $\mathbf{F}_1 X = 0, \qquad \mathbf{F}_1 \neq 0.$

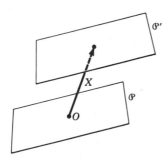

FIGURE 37

This is known as an **implicit** representation of $\mathcal{P}$. Let us now consider a plane $\mathcal{P}'$ not through the origin. It can be obtained from some plane $\mathcal{P}$ through the origin by adding some X_1 to each point, that is, through translation by X_1 (see Figure 37). Thus Y is in $\mathcal{P}'$ if and only if it is of the form $Y = X + X_1$, where X is in $\mathcal{P}$. But then

$$\mathbf{F}_1 Y = \mathbf{F}_1 X + \mathbf{F}_1 X_1 = \mathbf{F}_1 X_1 = c_1,$$

where c_1 is a number. Hence the points on $\mathcal{P}'$ are precisely the X satisfying

(4) $\mathbf{F}_1 X = c_1.$

This implicit representation is again not unique, since we can multiply through by a number, that is, $\mathbf{F}_1$ and c_1 may be replaced by $k\mathbf{F}_1$ and kc_1, for any nonzero k. For a given functional $\mathbf{F}_1$ the various planes obtained by taking various values for c_1 in the equation $\mathbf{F}_1 X = c_1$ are known as the **level planes** of the functional $\mathbf{F}_1$. All these level planes are parallel. And conversely, any two parallel planes can be represented as different level planes of the same functional.

To test whether a given point X_1 lies in the plane given by (4), we merely test whether it lies in the solution set of the equation, that is, whether $F_1 X_1 = c_1$ is true.

EXAMPLE 4. Does the point $\begin{pmatrix} 1 \\ 2 \\ 3 \end{pmatrix}$ lie in $(5 \quad 3 \quad -1)X = 2$? Since

$$(5 \quad 3 \quad -1) \begin{pmatrix} 1 \\ 2 \\ 3 \end{pmatrix} = 8,$$

the point is not in the plane. And since

$$(5 \quad 3 \quad -1) \begin{pmatrix} 1 \\ -1 \\ 0 \end{pmatrix} = 2,$$

the point $\begin{pmatrix} 1 \\ -1 \\ 0 \end{pmatrix}$ is in the plane.

Let us ask how one finds the intersection of the line $tX_1 + X_2$ with the plane $F_1 X = c_1$. The point(s) of intersection would have to be of the form $tX_1 + X_2$ and would have to lie in the solution set of the equation. Hence we look for one or more parameter values for which

$$(5) \qquad\qquad F_1(tX_1 + X_2) = tF_1 X_1 + F_1 X_2 = c_1,$$

where $F_1 X_1$ and $F_1 X_2$ are numbers. If $F_1 X_1 \neq 0$, we have a unique solution for (5), namely,

$$(6) \qquad\qquad t_0 = \frac{c_1 - F_1 X_2}{F_1 X_1} \quad \text{and} \quad X_0 = t_0 X_1 + X_2.$$

Thus t_0 is the parameter value of the point of intersection, and X_0 is the unique intersection point.

But the solution is entirely different if $F_1 X_1 = 0$. Then (5) reduces to $F_1 X_2 = c_1$, an expression that does not contain t. If this equation is true, then any value of t yields an intersection point; but if it is false, then no value of t will serve. Another way of putting it is to say that an equality between two numbers is either true for all X or false for all X, hence its set of solutions is either the set of all real numbers or the empty set.

From these considerations we deduce that $F_1X_1 = 0$ is the necessary and sufficient condition for the line $tX_1 + X_2$ to be parallel to the plane $F_1X = c_1$. If in addition $F_1X_2 = c_1$, then the line lies entirely in the plane.

Example 5. Consider the plane $(1\ 2\ 3)X = 6$, and lines $\mathcal{L}_1$, $\mathcal{L}_2$, $\mathcal{L}_3$ given parametrically as

$$
t\begin{pmatrix} 1 \\ 2 \\ 1 \end{pmatrix} + \begin{pmatrix} -1 \\ 0 \\ 1 \end{pmatrix}, \quad
t\begin{pmatrix} 1 \\ 1 \\ -1 \end{pmatrix} + \begin{pmatrix} -1 \\ 0 \\ 1 \end{pmatrix}, \quad
t\begin{pmatrix} 1 \\ 1 \\ -1 \end{pmatrix} + \begin{pmatrix} 1 \\ 1 \\ 1 \end{pmatrix},
$$

respectively. For $\mathcal{L}_1$,

$$
(1\ \ 2\ \ 3)\begin{pmatrix} 1 \\ 2 \\ 1 \end{pmatrix} = 8 \neq 0,
$$

hence we have a unique intersection;

$$
t_0 = \frac{6 - 2}{8} = \frac{1}{2} \quad \text{and} \quad X_0 = \frac{1}{2}\begin{pmatrix} 1 \\ 2 \\ 1 \end{pmatrix} + \begin{pmatrix} -1 \\ 0 \\ 1 \end{pmatrix} = \begin{pmatrix} -\frac{1}{2} \\ 1 \\ \frac{3}{2} \end{pmatrix}.
$$

For $\mathcal{L}_2$ and $\mathcal{L}_3$,

$$
(1\ \ 2\ \ 3)\begin{pmatrix} 1 \\ 1 \\ -1 \end{pmatrix} = 0,
$$

hence they are parallel to the plane. For $\mathcal{L}_3$ we also find

$$
(1\ \ 2\ \ 3)\begin{pmatrix} 1 \\ 1 \\ 1 \end{pmatrix} = 6 = c_1,
$$

hence it lies in the plane.

Next let us raise the question as to whether the lines $tX_1 + X_2$ and $tY_1 + Y_2$ are **coplanar**, that is whether there is a plane containing both of them. In general, one expects a negative answer, but under special conditions on X_1, X_2, Y_1, Y_2 such a plane may exist. Here we are searching for a nonzero $\mathbf{F}$ and a c such that the plane they determine contains both lines. This leads to five conditions:

$$\mathbf{F} \neq 0, \quad \mathbf{F}X_1 = 0, \quad \mathbf{F}Y_1 = 0, \quad \mathbf{F}X_2 = c, \quad \text{and} \quad \mathbf{F}Y_2 = c.$$

But we do not really care what the value of c is, as long as it exists. Hence the last two conditions reduce to $\mathbf{F}X_2 = \mathbf{F}Y_2$. Thus the conditions for the two lines to be coplanar may be written as:

(7) There is nonzero functional $\mathbf{F}$ such that $\mathbf{F}X_1 = 0$, $\mathbf{F}Y_1 = 0$, and
$\mathbf{F}(X_2 - Y_2) = 0$.

If these three equations for $\mathbf{F}$ have a common nonzero solution, then the lines are coplanar. If one solution is $\mathbf{F} = \mathbf{F}_0$, and we let $\mathbf{F}_0X_2 = c_0$, then the plane $\mathbf{F}_0X = c_0$ contains both lines.

EXAMPLE 6. Are the lines

$$t\begin{pmatrix} 1 \\ 1 \\ -1 \end{pmatrix} + \begin{pmatrix} 1 \\ 1 \\ 1 \end{pmatrix} \quad \text{and} \quad t\begin{pmatrix} 1 \\ -2 \\ 1 \end{pmatrix} + \begin{pmatrix} 2 \\ 5 \\ -2 \end{pmatrix}$$

coplanar? If we let $\mathbf{F} = (a_1 \quad a_2 \quad a_3)$, the conditions (7) become

$$a_1 + a_2 - a_3 = 0,$$

$$a_1 - 2a_2 + a_3 = 0,$$

$$-a_1 - 4a_2 + 3a_3 = 0.$$

One nonzero solution to these equations is $\mathbf{F}_0 = (1 \quad 2 \quad 3)$. Using this solution, we get $c_0 = 6$, and hence $(1 \quad 2 \quad 3)X = 6$ is an equation for the plane containing both lines. (We have already seen in Example 5 that the first line lies in this plane.)

EXERCISES

1. In representing the line $\mathcal{L}$ by the parametric expression

$$tX_1 + X_2, \qquad X_1 \neq 0.$$

show that X_2 may be chosen as any point on $\mathcal{L}$.

2. Show that in representing the line $\mathcal{L}$ by the parametric expression

$$tX_1 + X_2, \qquad X_1 \neq 0$$

X_1 may be replaced by any of its nonzero numerical multiples kX_1.

3. Give a geometric interpretation for the equations (7) for two lines to be coplanar.

4. Show that the following two parametric expressions represent the same line:

$$t\begin{pmatrix} 1 \\ 0 \\ -2 \end{pmatrix} + \begin{pmatrix} 1 \\ 2 \\ 3 \end{pmatrix}, \qquad t\begin{pmatrix} -2 \\ 0 \\ 4 \end{pmatrix} + \begin{pmatrix} 2 \\ 2 \\ 1 \end{pmatrix}.$$

5. Is the line through $\begin{pmatrix} 1 \\ 2 \\ 3 \end{pmatrix}$ and $\begin{pmatrix} 3 \\ -1 \\ 0 \end{pmatrix}$ parallel to the vector $\begin{pmatrix} 5 \\ -2 \\ 3 \end{pmatrix}$?

6. Represent parametrically the line through $\begin{pmatrix} 1 \\ 2 \\ 5 \end{pmatrix}$ parallel to the line

through $\begin{pmatrix} 1 \\ 0 \\ 3 \end{pmatrix}$ and $\begin{pmatrix} 0 \\ 1 \\ 2 \end{pmatrix}$.

7. Find an equation for the plane through

$$\begin{pmatrix} 1 \\ 2 \\ 3 \end{pmatrix}, \quad \begin{pmatrix} 0 \\ 0 \\ 1 \end{pmatrix}, \quad \begin{pmatrix} 0 \\ 1 \\ 0 \end{pmatrix}.$$

8. Which of the following points lie on the plane in Exercise 7 above?

$$\begin{pmatrix} 1 \\ 3 \\ 2 \end{pmatrix}, \quad \begin{pmatrix} 1 \\ 1 \\ 4 \end{pmatrix}, \quad \begin{pmatrix} 0 \\ 0 \\ 0 \end{pmatrix}, \quad \begin{pmatrix} 4 \\ -1 \\ 2 \end{pmatrix}.$$

9. Write an equation for a plane parallel to the plane in Exercise 7 and passing

through $\begin{pmatrix} 5 \\ -2 \\ 0 \end{pmatrix}$.

10. For each of the following lines and planes find the point(s) of intersection of the line with plane.

(a) $t \begin{pmatrix} 1 \\ 1 \\ 1 \end{pmatrix} + \begin{pmatrix} 1 \\ 0 \\ -1 \end{pmatrix}$; $(1 \quad 1 \quad 1)X = 3$. $\left[Ans. \begin{pmatrix} 2 \\ 1 \\ 0 \end{pmatrix}. \right]$

(b) $t \begin{pmatrix} 1 \\ 1 \\ 1 \end{pmatrix} + \begin{pmatrix} 1 \\ 0 \\ -1 \end{pmatrix}$; $(3 \quad 2 \quad 1)X = 6$.

(c) $t \begin{pmatrix} 1 \\ 0 \\ -1 \end{pmatrix} + \begin{pmatrix} 3 \\ 2 \\ 1 \end{pmatrix}$; $(1 \quad 1 \quad 1)X = 3$. $[Ans.$ None.$]$

(d) $t \begin{pmatrix} 1 \\ 0 \\ -1 \end{pmatrix} + \begin{pmatrix} 2 \\ 1 \\ 0 \end{pmatrix}$; $(1 \quad 1 \quad 1)X = 3$.

11. Which of the following pairs of lines are coplanar? For the coplanar pairs write an equation for the plane in which they lie.

(a) $t \begin{pmatrix} 1 \\ 0 \\ -1 \end{pmatrix} + \begin{pmatrix} 1 \\ 1 \\ 1 \end{pmatrix}$; $t \begin{pmatrix} 1 \\ -2 \\ 1 \end{pmatrix} + \begin{pmatrix} 3 \\ 0 \\ 0 \end{pmatrix}$.

$[Ans.$ Coplanar; $(1 \quad 1 \quad 1)X = 3.]$

(b) $t \begin{pmatrix} 1 \\ 0 \\ 0 \end{pmatrix} + \begin{pmatrix} 1 \\ 1 \\ 2 \end{pmatrix}$; $\quad t \begin{pmatrix} 0 \\ 1 \\ 0 \end{pmatrix} + \begin{pmatrix} 1 \\ 1 \\ 1 \end{pmatrix}$. $\quad$ [*Ans.* Not coplanar.]

(c) $t \begin{pmatrix} 1 \\ 1 \\ 1 \end{pmatrix} + \begin{pmatrix} 1 \\ 2 \\ 3 \end{pmatrix}$; $\quad t \begin{pmatrix} -1 \\ 1 \\ -1 \end{pmatrix}$.

(d) $t \begin{pmatrix} -1 \\ 1 \\ 1 \end{pmatrix} + \begin{pmatrix} 1 \\ 1 \\ 1 \end{pmatrix}$; $\quad t \begin{pmatrix} 1 \\ -2 \\ 1 \end{pmatrix} + \begin{pmatrix} 2 \\ 0 \\ 0 \end{pmatrix}$.

12. Let a line $\mathcal{L}$ be given by the parametric expression $Y_0 + tW_0$. Let Z_0 be some point not on $\mathcal{L}$. Write an equation for the plane that contains $\mathcal{L}$ and Z_0.

13. Given different level planes $\mathcal{P}_1$ and $\mathcal{P}_2$ of the same functional **F**, how can we recognize from c_1 and c_2 whether the planes are on the same or opposite sides of the origin?

14. FURTHER TOPICS IN VECTOR GEOMETRY

We know that any two points will determine a line and any three points not on a line will determine a plane in three dimensions. Let us see how we find the line and plane so determined.

Let Y_1 and Y_2 be any two points on $\mathcal{L}$, and let us look for a parametric representation of $\mathcal{L}$. From Figure 38 we see that $Y_1 - Y_2$ will serve as

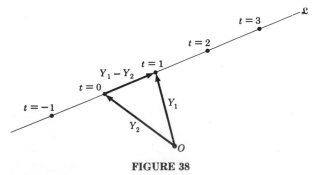

FIGURE 38

X_1 in the parametric representation, and either point will serve as X_2. Thus one easy way of writing down the parametric representation of $\mathcal{L}$ is

$$(1) \qquad\qquad t(Y_1 - Y_2) + Y_2.$$

We can also see from (1) directly that this is the desired line. If $t = 0$ we obtain Y_2, and if $t = 1$ we obtain Y_1, hence (1) represents a line containing both Y_1 and Y_2. It is also clear from (1) that Y_1 and Y_2 had to be distinct, otherwise t would disappear from the representation.

Let Y_1, Y_2, and Y_3 be three points which do not lie on a line. To find the plane containing them, we search for a nonzero $\mathbf{F}$ and a c such that

$$(2) \qquad\qquad \mathbf{F}Y_1 = c, \qquad \mathbf{F}Y_2 = c, \quad \text{and} \quad \mathbf{F}Y_3 = c.$$

We know from the nature of the problem that (2) determines a unique plane. Hence the equations will determine $\mathbf{F}$, up to a constant factor; that is, if $\mathbf{F} = \mathbf{F}_1$ is one solution, then the general solution is of the form $\mathbf{F} = k\mathbf{F}_1$, and then $c = k\mathbf{F}_1 Y_1$. Hence an equation of the plane will be $\mathbf{F}_1 X = \mathbf{F}_1 Y_1$.

EXAMPLE 1. Find the plane through the points

$$\begin{pmatrix} 1 \\ 1 \\ 1 \end{pmatrix}, \quad \begin{pmatrix} 0 \\ 0 \\ 2 \end{pmatrix}, \quad \text{and} \quad \begin{pmatrix} 10 \\ -2 \\ 0 \end{pmatrix}.$$

If $\mathbf{F} = (a_1 \quad a_2 \quad a_3)$, the conditions (2) become

$$a_1 + a_2 + a_3 = c,$$

$$2a_3 = c,$$

$$10a_1 - 2a_2 \qquad = c.$$

The general solution of these equations is $\mathbf{F} = c(\tfrac{1}{6} \ \tfrac{1}{3} \ \tfrac{1}{2})$. Choosing $c = 6$, we obtain the equation $(1 \quad 2 \quad 3)X = 6$.

Equations (2) can also be used when Y_1, Y_2, Y_3 lie on a line. In this case equations (2) will yield implicit equations for *all* planes through Y_1, Y_2, Y_3. Thus solving (2) automatically tells us whether Y_1, Y_2, Y_3 lie on a line; they do if and only if (2) does not determine $\mathbf{F}$ (up to a constant factor).

There is an alternative way of testing whether three points lie on a line. We know that the line through Y_1 and Y_2 has the equation (1). We then have to decide whether Y_3 lies on this line. This will happen if and only if $Y_3 - Y_2$ is a multiple of $Y_1 - Y_2$.

EXAMPLE 2. Do

$$\begin{pmatrix} 1 \\ 1 \\ 1 \end{pmatrix}, \begin{pmatrix} 1 \\ 0 \\ -1 \end{pmatrix}, \begin{pmatrix} 1 \\ 3 \\ 5 \end{pmatrix}$$

lie on a line? If $\mathbf{F} = (a_1 \quad a_2 \quad a_3)$, the conditions (2) become

$$a_1 + a_2 + a_3 = c,$$
$$a_1 \qquad - a_3 = c,$$
$$a_1 + 3a_2 + 5a_3 = c.$$

The general solutions to these equations can be written as

$$\mathbf{F} = (c + k \quad -2k \quad k).$$

Since $\mathbf{F}$ is not determined up to a constant factor by these points, we know that the given points lie on a line $\mathcal{L}$. Note that we have also found the equations of *all* planes through $\mathcal{L}$. They are of the form $(c + k \quad -2k \quad k)X = c$. For each k this is the equation of a plane through $\mathcal{L}$. By the alternate method we have to test whether

$$Y_3 - Y_2 = \begin{pmatrix} 0 \\ 3 \\ 6 \end{pmatrix}$$

is a multiple of

$$Y_1 - Y_2 = \begin{pmatrix} 0 \\ 1 \\ 2 \end{pmatrix},$$

which it clearly is.

Let us next suppose that we are given the planes $\mathbf{F}_1 X = c_1$ and $\mathbf{F}_2 X = c_2$, and we are asked to find their line of intersection. (A line represented as the intersection of two planes is said to be represented **implicitly**.) If Y is any point on their line of intersection, then it lies in both planes, and hence

(3) $$\mathbf{F}_1 Y = c_1 \quad \text{and} \quad \mathbf{F}_2 Y = c_2.$$

If $\mathbf{F}_2 \neq k\mathbf{F}_1$, then we know that the general solution of these two simultaneous equations is $Y = tX_1 + X_2$, where X_1 is a solution of the homogeneous equations, and X_2 is any one solution of the equations. And this solution is the parametric representation of the line of intersection.

If $\mathbf{F}_2 = k\mathbf{F}_1$, then (3) will have no solution unless $c_2 = kc_1$. And in the latter case the solution contains two parameters, and hence represents more than one line. Thus we may conclude that the necessary and sufficient condition for the two planes to be parallel is that $\mathbf{F}_2$ is a multiple of $\mathbf{F}_1$. If in addition c_2 is the same multiple of c_1, then the planes coincide. Since we can always divide the second equation by k, we may write parallel planes in the form $\mathbf{F}_1 X = c_1$ and $\mathbf{F}_1 X = c_2$, with the same $\mathbf{F}_1$. Then the planes coincide if and only if $c_1 = c_2$.

EXAMPLE 3. Find the line of intersection of $(1 \quad 2 \quad 3)X = 6$ with $(1 \quad 3 \quad 5)X = 9$. The equations (3) become

$$y_1 + 2y_2 + 3y_3 = 6,$$

$$y_1 + 3y_2 + 5y_3 = 9.$$

The general solution is

$$Y = t \begin{pmatrix} 1 \\ -2 \\ 1 \end{pmatrix} + \begin{pmatrix} 1 \\ 1 \\ 1 \end{pmatrix},$$

hence this is the parametric representation of the line of intersection.

One concept of the first type not yet discussed is the relation that Y lies **between** Y_1 and Y_2, that is, on the line segment connecting them. We know that (1) gives the entire line $\mathcal{L}$ in Figure 38, and that for $t = 0$ we obtain Y_2, while for $t = 1$ we obtain Y_1. It is easily seen from Figure 38 that the other points between Y_1 and Y_2 are given by intermediate values of t. Hence the parametric representation of the segment between Y_1 and Y_2 is

(4) $t(Y_1 - Y_2) + Y_2 = tY_1 + (1 - t)Y_2,$ $0 \le t \le 1.$

EXAMPLE 4. To find the points that trisect the segment joining

$$\begin{pmatrix} 1 \\ 2 \\ 3 \end{pmatrix} \text{ to } \begin{pmatrix} 1 \\ -1 \\ 0 \end{pmatrix},$$

we take $t = \frac{1}{3}$ and $t = \frac{2}{3}$ in the parametric formula for the segment. The

trisecting point close to $\begin{pmatrix} 1 \\ 2 \\ 3 \end{pmatrix}$ is

$$\frac{2}{3}\begin{pmatrix} 1 \\ 2 \\ 3 \end{pmatrix} + \frac{1}{3}\begin{pmatrix} 1 \\ -1 \\ 0 \end{pmatrix} = \begin{pmatrix} 1 \\ 1 \\ 2 \end{pmatrix}.$$

And the trisecting point close to $\begin{pmatrix} 1 \\ -1 \\ 0 \end{pmatrix}$ is

$$\frac{1}{3}\begin{pmatrix} 1 \\ 2 \\ 3 \end{pmatrix} + \frac{2}{3}\begin{pmatrix} 1 \\ -1 \\ 0 \end{pmatrix} = \begin{pmatrix} 1 \\ 0 \\ 1 \end{pmatrix}.$$

Notice that the coefficients $\frac{1}{3}$ and $\frac{2}{3}$ of the end-point vectors have sum 1, as they should, and that the "heavier" of the two coefficients goes with the nearer of the two end points.

All applications of vector methods that we have considered so far were carried out without the introduction of a coordinate system. Even in proving geometric theorems it may happen that these coordinate-free methods give a quick proof.

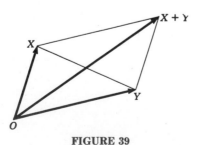

FIGURE 39

EXAMPLE 5. Suppose we want to show that the diagonals of a parallelogram bisect each other. Let us put the origin O at one vertex and vectors X and Y at the two adjacent vertices (see Figure 39). Then the fourth vertex is $X + Y$. The intersection of the two diagonals is some numerical multiple $w(X + Y)$ of the vector $X + Y$. Hence we have

$$w(X + Y) = (1 - t)X + tY,$$

$$wX + wY = (1 - t)X + tY.$$

Since X and Y are linearly independent, the coefficients of X must be equal, and the coefficients of Y must be equal.

$$w = 1 - t,$$

$$w = t.$$

Hence $t = 1 - t = w = \frac{1}{2}$, and we have proved that the intersection of the diagonals is the mid-point of each.

We thus see that a great many geometrical problems can be solved without introducing such concepts as length and angles. Actually, we can even introduce a limited concept of length by purely vector methods.

We know that the choice of a coordinate system is equivalent to the choice of a basis for the vector space. It is only when we require that the axes be perpendicular and that we have the "same" unit of length on all axes that we need concepts of the second type. These problems will be discussed in the next section.

While with vector methods alone we cannot compare the lengths of two vectors, we can compare their components. If we have a basis X_1, X_2, X_3 chosen for our 3-dimensional space, then all vectors are represented as numerical column vectors, and we can compare corresponding components. More generally, if two vectors are parallel, then one is a numerical multiple of the other, and hence we can compare their lengths.

Let us consider briefly how our basic tools generalize to n-dimensional geometry. In any number of dimensions a line through the origin is a 1-dimensional subspace, and hence can be represented as tX_1. Since any line is obtained from a line through the origin by translation, the parametric representation $tX_1 + X_2$ will be applicable in any number of dimensions.

The equation $F_1X = 0$ in n-dimensional space must represent an $(n - 1)$-dimensional subspace. This follows from the fact that F_1 is a transformation with a 1-dimensional range (assuming $F_1 \neq 0$), and hence its kernel must have dimension $n - 1$. (See Theorem 10.6.) Such a subspace, whose dimension is 1 less than the dimension of the entire space, is generally known as a **hyperplane**. Notice that the concept of line does not depend on the dimension of the space that contains it, while the concept of hyperplane does. It can be shown, using methods exactly analogous to those used in Section 13 that a hyperplane not through the origin is the set of solutions of an equation $F_1X = c_1$, with $c_1 \neq 0$.

Nearly all that we did in these last two sections carries over to n dimensions if for "line" we still read "line" and for "plane" we read "hyperplane."

It is interesting to step down from 3-dimensional space to 2-dimensional space. Here a coincidence occurs. Since a hyperplane is $(n - 1)$-dimensional, and since $n - 1 = 1$, hyperplanes are simply lines. This is the reason why in plane analytic geometry a line may be represented either implicitly by a single equation or parametrically. This leaves us with a great deal of freedom as to whether we think of a line as a line or as a hyperplane. But it also makes it hard to conjecture the proper n-dimensional generalizations of 2-dimensional theorems. The smallest "typical" space is 3-dimensional.

In higher-dimensional spaces there are, of course, nontrivial subspaces of all dimensions r between 1 and $n - 1$. Translates of these are sometimes called **flats** or sometimes simply **r-dimensional planes**. Each r-dimensional flat can be represented either parametrically or implicitly. (In particular, a plane in 3-space can be represented parametrically and a line in 3-space can be represented implicitly.) Parametrically, an r-dimensional flat is written

$$X_0 + t^{(1)}X_1 + \ldots + t^{(r)}X_r,$$

where X_0 is any fixed point on the flat, and $X_1, \ldots, X_r$ are any r linearly independent vectors parallel to the flat, and the parameters $t^{(1)}, \ldots, t^{(r)}$ run independently over all real numbers. Implicitly, an r-dimensional flat is written as the solution set of the conjunction of $n - r$ equations.

$$\mathbf{F}_1 X = c_1,$$

(5)

$$\mathbf{F}_{n-r} X = c_{n-r},$$

where the functionals $\mathbf{F}_1, \ldots, \mathbf{F}_{n-r}$ are linearly independent. That is, the flat is represented as the intersection of hyperplanes.

EXERCISES

1. Write a parametric expression for the line through

$$\begin{pmatrix} 1 \\ 2 \\ -3 \end{pmatrix} \quad \text{and} \quad \begin{pmatrix} 0 \\ 1 \\ 5 \end{pmatrix}.$$

2. Write another parametric expression for the line in Exercise 1.

3. Write an equation for the plane through

$$\begin{pmatrix} 2 \\ 2 \\ 3 \end{pmatrix}, \quad \begin{pmatrix} 2 \\ 3 \\ 3 \end{pmatrix}, \quad \begin{pmatrix} 2 \\ 3 \\ 4 \end{pmatrix}.$$

[Ans. $(1, 0, 0)X = 2.$]

4. Show that the points

$$\begin{pmatrix} 0 \\ -2 \\ -1 \end{pmatrix}, \quad \begin{pmatrix} 1 \\ 4 \\ 0 \end{pmatrix}, \quad \begin{pmatrix} 2 \\ 10 \\ 1 \end{pmatrix}$$

do not determine a unique plane.

5. Find a parametric expression for the line of intersection of the plane $(5 \quad 2 \quad 1)X = 0$ with the plane $(1 -1 \quad 0)X = 1$.

6. Find the plane parallel to $(5 \quad 2 \quad 1)X = 1$ that contains the point

$$\begin{pmatrix} 100 \\ 200 \\ 300 \end{pmatrix}.$$

[Ans. $(5 \quad 2 \quad 1)X = 1200.$]

7. Find the three points that divide the segment between $\begin{pmatrix} 1 \\ 9 \\ -2 \end{pmatrix}$ and

$\begin{pmatrix} 0 \\ 1 \\ 1 \end{pmatrix}$ into four equal parts. $\left[Ans. \begin{pmatrix} \frac{1}{4} \\ 3 \\ \frac{1}{4} \end{pmatrix}, \begin{pmatrix} \frac{1}{2} \\ 5 \\ -\frac{1}{2} \end{pmatrix}, \begin{pmatrix} \frac{3}{4} \\ 7 \\ -\frac{5}{4} \end{pmatrix}. \right]$

8. Check that each of the following points lies on the line through

$Y_0 = \begin{pmatrix} 1 \\ 2 \\ 3 \end{pmatrix}$ and $Z_0 = \begin{pmatrix} -1 \\ 0 \\ 2 \end{pmatrix}$. Which of them lie between Y_0 and Z_0?

$$\begin{pmatrix} 0 \\ 1 \\ \frac{5}{2} \end{pmatrix}, \quad \begin{pmatrix} -\frac{1}{2} \\ \frac{1}{2} \\ \frac{9}{4} \end{pmatrix}, \quad \begin{pmatrix} 2 \\ 3 \\ \frac{7}{2} \end{pmatrix}, \quad \begin{pmatrix} -3 \\ -2 \\ 1 \end{pmatrix}.$$

9. Check that all the following segments are parallel, and compare their lengths.

$$S_1 = \text{the segment joining} \begin{pmatrix} 1 \\ 2 \\ 0 \end{pmatrix} \quad \text{and} \quad \begin{pmatrix} 2 \\ 3 \\ -1 \end{pmatrix}.$$

$$S_2 = \text{the segment joining} \begin{pmatrix} 4 \\ 5 \\ -2 \end{pmatrix} \quad \text{and} \quad \begin{pmatrix} 6 \\ 7 \\ -4 \end{pmatrix}.$$

$$S_3 = \text{the segment joining} \begin{pmatrix} \frac{1}{2} \\ \frac{1}{2} \\ \frac{1}{2} \end{pmatrix} \quad \text{and} \quad \begin{pmatrix} 1 \\ 1 \\ 0 \end{pmatrix}.$$

[*Ans.* The length of S_2 is twice that of S_1 and the length of S_3 is $\frac{1}{2}$ that of S_1.]

10. Which of the following points lie in the plane determined by $\begin{pmatrix} 1 \\ 0 \\ 0 \end{pmatrix}$,

$$\begin{pmatrix} 0 \\ 1 \\ 0 \end{pmatrix}, \begin{pmatrix} 0 \\ 0 \\ 1 \end{pmatrix}?$$

$$\begin{pmatrix} 5 \\ -2 \\ -3 \end{pmatrix}, \begin{pmatrix} 4 \\ -2 \\ -1 \end{pmatrix}, \begin{pmatrix} \frac{1}{2} \\ \frac{1}{2} \\ \frac{1}{2} \end{pmatrix}, \begin{pmatrix} \frac{1}{3} \\ \frac{1}{3} \\ \frac{1}{3} \end{pmatrix}, \begin{pmatrix} \frac{1}{2} \\ \frac{1}{2} \\ 0 \end{pmatrix}, \begin{pmatrix} 0 \\ 0 \\ 0 \end{pmatrix}.$$

11. If X, Y, Z are linearly independent vectors, interpret geometrically the point $\frac{1}{3}X + \frac{1}{3}Y + \frac{1}{3}Z$.

12. Given a triangle, take one vertex as the origin and take the two adjacent sides as the vectors of a basis. What then are the coordinates of each of the other two vertices? What are the coordinates of the mid-points of each of the sides?

13. Find the points that trisect the segment joining $\begin{pmatrix} 1 \\ 2 \end{pmatrix}$ to $\begin{pmatrix} -3 \\ 0 \end{pmatrix}$.

14. Find a point X_0 on the segment between $Y_0 = \begin{pmatrix} 1 \\ 2 \\ 3 \end{pmatrix}$ and $Z_0 = \begin{pmatrix} \frac{1}{2} \\ \frac{1}{2} \\ \frac{1}{2} \end{pmatrix}$

such that X_0 is five times as far from Y_0 as it is from Z_0.

$$\left[Ans. \begin{pmatrix} \frac{7}{12} \\ \frac{3}{4} \\ \frac{11}{12} \end{pmatrix} \right].$$

15. Let F_0 be the functional that sends each column $\begin{pmatrix} x_1 \\ x_2 \\ x_3 \end{pmatrix}$ into $3x_1 + 2x_2 +$

x_3. What is an equation for the level plane of F_0 that passes through

$$\begin{pmatrix} 4 \\ -1 \\ 2 \end{pmatrix} ?$$

16. Let X_1, X_2, X_3 be any three linearly independent points in 3-dimensional space. Let W_1 be the mid-point of the segment from 0 to X_1. Let W_2 be the mid-point of the segment from X_1 to X_2. Let W_3 be the mid-point of the segment from X_2 to X_3. And let W_4 be the midpoint of the segment from X_3 to 0. Prove that a parallelogram is formed by drawing segments between W_1 and W_2, between W_2 and W_3, between W_3 and W_4, and between W_4 and W_1.

17. Write a parametric expression for the line of intersection of the planes

$$(1 \quad 2 \quad 3)X = 1 \quad \text{and} \quad (1 \quad 1 \quad -1)X = -1.$$

$$\left[Ans. \ t \begin{pmatrix} 5 \\ -4 \\ 1 \end{pmatrix} + \begin{pmatrix} -3 \\ 2 \\ 0 \end{pmatrix} \right].$$

18. Do the following three points lie on a line?

$$\begin{pmatrix} 2 \\ 3 \\ -4 \end{pmatrix}, \quad \begin{pmatrix} 2 \\ 1 \\ -1 \end{pmatrix}, \quad \begin{pmatrix} 2 \\ 7 \\ -10 \end{pmatrix}. \qquad [Ans. \text{ Yes.}]$$

19. Do the following four points lie on a plane?

$$\begin{pmatrix} 6 \\ 0 \\ -3 \end{pmatrix}, \quad \begin{pmatrix} -1 \\ 6 \\ -11 \end{pmatrix}, \quad \begin{pmatrix} 4 \\ 3 \\ -16 \end{pmatrix}, \quad \begin{pmatrix} 13 \\ -6 \\ 5 \end{pmatrix}.$$

20. The plane $\mathcal{P}$ goes through the points $\begin{pmatrix} 1 \\ 2 \\ 3 \end{pmatrix}$ and $\begin{pmatrix} -1 \\ 0 \\ 1 \end{pmatrix}$ and $\begin{pmatrix} 1 \\ 0 \\ 0 \end{pmatrix}$.

Write an equation for $\mathcal{P}$. $[Ans. \ (1 \ -3 \ 2)X = 1.]$

21. Write a parametric expression for the line of intersection of the planes determined by the following two equations:

$$x_1 - x_2 + x_3 = 1,$$
$$x_1 + 2x_2 + 3x_3 = 1.$$

22. Write an implicit equation for the plane that contains the line

$$X = t \begin{pmatrix} 1 \\ 0 \\ 5 \end{pmatrix} + \begin{pmatrix} 1 \\ 2 \\ -1 \end{pmatrix} \text{ and also contains the point } \begin{pmatrix} 1 \\ 0 \\ 1 \end{pmatrix}.$$

$$[Ans. \ (5 \ -1 \ -1)X = 4.]$$

23. Show that among all the level planes in 3-dimensional space of the functional $\mathbf{F}_0$, the level plane passing through Y_0 coincides with the solution set of $\mathbf{F}_0(X - Y_0) = 0$.

24. Let $\mathcal{L}_1$ and $\mathcal{L}_2$ be lines in the plane. Show that any one of the following three properties is sufficient to make $\mathcal{L}_1$ and $\mathcal{L}_2$ parallel.
   (a) The points in $\mathcal{L}_2$ are obtained by adding some fixed vector Y_0 to all the points in $\mathcal{L}_1$.
   (b) $\mathcal{L}_1$ and $\mathcal{L}_2$ are different level lines of the same functional F_0.
   (c) $\mathcal{L}_1$ and $\mathcal{L}_2$ never intersect.

25. Suppose the plane $\mathcal{P}_0$ goes through the origin and through the points

$$\begin{pmatrix} 1 \\ 2 \\ 3 \end{pmatrix} \text{ and } \begin{pmatrix} -1 \\ 0 \\ 1 \end{pmatrix}.$$ Suppose the plane $\mathcal{P}_1$ is parallel to $\mathcal{P}_0$ and goes

through the point $\begin{pmatrix} 3 \\ 7 \\ -9 \end{pmatrix}$. Determine whether the point $\begin{pmatrix} 5 \\ 8 \\ -7 \end{pmatrix}$

belongs to the plane $\mathcal{P}_1$.   [*Ans.* No.]

26. Show that as t varies over all real numbers (not only between 0 and 1) that

$$(*) \qquad\qquad tX_1 + (1 - t)X_2$$

represents the line through X_1 and X_2. The above expression can also be written

$$(**) \qquad\qquad t^{(1)}X_1 + t^{(2)}X_2$$

with the understanding that $t^{(1)}$ and $t^{(2)}$ are numerical variables subject only to the restriction $t^{(1)} + t^{(2)} = 1$.

27. Show that the following expression represents a plane through X_1 and X_2 and X_3 if the variables $t^{(1)}$ and $t^{(2)}$ and $t^{(3)}$ are. subject to the restriction $t^{(1)} + t^{(2)} + t^{(3)} = 1$, and X_1, X_2, X_3 are not on a line

$$(***) \qquad\qquad t^{(1)}X_1 + t^{(2)}X_2 + t^{(3)}X_3.$$

28. Show that if the variables $t^{(1)}$ and $t^{(2)}$ and $t^{(3)}$ in the expression $(***)$ above are also required to be nonnegative then we have a representation of the triangular region pictured in Figure 40.

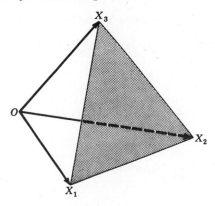

FIGURE 40

29. Prove by use of vector space ideas, and without setting up a coordinate system, that the three medians of a triangle intersect at a common point. (A "median" of a triangle is the segment joining one vertex to the midpoint of the opposite side.)

30. Prove by use of vector space ideas and without setting up a coordinate system that the point at which the three medians of a triangle intersect (see Exercise 29 above) divides each median in the ratio 2 to 1.

31. Given a parallelogram, take one vertex as the origin O and take the two adjacent sides as the vectors of a basis for the geometric plane. What then are the coordinates of each of the other three vertices? And of the point where the diagonals intersect? Do the same for a square, and compare.

32. In n-dimensional space show that the simultaneous implicit equations (5) define a flat of dimension exactly r if and only if the functionals $\mathbf{F}_1, \ldots, \mathbf{F}_{n-r}$ are linearly independent. (Hence, in particular, if $\mathbf{F}X = 0$ and $\mathbf{G}X = 0$ define the same hyperplane, then $\mathbf{G}$ is a numerical multiple of $\mathbf{F}$ and vice versa.)

33. In the situation of Exercise 32 above, what can we say about the dimension of the flat defined by Equations (5) when the functionals $\mathbf{F}_1, \ldots, \mathbf{F}_{n-r}$ are linearly dependent?

    [*Ans.* Either the solution set of these simultaneous equations is empty, or else the flat they define has dimension $> r$.]

34. Express the theorems stated in Exercises 32 and 33 above as theorems about simultaneous linear equations.

GRAPHICAL EXERCISES IN 2-DIMENSIONAL VECTOR GEOMETRY

In the following exercises the concepts of the last two sections are interpreted in direct geometric terms. Hence in order to be able to draw pictures, we state the questions always for a 2-dimensional space.

35. Write parametric expressions for the lines $\mathcal{L}$ and $\mathcal{L}_0$ pictured in Figure 41.

36. In Figure 42 what vector can be added to all the points on line $\mathcal{L}_1$ to give all points on line $\mathcal{L}_2$?   [*Ans.* $Y_2 - Y_1$.]

37. Show that line $\mathcal{L}_0$ in Figure 43 is represented by $tY_0 + (1 - t)Z_0$, as t runs over all real numbers. What is the relation between this representation and the representation $Y_0 + tW_0$ of line $\mathcal{L}_0$ in Figure 41?

38. Suppose that the vectors W_1 and W_2 in Figure 44 are chosen as basis for the plane, and that coordinates are assigned to every point in the plane relative to this basis. Show that then the line $\mathcal{L}_0$ in Figure 44 consists of all vectors of the form $\begin{pmatrix} t \\ 1 - t \end{pmatrix}$.

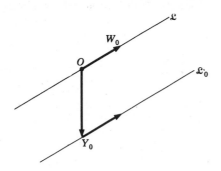

FIGURE 41

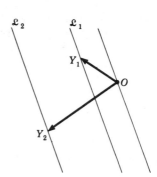

FIGURE 42

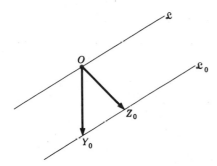

FIGURE 43

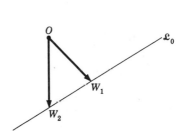

FIGURE 44

39. Relative to the basis $\{W_1,\ W_2\}$ in Exercise 38 above, choose $(a_1,\ a_2)$ so that $a_1x_1 + a_2x_2 = 1$, or $(a_1,\ a_2)X = 1$, is an implicit equation for the line $\mathcal{L}$ in Figure 45. $\left[Ans.\ a_1 = a_2 = 4.\right]$

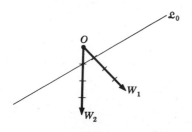

FIGURE 45

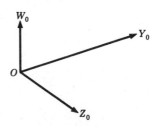

FIGURE 46

40. If W_0, Y_0, Z_0 are the plane vectors shown in Figure 46, sketch each of the following parametric lines:

$$W_0 + tY_0,$$

$$W_0 + tZ_0,$$

$$Y_0 + tW_0,$$

$$Z_0 + tW_0,$$

$$Z_0 + tZ_0,$$

$$tW_0,$$

$$(W_0 - Y_0) + tZ_0,$$

$$Z_0 + t(W_0 - Y_0).$$

41. Express each of the points X_1, X_2, X_3 pictured below in Figure 47 as a linear combination of Y_0 and Z_0. $\left[\textit{Partial Ans. } X_3 = \frac{5}{4}Y_0 - \frac{1}{4}Z_0.\right]$

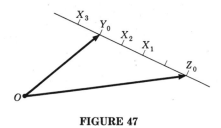

FIGURE 47

42. Imagine that the page on which these words are printed represents the plane that passes through the (tips of) linearly independent 3-dimensional vectors W, Y, Z. Locate in Figure 48, the points corresponding to

$$\tfrac{1}{2}W + \tfrac{1}{4}Y + \tfrac{1}{4}Z,$$

$$\tfrac{1}{3}W + \tfrac{1}{3}Y + \tfrac{1}{3}Z,$$

$$\tfrac{1}{2}W + \tfrac{1}{3}Y + \tfrac{1}{6}Z,$$

$$\tfrac{1}{2}W + \tfrac{1}{2}Y.$$

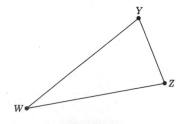

FIGURE 48

43. In Figure 49 we have drawn the "unit level line" $\mathcal{L}$ of a certain functional **F**. In other words, $\mathcal{L}$ is the set of solutions to the equation $\mathbf{F}X = 1$. Draw the lines represented by each of the following four equations:

$\mathbf{F}X = 2,$

$\mathbf{F}X = \frac{1}{2},$

$\mathbf{F}X = 0,$

$\mathbf{F}X = -1.$

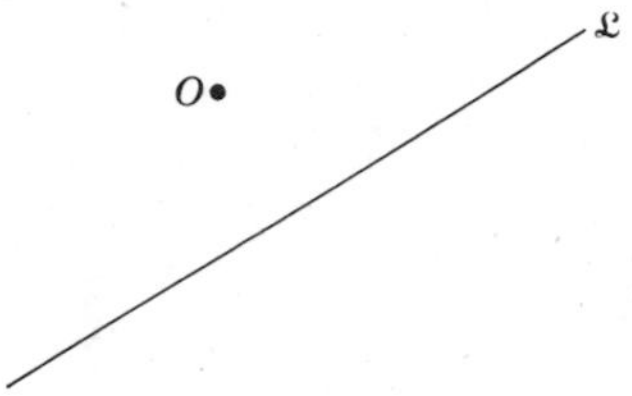

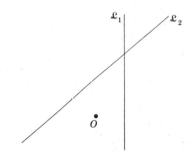

FIGURE 49

44. For the functional **F** of Exercise 43, pictured in Figure 49 draw the unit level lines of $2\mathbf{F}$, of $\frac{1}{2}\mathbf{F}$, and of $-\mathbf{F}$.

45. In Figure 50 we have drawn the unit level lines $\mathcal{L}_1$ and $\mathcal{L}_2$ of functionals $\mathbf{F}_1$ and $\mathbf{F}_2$. Draw the unit level line of $\mathbf{F}_1 + \mathbf{F}_2$.

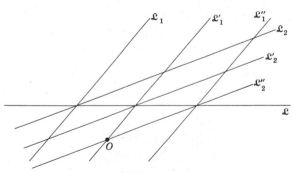

FIGURE 50

46. Let $\mathbf{F}_1$ and $\mathbf{F}_2$ have the unit level lines $\mathcal{L}_1$ and $\mathcal{L}_2$ in Figure 51 below, and let **F** have the unit level line $\mathcal{L}$. Express **F** as a linear combination of $\mathbf{F}_1$ and $\mathbf{F}_2$ making use of the various lines in Figure 51.

$$\left[Ans.\ \mathbf{F} = -\mathbf{F}_1 + 2\mathbf{F}_2.\right]$$

FIGURE 51

47. In Figure 52 are drawn the unit level lines $\mathcal{L}_1$ and $\mathcal{L}_2$ of functionals $\mathbf{F}_1$ and $\mathbf{F}_2$. Draw the unit level lines of $\frac{1}{2}\mathbf{F}_1 + \frac{1}{2}\mathbf{F}_2$, and of $\frac{1}{3}\mathbf{F}_1 + \frac{2}{3}\mathbf{F}_2$.

48. Given unit level lines $\mathcal{L}_1$ and $\mathcal{L}_2$ like those drawn in Figure 52, how can we describe geometrically the set of all unit level lines of linear combinations $c_1\mathbf{F}_1 + c_2\mathbf{F}_2$, $c_1 \geq 0$, $c_2 \geq 0$, $c_1 + c_2 = 1$?
[*Ans.* All the lines passing through P and not lying in the sector of the plane that contains the origin.]

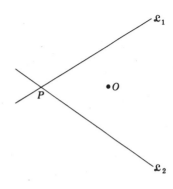

49. In Figure 52, draw a basis of vectors W_1 and W_2 "dual" to the functionals $\mathbf{F}_1$ and $\mathbf{F}_2$ of Exercise 47, i.e., such that $\mathbf{F}_1 W_1 = 1$, $\mathbf{F}_2 W_2 = 1$, $\mathbf{F}_1 W_2 = 0$, $\mathbf{F}_2 W_1 = 0$.

50. In Figure 51, draw a basis of vectors W_1 and W_2 "dual" to the functionals $\mathbf{F}_1$ and $\mathbf{F}_2$ of Exercise 46, and write an implicit equation of the line $\mathcal{L}$ in coordinate form.

FIGURE 52

15. EUCLIDEAN GEOMETRY

To allow the full application of abstract vector space ideas to euclidean geometry, we must find a means of introducing concepts of the second type (see Section 13), such as length, angle, perpendicularity, and cartesian coordinates. We will show in this section that all these concepts can be defined if in addition to our vector space concepts we introduce one new operation on vectors. If

$$X = \begin{pmatrix} x_1 \\ \cdot \\ \cdot \\ \cdot \\ x_n \end{pmatrix} \quad \text{and} \quad Y = \begin{pmatrix} y_1 \\ \cdot \\ \cdot \\ \cdot \\ y_n \end{pmatrix}$$

are vectors in $\mathfrak{R}^n$, we define the **dot product** or **inner product** of X and Y to be the number

$$X \cdot Y = x_1 y_1 + \ldots + x_n y_n.$$

From this we see immediately that the dot product is **symmetric** in X and Y, that is, $X \cdot Y = Y \cdot X$. Also it is clear that the dot product is **positive-definite**, that is $X \cdot X > 0$ when $X \neq 0$.

Let us first of all consider the length of a given vector X in $\mathcal{R}^3$. If

$$X = \begin{pmatrix} x_1 \\ x_2 \\ x_3 \end{pmatrix},$$

we think of the length of the vector as the distance from the origin to the point with coordinates

$$\begin{pmatrix} x_1 \\ x_2 \\ x_3 \end{pmatrix}.$$

In a general coordinate system the formula for this distance would be fairly complicated. But here is where we gain by the introduction of a **cartesian** coordinate system, that is, the choice of perpendicular axes and the same unit of length on each axis. In such a coordinate system the pythagorean theorem gives us a simple formula for the distance (see Figure 53). Letting $|X|$ stand for the length of the vector X, we have

(1) $|X|^2 = x_1^2 + x_2^2 + x_3^2.$

Thus we see that the **length** of the vector X can be expressed in terms of the dot product as $\sqrt{X \cdot X} = |X|$. Note that we use the same symbol for the length of a vector as for the absolute value of a number. Indeed, if we think of a number as a one-component vector, its length is its absolute value. In $\mathcal{R}^n$ we define the **length** of a vector by the same formula that works in $\mathcal{R}^3$: $|X| = \sqrt{X \cdot X}$.

Next we would like to express the angle between two nonzero vectors in $\mathcal{R}^n$. The usual convention is to take this angle θ to be in the interval $0 \leq \theta \leq \pi$ (see Exercise 1). The solution of this problem is provided by the following theorem.

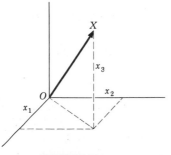

FIGURE 53

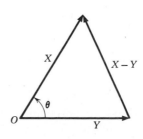

FIGURE 54

15.1 Theorem. If θ is the angle between X and Y, then

$$\cos \theta = X \cdot Y / |X| |Y|.$$

Proof. Let us apply the law of cosines to the triangle shown in Figure 54. It states that

$$|X - Y|^2 = |X|^2 + |Y|^2 - 2|X||Y|\cos\theta,$$

which we can rewrite, using $|X|^2 = X \cdot X$, as

$$(X - Y) \cdot (X - Y) = X \cdot X + Y \cdot Y - 2|X||Y|\cos\theta$$

Expanding the left-hand member, we obtain

$$X \cdot X - X \cdot Y - Y \cdot X + Y \cdot Y = X \cdot X + Y \cdot Y - 2|X||Y|\cos\theta$$

$$2X \cdot Y = 2|X||Y|\cos\theta$$

and from which the theorem follows by dividing by $2|X||Y|$.

We see from this theorem that $X \cdot Y$ in absolute value is at most $|X||Y|$, i.e., $|X \cdot Y| \leq |X||Y|$. This is known as the Cauchy-Schwarz inequality.

EXAMPLE 1. What is the angle θ between

$$X = \begin{pmatrix} 1 \\ 3 \end{pmatrix} \quad \text{and} \quad Y = \begin{pmatrix} -1 \\ 1 \end{pmatrix}?$$

We easily compute that

$$X \cdot X = 1^2 + 3^2 = 10,$$

$$Y \cdot Y = (-1)^2 + 1^2 = 2,$$

and

$$X \cdot Y = -1 + 3 = 2.$$

Hence

$$|X| = \sqrt{10}, \qquad |Y| = \sqrt{2}, \quad \text{and} \quad \cos\theta = \frac{1}{\sqrt{5}}.$$

By consulting a trigonometric table we find that $\theta = 1.1$ radians approximately (or about $63°$).

The theorem also provides a simple test for perpendicularity of two vectors. They are perpendicular if and only if $\theta = \pi/2$, and hence $\cos\theta = 0$. Thus the condition for perpendicularity is simply

$$(2) \qquad\qquad\qquad X \cdot Y = 0.$$

EXAMPLE 2. Let us find a vector X of length 2 perpendicular to

$$\begin{pmatrix} 1 \\ 2 \\ 3 \end{pmatrix} \quad \text{and to} \quad \begin{pmatrix} 1 \\ 0 \\ -1 \end{pmatrix}.$$

From geometric considerations we see that there will be two solutions, since if X is a solution, so is $-X$. (See Figure 55.) We have to write down

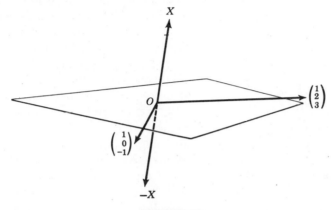

FIGURE 55

three conditions, two for the perpendicularity requirements, using (2), and a third condition to assure length 2:

$$x_1 + 2x_2 + 3x_3 = 0,$$

$$x_1 \qquad - \ x_3 = 0,$$

$$x_1^2 + \ x_2^2 + \ x_3^2 = 4.$$

These equations have the pair of solutions

$$X = \pm \begin{pmatrix} \sqrt{2/3} \\ -2\sqrt{2/3} \\ \sqrt{2/3} \end{pmatrix}.$$

We have thus succeeded in expressing the concepts of length, angle, and perpendicularity in terms of the dot product. Of course, all these formulas are subject to the assumption that the coordinates are cartesian.

In vector terminology this means that we have chosen a basis X_1, X_2, X_3 so that each basis vector has length 1 and each basis vector is perpendicular to both of the other basis vectors. Such a basis is called **orthonormal**. The significance of the choice of an orthonormal basis will be shown in the next section.

The test for the perpendicularity of two vectors may be applied also to test the perpendicularity of two lines. Let $tX_1 + X_2$ and $tY_1 + X_2$ be two lines $\mathcal{L}$, $\mathcal{L}'$ through X_2. We want to decide whether the lines are perpendicular. Clearly, this is equivalent to the question whether X_1 and Y_1 are perpendicular. (See Figure 56.) Hence the condition is given by (2).

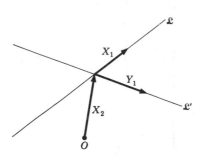

FIGURE 56

For many purposes it is convenient to "normalize" the vector X_1 in the parametric representation of $tX_1 + X_2$ of a line. Since it may be replaced by any nonzero multiple, we may as well choose it to be of unit length (in which case X_1 is determined up to a minus sign). This can be accomplished by dividing X_1 by its length, $|X_1|$. If the vectors X_1 and Y_1 are both chosen to be of unit length, then the cosine of the acute angle between the lines $\mathcal{L}$ and $\mathcal{L}'$ (see Figure 56) will simply be $|X_1 \cdot Y_1|$.

EXAMPLE 3. Let $\mathcal{L}$ be given by

$$t \begin{pmatrix} 3 \\ 0 \\ -4 \end{pmatrix} + \begin{pmatrix} 1 \\ 1 \\ 1 \end{pmatrix} \quad \text{and } \mathcal{L}' \text{ by} \quad t \begin{pmatrix} 12 \\ -3 \\ 4 \end{pmatrix} + \begin{pmatrix} 1 \\ 1 \\ 1 \end{pmatrix}.$$

In normalized form $\mathcal{L}$ is given by

$$t \begin{pmatrix} \frac{3}{5} \\ 0 \\ -\frac{4}{5} \end{pmatrix} + \begin{pmatrix} 1 \\ 1 \\ 1 \end{pmatrix} \quad \text{and } \mathcal{L}' \text{ by} \quad t \begin{pmatrix} \frac{12}{13} \\ -\frac{3}{13} \\ \frac{4}{13} \end{pmatrix} + \begin{pmatrix} 1 \\ 1 \\ 1 \end{pmatrix}.$$

These lines intersect at

$$\begin{pmatrix} 1 \\ 1 \\ 1 \end{pmatrix}.$$

What is the angle between them? The answer is

$$\cos \theta = \begin{pmatrix} \frac{3}{5} & 0 & -\frac{4}{5} \end{pmatrix} \begin{pmatrix} \frac{12}{13} \\ -\frac{3}{13} \\ \frac{4}{13} \end{pmatrix} = \frac{4}{13}.$$

Hence $\theta = 1.26$ radians (or about $72°$).

In euclidean geometry we have a simple geometric interpretation for a functional $\mathbf{F}_1$. Since $\mathbf{F}_1$ can be written as a row vector, we can identify it with the column vector X_1 having the same components, and then

$$\mathbf{F}_1 X = X_1 \cdot X, \qquad \text{for every } X.$$

We will now show that X_1 is the (common) direction of lines perpendicular to the plane $\mathbf{F}_1 X = c_1$. In other words, we wish to show that $tX_1 + X_2$ is perpendicular to the plane, for any X_2. It is a necessary and sufficient condition that this line be perpendicular to every line through X_2 which is parallel to the plane. Such a line has equation $tY_1 + X_2$, where $\mathbf{F}_1 Y_1 = X_1 \cdot Y_1 = 0$. But this is precisely the condition for the perpendicularity of the two lines.

Thus we will from now on (if we are doing euclidean geometry, and not simply vector geometry) write $X_1 \cdot X = c_1$ for the equation of a plane. Then we immediately know that the perpendicular line (or **normal**) passing through a given point X_2 is simply $tX_1 + X_2$.

EXAMPLE 4. The parametric representation of the normal to the plane

$$(1 \quad 2 \quad 3) X = 6 \text{ at the point } \begin{pmatrix} 1 \\ 1 \\ 1 \end{pmatrix} \text{ is } t \begin{pmatrix} 1 \\ 2 \\ 3 \end{pmatrix} + \begin{pmatrix} 1 \\ 1 \\ 1 \end{pmatrix}.$$

We recall that the equation $X_1 \cdot X = c_1$ for a plane is not unique, since we can multiply through by a number k. This suggests getting a unique representation by normalization, that is, by choosing X_1 to have length 1. Then X_1 will be a unit vector perpendicular to the plane. (Actually this still leaves two possible choices.) Such a choice has many advantages. For example, the normal $tX_1 + X_2$ will also appear in the normalized representation. The formula for the angle between two planes takes on a particularly simple form (see Exercise 4). And it leads to a simple formula for the distance from a point to the plane $\mathcal{P}$, or line in $\mathcal{R}^2$, as we will now show.

15.2 Theorem. If $X_1 \cdot X = c_1$ is the normalized equation of $\mathcal{P}$, and X_2 is any point, then the distance from X_2 to $\mathcal{P}$ is the absolute value of $c_1 - X_1 \cdot X_2$.

Proof. By definition, the distance is to be measured along a line from X_2 perpendicular to $\mathcal{P}$. This line is represented by $tX_1 + X_2$, and the intersection with $\mathcal{P}$ will occur for some $t = t_0$. The desired distance is then $|\,t_0X_1\,|$, which is simply the absolute value of t_0 since X_1 has unit length. (See Figure 57.) If $t_0X_1 + X_2$ lies in $\mathcal{P}$, then

$$X_1 \cdot (t_0X_1 + X_2) = c_1.$$

Remembering that $X_1 \cdot X_1 = 1$, we obtain $t_0 + X_1 \cdot X_2 = c_1$, from which the theorem follows.

EXAMPLE 5. Find the distance from

$$\begin{pmatrix} 1 \\ 1 \\ 1 \end{pmatrix} \quad \text{to the plane} \quad (3 \quad 0 \quad -4)X = -3.$$

The normalized equation of the plane is $(\tfrac{3}{5} \quad 0 \quad -\tfrac{4}{5})X = -\tfrac{3}{5}$. Then

$$c_1 - X_1 \cdot X_2 = -\tfrac{3}{5} - (\tfrac{3}{5} \quad 0 \quad -\tfrac{4}{5}) \begin{pmatrix} 1 \\ 1 \\ 1 \end{pmatrix} = -\tfrac{2}{5}.$$

Hence the distance is $\tfrac{2}{5}$.

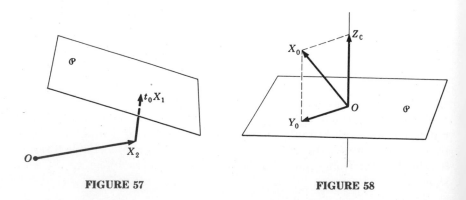

FIGURE 57   FIGURE 58

We now show that an arbitrary vector is the sum of one vector perpendicular to and one vector parallel to any given plane.

15.3 Theorem. If $\mathcal{P}$ is any plane and X_0 any vector, X_0 can be written uniquely as $X_0 = Y_0 + Z_0$, where Y_0 is parallel to $\mathcal{P}$ and Z_0 is perpendicular to $\mathcal{P}$.

Proof. Let $X_1 \cdot X = c_1$ be the normalized equation of the plane $\mathcal{P}$, and let $k = X_1 \cdot X_0$. First we will show that $Y_0 = X_0 - kX_1$ and $Z_0 = kX_1$ have all the desired properties. We see immediately that their sum is X_0, and that Z_0 is perpendicular to $\mathcal{P}$. By computing

$$X_1 \cdot Y_0 = X_1 \cdot X_0 - kX_1 \cdot X_1 = k - k = 0,$$

we see that Y_0 is parallel to $\mathcal{P}$.

Conversely, we must show that if $X_0 = Y + Z$, and Y is parallel to $\mathcal{P}$, and Z is perpendicular to $\mathcal{P}$, then $Y = Y_0$ and $Z = Z_0$. Since Y is parallel to $\mathcal{P}$, $X_1 \cdot Y = 0$. Then $k = X_1 \cdot X_0 = X_1 \cdot Z$. But Z is perpendicular to $\mathcal{P}$, hence

$$Z = cX_1, \qquad X_1 \cdot Z = cX_1 \cdot X_1 = c,$$

and thus $c = k$. Therefore

$$Z = Z_0, \quad \text{and} \quad Y = X_0 - Z_0 = Y_0.$$

When $\mathcal{P}$ is a plane through the origin, the vector Y_0 is the **projection** of X_0 on $\mathcal{P}$, and Z_0 is the projection of X_0 on the normal to $\mathcal{P}$ through the origin. (See Figure 58.)

EXERCISES

1. Show that each pair of nonzero vectors determines a unique angle θ such that $0 \le \theta \le \pi$.

2. Find an equation for the line in $\mathcal{R}^2$ perpendicular to the line $tX_1 + X_2$ that passes through the point Y_2.

3. Find the cosine of the angle between the planes $X_1 \cdot X = c_1$ and $Y_1 \cdot Y = c_2$.

4. Prove that if $X_1 \cdot X = c_1$ and $Y_1 \cdot Y = c_2$ are normalized equations of two planes, then the cosine of the angle between them is $X_1 \cdot Y_1$.

5. Show from Theorem 15.2 that distance from a point in $\mathcal{P}$ to $\mathcal{P}$ is 0.

6. Prove that if X_1 is any vector and tY_1 is the normalized equation of a line through the origin, then the length of the projection of X_1 on the line is $X_1 \cdot Y_1$.

7. Find the angle between the vectors $\begin{pmatrix} 1 \\ 1 \\ 1 \end{pmatrix}$ and $\begin{pmatrix} 1 \\ 0 \\ 1 \end{pmatrix}$. Interpret graphically.

8. Find a vector of unit length perpendicular to both vectors in Exercise 7.

$$\left[Ans. \begin{pmatrix} 1/\sqrt{2} \\ 0 \\ -1/\sqrt{2} \end{pmatrix} \right].$$

9. Find the normalized equation of the plane through $\begin{pmatrix} 1 \\ 2 \\ 3 \end{pmatrix}$ that is perpendicular to the vector of Exercise 8. Verify that both vectors in Exercise 7 are parallel to this plane.

10. Normalize the equations of the following pairs of planes, and use the result of Exercise 4 to find the angle between them.

(a) $(1 \quad 2 \quad 3)X = 6$; $(3 \quad 2 \quad 1)X = 6$.

(b) $(1 \quad 2 \quad 3)X = 6$; $(1 \quad 1 \quad -1)X = 1$.

(c) $(1 \quad 2 \quad 3)X = 6$; $(\frac{1}{6} \quad \frac{1}{2} \quad \frac{1}{3})X = 2$.

11. For each of the points and planes or lines listed below find the distance from the point to the plane or line.

(a) $\begin{pmatrix} 1 \\ 0 \\ -1 \end{pmatrix}$; $(1 \quad 1 \quad 1)X = 1$.

(b) $\begin{pmatrix} 1 \\ 0 \\ -1 \end{pmatrix}$; $(1 \quad 2 \quad 3)X = 1$.

(c) $\begin{pmatrix} 1 \\ 1 \\ 1 \end{pmatrix}$; $(1 \quad 2 \quad 3)X = 6.$

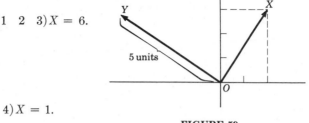

(d) $\begin{pmatrix} 1 \\ 2 \end{pmatrix}$; $(3 \quad 4)X = 1.$

FIGURE 59

12. Write $\begin{pmatrix} 1 \\ 1 \\ 1 \end{pmatrix}$ as the sum of vectors perpendicular and parallel to the plane

$(1 \quad 2 \quad 3)X = 6.$　　　　　　$\left[Ans. \begin{pmatrix} \frac{3}{7} \\ \frac{6}{7} \\ \frac{9}{7} \end{pmatrix} + \begin{pmatrix} \frac{4}{7} \\ \frac{1}{7} \\ -\frac{2}{7} \end{pmatrix} . \right]$

13. In Figure 59 we have drawn perpendicular vectors X and Y. The vector X has coordinates $\begin{pmatrix} 2 \\ 3 \end{pmatrix}$. The vector Y has length 5. What are the coordinates $\begin{pmatrix} y_1 \\ y_2 \end{pmatrix}$ of Y?　　　　　　$\left[Ans. \begin{pmatrix} -15/\sqrt{13} \\ 10/\sqrt{13} \end{pmatrix} . \right]$

14. Let θ be the angle between $X = \begin{pmatrix} 3 \\ -4 \end{pmatrix}$ and $Y = \begin{pmatrix} -12 \\ -5 \end{pmatrix}$. Show (without recourse to a table of cosines) that θ is between $90°$ and $120°$.

15. Find all vectors Z perpendicular to both $X = \begin{pmatrix} 1 \\ 2 \\ 0 \end{pmatrix}$ and $Y = \begin{pmatrix} 0 \\ -1 \\ 3 \end{pmatrix}$.

$\left[Ans. \ t \begin{pmatrix} -6 \\ 3 \\ 1 \end{pmatrix} . \right]$

16. In Figure 60 we have drawn a vector Y_0 in the plane. Suppose that we know this vector to be of length 2. Draw the line $\mathcal{L}$ having equation $Y_0 \cdot X = 2$. Draw also the line $\mathcal{L}_1$ having equation $Y_0 \cdot X = -4$.

FIGURE 60

17. In each of the figures below, state whether the inner product $X_0 \cdot Y_0$ is positive, negative, or zero.

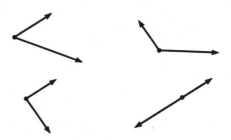

18. Show that if Z_1 has length 1 then $X \cdot Z_1$ is the length of the projection of X on the 1-dimensional subspace spanned by Z_1 (or else the negative of this length).

19. Prove, by using the inner product, the converse of the pythagorean theorem. [That is, prove that if a triangle has sides of lengths a, b, c with $a^2 + b^2 = c^2$, then the triangle has a right angle between the sides of lengths a and b, respectively.]

20. Find the distance between $\begin{pmatrix} 1 \\ 2 \end{pmatrix}$ and $\begin{pmatrix} 0 \\ 5 \end{pmatrix}$. Between $\begin{pmatrix} -1 \\ 2 \end{pmatrix}$ and $\begin{pmatrix} \frac{1}{2} \\ \frac{1}{2} \end{pmatrix}$.

Between the origin and $\begin{pmatrix} -1 \\ -3 \end{pmatrix}$. Between $\begin{pmatrix} 1 \\ 2 \\ 3 \end{pmatrix}$ and $\begin{pmatrix} -1 \\ 3 \\ 2 \end{pmatrix}$.

21. In Section 14 we learned that the mid-point $Z = \begin{pmatrix} z_1 \\ z_2 \end{pmatrix}$ of the segment connecting $X = \begin{pmatrix} x_1 \\ x_2 \end{pmatrix}$ and $Y = \begin{pmatrix} y_1 \\ y_2 \end{pmatrix}$ was $Z = \frac{1}{2}X + \frac{1}{2}Y$. Verify this fact now by computing the appropriate distances.

22. Determine x_2 so that $\begin{pmatrix} 1 \\ x_2 \end{pmatrix}$ is perpendicular to $\begin{pmatrix} \frac{1}{2} \\ -\frac{1}{2} \end{pmatrix}$.

23. Determine x_2 and x_3 so that $\begin{pmatrix} 5 \\ x_2 \\ x_3 \end{pmatrix}$ is perpendicular to both $\begin{pmatrix} 1 \\ 2 \\ 3 \end{pmatrix}$ and

$\begin{pmatrix} 1 \\ -2 \\ 1 \end{pmatrix}$. $\left[Ans.\ x_2 = \frac{5}{4},\ x_3 = -\frac{5}{2}.\right]$

24. Using tables of trigonometric functions find the angles between

(a) $\begin{pmatrix} 1 \\ 2 \end{pmatrix}$ and $\begin{pmatrix} -1 \\ -1 \end{pmatrix}$.   (b) $\begin{pmatrix} 1 \\ 0 \\ 1 \end{pmatrix}$ and $\begin{pmatrix} 1 \\ 2 \\ 0 \end{pmatrix}$.

25. In Figure 61 we have drawn the origin O and the "unit circle," which consists of all points that lie at distance 1 from the origin. Draw the

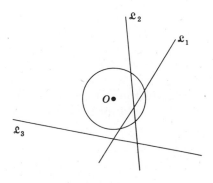

FIGURE 61

vectors Y_1 and Y_2 and Y_3 such that $\mathcal{L}_1$ has the equation $Y_1 \cdot X = 1$, $\mathcal{L}_2$ has the equation $Y_2 \cdot X = 1$, and $\mathcal{L}_3$ has the equation $Y_3 \cdot X = 1$.

26. What is the distance between the point $\begin{pmatrix} 1 \\ -3 \end{pmatrix}$ and the line whose equation

is $\begin{pmatrix} 2 \\ 5 \end{pmatrix} \cdot X = 1$? Between the point $\begin{pmatrix} 1 \\ 0 \\ 2 \end{pmatrix}$ and the plane whose equation is

$\begin{pmatrix} 1 \\ -2 \\ 1 \end{pmatrix} \cdot X = 3$?

$$\left[Ans. \ \frac{14}{\sqrt{29}}; 0. \right]$$

27. Show that in any parallelogram the sum of the squares of the lengths of the four sides equals the sum of the squares of the lengths of the diagonals. [*Hint*: Take the corners to be $O, X, Y, X + Y$.]

28. Show that if nonzero vectors X_1, X_2, X_3 are perpendicular to each other, then they are linearly independent.

16. ABSTRACT EUCLIDEAN VECTOR SPACES

It is easy to verify (see Exercise 7) that the dot product of vectors in $\Re^n$ has the following properties.

Positivity: $X \cdot X > 0$ except that $0 \cdot 0 = 0$.

Symmetry: $X \cdot Y = Y \cdot X$.

Additivity: $(X + Y) \cdot Z = X \cdot Z + Y \cdot Z$.

Homogeneity: $(aX) \cdot Y = a(X \cdot Y)$.

Because of the symmetry of the dot product it follows immediately that additivity and homogeneity hold for the second vector also, that is,

$$X \cdot (Y + Z) = X \cdot Y + X \cdot Z$$

and $$X \cdot (aY) = a(X \cdot Y).$$

Any finite-dimensional vector space on which there is defined a real-valued product with the above four properties will be called a **euclidean space**. More generally, we may drop the requirement that the dimension be finite and speak simply of a vector space with an inner product.

In terms of the inner product we can always define the length of a vector by

$$| X | = \sqrt{X \cdot X}.$$

Then length has the following properties.

Positivity: $| X | > 0$ except that $| 0 | = 0$ (1)

Homogeneity: $| aX | = | a | | X |$ (2)

Triangle Inequality: $| X + Y | \leq | X | + | Y |$ (3)

The proofs of (1) and (2) are easy and are left for the reader to check. The proof of (3) is harder and will be taken up later, though we remark here on its geometric significance. This can be seen by looking at Figure 62.

We have, in addition to $\mathbb{R}^n$, the following examples of vector spaces with inner products.

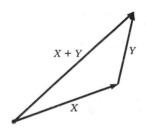

FIGURE 62

EXAMPLE 1. Let $\mathfrak{X}$ be the vector space of polynomials of degree ≤ 2. For two polynomials X and Y, let us define,

$$X \cdot Y = \int_0^1 X(x) Y(x) \, dx.$$

To prove that $X \cdot Y$ thus defined is an inner product, all we have to do is check that

$$\int_0^1 X(x)^2 \, dx > 0, \qquad \text{unless } X(x) = 0$$

$$\int_0^1 X(x) Y(x) \, dx = \int_0^1 Y(x) X(x) \, dx,$$

$$\int_0^1 [X(x) + Y(x)] Z(x) \, dx = \int_0^1 X(x) Z(x) \, dx + \int_0^1 Y(x) Z(x) \, dx$$

and $\quad \displaystyle\int_0^1 aX(x) Y(x) \, dx = a \int_0^1 X(x) Y(x) \, dx.$

It is obvious that these do hold. The length of a vector is then

$$| X | = \left(\int_0^1 X^2(x) \ dx \right)^{1/2}.$$

EXAMPLE 2. The vector space $\mathfrak{X}$ of all polynomials restricted to the unit interval is not finite-dimensional. However, it can be made into a space with an inner product by formally using the same definition that was used in Example 1. Thus if f and g are two polynomials in $\mathfrak{X}$, we can define

$$f \cdot g = \int_0^1 f(x)g(x) \ dx.$$

Checking that this is indeed an inner product differs from the verification in Example 1 only in the fact that here the integral is applied to more than fourth-degree polynomials.

EXAMPLE 3. For vectors

$$X = \begin{pmatrix} x_1 \\ x_2 \end{pmatrix} \quad \text{and} \quad Y = \begin{pmatrix} y_1 \\ y_2 \end{pmatrix}$$

in $\mathfrak{R}^2$, define

$$X \cdot Y = x_1 y_1 + 2 x_2 y_2.$$

Then in terms of this inner product the length of a vector is given by

$$| X | = \sqrt{x_1^2 + 2x_2^2}.$$

To ask for the set of points X satisfying $| X | = 1$ is to ask for a "unit circle" with respect to this new definition of length in $\mathfrak{R}^2$. In coordinates the equation becomes

$$x_1^2 + 2x_2^2 = 1,$$

and we can draw a picture of the new unit circle with respect to the usual perpendicular axes in $\mathfrak{R}^2$. The result is the ellipse shown in Figure 63.

Notice that whereas the vectors

$$E_1 = \begin{pmatrix} 1 \\ 0 \end{pmatrix} \quad \text{and} \quad E_2 = \begin{pmatrix} 0 \\ 1 \end{pmatrix}$$

satisfy $E_1 \cdot E_2 = 0$, that is, are **orthogonal**, or perpendicular, with respect to the new inner product, the vectors

$$\begin{pmatrix} 1 \\ 1 \end{pmatrix} \quad \text{and} \quad \begin{pmatrix} -1 \\ 1 \end{pmatrix}$$

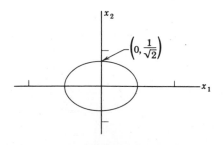

FIGURE 63

are not. In fact

$$\begin{pmatrix} 1 \\ 1 \end{pmatrix} \cdot \begin{pmatrix} -1 \\ 1 \end{pmatrix} = (1)(-1) + 2(1)(1) = 1.$$

Throughout the rest of the book we shall never use any inner product in $\mathfrak{R}^n$ except the one defined by

$$X \cdot Y = x_1 y_1 + \ldots + x_n y_n,$$

so there will be no ambiguity in the notation.

The fact that length has been defined in terms of an inner product leads to some properties of length that are not derivable from those already listed as (1)–(3). First we prove the

Cauchy-Schwarz inequality

$$| X \cdot Y | \leq | X | | Y |.$$

Proof. We assume first that X and Y are unit vectors, that is, that $| X | = | Y | = 1$. Then,

$$0 \leq | X - Y |^2 = (X - Y) \cdot (X - Y)$$
$$= | X |^2 - 2X \cdot Y + | Y |^2 = 2 - 2X \cdot Y$$

or $$X \cdot Y \leq 1.$$

Assuming that neither X nor Y is zero (for the inequality obviously holds if one of them *is* zero), we can replace X and Y by the unit vectors $X/| X |$ and $Y/| Y |$, getting

$$X \cdot Y \leq | X | | Y |.$$

Now replace X by $-X$ to get

$$-X \cdot Y \leq | X | | Y |.$$

The last two inequalities imply the Cauchy-Schwarz inequality.

Notice that if the Cauchy-Schwarz inequality is written as

$$\frac{| X \cdot Y |}{| X | | Y |} \leq 1,$$

then there will always be an angle θ such that

$$\cos \theta = \frac{X \cdot Y}{| X | | Y |}.$$

Defining the cosine of the angle θ between X and Y is more satisfactory than defining θ itself, because then we do not have to worry about whether the angle is

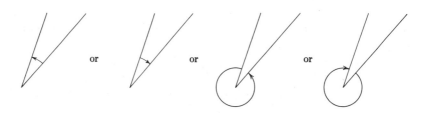

Using the Cauchy-Schwarz inequality, it is easy to give the deferred proof of the triangle inequality. For from

$$|X \cdot Y| \leq |X||Y|,$$

we get

$$|X + Y|^2 = (X + Y) \cdot (X + Y) = |X|^2 + 2X \cdot Y + |Y|^2$$

$$\leq |X|^2 + 2|X||Y| + |Y|^2 = (|X| + |Y|)^2,$$

from which follows

$$|X + Y| \leq |X| + |Y|.$$

Now we will show that $\mathcal{R}^n$ with its usual dot product is not essentially different from abstract euclidean vector spaces. Let $X_1, \ldots, X_n$ be non-zero vectors in a euclidean space such that each one is perpendicular to all the others. Then $X_1, \ldots, X_n$ are *automatically linearly independent.* For suppose that $c_1 X_1 + \ldots + c_n X_n = 0$. We want to prove that each c_k must be zero. To do this, we simply take the inner product of this linear combination with the vector X_k. Then

$$0 = X_k \cdot (c_1 X_1 + \ldots + c_k X_k + \ldots + c_n X_n)$$

$$= c_1 X_k \cdot X_1 + \ldots + c_k X_k \cdot X_k + \ldots + c_n X_k \cdot X_n$$

$$= c_k |X_k|^2,$$

since X_k is perpendicular to all the others. And then $c_k = 0$ because $|X_k| \neq 0$.

When the whole euclidean space $\mathcal{X}$ is n-dimensional, then $X_1, \ldots, X_n$ must form a basis for $\mathcal{X}$. It is natural also to require that each X_k have the length 1; for then any inner product $X \cdot Y$ is computed by the formula in Section 15, namely,

$$X \cdot Y = x_1 y_1 + \ldots + x_n y_n.$$

To see this, let

$$X = x_1 X_1 + \ldots + x_n X_n, \qquad Y = y_1 Y_1 + \ldots + y_n Y_n.$$

Then

$$X \cdot Y = (x_1 X_1 + \ldots + x_n X_n) \cdot (y_1 Y_1 + \ldots + y_n Y_n)$$

$$= \sum_{i,j=1}^{n} x_i y_j X_i \cdot X_j.$$

Now, if $i \neq j$, we have $X_i \cdot X_j = 0$. Hence all the terms in the sum drop out except

$$\sum_{i=1}^{n} x_i y_i X_i \cdot X_i.$$

Since we have taken $X_i \cdot X_i = |X_i|^2 = 1$, we get

$$X \cdot Y = \sum_{i=1}^{n} x_i y_i = x_1 y_1 + \ldots + x_n y_n.$$

Hence we can now identify X and Y with column vectors in $\mathfrak{R}^n$, and compute lengths and inner products coordinatewise. A basis for a euclidean space $\mathfrak{X}$ in which the basis vectors are perpendicular to each other and of length 1 is called an **orthonormal** basis. It is easy to prove the existence of such an orthonormal basis in any finite-dimensional euclidean space.

If $\mathfrak{X}$ is euclidean and $\mathfrak{X} \xrightarrow{A} \mathfrak{X}$ is a linear transformation, it makes sense to ask whether **A** preserves lengths and angles. Such a transformation is characterized by the identity,

$$(\mathbf{A}X) \cdot (\mathbf{A}Y) = X \cdot Y, \qquad \text{for every } X \text{ and } Y \text{ in } \mathfrak{X}.$$

This equation says that **A** preserves the inner product. Since length and angle are defined in terms of the inner product, they are also preserved. For example, it must also be true that $|\mathbf{A}X| = |X|$. If $\{X_1, \ldots, X_n\} = \Gamma$ is an orthonormal basis for $\mathfrak{X}$, then the matrix $\begin{pmatrix} \mathbf{A} \\ \Gamma\Gamma \end{pmatrix}$ must be such that each column, considered as a vector in the euclidean space $\mathfrak{R}^n$, has length 1 and is perpendicular to all the other columns. For these columns correspond to the vectors $\mathbf{A}X_1, \ldots, \mathbf{A}X_n$, which are (by the inner-product preserving nature of $\mathbf{A}$) perpendicular to each other and of length 1.

Conversely, if the columns of $\begin{pmatrix} \mathbf{A} \\ \Gamma\Gamma \end{pmatrix}$, Γ being an orthonormal basis for

the abstract euclidean space $\mathfrak{X}$, form an orthonormal basis for the euclidean space $\mathfrak{R}^n$ of column vectors, then $\mathbf{A}$ preserves length and angle. For it is clear that $\mathbf{A}$ preserves length and angle at least for the n vectors $X_1, \ldots, X_n$ that constitute the basis Γ. And then we can mechanically check, as in the paragraph above, that $\mathbf{A}$ preserves the inner product between any two vectors

$$X = a_1X_1 + \ldots + a_nX_n \quad \text{and} \quad Y = b_1X_1 + \ldots + b_nX_n.$$

Let us call a matrix whose columns form an orthonormal basis for $\mathfrak{R}^n$ an **orthogonal** matrix. It is very easy to compute the inverse of such a matrix. Suppose

$$A = \begin{pmatrix} a_{11} & a_{12} & \ldots \\ a_{21} & a_{22} & \ldots \\ \cdot & \cdot \\ \cdot & \cdot \\ \cdot & \cdot \end{pmatrix}$$

is orthogonal. Then its inverse is simply

$$A^{-1} = \begin{pmatrix} a_{11} & a_{21} & \ldots \\ a_{12} & a_{22} & \ldots \\ \cdot & \cdot \\ \cdot & \cdot \\ \cdot & \cdot \end{pmatrix}.$$

For when these two matrices are multiplied together in the order $A^{-1}A$, the result is the identity matrix I. Since we also have $AA^{-1} = I$, it is clear that the rows as well as the columns of an orthogonal matrix form an orthonormal basis.

The second of the above two matrices is obtained from the first by reflecting A across its main diagonal. When any two matrices are so related, we say that one is the **transpose** of the other. We denote the transpose of a matrix A by A^t. Thus, if

$$A = \begin{pmatrix} 1 & 2 & 3 \\ 4 & 5 & 6 \end{pmatrix}$$

then

$$A^t = \begin{pmatrix} 1 & 4 \\ 2 & 5 \\ 3 & 6 \end{pmatrix}.$$

Obviously,

$$(A^t)^t = A \qquad \textit{for any matrix } A.$$

Furthermore,

$$(AB)^t = B^t A^t \qquad \textit{whenever } AB \textit{ is defined.}$$

The proof is easy. Let c_{ij} be the ijth component of the product AB, and c_{ij}^t the ijth component of $(AB)^t$. Then

$$c_{ij}^t = c_{ji} = \sum_k a_{jk} b_{ki}$$

$$= \sum_k a_{kj}^t b_{ik}^t$$

$$= \sum_k b_{ik}^t a_{kj}^t$$

which completes the proof since the last sum is the ijth entry of $B^t A^t$.
We conclude the section with the following theorem.

16.1 Theorem. The matrix relating two orthonormal bases is an orthogonal matrix.

Proof. If $X_1, \ldots, X_n$ and $Y_1, \ldots, Y_n$ are orthonormal bases, then the matrix (a_{ij}) relating them in one direction is determined by the equation

$$Y_j = \sum_{i=1}^n a_{ij} X_i.$$

Then

$$Y_k \cdot Y_l = \left(\sum_{i=1}^n a_{ik} X_i \right) \cdot \left(\sum_{i=1}^n a_{il} X_i \right)$$

$$= \sum_{i=1}^n a_{ik} a_{il}$$

But $Y_k \cdot Y_l$ is 1 or 0 according as $k = l$ or $k \neq l$, so (a_{ij}) is orthogonal.

EXERCISES

1. Prove that in a euclidean space, length satisfies the PARALLELOGRAM LAW,

$$|X + Y|^2 + |X - Y|^2 = 2|X|^2 + 2|Y|^2.$$

State the geometric significance.

2. Show that if $|X| = |Y|$ in a euclidean space, then $X + Y$ is perpendicular to $X - Y$.

3. Let **A** be a linear transformation on a euclidean space $\mathfrak{X}$. Show that if $|\mathbf{A}X| = |X|$, for all X, then $(\mathbf{A}X) \cdot (\mathbf{A}Y) = X \cdot Y$, for all X and Y.

4. Show that the product of two orthogonal matrices is orthogonal.

5. In the vector space described in Example 1, find a first-degree polynomial orthogonal to the constant function 1.

6. Which of the following geometric ideas make sense in an abstract vector space, and which make sense only in a euclidean space?

(a) Bisect line segment.	(i) Trapezoid.
(b) Bisect angle.	(j) Ellipse.
(c) Medians of triangle.	(k) Circle.
(d) Altitudes of triangle.	(l) Hyperbola.
(e) Parallelogram.	(m) Regular polygon.
(f) Rhombus.	(n) Isosceles triangle.
(g) Rectangle.	(o) Acute angle.
(h) Square.	(p) Convex polygon.

[*Ans.* (a), (c), (e), (i), (j), (l), (p) are the ones that make sense in an abstract vector space.]

7. Prove that the dot product in $\mathfrak{R}^n$ has the properties listed at the beginning of the section.

8. Find a basis of orthogonal unit vectors for the euclidean space of Example 1 in the text. (Start with the constant function 1.)

17. A SURVEY OF DETERMINANTS

Here we shall define the determinant of a square matrix and mention some useful properties of determinants. In Appendix I the theory of determinants will be developed from a geometric point of view, and in particular the theorems that we use about determinants will be proved.

The definition of determinant can be made inductively. The determinant of a 2-by-2 matrix is

$$\det \begin{pmatrix} a_1 & b_1 \\ a_2 & b_2 \end{pmatrix} = a_1 b_2 - b_1 a_2.$$

The determinant of a 3-by-3 matrix is

$$\det \begin{pmatrix} a_1 & b_1 & c_1 \\ a_2 & b_2 & c_2 \\ a_3 & b_3 & c_3 \end{pmatrix} = a_1 \det \begin{pmatrix} b_2 & c_2 \\ b_3 & c_3 \end{pmatrix} - b_1 \det \begin{pmatrix} a_2 & c_2 \\ a_3 & c_3 \end{pmatrix}$$

$$+ c_1 \det \begin{pmatrix} a_2 & b_2 \\ a_3 & b_3 \end{pmatrix}.$$

Similarly, we can define the determinant of an n-by-n matrix using the formula for the determinant of an $(n - 1)$-by-$(n - 1)$ matrix. Thus, if

$$A = \begin{pmatrix} a_{11} & a_{12} & \dots & a_{1n} \\ a_{21} & a_{22} & & a_{2n} \\ \cdot & & & \cdot \\ \cdot & & & \cdot \\ \cdot & & & \cdot \\ a_{n1} & a_{n2} & \dots & a_{nn} \end{pmatrix}$$

then

$$\det A = \sum_{j=1}^{n} (-1)^{j+1} a_{1j} \det A_{1j}, \tag{1}$$

where A_{1j} is the matrix obtained from A by striking out the 1st row and the jth column. Notice that the elements a_{1j} come from the first row of A and that the plus and minus signs alternate. Also, the submatrix A_{1j} appears in the same term as the component a_{1j} whose column has been removed to get A_{1j}.

The determinant of a matrix is sometimes computed by a direct application of the above definition. More often, the computation is done using some of the following rules. Notice the connection with the elementary row operations used to solve systems of linear equations.

17.1 When an elementary numerical multiplication by c is performed on a matrix (that is, some row is multiplied by c), the determinant is multiplied by c.

17.2 When an elementary addition (or subtraction) is performed on a matrix, its determinant is unchanged.

17.3 When two rows of a matrix are interchanged, the determinant changes sign.

The notation for the determinant of a matrix in component form is often abbreviated by removing the symbol "det" and enclosing the matrix in straight vertical bars. For example,

$$\det \begin{pmatrix} a & b \\ c & d \end{pmatrix} = \begin{vmatrix} a & b \\ c & d \end{vmatrix}.$$

EXAMPLE. Let us illustrate the computation of a determinant using elementary row operations. Let

$$d = \begin{vmatrix} 3 & 12 & 9 \\ 2 & 5 & 4 \\ -1 & 3 & 2 \end{vmatrix}.$$

As in solving linear systems, we try to reduce the matrix to the unit matrix, keeping track of the effect of each operation. We have

$$\begin{vmatrix} 1 & 4 & 3 \\ 1 & \dfrac{5}{2} & 2 \\ 1 & -3 & -2 \end{vmatrix} = \left(\frac{1}{3}\right)\left(\frac{1}{2}\right)(-1)d = -\frac{d}{6}.$$

$$\begin{vmatrix} 1 & 4 & 3 \\ 0 & -\dfrac{3}{2} & -1 \\ 0 & -7 & -5 \end{vmatrix} = -\frac{d}{6}.$$

$$\begin{vmatrix} \dfrac{1}{4} & 1 & \dfrac{3}{4} \\ 0 & 1 & \dfrac{2}{3} \\ 0 & 1 & \dfrac{5}{7} \end{vmatrix} = \left(\frac{1}{4}\right)\left(-\frac{2}{3}\right)\left(-\frac{1}{7}\right)\left(-\frac{d}{6}\right) = -\frac{d}{252}.$$

$$\begin{vmatrix} \dfrac{1}{4} & 0 & \dfrac{1}{12} \\[2mm] 0 & 1 & \dfrac{2}{3} \\[2mm] 0 & 0 & \dfrac{1}{21} \end{vmatrix} = -\dfrac{d}{252}.$$

$$\begin{vmatrix} 3 & 0 & 1 \\[2mm] 0 & \dfrac{3}{2} & 1 \\[2mm] 0 & 0 & 1 \end{vmatrix} = (12)\left(\dfrac{3}{2}\right)(21)\left(-\dfrac{d}{252}\right) = -\dfrac{3}{2}d.$$

$$\begin{vmatrix} 3 & 0 & 0 \\[2mm] 0 & \dfrac{3}{2} & 0 \\[2mm] 0 & 0 & 1 \end{vmatrix} = -\dfrac{3}{2}d.$$

$$\begin{vmatrix} 1 & 0 & 0 \\[2mm] 0 & 1 & 0 \\[2mm] 0 & 0 & 1 \end{vmatrix} = \left(\dfrac{1}{3}\right)\left(\dfrac{2}{3}\right)\left(-\dfrac{3}{2}\right) = -\dfrac{d}{3}.$$

But the determinant of the identity matrix equals 1. Hence $1 = -d/3$, and $d = -3$. In the present example it is easier to compute d by direct use of the formula

$$d = 3 \det \begin{pmatrix} 5 & 4 \\ 3 & 2 \end{pmatrix} - 12 \det \begin{pmatrix} 2 & 4 \\ -1 & 2 \end{pmatrix} + 9 \det \begin{pmatrix} 2 & 5 \\ -1 & 3 \end{pmatrix}.$$

But for large matrices the elementary row operations provide a much simpler method of computation.

Recall that the *transpose* A^t of a matrix A is the matrix obtained by reflecting A across its main diagonal, that is, by interchanging every pair of components a_{ij} and a_{ji}. For instance, if

$$A = \begin{pmatrix} 3 & 12 & 9 \\ 2 & 5 & 4 \\ -1 & 3 & 2 \end{pmatrix}.$$

then

$$A^t = \begin{pmatrix} 3 & 2 & -1 \\ 12 & 5 & 3 \\ 9 & 4 & 2 \end{pmatrix}.$$

Computation shows that the above A and A^t have the same determinant. In general, we have

17.4 The determinant of an n-by-n matrix A is equal to the determinant of its transpose A^t.

Because of the transposition property, rules 17.1 through 17.3 hold for columns as well as rows, and we can use elementary column operations as well as elementary row operations to compute determinants. To see that an elementary column operation has the same effect as the corresponding row operation, we can proceed as follows: First, transpose the matrix, leaving the value of the determinant unchanged; Second, perform an elementary row operation; Third, transpose again.

The expansion formula (1) can be extended in such a way that an arbitrary row takes over the special role of the first row. For if in the matrix A we move the ith row to the top position, this change can be thought of as having been accomplished by $(i - 1)$ successive interchanges of adjacent rows. By rule 17.3, the determinant of the altered matrix is $(-1)^{i-1} \det A$. Now applying formula (1), we get

$$(-1)^{i-1} \det A = \sum_{j=1}^{n} (-1)^{i+1} a_{ij} \det A'_{1j},$$

where A'_{1j} is gotten from the altered matrix by striking out the new 1st row and the jth column. But $A'_{1j} = A_{ij}$, where A_{ij} is the submatrix of A obtained by striking out the ith row and the jth column. Hence

$$\det A = \sum_{j=1}^{n} (-1)^{i+j} a_{ij} \det A_{ij}. \tag{2}$$

The matrix A_{ij} is called the **minor** of the component a_{ij}, and the number $(-1)^{i+j} \det A_{ij}$ is called the **cofactor** of a_{ij}. By applying the transposition rule 17.4, we can modify equation (2) to an expansion by minors of an arbitrary column. Thus

$$\det A = \sum_{i=1}^{n} (-1)^{i+j} a_{ij} \det A_{ij}.$$

Notice that the plus or minus sign to be attached to the component a_{ij} (or to the determinant of its minor A_{ij}) can be found by taking the sign from the corresponding place in the square array

$$\begin{pmatrix} + & - & + & - & \cdots \\ - & + & - & + & \cdots \\ + & - & + & - & \cdots \\ - & + & - & + & \cdots \\ \cdot & \cdot & \cdot & \cdot \\ \cdot & \cdot & \cdot & \cdot \\ \cdot & \cdot & \cdot & \cdot \end{pmatrix}.$$

For example, in expanding the matrix

$$A = \begin{pmatrix} a_1 & b_1 & c_1 \\ a_2 & b_2 & c_2 \\ a_3 & b_3 & c_3 \end{pmatrix}$$

by using minors of the second column, we get

$$\det A = -b_1 \det \begin{pmatrix} a_2 & c_2 \\ a_3 & c_3 \end{pmatrix} + b_2 \det \begin{pmatrix} a_1 & c_1 \\ a_3 & c_3 \end{pmatrix} - b_3 \det \begin{pmatrix} a_1 & c_1 \\ a_2 & c_2 \end{pmatrix}.$$

We shall see later that if $\mathbf{A}$ is a linear transformation with matrix A, then $\det A$ is the constant factor by which $\mathbf{A}$ changes volume. Using this interpretation, the following rule becomes geometrically obvious.

17.5 If A and B are n-by-n matrices, then $\det AB = \det A \det B$.

To find the effect on volume of the transformation AB, first multiply by the factor corresponding to B and then by the factor corresponding to A.

If we assume that the square matrix A has an inverse, we can set $B = A^{-1}$ in the equation in 17.5. Then

$$\det A \ \det A^{-1} = \det I = 1,$$

and we immediately conclude that $\det A \neq 0$. In fact, the converse holds too.

17.6 The n-by-n matrix A has an inverse if and only if $\det A \neq 0$.

The proofs of the rules given in this section are all contained in Appendix I.

EXERCISES

1. Compute the following determinants.

(a) $\det \begin{pmatrix} 1 & 2 \\ -1 & 0 \end{pmatrix}$

(b) $\det \begin{pmatrix} 1 & 7 & 0 \\ 1 & -1 & 2 \\ 3 & 0 & 4 \end{pmatrix}$

(c) $\det \begin{pmatrix} -1 & 2 & -1 & 2 \\ 1 & 2 & 1 & 2 \\ 0 & 1 & 0 & 1 \\ 0 & -1 & 0 & -1 \end{pmatrix}$

(d) $\begin{vmatrix} 1 & 2 & 4 \\ 1 & 3 & 9 \\ 1 & 4 & 16 \end{vmatrix}$

2. Prove that

$$\det \begin{pmatrix} 1 & x_1 & x_1^2 & \cdots & x_1^{n-1} \\ 1 & x_2 & x_2^2 & \cdots & x_2^{n-1} \\ & \cdot & & & \\ & \cdot & & & \\ & \cdot & & & \\ 1 & x_n & x_n^2 & \cdots & x_n^{n-1} \end{pmatrix} = \prod_{i>j} (x_i - x_j) \qquad \text{(Vandermonde determinant)}.$$

3. Prove from the numerical multiplication and addition rules for determinants that if two rows of a matrix are interchanged, then the determinant changes sign. Prove the analogous statement for columns.

4. Prove that if two rows or columns of a matrix are the same, then the determinant of the matrix is zero.

5. Verify that

$$\det \begin{pmatrix} 1 & 2 \\ -1 & 4 \end{pmatrix} \det \begin{pmatrix} -5 & 1 \\ 0 & 1 \end{pmatrix} = \det \left[\begin{pmatrix} 1 & 2 \\ -1 & 4 \end{pmatrix} \begin{pmatrix} -5 & 1 \\ 0 & 1 \end{pmatrix} \right]$$

6. Prove using the product rule for determinants that for an invertible matrix A

$$\det A^{-1} = \frac{1}{\det A}.$$

7. Prove that the vectors

$$\begin{pmatrix} 1 \\ 0 \\ 1 \end{pmatrix}, \quad \begin{pmatrix} 1 \\ 1 \\ 0 \end{pmatrix}, \quad \text{and} \quad \begin{pmatrix} 0 \\ 1 \\ 1 \end{pmatrix}$$

are linearly independent.

8. Let $\mathfrak{X} \xrightarrow{\mathbf{L}} \mathfrak{X}$ be a linear transformation. Prove that if Γ and Δ are bases for $\mathfrak{X}$, then

$$\det \begin{pmatrix} \mathbf{L} \\ \Delta\Delta \end{pmatrix} = \det \begin{pmatrix} \mathbf{L} \\ \Gamma\Gamma \end{pmatrix}.$$

2

Differential Calculus

1. VECTOR FUNCTIONS

A function whose domain and range are subsets of vector spaces is a
vector function. The **domain** of a function is the set on which it is defined,
and the **range** is the set of values assumed by the function. A vector function f whose domain is a subset of a vector space $\mathfrak{X}$ and whose range is a
subset of a vector space $\mathcal{Y}$ will often be denoted by

$$\mathfrak{X} \xrightarrow{\ f\ } \mathcal{Y}.$$

The space $\mathfrak{X}$ is called the **domain space** of the function, and $\mathcal{Y}$ is called
the **range space**.

EXAMPLE 1. Let $\mathfrak{X}$ be the space $\mathfrak{R}^3$ of all 3-dimensional column vectors
and $\mathcal{Y}$ the space $\mathfrak{R}^2$ of all 2-dimensional column vectors. A vector function

159

$\mathcal{R}^3 \xrightarrow{f} \mathcal{R}^2$ is defined by

$$f\begin{pmatrix} x \\ y \\ z \end{pmatrix} = \begin{pmatrix} x^2 + y^2 + z^2 \\ x + y + z \end{pmatrix}.$$

Another function $\mathcal{R}^3 \xrightarrow{g} \mathcal{R}^2$ is defined by

$$g\begin{pmatrix} x \\ y \\ z \end{pmatrix} = \begin{pmatrix} 3x + 4y \\ 3y + 5z \end{pmatrix} = \begin{pmatrix} 3 & 4 & 0 \\ 0 & 3 & 5 \end{pmatrix}\begin{pmatrix} x \\ y \\ z \end{pmatrix}.$$

Notice that g is a linear transformation whereas f is not.

The class of vector functions is a large one. For example, every linear transformation is a vector function. The set $\mathcal{R}$ of all real numbers is a vector space of dimension 1, and, as a result, all of the ordinary functions of one-variable calculus are vector functions.

EXAMPLE 2. The following functions have domain space and range space equal to the set $\mathcal{R}$ of real numbers.

$$f(x) = 3x^3 + 5x^2 + 2,$$

$$g(x) = x^2 - 1,$$

$$h(x) = \sin^{-1} x, \qquad -1 \le x \le 1.$$

It is not necessary that the domain of a vector function equal its domain space; it can be a proper subset. The same is true of the range. In particular, the domain of f = the range of f = the domain of g = $\mathcal{R}$. On the other hand, the range of g consists of all real numbers $y \ge -1$, the domain of h is the interval $-1 \le x \le 1$, and the range of h is the interval $-\pi/2 \le y \le \pi/2$. The last three sets are all proper subsets of $\mathcal{R}$.

A vector X in $\mathcal{R}^n$ whose coordinates are the real numbers $x_1, \ldots, x_n$ will be written either as a horizontal n-tuple or as a column matrix. Thus, we shall write both

$$\begin{pmatrix} x_1 \\ \cdot \\ \cdot \\ \cdot \\ x_n \end{pmatrix} \quad \text{and} \quad (x_1, \ldots, x_n)$$

for the vector X. The practice of writing columns instead of horizontal tuples arises, of course, from the definition of matrix multiplication. If a transformation is determined by a matrix

$$\begin{pmatrix} a & b \\ c & d \end{pmatrix},$$

we usually write

$$\begin{pmatrix} a & b \\ c & d \end{pmatrix} \begin{pmatrix} x \\ y \end{pmatrix}$$

for the value of the transformation at

$$\begin{pmatrix} x \\ y \end{pmatrix} \text{ or } (x, y).$$

A function whose range is a subset of the space $\mathcal{R}$ of all real numbers is called **real-valued**. Every function $\mathcal{R}^n \xrightarrow{f} \mathcal{R}^m$ defines a set of real-valued functions $f_1, \ldots, f_m$, called the **coordinate functions** of f. The definition is as follows: For every X in the domain of f and each $i = 1, \ldots, m$, we set $f_i X$ equal to the ith coordinate of fX. Thus,

$$fX = (f_1 X, \ldots, f_m X),$$

for every X in the domain of f.

EXAMPLE 3. Consider the vector function

$$f\begin{pmatrix} x \\ y \\ z \end{pmatrix} = \begin{pmatrix} x + y + z \\ xy + yz + zx \\ xyz \end{pmatrix}.$$

The coordinate functions of f are the three real-valued functions

$$f_1(x, y, z) = x + y + z,$$
$$f_2(x, y, z) = xy + yz + zx,$$
$$f_3(x, y, z) = xyz.$$

The **graph** of any function f whatever is defined to be the set of all ordered pairs (X, fX) where X is in the domain of f. In studying real-valued functions of one real variable, graphs are a considerable aid to understanding. For example, the graph of the function defined by $f(x) =$

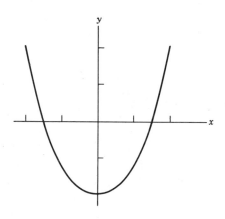

FIGURE 1

$x^2 - 2$ is the set of all ordered pairs (x, y) with $y = x^2 - 2$, that is, it is the subset of the xy-plane consisting of the parabola shown in Figure 1. More generally, the graph of a function $\Re^n \xrightarrow{f} \Re^m$ is the subset of $\Re^{n+m}$ consisting of all points $(x_1, \ldots, x_n, y_1, \ldots, y_m)$ such that

$$y_1 = f_1(x_1, \ldots, x_n)$$
$$\cdots$$
$$y_m = f_m(x_1, \ldots, x_n),$$

where $f_1, \ldots, f_m$ are the coordinate functions of f. As a practical means of increasing understanding by visualization, the usefulness of the graph is largely limited to functions $\Re^n \xrightarrow{f} \Re^m$ for which $m + n \leq 3$.

EXAMPLE 4. The length $|X|$ of a vector X in $\Re^2$ is defined by

$$|X| = |(x, y)| = \sqrt{x^2 + y^2}.$$

The graph of the function f defined by $fX = |X|^2$ is the subset of $\Re^3$ pictured in Figure 2. Notice that we have drawn the z-axis perpendicular to the xy-plane. This choice enables us to draw a recognizable graph, but is not logically necessary.

EXAMPLE 5. Consider the function $\Re \xrightarrow{f} \Re^2$ defined by

$$f(t) = \begin{pmatrix} \cos t \\ \sin t \end{pmatrix}, \qquad \text{for every } t \text{ in } \Re.$$

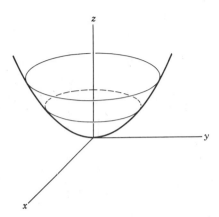

FIGURE 2

Assuming that the length $|\,X\,|$ of a vector

$$X = \begin{pmatrix} x \\ y \end{pmatrix}$$

is given by

$$|\,X\,| = \sqrt{x^2 + y^2},$$

we have

$$|\,f(t)\,| = \sqrt{\cos^2 t + \sin^2 t} = 1.$$

Thus the range of f is a subset of the unit circle $|\,X\,| = 1$ in $\mathcal{R}^2$. The number t is interpreted geometrically as the angle in radians between the vector $f(t)$ and the positive x-axis. As t runs through $\mathcal{R}$, the unit circle is covered infinitely often. It follows that the range of f is the whole unit circle. The circle is not, however, the graph of f. The latter is a subset of $\mathcal{R}^3$ and is a spiral, the axis of which is the t-axis. See Figure 3.

We recall that the euclidean structure on $\mathcal{R}^n$ consists of an inner product and a norm defined on the vector space $\mathcal{R}^n$ of n-tuples. The **inner product** $X \cdot Y$ of $X = (x_1, \ldots, x_n)$ and $Y = (y_1, \ldots, y_n)$ is defined by

$$X \cdot Y = x_1 y_1 + \ldots + x_n y_n.$$

A real-valued function, called the **euclidean norm**, is defined by

$$|\,X\,| = \sqrt{X \cdot X}.$$

The **length** of X is defined to be $|\,X\,|$, the **distance** between X and Y is $|\,X - Y\,|$, and if X and Y are nonzero, the **angle** between them is deter-

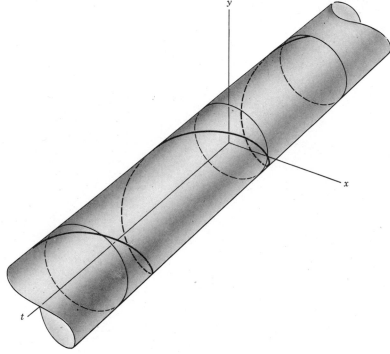

FIGURE 3

mined so that

$$\cos \theta = \frac{X \cdot Y}{|X||Y|}.$$

According to these definitions the coordinate axes are mutually perpendicular, and the basis vectors $(1, 0, \ldots, 0)$, $(0, 1, \ldots, 0)$, ..., $(0, 0, \ldots, 1)$ each have length equal to 1. In the examples that follow we shall make use of euclidean as well as vector geometry whenever it is convenient.

EXAMPLE 6. Let the vector function f be defined by

$$f(t) = \begin{pmatrix} x \\ y \\ z \end{pmatrix} = \begin{pmatrix} t \\ t^2 \\ t^3 \end{pmatrix}, \qquad -\infty < t < \infty.$$

The graph of f is a subset of $\mathfrak{R}^4$, so we shall not attempt to draw it. Instead we shall sketch the range. By setting $z = 0$, we obtain the equations $x = t$, $y = t^2$ which are equivalent to $y = x^2$. Thus the projected image, on the xy-plane, of the range of f is the graph of $y = x^2$. Similarly, in the yz-plane we obtain $y = z^{2/3}$, and in the xz-plane we get $z = x^3$. From this information, we have drawn in Figure 4 that part of the range of f that lies above the first quadrant of the xy-plane.

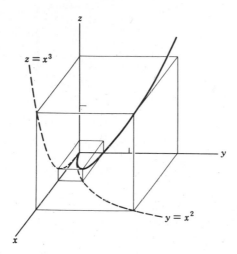

FIGURE 4

In drawing Figure 4 we have labeled the axes in the manner usually associated with a right-hand orientation. Of course, if we were to interchange x and y in this labeling, the picture would look different. A similar change in Figure 5(b) would result in a ramp that spirals down turning always to the left instead of to the right. In order to make it easy to see the relationship between the pictures, we have always chosen the right-hand orientation for the axes in the 3-dimensional ones. For a discussion of orientation see Section 1 of Appendix I.

EXAMPLE 7. Consider the function

$$f\begin{pmatrix} u \\ v \end{pmatrix} = \begin{pmatrix} x \\ y \\ z \end{pmatrix} = \begin{pmatrix} u\cos v \\ u\sin v \\ v \end{pmatrix} \qquad \begin{matrix} 0 \leq u \leq 4. \\ \\ 0 \leq v \leq 2\pi. \end{matrix}$$

The domain of f is the shaded rectangle in Figure 5(a). In order to sketch the range, we proceed as follows: Choose a number a in the interval

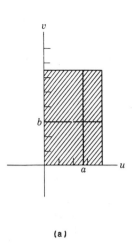

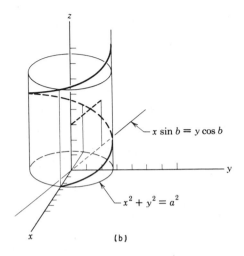

FIGURE 5

$0 \le u \le 4$, and set $u = a$. Then,

$$x = a \cos v,$$

$$y = a \sin v, \qquad 0 \le v \le 2\pi,$$

$$z = v,$$

and $x^2 + y^2 = a^2$. We interpret v both as distance along the z-axis and as the angle between $(x, y, 0)$ and the x-axis. It follows that the image under f of the line segment $u = a$, $0 \le v \le 2\pi$ [see Figure 5(a)] is the spiral whose projection on the xy-plane is the circle of radius a and whose axis is the z-axis [see Figure 5(b)]. Next, choose a number b in the interval $0 \le v \le 2\pi$, and set $v = b$. Then,

$$x = u \cos b,$$

$$y = u \sin b, \qquad 0 \le u \le 4,$$

$$z = b,$$

and $x^2 + y^2 = u^2$. The image under f of the line segment $v = b$, $0 \le u \le 4$ [see Figure 5(a)] is the line segment $x \sin b = y \cos b$, $z = b$ of length 4 where x runs from 0 to $4 \cos b$ [see Figure 5(b)]. Letting a and b vary, we obtain the range of f as the spiral surface shown in Figure 6.

Notice that the range of f in Examples 5 and 6 is a curve, whereas in Example 7 it is a surface. Similarly, the graph of f in Example 4 is a surface, but in Example 5 it is a curve. The evidence suggests that when the dimen-

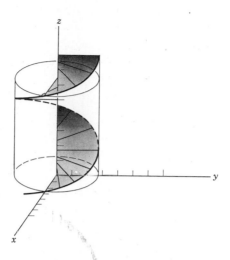

FIGURE 6

sion of the domain space is 1, one gets a curve, and when it is 2, one gets a surface. Exceptions to this will be discussed in Section 5.

The curves and surfaces pictured in Figures 2, 3, 4, and 6 are related to the vector functions that define them in two essentially different ways. The bowl-shaped surface in Figure 2 is just the graph of the function which defines it, and the same is true for the spiral curve in Figure 3. For this reason, we shall say that both curve and surface are defined **explicitly**. On the other hand, the curve in Figure 4 and the surface in Figure 6 are the ranges of their defining functions. They are therefore said to be defined **parametrically**. This terminology is standard in discussing real-valued functions of one real variable. For example, the function

$$f(x) \;=\; \sqrt{16 - x^2}$$

explicitly defines the upper half of the circle of radius 4, and the same curve is defined parametrically by the pair of functions

$$\begin{cases} x(t) \;=\; 4\cos t, \\[2pt] y(t) \;=\; 4\sin t, \end{cases} \qquad 0 \le t \le \pi.$$

Parametric representations of lines in 3-dimensional space have been studied in Chapter 1. Let X_1 and X_2 be any two vectors in $\Re^3$. If $X_1 \ne 0$, the range of the function $\Re \xrightarrow{f} \Re^3$ defined by

$$f(t) \;=\; tX_1 + X_2, \qquad -\infty < t < \infty,$$

is a parametrically defined line.

Curves and surfaces can also be defined **implicitly**. In particular, implicitly defined planes were discussed in Chapter 1. Let $(a \quad b \quad c)$ be a nonzero 1-by-3 matrix, and let $\mathfrak{R}^3 \xrightarrow{F} \mathfrak{R}$ be the linear functional defined, for any

$$X = \begin{pmatrix} x \\ y \\ z \end{pmatrix},$$

by

$$FX = (a \quad b \quad c) \begin{pmatrix} x \\ y \\ z \end{pmatrix}.$$

For any real number d, the set of all X such that

$$FX = ax + by + cz = d$$

is an implicitly defined plane.

EXAMPLE 8. Consider the function f defined by $f(x, y, z) = xy + yz + zx$. The subset S of $\mathfrak{R}^3$ consisting of all points (x, y, z) that satisfy

$$f(x, y, z) = xy + yz + zx = 1 \tag{1}$$

is said to be defined **implicitly** by Equation (1). Setting $z = 0$ in (1) we obtain the equation $xy = 1$, which implicitly defines a hyperbola in the xy-plane. This hyperbola is the intersection of S and the xy-plane. Since $f(x, y, z)$ is symmetric in x, y, z, the other coordinate planes also intersect S in hyperbolas, as shown in Figure 7. More generally, the intersection of

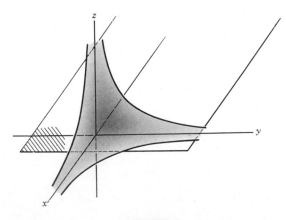

FIGURE 7

S with the plane $z = a$ is given by $xy + ya + ax = 1$. This equation is equivalent to

$$(x + a)(y + a) = xy + ya + ax + a^2 = a^2 + 1.$$

By substituting $u = x + a$ and $v = y + a$, we obtain the equation $uv = a^2 + 1$ of the hyperbola shown in Figure 8. It follows by symmetry that

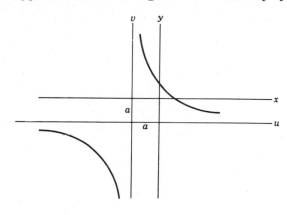

FIGURE 8

the intersection of S with any plane parallel to a coordinate plane is a hyperbola. We conclude that S looks like a surface, and the part of it that lies in the octant $x \geq 0$, $y \geq 0$, $z \geq 0$ is drawn in Figure 7.

EXAMPLE 9. Let $\mathfrak{R}^3 \xrightarrow{f} \mathfrak{R}^2$ be the function defined by

$$f\begin{pmatrix} x \\ y \\ z \end{pmatrix} = \begin{pmatrix} xy + yz + zx \\ x + y - z \end{pmatrix}.$$

Consider the subset C of $\mathfrak{R}^3$ implicitly defined by the equation

$$fX = \begin{pmatrix} 1 \\ 1 \end{pmatrix}.$$

That is, C consists of all $X = \begin{pmatrix} x \\ y \\ z \end{pmatrix}$ such that

$$xy + yz + zx = 1,$$
$$x + y - z = 1.$$

We have seen in Example 8 that $xy + yz + zx = 1$ implicitly defines the surface pictured in Figure 7. The equation $x + y - z = 1$ implicitly defines the plane in Figure 9. The set C of points that satisfy both equations is the curve in which the surface and the plane intersect.

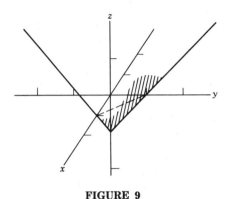

FIGURE 9

The distinctions among explicit, parametric, and implicit representations are not limited to dimensions 2 and 3. For any two integers n and m, an n-dimensional surface S is defined

(1) **explicitly** if S is the **graph** in $\Re^{n+m}$ of a function

$$\Re^n \xrightarrow{f} \Re^m,$$

(2) **parametrically** if S is the **range** in $\Re^m$ of a function

$$\Re^n \xrightarrow{f} \Re^m,$$

(3) **implicitly** if, for some function

$$\Re^{n+m} \xrightarrow{f} \Re^m$$

and point Z_0 in $\Re^m$, S is the set of all X in the **domain** of f such that $fX = Z_0$.

A 1-dimensional surface is a curve, and a 2-dimensional surface is what we usually refer to as simply a surface. The reason for giving the definitions for arbitrary dimensions in this book is not that we wish to study, for example, any particular 4-dimensional surface in 7-dimensional space. It is rather the desirability of expressing what is one idea in one definition.

When the domain and range spaces of a vector function are the same, it is often helpful to picture the domain vectors X as points and the image

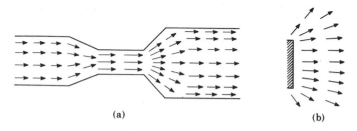

FIGURE 10

vectors fX as arrows or free vectors. We picture fX as an arrow with its tail at X. One would do this, for example, in representing a 2-dimensional fluid flow in which the image vector at each point is the velocity and direction of the flow. See Figure 10(a). Another example is an electric field, where the value of the function at a point is the vector giving the force exerted by the field on a unit charge. See Figure 10(b). Vector functions looked at in this way are sometimes called **vector fields**.

EXERCISES

1. The vector function f is defined by

$$f\begin{pmatrix} x \\ y \end{pmatrix} = \begin{pmatrix} x^2 - y^2 \\ 2xy \end{pmatrix}.$$

What are the coordinate functions of f? Consider the domain space to be the xy-plane and the range space to be the uv-plane.

(a) Find the image of the segment of the line $y = x$ between

$$\begin{pmatrix} 0 \\ 0 \end{pmatrix} \quad \text{and} \quad \begin{pmatrix} 1 \\ 1 \end{pmatrix}.$$

(b) Find the image of the region defined by $0 < x$, $0 < y$, and $x^2 + y^2 < 1$.
(c) Find the angle between the images of the lines $y = 0$ and $y = (1/\sqrt{3})x$.
$$[Ans.\ \pi/3.]$$

2. A vector function f from the xy-plane to the uv-plane is defined by

$$f\begin{pmatrix} x \\ y \end{pmatrix} = \begin{pmatrix} u \\ v \end{pmatrix} = \begin{pmatrix} x \\ (x+y)^2 \\ 4x \end{pmatrix}, \qquad x \neq 0.$$

What are the coordinate functions of f? Find the image of the region bounded by the lines $x = y$, $y = x - 8$, $x = -y$, $y = 8 - x$.

3. Consider the function $f(x, y) = \sqrt{4 - x^2 - y^2}$.

(a) Sketch the domain of f (take it as large as possible.)

(b) Sketch the graph of f.

(c) Sketch the range of f.

4. The function $\mathcal{R} \xrightarrow{g} \mathcal{R}^2$ is defined by

$$g(t) = \begin{pmatrix} 2 \cos t \\ 3 \sin t \end{pmatrix}, \qquad 0 \leq t \leq 2\pi.$$

(a) Draw the range of g.

(b) Draw the graph of g.

5. A transformation from the xy-plane to the uv-plane is defined by

$$f\begin{pmatrix} x \\ y \end{pmatrix} = \begin{pmatrix} u \\ v \end{pmatrix} = \begin{pmatrix} x \\ y(1 + x^2) \end{pmatrix}.$$

What are the images of horizontal lines in the xy-plane?

6. For each of the following linear transformations: (α) What is the domain? (β) Describe and sketch the range. (γ) Describe and sketch the set implicitly defined by the equation $LX = 0$. What is this set usually called?

(a) $L\begin{pmatrix} x \\ y \end{pmatrix} = \begin{pmatrix} 2 & 1 \\ 4 & 3 \end{pmatrix}\begin{pmatrix} x \\ y \end{pmatrix}$

(b) $L\begin{pmatrix} x \\ y \end{pmatrix} = \begin{pmatrix} 2 & 1 \\ 4 & 2 \end{pmatrix}\begin{pmatrix} x \\ y \end{pmatrix}$

(c) $L\begin{pmatrix} x \\ y \\ z \end{pmatrix} = \begin{pmatrix} 1 & 0 & 2 \\ 3 & 2 & 1 \end{pmatrix}\begin{pmatrix} x \\ y \\ z \end{pmatrix}$

(d) $L\begin{pmatrix} x \\ y \\ z \end{pmatrix} = \begin{pmatrix} 1 & 2 & 3 \\ -1 & 4 & 2 \\ 5 & -8 & 0 \end{pmatrix}\begin{pmatrix} x \\ y \\ z \end{pmatrix}$

7. Draw the surfaces defined explicitly by the following functions.

(a) $f\begin{pmatrix} x \\ y \end{pmatrix} = 2 - x^2 - y^2$

(b) $h\begin{pmatrix} x \\ y \end{pmatrix} = \dfrac{1}{x^2 + y^2}$

(c) $g(x, y) = \sin x$

(d) $f(x, y) = 0$

(e) $f(x, y) = e^{x+y}$

(f) $g(x, y) = \begin{cases} 1 & \text{if } |x| < |y| \\ 0 & \text{if } |x| \geq |y| \end{cases}$

8. Draw the curves defined parametrically by the following functions.

(a) $f(t) = \begin{pmatrix} 1 \\ 2 \\ 0 \end{pmatrix} t + \begin{pmatrix} 1 \\ 1 \\ 1 \end{pmatrix}, \quad -\infty < t < \infty.$

(b) $g(t) = \begin{pmatrix} 1 \\ 1 \\ 1 \end{pmatrix} t + \begin{pmatrix} 1 \\ 2 \\ 3 \end{pmatrix} (1 - t), 0 \leq t \leq 1.$

(c) $X = \begin{pmatrix} 1 \\ 0 \\ 2 \end{pmatrix} t + \begin{pmatrix} -1 \\ 0 \\ -2 \end{pmatrix}, 0 \leq t \leq 2.$

(d) $f(t) = \begin{pmatrix} t \\ t^2 \\ t^3 \end{pmatrix}, 0 \leq t \leq 1.$

(e) $f(t) = (2t, t), -1 \leq t \leq 1.$

(f) $g(t) = \begin{pmatrix} \cos t \\ \sin t \\ t^2 \end{pmatrix}, 0 \leq t \leq 2\pi.$

(g) $h(t) = (t, t, t^2)$, $-1 \le t \le 2$.

(h) $f(t) = \begin{pmatrix} 2t \\ |t| \end{pmatrix}$, $-1 \le t \le 2$.

9. Draw the surfaces defined parametrically by the following functions:

(a) $L\begin{pmatrix} u \\ v \end{pmatrix} = \begin{pmatrix} x \\ y \\ z \end{pmatrix} = \begin{pmatrix} 1 & 0 \\ 0 & 1 \\ 1 & 0 \end{pmatrix}\begin{pmatrix} u \\ v \end{pmatrix}$, $\begin{cases} -\infty < u < \infty, \\ -\infty < v < \infty. \end{cases}$

(b) $f\begin{pmatrix} u \\ v \end{pmatrix} = \begin{pmatrix} x \\ y \\ z \end{pmatrix} = \begin{pmatrix} 1 & 0 \\ 0 & 1 \\ 1 & 0 \end{pmatrix}\begin{pmatrix} u \\ v \end{pmatrix} + \begin{pmatrix} 1 \\ 1 \\ 1 \end{pmatrix}$, $\begin{cases} -\infty < u < \infty, \\ -\infty < v < \infty. \end{cases}$

(c) $f\begin{pmatrix} u \\ v \end{pmatrix} = \begin{pmatrix} x \\ y \\ z \end{pmatrix} = \begin{pmatrix} 1 & 1 \\ 2 & 3 \\ 1 & 2 \end{pmatrix}\begin{pmatrix} u \\ v \end{pmatrix} + \begin{pmatrix} 0 \\ 1 \\ 0 \end{pmatrix}$, $\begin{cases} -\infty < u < \infty, \\ -\infty < v < \infty. \end{cases}$

(d) $g\begin{pmatrix} u \\ v \end{pmatrix} = \begin{pmatrix} x \\ y \\ z \end{pmatrix} = \begin{pmatrix} \cos u \sin v \\ \sin u \sin v \\ \cos v \end{pmatrix}$, $\begin{cases} 0 \le u \le 2\pi. \\ 0 \le v \le \pi/2. \end{cases}$

(e) $\begin{pmatrix} x \\ y \\ z \end{pmatrix} = \begin{pmatrix} \cos u \cosh v \\ \sin u \cosh v \\ \sinh v \end{pmatrix}$, $\begin{cases} 0 \le u \le 2\pi, \\ -\infty < v < \infty. \end{cases}$

(f) $\begin{pmatrix} x \\ y \\ z \end{pmatrix} = \begin{pmatrix} \cosh v \\ \cos u \sinh v \\ \sin u \sinh v \end{pmatrix}$, $\begin{cases} 0 \le u \le 2\pi, \\ -\infty < v < \infty. \end{cases}$

$$(g) \quad \begin{pmatrix} x \\ y \\ z \end{pmatrix} = \begin{pmatrix} 2\cos u + v \sin (u/2) \cos u \\ 2 \sin u + v \sin (u/2) \sin u \\ v \cos u/2 \end{pmatrix}, \quad \begin{cases} 0 \le u \le 2\pi, \\ -1 \le v \le 1. \end{cases}$$

Möbius strip

10. Draw the following implicitly defined curves and surfaces. The surface (or curve) implicitly defined by a vector equation $FX = K$ is called the **level surface** of F at the level K.

(a) $f(x, y) = x + y = 1$.

(b) $g(x, y) = \dfrac{x^2}{a^2} + \dfrac{y^2}{b^2} = 1$.

(c) $f(x, y) = (x^2 + y^2 + 1)^2 - 4x^2 = 0$.

(d) $FX = (1 \quad 2 \quad 1) \begin{pmatrix} x \\ y \\ z \end{pmatrix} = 0$.

(e) $FX = (1 \quad 0 \quad 1) \begin{pmatrix} x \\ y \\ z \end{pmatrix} = 1$.

(f) $f(x, y, z) = xyz = 1$.

(g) $xyz = 0$.

(h) $g(x, y, z) = x^2 - y^2 = 2$.

(i) $f \begin{pmatrix} x \\ y \\ z \end{pmatrix} = \begin{pmatrix} x - y \\ y + z \end{pmatrix} = \begin{pmatrix} 0 \\ 0 \end{pmatrix}$.

(j) $\begin{cases} 2x + y + z = 2, \\ x \quad\quad - z = 3. \end{cases}$

(k) $g \begin{pmatrix} x \\ y \\ z \end{pmatrix} = \begin{pmatrix} xyz \\ x + y \end{pmatrix} = \begin{pmatrix} 1 \\ 0 \end{pmatrix}$.

$$(1) \quad f\begin{pmatrix} x \\ y \\ z \end{pmatrix} = \begin{pmatrix} xy + yz + zx \\ x + y \end{pmatrix} = \begin{pmatrix} 1 \\ 4 \end{pmatrix}.$$

11. Sketch the indicated vector fields.

(a) $f\begin{pmatrix} x \\ y \end{pmatrix} = \begin{pmatrix} 1 \\ x \end{pmatrix}$ for $-1 \leq x \leq 2$, $y = 0$, $y = 1$.

(b) $f\begin{pmatrix} x \\ y \end{pmatrix} = \begin{pmatrix} -x \\ y \end{pmatrix}$ for $x^2 + y^2 \leq 4$.

(c) $f\begin{pmatrix} x \\ y \end{pmatrix} = \begin{pmatrix} y \\ x \end{pmatrix}$ for $x^2 + y^2 \leq 4$.

(d) $f\begin{pmatrix} x \\ y \end{pmatrix} = \dfrac{1}{x^2 + y^2}\begin{pmatrix} 1 \\ 1 \end{pmatrix}$ for $x^2 + y^2 \leq 4$.

12. Derive a parametric representation of the plane containing the point X_0 in $\mathfrak{R}^3$ and parallel to the subspace of $\mathfrak{R}^3$ spanned by the linearly independent vectors X_1 and X_2.

13. Let a transformation from the euclidean xy-plane to itself be given by

$$f\begin{pmatrix} x \\ y \end{pmatrix} = \begin{pmatrix} x + y \\ -x + y \end{pmatrix}.$$

Show that f accomplishes an expansion out from the origin by a factor $\sqrt{2}$ and a rotation through an angle $\pi/4$.

2. LIMITS AND CONTINUITY

Any definition of limit is based on a notion of proximity. To assert for example, that

$$\lim_{x \to 0} \frac{\sin x}{x} = 1$$

is to say that $(\sin x)/x$ is arbitrarily close to 1 provided x is sufficiently close to 0. (We rule out $x = 0$ since $(\sin 0)/0$ is not defined.) Proximity on the real-number line can be expressed by inequalities. For example,

FIGURE 11

$| x - 3 | < 0.4$ says that the distance between the number x and the number 3 is less than 0.4, or, equivalently, that x lies in the interior of the interval with center 3 and half-length 0.4. See Figure 11. The statement "$(\sin x)/x$ is arbitrarily close to 1 provided x is sufficiently close to 0" is translated in terms of inequalities as: For any positive number ϵ, there exists a positive number δ such that if

$$0 < | x - 0 | = | x | < \delta,$$

then
$$\left| \frac{\sin x}{x} - 1 \right| < \epsilon.$$

In a vector space of arbitrary finite dimension a definition of limit also requires the means of asserting that one point is close to another. Distance will be defined with respect to the euclidean norm. For any $\epsilon > 0$ and point X_0 in $\mathfrak{R}^n$, the set of all vectors X in $\mathfrak{R}^n$ that satisfy the inequality

$$| X - X_0 | < \epsilon$$

is a spherical ball with radius ϵ and center X_0. For example, if $X_0 = (1, 2, 1)$, the set of all X in $\mathfrak{R}^3$ such that

$$| X - X_0 | = \sqrt{(x - 1)^2 + (y - 2)^2 + (z - 1)^2} < 0.5$$

is the ball shown in Figure 12.

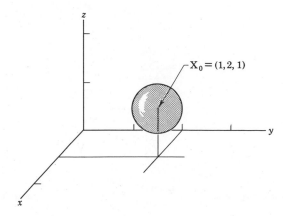

FIGURE 12

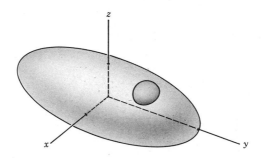

FIGURE 13

Let S be a subset of $\mathcal{R}^n$ and X a point in $\mathcal{R}^n$. Then X is a **limit point** of S if, for any $\epsilon > 0$, there exists a point Y in S such that $0 < |X - Y| < \epsilon$. Translated into English, the definition says that X is a limit point of S if there are points in S other than X that are contained in a ball of arbitrarily small radius with center at X. If, for example, E is the solid ellipsoid implicitly defined by $x^2 + y^2/4 + z^2 < 1$, then the set of limit points of E consists of E together with the skin $x^2 + y^2/4 + z^2 = 1$. See Figure 13.

We come now to the definition of limit for a function $\mathcal{R}^n \xrightarrow{f} \mathcal{R}^m$. Let Y_0 be a point in $\mathcal{R}^m$ and X_0 a limit point of the domain of f. Then Y_0 **is the limit of f at X_0**, abbreviated

$$\lim_{X \to X_0} fX = Y_0,$$

if, for any $\epsilon > 0$, there exists $\delta > 0$ such that if X is in the domain of f and $0 < |X - X_0| < \delta$, then $|fX - Y_0| < \epsilon$. The definition means

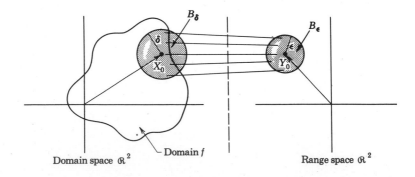

FIGURE 14

that if the limit exists, then fX is arbitrarily close to Y_0 provided X is sufficiently close to X_0. Geometrically the idea is this: Given any ϵ-ball B_ϵ centered at Y_0, there exists a δ-ball B_δ centered at X_0 whose intersection with the domain of f is mapped by f into B_ϵ. A 2-dimensional example is pictured in Figure 14. The statement

$$\lim_{X \to X_0} fX = Y_0$$

is also commonly read "The limit of fX, as X approaches X_0, is Y_0." To see why we have required that X_0 be a limit point of the domain of f, consider a 1-dimensional example. The function $(\sin^{-1} x)/x$, the graph of

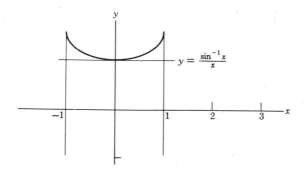

FIGURE 15

which is drawn in Figure 15, has as its domain the broken interval $-1 \leq x \leq 1$, $x \neq 0$. Clearly we want

$$\lim_{x \to 1/2} \frac{\sin^{-1} x}{x} = \frac{\pi}{6} \bigg/ \frac{1}{2} = \frac{\pi}{3},$$

$$\lim_{x \to 0} \frac{\sin^{-1} x}{x} = 1.$$

But it makes no sense to ask for

$$\lim_{x \to 3} \frac{\sin^{-1} x}{x}.$$

EXAMPLE 1. Consider the real-valued function

$$f\begin{pmatrix} x \\ y \end{pmatrix} = x \frac{x^2 - y^2}{x^2 + y^2}.$$

The domain of f is all of $\mathcal{R}^2$ except the origin. Then,

$$\lim_{X \to \binom{0}{0}} fX = 0$$

because

$$\left| f\binom{x}{y} \right| = \left| x \frac{x^2 - y^2}{x^2 + y^2} \right|,$$

and

$$\left| x \frac{x^2 - y^2}{x^2 + y^2} \right| = |x| \left| \frac{x^2 - y^2}{x^2 + y^2} \right| \le |x| \le \sqrt{x^2 + y^2},$$

and so

$$\left| f\binom{x}{y} \right| \le \left| \binom{x}{y} \right|.$$

For any $\epsilon > 0$, we may choose $\delta = \epsilon$.

EXAMPLE 2. The range space and the domain are the same as in Example 1 and

$$f\binom{x}{y} = \frac{e^{x+y}}{x^2 + y^2}.$$

There is no limit as

$$\binom{x}{y} \longrightarrow \binom{0}{0},$$

for example, along the line $y = x$. We can write

$$\lim_{X \to \binom{0}{0}} fX = \infty$$

to describe what happens.

EXAMPLE 3. The range space and the domain are the same as in the preceding two examples and

$$f\binom{x}{y} = \frac{x^2 - y^2}{x^2 + y^2}.$$

There is no limit as

$$\binom{x}{y} \longrightarrow \binom{0}{0}.$$

If $\begin{pmatrix} x \\ y \end{pmatrix}$ approaches $\begin{pmatrix} 0 \\ 0 \end{pmatrix}$ along the line $y = \alpha x$, we obtain

$$\lim_{X \to 0} \frac{x^2 - y^2}{x^2 + y^2} = \lim_{x \to 0} \frac{x^2(1 - \alpha^2)}{x^2(1 + \alpha^2)} = \frac{1 - \alpha^2}{1 + \alpha^2}.$$

The limit is obviously not independent of α; it equals 0 if $\alpha = 1$, and 1 if $\alpha = 0$.

The functions in the above three examples are all real-valued. The following theorem shows that the problem of the existence and evaluation of a limit for any function $\mathfrak{R}^n \xrightarrow{f} \mathfrak{R}^m$ reduces to the same problem for the coordinate functions. The latter are, of course, real-valued.

2.1 Theorem. Given $\mathfrak{R}^n \xrightarrow{f} \mathfrak{R}^m$, with coordinate functions $f_1, \ldots, f_m$, and a point $Y_0 = (b_1, \ldots, b_m)$ in $\mathfrak{R}^m$, then

$$\lim_{X \to X_0} fX = Y_0 \tag{1}$$

if and only if

$$\lim_{X \to X_0} f_i X = b_i, \qquad i = 1, \ldots, m. \tag{2}$$

Proof. Since the domain of f equals the domain of f_i, $i = 1, \ldots, m$, the vector X_0 is a limit point of the domain of f if and only if it is a limit point of the domain of each f_i. Suppose Equation (1) holds and $\epsilon > 0$ is given. Then there exists $\delta > 0$ such that if X is in the domain of f and $0 < |X - X_0| < \delta$, then $|fX - Y_0| < \epsilon$. Hence,

$$|f_i X - b_i| \leq |fX - Y_0| < \epsilon, \qquad i = 1, \ldots, m,$$

and so Equation (2) holds. Conversely, assume (2) and let $\epsilon > 0$ be given. Then there exists $\delta_i > 0$ such that if X is in the domain of f_i and $0 < |X - X_0| < \delta_i$, then

$$|f_i X - b_i| < \frac{\epsilon}{\sqrt{m}}.$$

We set $\delta = \min \{\delta_1, \ldots, \delta_m\}$. If X is in the domain of f and

$$0 < |X - X_0| < \delta,$$

then
$$\max \{|f_i X - b_i|\} < \frac{\epsilon}{\sqrt{m}}.$$

We now use the fact that, for any vector $X = (x_1, \ldots, x_n)$,

$$|X| \leq \sqrt{n} \max \{|x_1|, \ldots, |x_n|\}.$$

Then

$$|fX - Y_0| \leq \sqrt{m} \max \{|f_iX - b_i|\} < \epsilon.$$

This completes the proof.

EXAMPLE 4. Vector functions f_1 and f_2 are defined by

$$f_1(t) = \begin{pmatrix} t \\ t^2 \\ \sin t \end{pmatrix}, \qquad f_2(t) = \begin{pmatrix} t \\ t^2 \\ \sin \dfrac{1}{t} \end{pmatrix}.$$

Then,

$$\lim_{t \to 0} f_1(t) = \begin{pmatrix} 0 \\ 0 \\ 0 \end{pmatrix},$$

but $\lim f_2(t)$ does not exist because the coordinate function $\sin (1/t)$ has no limit at $t = 0$.

The concept of continuity is essential in calculus. Roughly speaking, a continuous function f is one whose values do not change abruptly. That is, if X is close to X_0, then fX must be close to fX_0. This idea is related to the notion of limit, and the definition of continuity is as follows: **A function f is continuous at** X_0 if X_0 is in the domain of f and $\lim_{X \to X_0} fX = fX_0$. It is an immediate corollary of (2.1) that

2.2 Corollary. A vector function is continuous at a point if and only if its coordinate functions are continuous there.

EXAMPLE 5. The function

$$f_1(t) = \begin{pmatrix} t \\ t^2 \\ \sin t \end{pmatrix}$$

is continuous at every value of t. On the other hand, the function

$$f_2(t) = \begin{pmatrix} t \\ t^2 \\ \sin \dfrac{1}{t} \end{pmatrix}$$

is continuous except at $t = 0$. Consider the function of Example 1 defined by

$$f\begin{pmatrix} x \\ y \end{pmatrix} = x\,\frac{x^2 - y^2}{x^2 + y^2}.$$

As it stands f is not continuous at $\begin{pmatrix} 0 \\ 0 \end{pmatrix}$ because it is not defined there.

However, it is easy to extend the domain by setting

$$f\begin{pmatrix} x \\ y \end{pmatrix} = \begin{cases} x\,\dfrac{x^2 - y^2}{x^2 + y^2}, & \text{if } \begin{pmatrix} x \\ y \end{pmatrix} \neq \begin{pmatrix} 0 \\ 0 \end{pmatrix}. \\[2em] 0, & \text{if } \begin{pmatrix} x \\ y \end{pmatrix} = \begin{pmatrix} 0 \\ 0 \end{pmatrix}. \end{cases}$$

The extended function is continuous at every $\begin{pmatrix} x \\ y \end{pmatrix}$.

A function is simply called **continuous** if it is continuous at every point of its domain.

Many proofs involving the euclidean norm actually use only three of its properties. Established in Chapter 1, they are

2.3 $|X| > 0$, except that $|0| = 0$.

2.4 $|aX| = |a||X|$.

2.5 $|X + Y| \leq |X| + |Y|$.

By abstracting from these properties, we arrive at the general concept of a norm. Specifically, a **norm** on a vector space $\mathfrak{X}$ is a real-valued function $\|\ \ \|$ with domain $\mathfrak{X}$ and the following three properties:

Positivity: $\| X \| > 0$, except that $\| 0 \| = 0$.

Homogeneity: $\| aX \| = | a | \, \| X \|$.

Triangle inequality: $\| X + Y \| \leq \| X \| + \| Y \|$.

An example of a norm on $\mathfrak{R}^n$ different from the euclidean norm is the so-called **box norm** defined, for any $X = (x_1, \ldots, x_n)$, by

$$\| X \| = \max \{| x_1 |, \ldots, | x_n |\}.$$

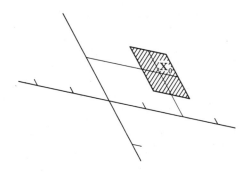

FIGURE 16

If $X_0 = (2, 1)$, the set of all X in $\mathfrak{R}^2$ such that $\| X - X_0 \| < 0.5$ is the parallelogram shown in Figure 16. We have purposely drawn nonperpendicular coordinate axes with different scale to emphasize the fact that this norm is not euclidean. See Exercise 9. Actually any norm whatever can serve as the basis of a definition of limit in a vector space. An important theorem, proved in the Appendix, is that, for a finite-dimensional vector space, the definition of limit is independent of the choice of norm.

2.6 Theorem. For any linear transformation $\mathfrak{R}^n \xrightarrow{L} \mathfrak{R}^m$, there exists a positive real number k such that

$$| LX | \leq k | X |, \qquad \text{for every } X \text{ in } \mathfrak{R}^n.$$

Proof. The domain space $\mathfrak{R}^n$ has the natural basis

$$E_1 = (1, 0, \ldots, 0), \quad E_2 = (0, 1, \ldots, 0), \quad \ldots, \quad E_n = (0, 0, \ldots, 1).$$

Choose for k any positive number such that $k \geq |LE_1| + \ldots + |LE_n|$. Then, for every $X = (x_1, \ldots, x_n)$,

$$LX = x_1 LE_1 + \ldots + x_n LE_n.$$

Norm properties (2.4) and (2.5) imply

$$|LX| \leq |x_1| |LE_1| + \ldots + |x_n| |LE_n|$$
$$\leq (|LE_1| + \ldots + |LE_n|) \max_i \{|x_i|\}$$
$$\leq k \max_i \{|x_i|\}.$$

Since $|x_i| \leq |X|, i = 1, \ldots, n$, we conclude that $|LX| \leq k|X|$.

An immediate corollary is

2.7 Corollary. Every linear transformation is a continuous vector function.

A vector X_0 is an interior point of a subset of a vector space if all points sufficiently close to X_0 are also in the subset. Consider, for example, the subset S of $\mathfrak{R}^2$ consisting of all points (x, y) such that $0 < x \leq 2$ and $-1 \leq y < 1$ (cf. Figure 17). The points $(1, 0)$, $(\frac{1}{2}, \frac{1}{2})$, $(1, -1)$, $(2, 0)$ all belong to S. The first two are interior points and the last two are not. More generally, the interior points of S are precisely those (x, y) that satisfy the inequalities $0 < x < 2$ and $-1 < y < 1$. The formal definition is as follows: X_0 is an **interior point** of a subset S of $\mathfrak{R}^n$ if there exists a positive real number δ such that X belongs to S whenever $|X - X_0| < \delta$.

A subset of $\mathfrak{R}^n$, all of whose points are interior, is called **open**. Notice that according to this definition the whole space $\mathfrak{R}^n$ is an open set. So also is the empty subset ϕ of $\mathfrak{R}^n$. Since ϕ contains no points, the condition for openness is vacuously satisfied. An open set containing a particular point is often called a **neighborhood** of that point.

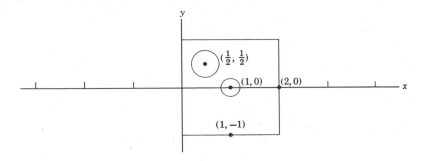

FIGURE 17

EXAMPLE 6. For any $\epsilon > 0$ and any X_0 in $\mathfrak{R}^n$, the set B_ϵ of all vectors X such that $|X - X_0| < \epsilon$ is open. In 3-dimensional space, for example, B_ϵ is the ϵ-ball pictured in Figure 12 for $\epsilon = 0.5$. Let X_1 be an arbitrary point in B_ϵ. Then $|X_1 - X_0| < \epsilon$. We must show that every vector sufficiently close to X_1 is in B_ϵ. Set

$$\delta = \epsilon - |X_1 - X_0|.$$

Then δ is positive. Suppose X is any vector such that $|X - X_1| < \delta$. By the triangle inequality (2.5),

$$|X - X_0| = |(X - X_1) + (X_1 - X_0)|$$

$$\leq |X - X_1| + |X_1 - X_0|$$

$$< \delta + (\epsilon - \delta) = \epsilon.$$

Hence, X is in B_ϵ, and the proof is complete.

EXAMPLE 7. Let I be a finite set of points in $\mathfrak{R}^n$. Then the set consisting of all points in $\mathfrak{R}^n$ that are not in I is open. Thus a vector function that is defined at all points of $\mathfrak{R}^n$ except for some finite set has for its domain an open subset of $\mathfrak{R}^n$.

Two basic properties of open sets are described in the following simple theorems. The proof of the first is easy and is left as an exercise.

2.8 Theorem. The union of two open subsets of $\mathfrak{R}^n$ is open.

2.9 Theorem. The intersection of two open subsets of $\mathfrak{R}^n$ is open.

> *Proof* (of Theorem 2.9). Consider a point X_0 belonging to both of two open subsets S_1 and S_2 of $\mathfrak{R}^n$. Since S_i is open, $i = 1, 2$, there exists $\delta_i > 0$ such that if $|X - X_0| < \delta_i$, then X is in S_i. Set $\delta = \min\{\delta_1, \delta_2\}$. Clearly, if $|X - X_0| < \delta$ then X belongs to $S_1 \cap S_2$.

Theorems 2.8 and 2.9 imply, of course, that the union and intersection of any finite number of open subsets of $\mathfrak{R}^n$ are open.

A point X is a **boundary point** of a subset S of $\mathfrak{R}^n$ if it is neither an interior point of S nor an interior point of the complement of S. The set of all boundary points of a set is its **boundary**. A **closed set** is one that contains its boundary.

EXERCISES

In Exercises 1 and 2 take the domains of the functions to be as large as possible.

1. At which points do the following functions fail to have limits?

(a) $f\begin{pmatrix} x \\ y \end{pmatrix} = \begin{pmatrix} y + \tan x \\ \ln (x + y) \end{pmatrix}.$

(b) $f\begin{pmatrix} x \\ y \end{pmatrix} = \begin{pmatrix} \dfrac{y}{x^2 + 1} \\ \dfrac{x}{y^2 - 1} \end{pmatrix}.$

(c) $f(x, y) = \dfrac{x}{\sin x} + y.$

(d) $f(x, y) = \begin{cases} \dfrac{x}{\sin x} + y, & \text{if } x \neq 0. \\ 2 + y, & \text{if } x = 0. \end{cases}$

(e) $f(t) = \begin{pmatrix} \sin t \\ \cos t \\ \sin \dfrac{1}{t^2} \end{pmatrix}$

2. At which points do the following functions fail to be continuous?

(a) $f\begin{pmatrix} x \\ y \end{pmatrix} = \begin{pmatrix} \dfrac{1}{x^2} + \dfrac{1}{y^2} \\ x^2 + y^2 \end{pmatrix}$

(b) $f\begin{pmatrix} u \\ v \end{pmatrix} = \begin{pmatrix} 3u - 4v \\ u + 8v \end{pmatrix}$

(c) $f(x, y) = \begin{cases} \dfrac{\sin x}{x} + y, & \text{if } x \neq 0. \\ 1 + y & \text{if } x = 0. \end{cases}$

(d) $f\begin{pmatrix} x \\ y \end{pmatrix} = \begin{cases} \dfrac{x^2 - y^2}{x^2 + y^2}, & \text{if } x^2 + y^2 \neq 0 \\ 0, & \text{if } x^2 + y^2 = 0 \end{cases}$

(e) $f\begin{pmatrix} u \\ v \end{pmatrix} = \begin{pmatrix} v \tan u \\ u \sec v \\ v \end{pmatrix}$

(f) $fX = \dfrac{|X|}{1 - |X|^2}$

3. Can the curve shown in Figure 18 be defined parametrically by a continuous vector function?

FIGURE 18

4. When $X_0 = (1, 2)$, draw the set of all vectors X in $\mathfrak{R}^2$ such that

(a) $|X - X_0| \leq 3$

(b) $|X - X_0| = 3$

(c) $|X + X_0| < 3$

5. Identify as open, closed, or neither the subset of $\mathfrak{R}^2$ consisting of all vectors

$X = \begin{pmatrix} x \\ y \end{pmatrix}$ such that

(a) $\left| X - \begin{pmatrix} 1 \\ 2 \end{pmatrix} \right| \leq 0.5.$

(b) $\left| X - \begin{pmatrix} 1 \\ 2 \end{pmatrix} \right| < 0.5.$

(c) $\left| X - \begin{pmatrix} 1 \\ 2 \end{pmatrix} \right| < -0.5.$

(d) $0 < x < 3$ and $0 < y < 2$.

(e) $2 \leq x < 3$ and $0 < y < 2$.

(f) $\dfrac{x^2}{a^2} + \dfrac{y^2}{b^2} < 1.$

(g) X is none of $\left\{ \begin{pmatrix} 0 \\ 0 \end{pmatrix}, \begin{pmatrix} 0 \\ 1 \end{pmatrix}, \begin{pmatrix} 1 \\ 0 \end{pmatrix} \right\}.$

(h) $x^2 + y^2 > 0.$

(i) $x > 0.$

(j) $x > y.$

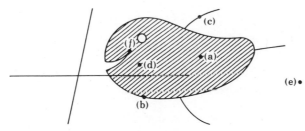

FIGURE 19

6. Which of the points (a)–(f) of the subset of $\Re^2$ shown in Figure 19 are interior points and which are boundary points?

7. Prove Theorem 2.8.

8. Prove that X is a boundary point of a set S if and only if every neighborhood of X contains a point of S and a point of the complement of S.

9. Show that the box norm, $\| X \| = \max \{| x_1 |, \ldots, | x_n |\}$, satisfies properties 2.3, 2.4, and 2.5 but does not satisfy the parallelogram law that holds for the euclidean norm. By the parallelogram law we mean

$$2 | X |^2 + 2 | Y |^2 = | X + Y |^2 + | X - Y |^2.$$

10. Let $X_0 = (1, 1, 1)$.
  (a) Draw the sphere consisting of all points X such that $| X - X_0 | = 2$.
  (b) Draw the "sphere" consisting of all points X such that

$$\| X - X_0 \| = 2,$$

  where $\| X \| = \max \{| x |, | y |, | z |\}.$

11. Prove that every linear transformation is a continuous vector function. That is, prove (as is claimed in the text) that statement 2.7 is a corollary of Theorem 2.6.

12. A vector function f is said to have a **removable discontinuity** at X_0 if (a) f is not continuous at X_0, (b) there is a vector Y_0 such that $\lim\limits_{X \to X_0} fX = Y_0$. Give an example of a function f and a point X_0 such that f is not continuous at X_0 and (1) f has a removable discontinuity at X_0. (2) f does not have a removable discontinuity at X_0.

13. Prove that every translation is a continuous vector function. A vector function $\mathcal{R}^n \xrightarrow{f} \mathcal{R}^n$ is a **translation** if there exists a vector Y in $\mathcal{R}^n$ such that $fX = X + Y$ for all X in $\mathcal{R}^n$.

14. Let f be the real-valued function defined by $fX = \| X \|$, for all X in $\mathcal{R}^n$. Prove that f is continuous, with respect to the euclidean norm.

15. If f and g are vector functions with the same domain and same range, prove

$$\lim_{X \to X_0} (fX + gX) = \lim_{X \to X_0} fX + \lim_{X \to X_0} gX,$$

provided that $\lim\limits_{X \to X_0} fX$ and $\lim\limits_{X \to X_0} gX$ exist.

16. Prove that there exist positive numbers k and K such that, for any X in $\mathcal{R}^n$,

$$k \, | X | \leq \| X \| \leq K \, | X |,$$

where $\| \ \ \|$ is the box norm.

17. Let $\mathcal{L}$ be a line and $\mathcal{P}$ a plane in $\mathcal{R}^3$. Is either $\mathcal{P}$ or $\mathcal{L}$ an open subset?

18. Let S be a subset of $\mathcal{R}^n$ that contains all its limit points. Prove that the complement of S in $\mathcal{R}^n$ is open.

19. Converse of Exercise 18: If S is an open subset of $\mathcal{R}^n$, show that the complement of S in $\mathcal{R}^n$ contains all its limit points.

3. PARTIAL DERIVATIVES

Let f be a real-valued function with domain space $\mathcal{R}^n$. For each $i = 1, \ldots, n$, we define a new real-valued function called the **partial derivative of f with respect to the ith variable** and denoted by $\partial f / \partial x_i$. For each $X = (x_1, \ldots, x_n)$ in the domain of f, the number $(\partial f / \partial x_i) X$ is by definition

$$\frac{\partial f}{\partial x_i} X = \lim_{t \to 0} \frac{f(x_1, \ldots, x_i + t, \ldots, x_n) - f(x_1, \ldots, x_i, \ldots, x_n)}{t}.$$

The domain space of $\partial f/\partial x_i$ is $\mathfrak{R}^n$, and the domain of $\partial f/\partial x_i$ is the subset of the domain of f consisting of all X for which the above limit exists. Thus the domain of $\partial f/\partial x_i$ could conceivably be the empty set. The number $(\partial f/\partial x_i) X$ is simply the derivative at x_i of the function of one variable obtained by holding $x_1, \ldots, x_{i-1}, x_{i+1}, \ldots, x_n$ fixed and considering f to be a function of the ith variable only.

EXAMPLE 1. Let $f(x, y, z) = x^2y + y^2z + z^2x$. Then,

$$\frac{\partial f}{\partial x}(x, y, z) = 2xy + z^2,$$

$$\frac{\partial f}{\partial y}(x, y, z) = x^2 + 2yz,$$

$$\frac{\partial f}{\partial z}(x, y, z) = y^2 + 2zx.$$

The partial derivatives at $X = (1, 2, 3)$ are

$$\frac{\partial f}{\partial x}(1, 2, 3) = 4 + 9 = 13,$$

$$\frac{\partial f}{\partial y}(1, 2, 3) = 1 + 12 = 13,$$

$$\frac{\partial f}{\partial z}(1, 2, 3) = 4 + 6 = 10.$$

EXAMPLE 2. Let $f(u, v) = \sin u \cos v$. Then

$$\frac{\partial f}{\partial u} = \frac{\partial \sin u \cos v}{\partial u} = \cos u \cos v,$$

$$\frac{\partial f}{\partial v} = \frac{\partial \sin u \cos v}{\partial v} = -\sin u \sin v,$$

$$\frac{\partial f}{\partial u}(0, 0) = \frac{\partial \sin u \cos v}{\partial u}(0, 0) = \cos 0 \cos 0 = 1,$$

$$\frac{\partial f}{\partial v}\left(\frac{\pi}{2}, \frac{\pi}{2}\right) = \frac{\partial \sin u \cos v}{\partial v}\left(\frac{\pi}{2}, \frac{\pi}{2}\right) = -\sin\frac{\pi}{2}\sin\frac{\pi}{2} = -1.$$

One can compound the operation of taking partial derivative. The partial derivative of $\partial f/\partial x_i$ with respect to the jth variable is $\partial/\partial x_j\,(\partial f/\partial x_i)$ and is denoted by $\partial^2 f/\partial x_j \partial x_i$. The compounding can be repeated indefinitely, provided the derivatives exist. An alternative notation for higher-order partial derivatives is illustrated below.

$$\frac{\partial f}{\partial x_i} = f_{x_i}$$

$$\frac{\partial}{\partial x_j}\left(\frac{\partial f}{\partial x_i}\right) = \frac{\partial^2 f}{\partial x_j\,\partial x_i} = f_{x_i x_j}$$

$$\frac{\partial}{\partial x_i}\left(\frac{\partial f}{\partial x_i}\right) = \frac{\partial^2 f}{\partial x_i^2} = f_{x_i x_i}$$

$$\frac{\partial}{\partial x_i}\left(\frac{\partial^2 f}{\partial x_j\,\partial x_i}\right) = \frac{\partial^3 f}{\partial x_i\,\partial x_j\,\partial x_i} = f_{x_i\,x_j x_i}.$$

EXAMPLE 3. Consider $f\begin{pmatrix} x \\ y \end{pmatrix} = xy - x^2.$

$$f_x = \frac{\partial f}{\partial x} = y - 2x$$

$$f_{xy} = \frac{\partial^2 f}{\partial y\,\partial x} = 1$$

$$f_{xx} = \frac{\partial^2 f}{\partial x^2} = -2$$

$$f_{yxx} = \frac{\partial^3 f}{\partial x^2\,\partial y} = 0.$$

Consider a surface in 3-dimensional euclidean space defined explicitly by the function $f(x, y)$. A typical example is shown in Figure 20. The intersection of the surface with the plane $y = b$ is a curve, defined implicitly by the equations

$$z = f(x, y), \qquad y = b.$$

Consider as a subset of 2-dimensional space the curve defined by the

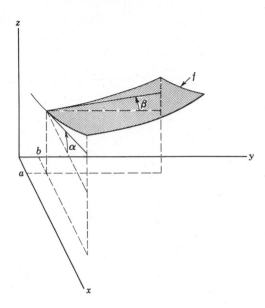

FIGURE 20

function $g(x) = f(x, b)$. Its slope at $x = a$ is

$$g'(a) = \frac{\partial f}{\partial x}(a, b).$$

Similarly, at $y = b$ the curve defined by $h(y) = f(a, y)$ has slope equal to

$$h'(b) = \frac{\partial f}{\partial y}(a, b).$$

The angles α and β shown in Figure 20 therefore satisfy

$$\tan \alpha = \frac{\partial f}{\partial x}(a, b), \qquad \tan \beta = \frac{\partial f}{\partial y}(a, b).$$

It is an important theorem that if certain conditions of differentiability and continuity are satisfied, then the higher-order partial derivatives of $\mathfrak{R}^n \xrightarrow{f} \mathfrak{R}$ are independent of the order of differentiation. A precise statement is

3.1 Theorem. Let $f(x, y)$ be a real-valued function such that f_x, f_y, and f_{xy} (or f_{yx}) are continuous at every point of an open subset S of $\mathfrak{R}^2$. Then, at every point of S, the derivative f_{yx} (or f_{xy}) exists and $f_{xy} = f_{yx}$.*

* A proof is given in T. M. Apostol, *Mathematical Analysis*, Addison-Wesley, 1957, p. 121.

The theorem can be applied successively to still higher-order partial derivatives, provided the analogous differentiability and continuity requirements are satisfied. Moreover, by considering only two variables at a time, we can apply it to functions $\mathfrak{R}^n \xrightarrow{f} \mathfrak{R}$ where $n > 2$. Thus, for the commonly encountered functions, which have partial derivatives of arbitrarily high order, we have typically

$$\frac{\partial^2 f}{\partial x\, \partial y} = \frac{\partial^2 f}{\partial y\, \partial x}$$

$$\frac{\partial^3 g}{\partial x\, \partial y\, \partial x} = \frac{\partial^3 g}{\partial x^2\, \partial y}$$

$$\frac{\partial^4 h}{\partial z\, \partial x\, \partial y\, \partial z} = \frac{\partial^4 h}{\partial x\, \partial y\, \partial z^2}$$

et cetera.

EXAMPLE 4. The partial derivatives f_{xy} and f_{yx} of the function

$$f(x, y) = \begin{cases} 2xy\, \dfrac{x^2 - y^2}{x^2 + y^2}, & \text{if } x^2 + y^2 \neq 0 \\[4mm] 0, & \text{if } x = y = 0 \end{cases}$$

are *not* equal at the origin. Except at $(0, 0)$, of course, the partial derivatives of f of arbitrarily high order are all continuous. Hence, by Theorem 3.1,

$$f_{xy}(x, y) = f_{yx}(x, y), \qquad \text{if } (x, y) \neq (0, 0).$$

Moreover, if $(x, y) \neq (0, 0)$,

$$f_x(x, y) = 2y\, \frac{x^2 - y^2}{x^2 + y^2} + 2xy\, \frac{4xy^2}{(x^2 + y^2)^2},$$

$$f_y(x, y) = 2x\, \frac{x^2 - y^2}{x^2 + y^2} - 2xy\, \frac{4x^2 y}{(x^2 + y^2)^2}.$$

At the origin the formal rules of differentiation are not applicable since the denominator $x^2 + y^2$ is zero there. Turning to the definition of the partial derivative, we obtain

$$f_x(0, 0) = \lim_{t \to 0} \frac{f(t, 0) - f(0, 0)}{t} = \lim_{t \to 0} \frac{0}{t} = 0$$

$$f_y(0, 0) = \lim_{t \to 0} \frac{f(0, t) - f(0, 0)}{t} = \lim_{t \to 0} \frac{0}{t} = 0$$

$$f_{yx}(0, 0) = \lim_{t \to 0} \frac{f_y(t, 0) - f_y(0, 0)}{t} = \lim_{t \to 0} \frac{2t}{t} = 2$$

$$f_{xy}(0, 0) = \lim_{t \to 0} \frac{f_x(0, t) - f_x(0, 0)}{t} = \lim_{t \to 0} \frac{-2t}{t} = -2.$$

EXERCISES

1. Find $\dfrac{\partial f}{\partial x}$ and $\dfrac{\partial f}{\partial y}$, where $f(x, y)$ is:

(a) $x^2 + x \sin (x + y)$.

(b) $\sin x \cos (x + y)$.

(c) e^{x+y+1}.

(d) $\arctan (y/x)$.

(e) x^y.

(f) $\log_x y$.

$$\left[\text{Ans.} \quad \frac{\partial f}{\partial x} = -\frac{\ln y}{x(\ln x)^2}. \right]$$

2. Find $\dfrac{\partial^2 f}{\partial y \, \partial x}$ and $\dfrac{\partial^2 f}{\partial x \, \partial y}$ where f is

(a) $xy + x^2 y^3$.   (b) $\sin (x^2 + y^2)$.   (c) $\dfrac{1}{x^2 + y^2}$.

3. Find the first-order partial derivatives of the following functions:

(a) $f(x, y, z) = x^2 e^{x+y+z} \cos y$.

(b) $f(x, y, z, w) = \dfrac{x^2 - y^2}{z^2 + w^2}$.

(c) $f(x, y, z) = x^{(y^z)}$.

4. Find $\dfrac{\partial^3 f(x, y)}{\partial x^2 \, \partial y}$ if $f(x, y) = \log (x + y)$.

5. Show that $\dfrac{\partial^2 f}{\partial x^2} + \dfrac{\partial^2 f}{\partial y^2} = 0$ is satisfied by

(a) $\log (x^2 + y^2)$.

(b) $x^3 - 3xy^2$.

6. If $f(x, y, z) = 1/(x^2 + y^2 + z^2)^{1/2}$, show that

$$f_{xx} + f_{yy} + f_{zz} = 0.$$

7. If $f(x_1, x_2, \ldots, x_n) = 1/(x_1^2 + x_2^2 + \ldots + x_n^2)^{(n-2)/2}$, show that

$$f_{x_1^2} + f_{x_2^2} + \ldots + f_{x_n^2} = 0.$$

8. Why does Example 4 in the text not contradict Theorem 3.1?

9. Prove directly that if $f(x, y)$ is a polynomial then

$$\frac{\partial^2 f}{\partial x\, \partial y} = \frac{\partial^2 f}{\partial y\, \partial x}.$$

10. If

$$f(x, y) = \begin{cases} x^2 \operatorname{arcsinh} \dfrac{y}{x} - y^2 \operatorname{arcsinh} \dfrac{x}{y}, & \text{if } xy \neq 0, \\[2mm] 0, & \text{if } xy = 0, \end{cases}$$

prove that $\dfrac{\partial^2 f}{\partial y\, \partial x}(0, 0) = -1$ and $\dfrac{\partial^2 f}{\partial x\, \partial y}(0, 0) = 1$.

11. Let f be defined by

$$f(x, y) = \begin{cases} x^3 \sin \dfrac{y}{x} - y^2 \sin \dfrac{x}{y}, & \text{if } xy \neq 0, \\[2mm] 0, & \text{if } xy = 0. \end{cases}$$

Prove that $\dfrac{\partial^2 f}{\partial y\, \partial x}(0, 0) = -1$ and $\dfrac{\partial^2 f}{\partial x\, \partial y}(0, 0) = 0$.

4. THE DIFFERENTIAL

The simplest vector functions with domain space $\mathfrak{X}$ and range space $\mathcal{Y}$ are the constant functions: for a fixed Y_0 in $\mathcal{Y}$,

$$fX = Y_0, \qquad \text{for every } X \text{ in } \mathfrak{X}.$$

Next in complexity are the linear transformations $\mathfrak{X} \xrightarrow{L} \mathcal{Y}$. The sum of a constant function and a linear transformation is called an **affine transformation**. It is the generalization to arbitrary dimensions of the 1-variable function $ax + b$. Thus a function $\mathfrak{X} \xrightarrow{A} \mathcal{Y}$ is an affine transformation if there exists a linear transformation $\mathfrak{X} \xrightarrow{L} \mathcal{Y}$ and a vector Y_0 in $\mathcal{Y}$ such that

$$AX = LX + Y_0, \qquad \text{for every } X \text{ in } \mathfrak{X}.$$

We shall see that affine transformations form the basis of the differential calculus of vector functions.

EXAMPLE 1. In terms of coordinate variables an affine transformation is a function that is defined by linear equations. For example, consider the point

$$Y_0 = \begin{pmatrix} 1 \\ 2 \\ 0 \end{pmatrix}$$

and the linear transformation $\mathcal{R}^4 \xrightarrow{L} \mathcal{R}^3$ defined by the matrix

$$\begin{pmatrix} 2 & 3 & 0 & 1 \\ 1 & 0 & 5 & 2 \\ 1 & 2 & 0 & 3 \end{pmatrix}.$$

The affine transformation

$$\begin{pmatrix} u \\ v \\ w \end{pmatrix} = LX + Y_0, \quad \text{for every } X = \begin{pmatrix} x \\ y \\ z \\ t \end{pmatrix}$$

is described by the equations

$$u = 2x + 3y + t + 1$$
$$v = x + 5z + 2t + 2$$
$$w = x + 2y + 3t.$$

Since any system of linear equations can be systematically solved, any affine transformation can be completely and effectively analyzed.

We shall now study the possibility of approximating an arbitrary vector function f near a point X_0 of its domain by an affine transformation A. The general idea is the possibility of replacing near X_0 what may be a very complicated function by a simple one. Before trying to decide whether or not an approximation exists, we first have to say what we shall mean by an approximation. We begin by requiring that $fX_0 = AX_0$. Since $AX = LX + Y_0$, where L is a linear transformation, we obtain $fX_0 = LX_0 + Y_0$ and so

$$AX = L(X - X_0) + fX_0. \tag{1}$$

The next requirement is that

$$\lim_{X \to X_0} (fX - AX) = 0. \tag{2}$$

At first glance, Equation (2) may appear to say more than it really does. From (1) we obtain

$$fX - AX = fX - fX_0 - L(X - X_0).$$

Now every linear transformation is continuous (see Theorem 2.7), so $\lim_{X \to X_0} L(X - X_0) = L0 = 0$. Hence,

$$\lim_{X \to X_0} (fX - AX) = \lim_{X \to X_0} (fX - fX_0).$$

It follows that Equation (2) is precisely the statement that the vector function f is continuous at X_0. This is significant, but it says nothing whatever about how good an approximation to f the affine transformation A is. In fact, it says nothing about A at all. To say the same thing another way: If f is continuous at X_0 and L is any linear transformation whatever of the domain space of f into the range space, we may define $AX = L(X - X_0) + fX_0$, and it will be true that $\lim_{X \to X_0} (fX - AX) = 0$. Thus, in order for our notion of approximation to distinguish one affine transformation from another or to measure in any way how well A approximates f, some additional requirement is necessary. A natural condition, and the one we shall require, is that $fX - AX$ approach 0 faster than X approaches X_0. That is, we demand that

$$\lim_{X \to X_0} \frac{fX - AX}{|X - X_0|} = 0$$

or, equivalently,

$$\lim_{X \to X_0} \frac{fX - fX_0 - L(X - X_0)}{|X - X_0|} = 0.$$

A function $\Re^n \xrightarrow{f} \Re^m$ will be called **differentiable** at X_0 if

(1) X_0 is an interior point of the domain of f.
(2) There is an affine transformation that approximates f near X_0. That is, there exists a linear transformation $\Re^n \xrightarrow{L} \Re^m$ such that

$$\lim_{X \to X_0} \frac{fX - fX_0 - L(X - X_0)}{|X - X_0|} = 0.$$

The linear transformation L is called the **differential** of f at X_0. The function f is said simply to be **differentiable** if it is differentiable at every point of its domain.

According to the definition, the domain of a differentiable function is an open set. It is, however, convenient to extend the definition sufficiently to speak of a differentiable function f defined on an arbitrary subset S of the domain space. By such an f we shall mean the restriction to S of a differentiable function whose domain is open.

EXAMPLE 2. The function f defined by $f(x, y) = \sqrt{1 - x^2 - y^2}$ has for its domain the disc $x^2 + y^2 \leq 1$. Its graph is shown in Figure 21. The interior points of the domain are those (x, y) such that $x^2 + y^2 < 1$. We shall see that this function is differentiable at every interior point of its domain.

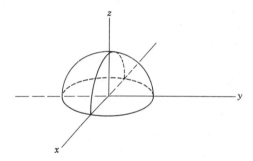

FIGURE 21

The next theorem shows that if a function is differentiable at a point, then there is just one affine transformation that approximates it there. This is certainly a desirable result. The fact that it can be proved from the definitions we have made is in itself an indication that they are the right ones.

4.1 Theorem. If f is differentiable at X_0, then the differential there is unique.

Proof. Suppose there are two different differentials L_1 and L_2 of f at X_0. We define the remainders

$$R_i = fX - fX_0 - L_i(X - X_0), \qquad i = 1, 2.$$

Then

$$R_2 - R_1 = (L_1 - L_2)(X - X_0).$$

Since L_1 and L_2 are assumed to be distinct, there exists a vector Y such that $(L_1 - L_2)Y \neq 0$. Since X_0 is an interior point of the domain of f, it follows that, for sufficiently small values of the real number t, the vector $X = X_0 + tY$ is in the domain of f. Hence,

$$R_2 - R_1 = (L_1 - L_2)(X - X_0) = t(L_1 - L_2)Y.$$

Since by the homogeneity property of the norm $|X - X_0| = |t||Y|$, we have, for positive t,

$$\frac{R_2 - R_1}{|X - X_0|} = \frac{R_2 - R_1}{t|Y|} = \frac{(L_1 - L_2)Y}{|Y|}.$$

Notice that $|Y| \neq 0$, because $Y \neq 0$. These equations contain the contradiction we are after. The right-hand side is a nonzero vector that is independent of t. On the other hand, because f is differentiable,

$$\lim_{t \to 0} \frac{R_2 - R_1}{|X - X_0|} = \lim_{X \to X_0} \frac{R_2 - R_1}{|X - X_0|} = 0.$$

The initial assumption $L_1 \neq L_2$ is therefore false, and this completes the proof.

Because the differential is unique, we speak of *the* differential at X_0, and we denote it by $d_{X_0} f$. Notice that the proof of the uniqueness of the differential of a function uses the assumption that X_0 is an interior point of the domain of the function.

In dimension 1 an affine transformation is a function of the form $ax + b$. Hence a real-valued function $f(x)$ of a real variable x that is differentiable at x_0 can be approximated near x_0 by a function $A(x) = ax + b$. Since $f(x_0) = A(x_0) = ax_0 + b$, we obtain

$$A(x) = ax + b = a(x - x_0) + f(x_0).$$

The linear part of A (denoted earlier by L) is in this case just multiplication by the real number a. The euclidean norm of a real number is its absolute value, so condition (2) of the definition of differentiability becomes

$$\lim_{x \to x_0} \frac{f(x) - f(x_0) - a(x - x_0)}{|x - x_0|} = 0.$$

This is equivalent to

$$\lim_{x \to x_0} \frac{f(x) - f(x_0)}{x - x_0} = a.$$

The number a is commonly denoted by $f'(x_0)$ and is called the **derivative of** f at x_0. The affine transformation A is therefore given by

$$A(x) = f(x_0) + f'(x_0)(x - x_0).$$

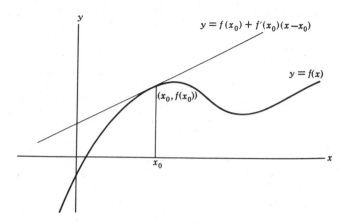

FIGURE 22

Its graph is the **tangent line** to the graph of f at x_0, and a typical example is drawn in Figure 22. Thus we have seen that the general definition of differentiability for vector functions reduces in dimension 1 to the definition usually encountered in a one-variable calculus course. The same is true of the differential. According to our definition, $d_{x_0} f$ is the linear function defined by

$$d_{x_0} f(x) = ax = f'(x_0)x, \qquad \text{for any } x.$$

If we omit the subscript x_0 on the differential (as is usually done) and fail to distinguish notationally between a function and its value (as is also usually done), we obtain the familiar formula

$$dy = df(\Delta x) = f'(x_0) \, \Delta x,$$

where $y = f(x)$ and Δx is any real number.

The differential of a function $\Re^n \xrightarrow{f} \Re^m$ at a point is a linear transformation and is therefore defined by a matrix. If $f_1, \ldots, f_m$ are the coordinate functions of f, the matrix of partial derivatives

$$\begin{pmatrix} \dfrac{\partial f_1}{\partial x_1} X & \cdots & \dfrac{\partial f_1}{\partial x_n} X \\[2mm] \dfrac{\partial f_2}{\partial x_1} X & \cdots & \dfrac{\partial f_2}{\partial x_n} X \\[2mm] \cdots & & \cdots \\[2mm] \dfrac{\partial f_m}{\partial x_1} X & \cdots & \dfrac{\partial f_m}{\partial x_n} X \end{pmatrix}$$

is called the **Jacobian matrix of f at X**. The Jacobian is the matrix of the differential, and we state the fact as a theorem.

4.2 Theorem. If the function $\Re^n \xrightarrow{f} \Re^m$ is differentiable at X_0, then the Jacobian matrix of f at X_0 is the matrix of the differential $d_{X_0} f$.

Proof. The domain space $\Re^n$ has the natural basis

$$
E_1 = \begin{pmatrix} 1 \\ 0 \\ \vdots \\ 0 \end{pmatrix}, \quad
E_2 = \begin{pmatrix} 0 \\ 1 \\ \vdots \\ 0 \end{pmatrix}, \quad \cdots, \quad
E_n = \begin{pmatrix} 0 \\ 0 \\ \vdots \\ 1 \end{pmatrix}.
$$

Since X_0 is an interior point of the domain of f, the vectors

$$
X_j = X_0 + tE_j, \qquad j = 1, \cdots, n,
$$

are in the domain of f for all sufficiently small t. By the defining property of the differential, i.e., condition (2) of the definition of differentiability, it follows that

$$
\lim_{t \to 0} \frac{fX_j - fX_0 - (d_{X_0} f)tE_j}{t} = 0, \qquad j = 1, \ldots, n.
$$

This is equivalent, by the linearity of $d_{X_0} f$, to

$$
\lim_{t \to 0} \frac{fX_j - fX_0}{t} = (d_{X_0} f) E_j, \qquad j = 1, \ldots, n. \tag{3}
$$

Let (a_{ij}), $i = 1, \ldots, m, j = 1, \ldots, n$, be the matrix of the linear transformation $d_{X_0} f$. Then,

$$
(d_{X_0} f) E_j = \begin{pmatrix} a_{11} & \cdots & a_{1n} \\ a_{21} & \cdots & a_{2n} \\ \cdots & & \cdots \\ a_{m1} & & a_{mn} \end{pmatrix} \begin{pmatrix} 0 \\ \vdots \\ 1 \\ \vdots \\ 0 \end{pmatrix} = \begin{pmatrix} a_{1j} \\ a_{2j} \\ \vdots \\ a_{mj} \end{pmatrix}
$$

so the ith coordinate of $(d_{X_0} f) E_j$ is simply a_{ij}. Let $f_1, \ldots, f_m$ be the coordinate functions of f. It follows from Equation (3) that, for each f_i, $i = 1, \ldots, m$,

$$
\lim_{t \to 0} \frac{f_i X_j - f_i X_0}{t} = a_{ij}, \qquad j = 1, \ldots, n.
$$

The vector X_j differs from X_0 in only the jth coordinate, and in that coordinate the difference is just t. Therefore, the left-hand side of the last equation is precisely the partial derivative $(\partial f_i/\partial x_j)X_0$, and this completes the proof.

EXAMPLE 3. Consider the function

$$f\begin{pmatrix} x \\ y \\ z \end{pmatrix} = \begin{pmatrix} x^2 + e^y \\ x + y \sin z \end{pmatrix}.$$

The coordinate functions are

$$f_1\begin{pmatrix} x \\ y \\ z \end{pmatrix} = x^2 + e^y, \qquad f_2\begin{pmatrix} x \\ y \\ z \end{pmatrix} = x + y \sin z,$$

and the Jacobian matrix is

$$\begin{pmatrix} 2x & e^y & 0 \\ 1 & \sin z & y \cos z \end{pmatrix}.$$

The differential of f at $\begin{pmatrix} 1 \\ 1 \\ \pi \end{pmatrix}$ is the linear transformation whose matrix is

$$\begin{pmatrix} 2 & e & 0 \\ 1 & 0 & -1 \end{pmatrix}.$$

EXAMPLE 4. The function f defined by

$$f(x, y) = (x^2 + 2xy + y^2, xy^2 + x^2y)$$

has a differential $d_X f$ at $X = (x, y)$ represented by the Jacobian matrix

$$\begin{pmatrix} 2x + 2y & 2x + 2y \\ y^2 + 2xy & 2xy + x^2 \end{pmatrix}.$$

How can one tell whether or not a vector function is differentiable? Theorem 4.2 says only that if f is differentiable, then the differential is represented by the Jacobian matrix. It does not go the other way. Thus Examples 3 and 4 are inconclusive to the extent that we have simply assumed that the functions appearing in them have differentials. Just as the derivative of a real-valued function of one variable may fail to exist, so in general a vector function need not possess a differential at every point. Our next objective is a convenient criterion for differentiability.

4.3 Theorem. If the domain of $\mathfrak{R}^n \xrightarrow{f} \mathfrak{R}^m$ is an open set on which the partial derivatives $\partial f_i/\partial x_j$ of the coordinate functions are continuous, then f is differentiable and, for any X_0 in the domain of f, the differential $d_{X_0}f$ is represented by the Jacobian matrix of f at X_0.

Proof. Let L be the linear transformation defined by the matrix of $d_{X_0}f$. The theorem will have been proved if it can be shown that L satisfies

$$\lim_{X \to X_0} \frac{fX - fX_0 - L(X - X_0)}{|X - X_0|} = 0. \tag{4}$$

Since by Theorem 2.1 a vector function approaches a limit if and only if the coordinate functions approach the coordinates of the limit, it is enough to prove the theorem for the coordinate functions of f, or, what is notationally simpler, to prove it under the assumption that f is real-valued. If

$$X = (x_1, \ldots, x_n) \quad \text{and}$$
$$X_0 = (a_1, \ldots, a_n),$$

set

$$Y_k = (x_1, \ldots, x_k, a_{k+1}, \ldots, a_n),$$
$$k = 0, 1, \ldots, n,$$

so that $Y_0 = X_0$ and $Y_n = X$. These vectors are illustrated for three dimensions in Figure 23. Then

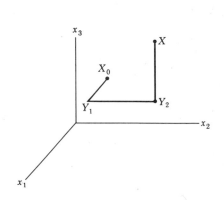

FIGURE 23

$$fX - fX_0 = \sum_{k=1}^{n} (fY_k - fY_{k-1}).$$

Because Y_k and Y_{k-1} differ only in their kth coordinates, we can apply the mean-value theorem for real functions of a real variable to get

$$fY_k - fY_{k-1} = (x_k - a_k) \frac{\partial f}{\partial x_k} Z_k,$$

where Z_k is a point on the segment joining Y_k and Y_{k-1}. Then

$$fX - fX_0 = \sum_{k=1}^{n} (x_k - a_k) \frac{\partial f}{\partial x_k} Z_k.$$

We also have

$$L(X - X_0) = \left(\frac{\partial f}{\partial x_1} X_0, \ldots, \frac{\partial f}{\partial x_n} X_0 \right) \begin{pmatrix} x_1 - a_1 \\ \cdot \\ \cdot \\ \cdot \\ x_n - a_n \end{pmatrix}$$

$$= \sum_{k=1}^{n} (x_k - a_k) \frac{\partial f}{\partial x_k} X_0.$$

Hence

$$| fX - fX_0 - L(X - X_0) | = \left| \sum_{k=1}^{n} \left(\frac{\partial f}{\partial x_k} Z_k - \frac{\partial f}{\partial x_k} X_0 \right)(x_k - a_k) \right|$$

$$\leq \sum_{k=1}^{n} \left| \frac{\partial f}{\partial x_k} Z_k - \frac{\partial f}{\partial x_k} X_0 \right| | X - X_0 |,$$

where we have used the triangle inequality and the fact that

$$| x_k - a_k | \leq | X - X_0 | \qquad \text{for } k = 1, 2, \ldots, n.$$

Since the partial derivatives are continuous at X_0, and the Z_k tend to X_0 as X does, the limit equation (4) follows immediately.

The entries in the Jacobian matrices that appear in Examples 3 and 4 are certainly continuous functions. As a result of the theorem just proved we conclude that the two functions in those examples are differentiable.

EXAMPLE 5. The function

$$f(x, y) = \sqrt{1 - x^2 - y^2}$$

defined for all (x, y) such that $x^2 + y^2 < 1$ is the same as in Example 2 except that we have removed the boundary of the disc so that the domain is an open set. The Jacobian matrix is

$$(f_x \quad f_y) = \left(\frac{-x}{\sqrt{1 - x^2 - y^2}} \quad \frac{-y}{\sqrt{1 - x^2 - y^2}} \right).$$

The entries are continuous on the open disc, and we conclude, by Theorem 4.3, that f is differentiable there.

EXAMPLE 6. Consider the function

$$f(t) = \begin{pmatrix} \cos t \\ \sin t \end{pmatrix}, \qquad -\infty < t < \infty.$$

The differential $d_{t_0} f$ is defined by the 2-by-1 matrix

$$\begin{pmatrix} -\sin t_0 \\ \cos t_0 \end{pmatrix}.$$

It is instructive to consider the matrix as a vector in the range space of f and to draw it with its tail at the image point $f(t_0)$. For $t_0 = 0, \pi/4, \pi/3, \pi/2$, and π, the respective matrices of the differential $d_{t_0} f$ are

$$\begin{pmatrix} 0 \\ 1 \end{pmatrix}, \quad \begin{pmatrix} -\dfrac{\sqrt{2}}{2} \\ \dfrac{\sqrt{2}}{2} \end{pmatrix}, \quad \begin{pmatrix} -\dfrac{\sqrt{3}}{2} \\ \dfrac{1}{2} \end{pmatrix}, \quad \begin{pmatrix} -1 \\ 0 \end{pmatrix}, \quad \text{and} \quad \begin{pmatrix} 0 \\ -1 \end{pmatrix}.$$

These vectors, drawn with their tails at their corresponding image points under f, are shown in Figure 24. Evidently, for curves at least, the differential is related to the notion of a tangent vector. The linear transformation that best approximates $f(t)$ in the neighborhood of t_0 is the vector function

$$(d_{t_0} f)(t - t_0) + f(t_0)$$

which in terms of matrices becomes

$$t \begin{pmatrix} -\sin t_0 \\ \cos t_0 \end{pmatrix} + \begin{pmatrix} \cos t_0 + t_0 \sin t_0 \\ \sin t_0 - t_0 \cos t_0 \end{pmatrix}.$$

This is the equation of a straight line. It is the line tangent to f at t_0. We shall study tangents to curves in greater detail in the next section.

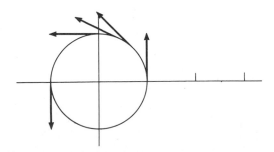

FIGURE 24

The criterion for differentiability of a vector function established in Theorem 4.3 requires the continuity of the partial derivatives of the coordinate functions. There is a similar condition of continuous differentiability for vector functions that is stronger than simple differentiability. The definition is: A vector function f is **continuously differentiable** at X_0 if the function which assigns to each X the differential $d_X f$ is continuous at X_0. This says (what continuity always says) that if X is close to X_0, then $d_X f$ is close to $d_{X_0} f$. The definition therefore presupposes a notion of proximity between differentials. But this notion is already available. It was pointed out in Chapter 1 that the *set of linear transformations from one vector space to another is itself a vector space.* Addition and numerical multiplication of linear transformations are defined by

$$(L_1 + L_2)X = L_1 X + L_2 X, \qquad (aL)X = a(LX)$$

and the axioms for a vector space are satisfied. Moreover, *the coordinates of a linear transformation* $\mathcal{R}^n \xrightarrow{L} \mathcal{R}^m$ *are simply the entries of the matrix that defines* L. It follows that the coordinate functions of the vector function $X \to d_X f$ are just the partial derivatives that appear in the Jacobian matrix. We have seen (see Theorem 2.2) that a vector function is continuous if and only if its coordinate functions are continuous. Furthermore, (see Theorem 4.3) the continuity of the entries $\partial f_i / \partial x_j$ of the Jacobian matrix ensures the existence of the differential. Thus we have proved

4.4 Theorem. Let $\mathcal{R}^n \xrightarrow{f} \mathcal{R}^m$ be a function whose domain D is open. Then, f is continuously differentiable on D if and only if the entries of the Jacobian matrix of f are continuous on D.

The last theorem can be summarized in the statement that *continuity of a vector function is equivalent to continuous differentiability of the entries of the Jacobian matrix.* If continuity is omitted the theorem is false. It is not true that the existence of the partial derivatives which constitute the Jacobian matrix implies the differentiability of the vector function. The converse does hold and is stated as Theorem 4.2.

EXERCISES

1. A linear transformation $\mathcal{R}^n \xrightarrow{L} \mathcal{R}^m$ is defined by a matrix (a_{ij}), and

$$Y_0 = \begin{pmatrix} b_1 \\ \cdot \\ \cdot \\ \cdot \\ b_m \end{pmatrix}$$

is a vector in $\mathcal{R}^m$. Construct a specific example by choosing m and n, a matrix (a_{ij}), and a vector

$$\begin{pmatrix} b_1 \\ \cdot \\ \cdot \\ \cdot \\ b_m \end{pmatrix}$$

so that the affine transformation

$$AX = LX + Y_0, \quad \text{all } X \text{ in } \mathcal{R}^n,$$

(a) explicitly defines a line in $\mathcal{R}^2$.
(b) explicitly defines a line in $\mathcal{R}^3$.
(c) explicitly defines a plane in $\mathcal{R}^3$.
(d) parametrically defines a line in $\mathcal{R}^3$.
(e) parametrically defines a plane in $\mathcal{R}^3$.
What condition must the matrix (a_{ij}) satisfy in order to give an example for (e)?

2. If f is the vector function defined by

$$f\begin{pmatrix} x \\ y \end{pmatrix} = \begin{pmatrix} x^2 - y^2 \\ 2xy \end{pmatrix},$$

find the matrix of the differential of f at the following points:

(a) $\begin{pmatrix} x \\ y \end{pmatrix}$,   (b) $\begin{pmatrix} a \\ b \end{pmatrix}$,   (c) $\begin{pmatrix} 1 \\ 0 \end{pmatrix}$,   (d) $\begin{pmatrix} \dfrac{1}{\sqrt{2}} \\ \dfrac{1}{\sqrt{2}} \end{pmatrix}$.

$$\left[Ans. \ (c) \ \begin{pmatrix} 2 & 0 \\ 0 & 2 \end{pmatrix} \right]$$

3. Find the matrix of the differential of each of the following functions at the indicated points.

(a) $f\begin{pmatrix} x \\ y \end{pmatrix} = x^2 + y^2$ at $\begin{pmatrix} x \\ y \end{pmatrix} = \begin{pmatrix} 1 \\ 1 \end{pmatrix}$.

(b) $g(x, y, z) = xyz$ at $(x, y, z) = (1, 0, 0)$.

(c) $f(t) = \begin{pmatrix} \sin t \\ \cos t \end{pmatrix}$ at $t = \dfrac{\pi}{4}$. $\left[Ans. \ \begin{pmatrix} \dfrac{1}{\sqrt{2}} \\ \dfrac{-1}{\sqrt{2}} \end{pmatrix} \right]$

(d) $f(t) = \begin{pmatrix} e^t \\ t \\ t^2 \end{pmatrix}$ at $t = 1$.

(e) $g(x, y) = \begin{pmatrix} x + y \\ x^2 + y^2 \end{pmatrix}$ at $(x, y) = (1, 2)$.

(f) $A\begin{pmatrix} u \\ v \end{pmatrix} = \begin{pmatrix} u + v \\ u - v \\ 1 \end{pmatrix}$ at $\begin{pmatrix} u \\ v \end{pmatrix} = \begin{pmatrix} 1 \\ 0 \end{pmatrix}$.

(g) $T\begin{pmatrix} u \\ v \end{pmatrix} = \begin{pmatrix} u \cos v \\ u \sin v \\ v \end{pmatrix}$ at $\begin{pmatrix} u \\ v \end{pmatrix} = \begin{pmatrix} 1 \\ \pi \end{pmatrix}$. $\left[Ans. \begin{pmatrix} -1 & 0 \\ 0 & -1 \\ 0 & 1 \end{pmatrix} \right].$

(h) $f(x, y, z) = (x + y + z, xy + yz + zx, xyz)$ at (x, y, z).

4. Let T be a transformation from three-dimensional to two-dimensional euclidean space defined by

$$T\begin{pmatrix} x \\ y \\ z \end{pmatrix} = \begin{pmatrix} x \\ y \end{pmatrix}.$$

(a) What is the geometric interpretation of this transformation?

(b) Show that T is differentiable at all points and find the matrix of the differential of T at $\begin{pmatrix} 1 \\ 1 \\ 1 \end{pmatrix}$. $\left[Ans. \begin{pmatrix} 1 & 0 & 0 \\ 0 & 1 & 0 \end{pmatrix} \right].$

5. (a) Draw the curve in $\mathfrak{R}^2$ defined parametrically by the function

$$g(t) = (t - 1, t^2 - 3t + 2), \qquad -\infty < t < \infty.$$

(b) Find the affine transformation that approximates g

(1) near $t = 0$.   (2) near $t = 2$. $[Ans.\ A(t) = (t - 1, t - 2).]$

(c) Draw the curve defined parametrically by the affine transformation.

6. Let f be the function given in Exercise 2, and let

$$X_0 = \begin{pmatrix} 1 \\ 0 \end{pmatrix}, \qquad Y_1 = \begin{pmatrix} 0.1 \\ 0 \end{pmatrix}, \qquad Y_2 = \begin{pmatrix} 0 \\ 0.1 \end{pmatrix}, \qquad \text{and} \quad Y_3 = \begin{pmatrix} 0.1 \\ 0.1 \end{pmatrix}.$$

(a) Compute $f(X_0 + Y_i)$ for $i = 1, 2, 3$.

(b) Find the affine transformation A that approximates f near X_0.

(c) Use A to find approximations to the vectors

$$f(X_0 + Y_i), \qquad i = 1, 2, 3.$$

7. (a) Sketch the surface in $\Re^3$ defined explicitly by the function

$$f(x, y) = 4 - x^2 - y^2.$$

(b) Find the affine transformation that approximates f

(1) near $(0, 0)$.   (2) near $(2, 0)$. $[Ans.\ A(x, y) = 8 - 4x.]$

(c) Draw the graph of the affine transformation.

8. What is the matrix of the differential of the affine transformation

$$\begin{pmatrix} a_1 & a_2 & a_3 \\ b_1 & b_2 & b_3 \\ c_1 & c_2 & c_3 \end{pmatrix} \begin{pmatrix} x \\ y \\ z \end{pmatrix} + \begin{pmatrix} a_0 \\ b_0 \\ c_0 \end{pmatrix}?$$

9. Prove that every linear transformation is its own differential.

10. Prove that if the vector function f is differentiable at X_0, then

$$(d_{X_0} f) X = \lim_{t \to 0} \frac{f(X_0 + tX) - fX_0}{t}.$$

11. Prove that if a vector function is differentiable at a point, then it is continuous there.

12. At which points do the following functions fail to be differentiable? Why?

(a) $f\begin{pmatrix} x \\ y \end{pmatrix} = \begin{pmatrix} \dfrac{1}{x^2} + \dfrac{1}{y^2} \\ x^2 + y^2 \end{pmatrix}.$ (b) $g\begin{pmatrix} x \\ y \end{pmatrix} = \begin{pmatrix} \sqrt{x^2 - y^2} \\ x + y \end{pmatrix}.$

(c) $f(u, v) = |u + v|.$

(d) $h(x, y) = \begin{cases} (x \sin(1/x),\ x^2 + y^2), & \text{if } x \neq 0. \\ (0,\ x^2 + y^2), & \text{if } x = 0. \end{cases}$

13. Prove that every translation is differentiable. What is the differential?

14. Consider the function $\mathfrak{R}^n \xrightarrow{f} \mathfrak{R}$ defined by $fX = |X|^2 = X \cdot X$. Prove that

$$(d_X f) Y = 2X \cdot Y, \text{ for any } X \text{ and } Y \text{ in } \mathfrak{R}^n.$$

15. Is the function $\mathfrak{R}^n \xrightarrow{g} \mathfrak{R}$ defined by $gX = |X|$ differentiable at every point of its domain?

16. Consider the function that assigns the box norm,

$$\| X \| = \max \{ |x_1|, \ldots, |x_n| \},$$

to each $X = (x_1, \ldots, x_n)$ in $\mathfrak{R}^n$. For what points does the function fail to be differentiable? Answer for (a) $n = 1$, (b) $n = 2$, (c) arbitrary n.

17. Show that the operation of taking the differential is a linear transformation on a vector space of functions. That is, show that if f and g are differentiable at X_0 and a is a real number, then $f + g$ and af are differentiable at X_0 and
(a) $d_{X_0}(f + g) = d_{X_0}f + d_{X_0}g$.
(b) $d_{X_0}(af) = a(d_{X_0}f)$.
The domain of $f + g$ is the intersection of the domains of f and g. [*Hint.* This is not a difficult problem. Use the uniqueness theorem (Theorem 4.1).]

18. Verify that the function

$$f(x, y) = \begin{cases} \dfrac{xy}{x^2 - y^2}, & x \neq \pm y, \\[2ex] 0, & x = \pm y, \end{cases}$$

has a Jacobian matrix at $(0, 0)$, but that it is not differentiable there.

19. Give an example of a vector function that is differentiable at a point but not continuously differentiable there.

20. Show that the function defined by

$$x^2 \sin \frac{1}{x}, \quad x \neq 0$$

$$0, \quad x = 0$$

is differentiable for all x, but is not continuously differentiable at $x = 0$.

5. TANGENT LINES AND PLANES

A curve may have a tangent line at all of its points, at some of them, or at none of them. Similarly, at a given point on a surface there may or may not be a tangent plane. It was remarked in the preceding section (see p. 201) that an explicitly defined curve in $\mathcal{R}^2$ has a tangent line at a point if the function that defines the curve has a derivative there. In general, the existence of a tangent n-dimensional plane to an n-dimensional surface is the geometric counterpart to the analytic condition of differentiability of the vector function that defines the surface. The principle is this: *If a surface* (of any dimension) *has a tangent plane* (of the same dimension) *at some point and is defined by a vector function f, then f is differentiable there and the tangent plane is defined by the affine transformation that approximates f near that point.* Notice that because of the essential role played by differentiability it is important that the function representing the curve or surface be kept clearly in mind. For example, the boundary of the disk $x^2 + y^2 < 1$ can be represented in several ways near each of its points, and it is usually a good idea to pick a representation by a differentiable function. In what follows we shall state the above principle in detail for each of the three ways in which we have considered surfaces to be defined: parametrically, explicitly, and implicitly.

An n-**dimensional plane** or **flat** $\mathcal{P}$ is the image under a translation of an n-dimensional subspace $\mathcal{P}_0$ of a vector space $\mathcal{X}$. For some fixed vector X_0 in $\mathcal{X}$, we write

$$\mathcal{P} = \mathcal{P}_0 + X_0.$$

The expression $\mathcal{P}_0 + X_0$ is an abbreviation for the set of vectors $X + X_0$ where X ranges over all vectors X in $\mathcal{P}_0$. A 0-dimensional plane is just a point, a 1-dimensional plane is a line, and a 2-dimensional plane is called simply a plane. Since the range of any linear transformation is a subspace of a vector space, it follows that the range of every affine transformation is an n-dimensional plane, or flat, for some integer n.

I. Parametrically defined surfaces. Let an n-dimensional surface S be defined parametrically by a vector function $\mathcal{R}^n \xrightarrow{f} \mathcal{R}^m$. According to the definition in Section 1, this means that S is the range of f. If f is differentiable at X_0, then the affine transformation A that approximates f near X_0 is defined by

$$AX = fX_0 + (d_{X_0}f)(X - X_0), \qquad \text{for all } X \text{ in } \mathcal{R}^n.$$

We shall say that the surface S **has a tangent at** fX_0 if f is differentiable at X_0 and if A parametrically defines an n-dimensional plane. If it exists, this plane is **the tangent to** S at fX_0.

EXAMPLE 1. Consider the surface S in 3-dimensional space $\mathfrak{R}^3$ defined parametrically by

$$f\begin{pmatrix} u \\ v \end{pmatrix} = \begin{pmatrix} x \\ y \\ z \end{pmatrix} = \begin{pmatrix} u \cos v \\ u \sin v \\ v \end{pmatrix}, \qquad \begin{cases} 0 \le u \le 4, \\ 0 \le v \le 2\pi. \end{cases}$$

This function is discussed in Example 7, Section 1, and its range, which is the surface S, is pictured in Figure 6. At

$$X_0 = \begin{pmatrix} u_0 \\ v_0 \end{pmatrix} = \begin{pmatrix} 2 \\ \pi/2 \end{pmatrix}$$

the matrix of the differential $d_{X_0} f$ is

$$\begin{pmatrix} \cos v_0 & -u_0 \sin v_0 \\ \sin v_0 & u_0 \cos v_0 \\ 0 & 1 \end{pmatrix} = \begin{pmatrix} 0 & -2 \\ 1 & 0 \\ 0 & 1 \end{pmatrix}.$$

The affine transformation $AX = fX_0 + (d_{X_0}f)(X - X_0)$ that approximates f near X_0 is therefore given by

$$A\begin{pmatrix} u \\ v \end{pmatrix} = \begin{pmatrix} x \\ y \\ z \end{pmatrix} = \begin{pmatrix} 0 \\ 2 \\ \pi/2 \end{pmatrix} + \begin{pmatrix} 0 & -2 \\ 1 & 0 \\ 0 & 1 \end{pmatrix} \begin{pmatrix} u - 2 \\ v - \pi/2 \end{pmatrix}$$

$$= u\begin{pmatrix} 0 \\ 1 \\ 0 \end{pmatrix} + v\begin{pmatrix} -2 \\ 0 \\ 1 \end{pmatrix} + \begin{pmatrix} \pi \\ 0 \\ 0 \end{pmatrix},$$

for all u and v. Since the vectors

$$\begin{pmatrix} 0 \\ 1 \\ 0 \end{pmatrix} \quad \text{and} \quad \begin{pmatrix} -2 \\ 0 \\ 1 \end{pmatrix}$$

are linearly independent, we conclude that the range of A is a plane. Hence, the surface S has a tangent plane at

$$\begin{pmatrix} 0 \\ 2 \\ \pi/2 \end{pmatrix}.$$

Eliminating u and v from the equations

$$x = \quad -2v + \pi$$
$$y = u$$
$$z = \quad\quad v$$

we obtain

$$x = -2z + \pi$$

as the equation that implicitly defines the tangent plane to S at

$$\begin{pmatrix} 0 \\ 2 \\ \pi/2 \end{pmatrix};$$

see Figure 25.

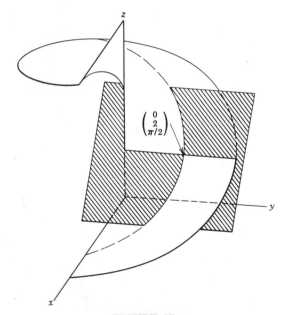

FIGURE 25

For a function $\mathcal{R} \xrightarrow{f} \mathcal{R}^m$ of one variable, we define the **derivative** df/dt to be the function whose value at t_0 is given by

$$\frac{df}{dt}(t_0) = (d_{t_0}f)1.$$

This definition extends the familiar derivative of a real-valued function of one variable to vector-valued functions of one variable. (See Exercise 6.)

EXAMPLE 2. The function of f defined by

$$f(t) = \begin{pmatrix} x \\ y \\ z \end{pmatrix} = \begin{pmatrix} t \\ t^2 \\ t^3 \end{pmatrix}, \qquad -\infty < t < \infty,$$

and discussed in Example 6, Section 1, parametrically defines the curve shown in Figure 26. The differential of f at t_0 is defined by the Jacobian matrix

$$\begin{pmatrix} 1 \\ 2t_0 \\ 3t_0^2 \end{pmatrix},$$

and the affine transformation

$$A(t) = f(t_0) + (d_{t_0}f)(t - t_0)$$

$$= f(t_0) + (t - t_0)\frac{df}{dt}(t_0)$$

that approximates f near t_0 is given by

$$A(t) = \begin{pmatrix} t_0 \\ t_0^2 \\ t_0^3 \end{pmatrix} + (t - t_0)\begin{pmatrix} 1 \\ 2t_0 \\ 3t_0^2 \end{pmatrix}$$

$$= t\begin{pmatrix} 1 \\ 2t_0 \\ 3t_0^2 \end{pmatrix} - \begin{pmatrix} 0 \\ t_0^2 \\ 2t_0^3 \end{pmatrix}, \qquad -\infty < t < \infty.$$

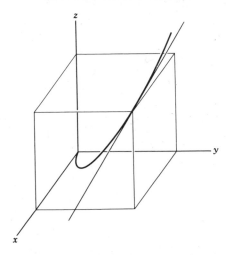

FIGURE 26

Since

$$\begin{pmatrix} 1 \\ 2t_0 \\ 3t_0^2 \end{pmatrix} \neq 0,$$

it follows that the range of A is the tangent line to the curve at $f(t_0)$. Figure 26 shows the curve and the tangent line to it at

$$f(1) = \begin{pmatrix} 1 \\ 1 \\ 1 \end{pmatrix}.$$

A **tangent vector** to a curve at a point is any vector in the direction of the tangent line at that point. Thus Z is a tangent vector to a curve C at a point Y_0 if there exist points Y_1 and Y_2 on the tangent line to C at Y_0 such that $Z = Y_1 - Y_2$. If the tangent line to a curve at a point is defined parametrically by an affine transformation

$$A(t) = tX_1 + X_2, \qquad X_1 \neq 0,$$

then $X_1 = A(1) - A(0)$ is a tangent vector at that point. In Example 2 above,

$$\begin{pmatrix} 1 \\ 2t_0 \\ 3t_0^2 \end{pmatrix}$$

is a tangent vector to the curve at $f(t_0)$.

Our definition of a parametrically defined surface and the evidence of the examples up to this point both suggest that the range of a function $\mathfrak{R}^2 \xrightarrow{f} \mathfrak{R}^3$ is the sort of object we want to call a surface. It is however, very easy to construct many functions with domain space $\mathfrak{R}^2$ and range space $\mathfrak{R}^3$ whose ranges in no way resemble the ordinary geometric idea of a surface. Consider, for example, the following functions:

$$f\begin{pmatrix} u \\ v \end{pmatrix} = \begin{pmatrix} 0 \\ 0 \\ 0 \end{pmatrix}, \quad g\begin{pmatrix} u \\ v \end{pmatrix} = \begin{pmatrix} \sin u \\ 0 \\ 0 \end{pmatrix}, \quad h\begin{pmatrix} u \\ v \end{pmatrix} = \begin{pmatrix} u + v \\ u + v \\ u + v \end{pmatrix}.$$

The range of f is a point, the range of g is a line segment, and the range of h is a line. Two more examples are

$$T\begin{pmatrix} u \\ v \end{pmatrix} = \begin{pmatrix} \cos u \sin v \\ \sin u \sin v \\ \cos v \end{pmatrix}, \quad 0 \le u \le 2\pi, v = \pi/2,$$

$$H\begin{pmatrix} u \\ v \end{pmatrix} = \begin{pmatrix} u \\ v \\ q \end{pmatrix}, \quad \begin{array}{l} 0 \le u \le 1, 0 \le v \le 1, \\ q \text{ is 0 or 1 according as } u \text{ is} \\ \text{a rational or irrational} \\ \text{number.} \end{array}$$

The function T has for its range the circle of radius 1 in the xy-plane, and the range of H cannot really be pictured at all.

Examples of surfaces also exist for which the dimension of the range is greater than the dimension of the domain space. For every positive integer n, it is possible to define a continuous function with domain space $\mathfrak{R}^2$ whose range is the entire space $\mathfrak{R}^n$. Moreover, examples of this kind are not limited to surfaces. There also exist space-filling curves, that is, there exists a continuous function of a real variable whose range contains every point of a vector space of arbitrarily high dimension. These functions are called **Peano** curves after their discoverer, Giuseppe Peano.*

The unusual behavior of the examples mentioned in the preceding paragraphs is due to a variety of causes. The functions f, g, and h all have the common feature that they are not really functions of two independent variables. The transformation T was constructed by artificially restricting every point of its domain. The trouble with the so-called space-filling curves and surfaces lies deeper, but can be attributed to the fact that they are wildly nondifferentiable. All of these troubles are eliminated by requiring the existence of a tangent line or plane. The criterion follows immediately from the definition of tangent.

5.1 Theorem. An n-dimensional surface defined parametrically by a function $\Re^n \xrightarrow{f} \Re^m$ has an n-dimensional tangent at fX_0 if and only if $d_{X_0}f$ exists and has an n-dimensional range.

In order to use the preceding theorem it is, of course, necessary to be able to recognize when the range of $d_{X_0}f$ is n-dimensional. We recall [Chapter 1, Section 11, Exercise 21(a)] that

5.2 Theorem. A linear transformation, defined by a matrix

$$\begin{pmatrix} a_{11} & \cdots & a_{1n} \\ \cdot & & \cdot \\ \cdot & & \cdot \\ \cdot & & \cdot \\ a_{m1} & \cdots & a_{mn} \end{pmatrix},$$

has n-dimensional range if and only if the column vectors

$$\begin{pmatrix} a_{11} \\ \cdot \\ \cdot \\ \cdot \\ a_{m1} \end{pmatrix}, \cdots, \begin{pmatrix} a_{1n} \\ \cdot \\ \cdot \\ \cdot \\ a_{mn} \end{pmatrix}$$

are linearly independent.

What are the implications of Theorems 5.1 and 5.2 for curves and surfaces in 3-dimensional space? A single vector forms a linearly independent set if and only if it is not zero. Hence a curve defined parametrically

* M. H. A. Newman, *Topology of Plane Sets of Points*, Cambridge University Press, 1951, p. 89.

by $\mathcal{R} \xrightarrow{f} \mathcal{R}^3$ has a tangent line at $f(t_0)$ if and only if $d_{t_0} f$ exists and the 3-by-1 Jacobian matrix of f at t_0 is not equal to

$$\begin{pmatrix} 0 \\ 0 \\ 0 \end{pmatrix}.$$

Similarly, a surface defined parametrically by $\mathcal{R}^2 \xrightarrow{f} \mathcal{R}^3$ has a tangent plane at fX_0 if and only if $d_{X_0} f$ exists and the columns of the 3-by-2 Jacobian matrix of f at X_0 are linearly independent.

EXAMPLE 3. The surfaces defined by

$$f\begin{pmatrix} u \\ v \end{pmatrix} = \begin{pmatrix} 0 \\ 0 \\ 0 \end{pmatrix}, \quad g\begin{pmatrix} u \\ v \end{pmatrix} = \begin{pmatrix} \sin u \\ 0 \\ 0 \end{pmatrix}, \quad h\begin{pmatrix} u \\ v \end{pmatrix} = \begin{pmatrix} u + v \\ u + v \\ u + v \end{pmatrix},$$

$$\begin{cases} -\infty < u < \infty \\ -\infty < v < \infty \end{cases}$$

fail to have tangent planes at any point. The matrices of the differentials of f, g, and h are, respectively,

$$\begin{pmatrix} 0 & 0 \\ 0 & 0 \\ 0 & 0 \end{pmatrix}, \quad \begin{pmatrix} \cos u & 0 \\ 0 & 0 \\ 0 & 0 \end{pmatrix}, \quad \begin{pmatrix} 1 & 1 \\ 1 & 1 \\ 1 & 1 \end{pmatrix}.$$

Theorem 5.2 shows that none of these has 2-dimensional range.

II. Explicitly defined surfaces. Suppose an n-dimensional surface S is defined explicitly by a function $\mathcal{R}^n \xrightarrow{f} \mathcal{R}^m$. This means that S is the graph of f in $\mathcal{R}^{n+m}$. Then the surface S **has a tangent at** (X_0, fX_0) if f is differentiable at X_0 and the affine transformation

$$AX = fX_0 + (d_{X_0} f)(X - X_0)$$

explicitly defines an n-dimensional plane. If it exists, this plane is the

tangent to S at (X_0, fX_0). Notice that the ordered pair (X_0, fX_0) is a point in $\Re^{n+m}$ on the surface S. Specifically, if

$$X = (x_1, \ldots, x_n) \quad \text{and} \quad Y = (y_1, \ldots, y_m),$$

then

$$(X, Y) = (x_1, \ldots, x_n, y_1, \ldots, y_m).$$

The complication in the parametric theory that necessitates checking that the differential has n-dimensional range does not arise here. If $d_{X_0} f$ exists, then the transformation A always explicitly defines a plane.

5.3 Theorem. The graph of every affine transformation $\Re^n \xrightarrow{A} \Re^m$ is an n-dimensional plane.

Proof. By the definition of an affine transformation, there exists a linear transformation $\Re^n \xrightarrow{L} \Re^m$ and a vector Y_0 in $\Re^m$ such that

$$AX = LX + Y_0, \quad \text{for all } X \text{ in } \Re^n.$$

The graph of A is the set of all points

$$(X, AX) = (X, LX) + (0, Y_0), \quad X \text{ in } \Re^n.$$

It is therefore the image under translation by $(0, Y_0)$ of the graph of L. Hence, the graph of A is an n-dimensional plane if and only if the graph of L, which is a subspace of $\Re^{n+m}$, has dimension n. We define a linear transformation $\Re^n \xrightarrow{L'} \Re^{n+m}$ by setting $L'X = (X, LX)$, for every X in $\Re^n$. The range of L' is equal to the graph of L. Furthermore, L' is obviously one-one, so its kernel has dimension zero. Then

$$n = 0 + \text{dimension of range of } L' = \text{dimension of graph of } L.$$

This completes the proof.

EXAMPLE 4. The curve defined explicitly by the function

$$f(t) = \begin{pmatrix} t^2 \\ t^2 \end{pmatrix}, \quad -\infty < t < \infty,$$

is drawn in Figure 27. The tangent line to the curve at

$$\begin{pmatrix} t_0 \\ f(t_0) \end{pmatrix} = \begin{pmatrix} 1 \\ 1 \\ 1 \end{pmatrix}$$

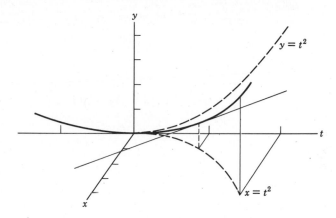

FIGURE 27

is explicitly defined by

$$A(t) = f(t_0) + (d_{t_0}f)(t - t_0)$$

$$= \begin{pmatrix} 1 \\ 1 \end{pmatrix} + \begin{pmatrix} 2 \\ 2 \end{pmatrix}(t - 1)$$

$$= t\begin{pmatrix} 2 \\ 2 \end{pmatrix} - \begin{pmatrix} 1 \\ 1 \end{pmatrix}.$$

EXAMPLE 5. The hemisphere shown in Figure 28 is defined explicitly by

$$g\begin{pmatrix} x \\ y \end{pmatrix} = \sqrt{9 - x^2 - y^2}.$$

The differential of g at $X_0 = \begin{pmatrix} 2 \\ 1 \end{pmatrix}$ is defined by the Jacobian matrix

$$\left(\frac{-x}{\sqrt{9 - x^2 - y^2}} \quad \frac{-y}{\sqrt{9 - x^2 - y^2}}\right)_{x=2,y=1} = \left(-1 \quad -\frac{1}{2}\right).$$

The tangent plane to the hemisphere at $(2, 1, 2)$ is the graph of the approximating affine transformation

$$AX = gX_0 + (d_{X_0}g)(X - X_0)$$

$$= 2 + \left(-1 \quad -\frac{1}{2}\right)\begin{pmatrix} x - 2 \\ y - 1 \end{pmatrix}$$

$$= \frac{9}{2} - x - \frac{1}{2}y.$$

The plane is implicitly defined by the equation $z = AX$, that is, by

$$2x + y + 2z = 9.$$

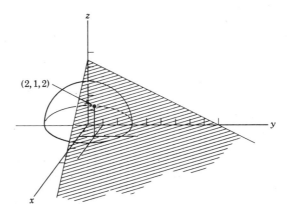

FIGURE 28

A good geometric picture of the differential of a real-valued function $f(x, y)$ at $X_0 = (x_0, y_0)$ is obtained by looking at the surface defined explicitly by f, and at the tangent plane to the surface at $(x_0, y_0, f(X_0))$. An example is shown in Figure 29. The tangent plane is the graph of the affine transformation defined by

$$A(x, y) = f(x_0, y_0) + (d_{X_0}f)(x - x_0, y - y_0), \quad \text{all } (x, y) \text{ in } \Re^2.$$

The difference $A(x, y) - f(x_0, y_0) = (d_{X_0}f)(x - x_0, y - y_0)$ is a good approximation to the increment $f(x, y) - f(x_0, y_0)$ provided (x, y) is close to (x_0, y_0). Figure 29 is the analogue of a similar picture, included in many one-variable calculus texts, that exhibits the differential for real-valued functions of one variable.*

* See, for example, G. B. Thomas, Jr., *Calculus and Analytic Geometry*, 3rd ed., Addison-Wesley, 1960, p. 83.

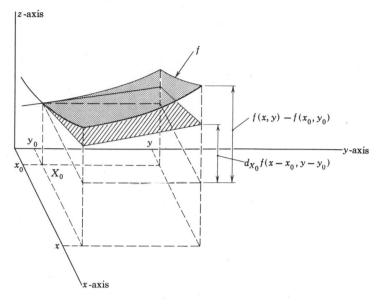

FIGURE 29

III. Implicitly defined surfaces. Consider a function $\mathfrak{R}^{n+m} \xrightarrow{F} \mathfrak{R}^m$ and a point Z_0 in $\mathfrak{R}^m$. Let S be an n-dimensional surface defined implicitly by the equation $FX = Z_0$. That is, S is the set of all points X in $\mathfrak{R}^{n+m}$ such that $FX = Z_0$. Following the basic principle stated in the first paragraph of this section, we say that S **has a tangent at** X_0 if $FX_0 = Z_0$ (i.e., X_0 is a point on the surface), F is differentiable at X_0, and an n-dimensional plane is implicitly defined by the equation

$$AX = Z_0, \tag{1}$$

where A is the approximating affine transformation

$$AX = FX_0 + (d_{X_0}F)(X - X_0).$$

Since $FX_0 = Z_0$, Equation (1) is equivalent to

$$(d_{X_0}F)(X - X_0) = 0. \tag{2}$$

The critical condition is therefore that the set of all vectors X in $\mathfrak{R}^{n+m}$ that satisfy Equation (2) should be an n-dimensional plane. If it exists, this plane is **the tangent** to S at X_0.

EXAMPLE 6. The equation $x^2 + y^2 + z^2 = 9$ implicitly defines a sphere of radius 3 with center at the origin in 3-dimensional euclidean space.

An equation of the tangent plane to the sphere at

$$X_0 = (x_0, y_0, z_0) = (2, 1, 2)$$

is determined as follows: If $F(x, y, z) = x^2 + y^2 + z^2$, the Jacobian matrix that defines $d_{X_0}F$ is

$$(2x_0 \quad 2y_0 \quad 2z_0) = (4 \quad 2 \quad 4).$$

Equation (2), which implicitly defines the tangent plane, is therefore

$$(4 \quad 2 \quad 4) \begin{pmatrix} x - 2 \\ y - 1 \\ z - 2 \end{pmatrix} = 0.$$

This is equivalent to $4x + 2y + 4z = 18$ and thence to $2x + y + 2z = 9$. Notice that we have found the same equation as that obtained for the tangent plane in Example 5.

The surface $\mathcal{P}$ implicitly defined by the equation $(d_{X_0}F)(X - X_0) = 0$ is not necessarily an n-dimensional plane. If it is not, then by our definition the surface defined by $FX = Y_0$ does not have a tangent plane at X_0. The situation is entirely analogous to the complication in the parametric theory that gave rise to Theorems 5.1 and 5.2. It is straightforward to check that $\mathcal{P}$ is the image of the kernel of $d_{X_0}F$ under translation by X_0, that is,

$$\mathcal{P} = (\text{kernel of } d_{X_0}F) + X_0.$$

Hence, $\mathcal{P}$ *is an n-dimensional plane if and only if the dimension of the kernel of $d_{X_0}F$ is equal to n.* To apply this fact, which is the analogue of Theorem 5.1, we have from Chapter 1, Section 11, Exercise 21(b), the following analogue of Theorem 5.2.

5.4 Theorem. The dimension of the kernel of a linear transformation defined by a matrix

$$A = \begin{pmatrix} a_{11} & \cdots & a_{1,n+m} \\ \cdot & & \cdot \\ \cdot & & \cdot \\ \cdot & & \cdot \\ a_{m,1} & \cdots & a_{m,n+m} \end{pmatrix}$$

is equal to n if and only if some m columns of A are linearly independent.

A **normal**, or perpendicular, vector to a surface S at a point X_0 is any vector Y_0 that is perpendicular to the tangent plane to S at X_0. Notice that, while the notion of perpendicularity is used in the definition of normal, it is not used in the definition of tangent.

EXAMPLE 7. Let the surface S in $\mathcal{R}^3$ be defined implicitly with respect to a function $\mathcal{R}^3 \xrightarrow{F} \mathcal{R}$ by the equation $FX = 0$. If S has a tangent plane at X_0, it is implicitly defined by

$$(d_{X_0}F)(X - X_0) = 0.$$

The vector

$$Y_0 = \left(\frac{\partial F}{\partial x} X_0, \ \frac{\partial F}{\partial y} X_0, \ \frac{\partial F}{\partial z} X_0 \right)$$

is perpendicular to the tangent plane and is therefore a normal to S at X_0.

As a final application of the ideas in this section, consider a real-valued function $f(x, y)$. The surface S defined explicitly by f is the same as that defined implicitly by the equation $z = f(x, y)$. The tangent plane to S at $X_0 = (x_0, y_0, z_0)$, where $z_0 = f(x_0, y_0)$, can be found as follows. Set $F(x, y, z) = f(x, y) - z$. The differential $d_{X_0}F$ is defined by the Jacobian matrix

$$M = \left(\frac{\partial f}{\partial x}(x_0, y_0) \quad \frac{\partial f}{\partial y}(x_0, y_0) \quad -1 \right).$$

The equation of the tangent plane is therefore

$$(d_{X_0}F)(X - X_0) = M \begin{pmatrix} x - x_0 \\ y - y_0 \\ z - z_0 \end{pmatrix} = 0,$$

which is equivalent to

$$z - z_0 = (x - x_0) \frac{\partial f}{\partial x}(x_0, y_0) + (y - y_0) \frac{\partial f}{\partial y}(x_0, y_0).$$

The points (x, y, z) that satisfy this equation are, of course, precisely the graph of the affine transformation that approximates f near (x_0, y_0). Thus both the implicit and explicit approach to the tangent plane have led to the same result.

EXERCISES

1. Find a parametric representation $tX_1 + X_2$ for the tangent line to each of the curves defined parametrically by the following functions at the points indicated. In (a), (b), and (c) sketch the curve and the tangent line.

(a) $f(t) = \begin{pmatrix} t \\ e^t \end{pmatrix}$, at $f(0)$.

$$\left[Ans. \ t \begin{pmatrix} 1 \\ 1 \end{pmatrix} + \begin{pmatrix} 0 \\ 1 \end{pmatrix}. \right]$$

(b) $g(t) = \begin{pmatrix} x \\ y \\ z \end{pmatrix} = \begin{pmatrix} t^2 + 1 \\ t - 1 \\ t^2 \end{pmatrix}$, at $\begin{pmatrix} 2 \\ 0 \\ 1 \end{pmatrix}$.

(c) $\begin{pmatrix} x \\ y \\ z \end{pmatrix} = \begin{pmatrix} \cos t \\ \sin t \\ t^2 \end{pmatrix}$, at $\begin{pmatrix} 0 \\ 1 \\ \dfrac{\pi^2}{4} \end{pmatrix}$.

(d) $f(t) = \begin{pmatrix} t \\ 2t \\ 3t \\ t + 1 \end{pmatrix}$, at $f(2)$. $Ans.\ t \begin{bmatrix} \begin{pmatrix} 1 \\ 2 \\ 3 \\ 1 \end{pmatrix} + \begin{pmatrix} 0 \\ 0 \\ 0 \\ 1 \end{pmatrix} \end{bmatrix}$.

2. Find the tangent plane to each of the surfaces defined parametrically by the following functions at the points indicated. Sketch the surface and the tangent plane in (a) and (b).

(a) $f \begin{pmatrix} u \\ v \end{pmatrix} = \begin{pmatrix} u + v \\ u - v \\ u^2 - v^2 \end{pmatrix}$, $\begin{Bmatrix} 1 \le u \le 2 \\ 0 \le v \le 1 \end{Bmatrix}$ at $f \begin{pmatrix} 1 \\ 1 \end{pmatrix}$.

$Ans. \begin{bmatrix} \begin{pmatrix} u + v \\ u - v \\ 2u - 2v \end{pmatrix} \end{bmatrix}$.

(b) $g \begin{pmatrix} u \\ v \end{pmatrix} = \begin{pmatrix} x \\ y \\ z \end{pmatrix} = \begin{pmatrix} \cos u \sin v \\ \sin u \sin v \\ \cos v \end{pmatrix}$, $\begin{Bmatrix} 0 \le u \le 2\pi \\ 0 \le v \le \pi/2 \end{Bmatrix}$ at $g \begin{pmatrix} \pi \\ \pi/4 \end{pmatrix}$.

(c) $\begin{pmatrix} x \\ y \\ z \end{pmatrix} = \begin{pmatrix} u + v + 1 \\ 2u + 3v \\ u + 2v - 2 \end{pmatrix}$, at $\begin{pmatrix} 3 \\ 5 \\ 1 \end{pmatrix}$.

(d) $f\begin{pmatrix} u \\ v \end{pmatrix} = \begin{pmatrix} 4u^2 + v^2 \\ uv^2 + uv - v^2 \\ uv + 1 \end{pmatrix}$, at $f\begin{pmatrix} 0 \\ 1 \end{pmatrix}$.

3. Find the tangent plane or tangent line to each of the following explicitly defined curves and surfaces at the points indicated.

   (a) $f(x) = (x - 1)(x - 2)(x - 3)$, at $(0, -6)$.

   (b) $f(x, y) = \dfrac{1}{x^2 + y^2}$, at $(x_0, y_0, f(x_0, y_0)) = \left(0, 2, \dfrac{1}{4}\right)$.

   (c) $g(t) = \begin{pmatrix} t \\ e^t \end{pmatrix}$, at $\begin{pmatrix} 1 \\ 1 \\ e \end{pmatrix}$. $\left[Ans.\ L(t) = t\begin{pmatrix} 1 \\ e \end{pmatrix} \right]$

   (d) $g(x, y) = \cosh(x^2 + y^2)$, at $(x_0, y_0, g(x_0, y_0)) = (1, 2, \cosh 5)$.

   (e) $f\begin{pmatrix} x \\ y \end{pmatrix} = \begin{cases} 1 \text{ if } |x| < |y| \\ 0 \text{ if } |x| \geq |y| \end{cases}$ at $\begin{pmatrix} 1 \\ 2 \\ 1 \end{pmatrix}$.

4. Find the tangent line or tangent plane to each of the following implicitly defined curves and surfaces at the points indicated. Sketch the curve or surface and the tangent in (b), (d), (f), and (g).

   (a) $F\begin{pmatrix} x \\ y \\ z \end{pmatrix} = xy + yz + zx = 1$, at $X_0 = \begin{pmatrix} 2 \\ -1 \\ 3 \end{pmatrix}$.

   (Cf. Section 1, Example 8.)

   (b) $F\begin{pmatrix} x \\ y \\ z \end{pmatrix} = \dfrac{x^2}{4} + \dfrac{y^2}{9} + z^2 = 1$, at $X_0 = \begin{pmatrix} 1 \\ 0 \\ \dfrac{\sqrt{3}}{2} \end{pmatrix}$. $\left[Ans.\ \dfrac{x}{2} + \sqrt{3}\,z = 2 \right]$

(c) $5x + 5y + 2z = 8$, at $(1, 1, -1)$.

(d) $\dfrac{x^2}{a^2} + \dfrac{y^2}{b^2} = 1$, at $(x_0, y_0) = \left(\dfrac{\sqrt{3}\,a}{2}, \dfrac{b}{2}\right)$.

(e) $T\begin{pmatrix} x \\ y \\ z \end{pmatrix} = \begin{pmatrix} xy + yz + zx \\ x + y - z \end{pmatrix} = \begin{pmatrix} 1 \\ -2 \end{pmatrix}$, at $X_0 = \begin{pmatrix} 2 \\ -1 \\ 3 \end{pmatrix}$.

(Compare with Example 9 in Section 1.)

(f) $F\begin{pmatrix} x \\ y \\ z \end{pmatrix} = \begin{pmatrix} x^2 + y^2 + z^2 \\ x^2 + y^2 \end{pmatrix} = \begin{pmatrix} 9 \\ 5 \end{pmatrix}$, at $X_0 = \begin{pmatrix} 1 \\ 2 \\ 2 \end{pmatrix}$.

(g) $F\begin{pmatrix} x \\ y \\ z \end{pmatrix} = \begin{pmatrix} x^2 + y^2 + z^2 \\ x + y \end{pmatrix} = \begin{pmatrix} 9 \\ 3 \end{pmatrix}$, at $X_0 = \begin{pmatrix} 2 \\ 1 \\ 2 \end{pmatrix}$.

$$\left[Ans. \begin{pmatrix} 4 & 2 & 4 \\ 1 & 1 & 0 \end{pmatrix} \begin{pmatrix} x \\ y \\ z \end{pmatrix} = \begin{pmatrix} 18 \\ 3 \end{pmatrix}. \right]$$

5. In each of Exercises 1(a), 2(a), 2(b), 4(b), 4(f), find a normal to the

given curve or surface at the point indicated. $\left[Ans.\ 1\text{(a)} \begin{pmatrix} 1 \\ -1 \end{pmatrix}. \right]$

6. Consider a curve in $\mathfrak{R}^3$ defined parametrically by a vector function f and having a tangent line at $f(t_0)$.

   (a) On a drawing of such a curve show the points $f(t_0)$ and $f(t)$ and draw the vectors $f(t) - f(t_0)$ and $\dfrac{f(t) - f(t_0)}{t - t_0}$, for a value of t close to t_0.

   (b) Show that $\lim\limits_{t \to t_0} \dfrac{f(t) - f(t_0)}{t - t_0}$ is a tangent vector to the curve at $f(t_0)$.

7. Each of the following curves and surfaces fails, according to our definitions, to have a tangent line or plane at the indicated point. Why?

(a) $f(t) = \begin{pmatrix} t \\ |t| \\ t^2 \end{pmatrix}$, at $f(0)$.

(b) $g(t) = \begin{pmatrix} t^2 - 2t \\ t^3 - 3t \\ t^4 - t^3 - t \end{pmatrix}$, at $\begin{pmatrix} -1 \\ -2 \\ -1 \end{pmatrix}$.

(c) $f\begin{pmatrix} u \\ v \end{pmatrix} = \begin{pmatrix} u^2 v^4 \\ uv^2 \\ u^2 + v^4 \end{pmatrix}$, at $f\begin{pmatrix} 1 \\ 1 \end{pmatrix}$.

(d) $f(x, y) = \sqrt{1 - x^2 - y^2}$, at $\left(\dfrac{\sqrt{2}}{2}, \dfrac{\sqrt{2}}{2}, 0 \right)$.

(e) $F\begin{pmatrix} x \\ y \\ z \end{pmatrix} = \begin{pmatrix} z^2 e^{x+y} \\ 2xyz^2 \end{pmatrix} = \begin{pmatrix} 4e^2 \\ 8 \end{pmatrix}$, at $X_0 = \begin{pmatrix} 1 \\ 1 \\ 2 \end{pmatrix}$.

8. Find all points at which the surface defined parametrically by the function

$$f\begin{pmatrix} u \\ v \end{pmatrix} = \begin{pmatrix} u^2 v^2 \\ uv \\ uv + 1 \end{pmatrix}$$

fails to have a tangent plane.

9. Assume that a surface S implicitly defined by the equation $GX = 0$, with respect to $\Re^{n+m} \xrightarrow{G} \Re^m$, has a tangent plane $\mathcal{P}$ at X_0. With respect to the coordinate functions $G_1, \ldots, G_m$, let S_k be defined by $G_k X = 0$, $k = 1, \ldots, m$.

(a) Show that S_k has a tangent plane $\mathcal{P}_k$ at X_0 and that

$$\mathcal{P} = \mathcal{P}_1 \cap \ldots \cap \mathcal{P}_m.$$

(b) If Y_k is normal to S_k at X_0, prove that any vector Y in the subspace $\mathcal{Y}$ generated by $Y_1, \ldots, Y_m$ is perpendicular to S at X_0.

(c) What is the dimension of $\mathcal{Y}$?

10. Different vector functions can define the same curve or surface. Show that the functions

$$f_1(t) = (\cos t, \sin t), \qquad\qquad 0 < t < 2\pi,$$

$$f_2(s) = \left(\frac{s^2 - 1}{s^2 + 1}, \frac{2s}{s^2 + 1}\right) \qquad -\infty < s < \infty,$$

parametrically define the same curve in 2-dimensional euclidean space.

11. Consider the vector functions

$$f(t) = \begin{pmatrix} t^3 \\ t^3 \\ t^3 \end{pmatrix}, \qquad -\infty < t < \infty,$$

$$g\begin{pmatrix} u \\ v \end{pmatrix} = \begin{pmatrix} u^3 \\ v^3 \\ 0 \end{pmatrix}, \qquad \begin{cases} -\infty < u < \infty, \\ -\infty < v < \infty. \end{cases}$$

(a) What curve and what surface are parametrically defined by f and g, respectively?

(b) Show that according to our definition the curve does not have a tangent line and the surface does not have a tangent plane at

$$\begin{pmatrix} 0 \\ 0 \\ 0 \end{pmatrix}.$$

(This does not mean that we have to throw out our definition. These examples do show, however, that our notion of tangent reflects more than the simple picture in the range space. The parametrization is an essential feature. A natural physical interpretation of f is to regard $f(t)$ as the position in $\mathfrak{R}^3$ of a particle at time t. A tangent vector at $f(t_0)$ gives the instantaneous direction of motion at t_0. Since the velocity is zero at $t_0 = 0$, there is no direction of motion then and hence no tangent line.)

12. Let

$$f(t) = \begin{pmatrix} t^3 \\ t^3 \end{pmatrix}, \qquad -\infty < t < \infty.$$

(a) Show that the curve in $\mathfrak{R}^3$ defined explicitly by f has a tangent line at every point.

(b) Show that the curve in $\mathcal{R}^2$ defined parametrically by f fails to have a tangent line at one point.

(c) Interpret (a) and (b) geometrically. What is the relation between the tangent line in (a) and in (b)?

13. Let $Y_0 = 0$ lie in the range of a function $\mathcal{R}^n \xrightarrow{F} \mathcal{R}^m$. The surface S defined implicitly by the equation $FX = 0$ is assumed to have a tangent $\mathfrak{I}$ at X_0.

(a) Check that the surface S' in $\mathcal{R}^{n+m}$ defined explicitly by F has a tangent $\mathfrak{I}'$ at (X_0, Y_0).

(b) Let $\mathcal{P}$ be the plane in $\mathcal{R}^{n+m}$ defined by the equation $Y = 0$, and show that $S = S' \cap \mathcal{P}$.

(c) Prove that $\mathfrak{I} = \mathfrak{I}' \cap \mathcal{P}$.

(d) Using the equation $F(x, y) = x^2 + y^2 - 2 = 0$ and the point $X_0 = (1, 1)$, draw a picture illustrating S, $\mathfrak{I}$, S', $\mathfrak{I}'$, and $\mathcal{P}$.

(e) Using the equation $F(x, y) = 4x^2 - 4xy + y^2 = 0$ and the point $X_0 = (1, 2)$, draw a picture illustrating S, S', $\mathfrak{I}'$, and $\mathcal{P}$. What happens to $\mathfrak{I}$?

14. The surface defined explicitly by the real-valued function $f(x, y)$ is also defined parametrically by the function

$$ g\begin{pmatrix} x \\ y \end{pmatrix} = \begin{pmatrix} x \\ y \\ f(x, y) \end{pmatrix}. $$

Show that the tangent plane at

$$ \begin{pmatrix} x_0 \\ y_0 \\ f(x_0, y_0) \end{pmatrix} $$

is the same whether computed directly from f or from g.

15. Prove that if a parametrically defined curve in $\mathcal{R}^3$ has a tangent line at all its points and all these lines are identical, then the curve is a straight line. (Assume that the function that determines the curve is defined on an interval.)

16. A straight line $\mathcal{L}$ in $\mathcal{R}^3$ defined parametrically by

$$ X(t) = tX_1 + X_2, \qquad X_1 \neq 0, $$

lies on the surface explicitly defined by a real-valued function $f(x, y)$. Assuming that it exists, prove that the tangent plane to the surface at X_2 contains the line $\mathcal{L}$.

6. DERIVATIVE WITH RESPECT TO A VECTOR

Let $\mathfrak{R}^n \xrightarrow{f} \mathfrak{R}^m$ be a vector function, and let Y be a vector in the domain space $\mathfrak{R}^n$. The **derivative of f with respect to** Y, denoted by $\partial f/\partial Y$, is the vector function defined by

$$\frac{\partial f}{\partial Y} X = \lim_{t \to 0} \frac{f(X + tY) - fX}{t}.$$

The domain of $\partial f/\partial Y$ is the subset of the domain of f for which the above limit exists. The domain space and range space of $\partial f/\partial Y$ are the same as those of f.

The connection between the derivative with respect to a vector and the differential is provided in the following theorem.

6.1 Theorem. If f is differentiable at X, then

$$\frac{\partial f}{\partial Y} X = (d_X f) Y, \qquad \text{for every } Y \text{ in } \mathfrak{R}^n.$$

Proof. If $Y = 0$, then $(\partial f/\partial Y) X = 0 = (d_X f) Y$. Hence, in the remainder of the proof we assume that $Y \neq 0$. The existence of the differential $d_X f$ implies that

$$\lim_{t \to 0} \frac{f(X + tY) - fX - (d_X f)(tY)}{|tY|} = 0,$$

which is equivalent to

$$\lim_{t \to 0} \frac{1}{|Y|} \left| \frac{f(X + tY) - fX}{t} - (d_X f) Y \right| = 0.$$

This in turn is equivalent to

$$\lim_{t \to 0} \frac{f(X + tY) - fX}{t} = (d_X f) Y,$$

and the proof is finished.

The equation

$$\frac{\partial f}{\partial Y} X = (d_X f) Y$$

shows that for a differentiable function the derivative with respect to a vector involves nothing really new. However, it does represent a change in viewpoint. In a typical discussion of $(d_X f) Y$, the vector Y will be regarded as the variable, and X will be considered fixed. In $(\partial f/\partial Y)X$ the opposite is true.

EXAMPLE 1. Let f be the vector function defined by

$$f\begin{pmatrix} x \\ y \end{pmatrix} = \begin{pmatrix} x \sin y \\ y \sin x \end{pmatrix}, \qquad \begin{cases} -\infty < x < \infty, \\ -\infty < y < \infty, \end{cases}$$

and take $Y = \begin{pmatrix} 1 \\ 3 \end{pmatrix}$. Setting $X = \begin{pmatrix} x \\ y \end{pmatrix}$, we have

$$\frac{\partial f}{\partial Y}\begin{pmatrix} x \\ y \end{pmatrix} = (d_X f)\, Y = \begin{pmatrix} \sin y & x \cos y \\ y \cos x & \sin x \end{pmatrix}\begin{pmatrix} 1 \\ 3 \end{pmatrix}$$

$$= \begin{pmatrix} \sin y + 3x \cos y \\ y \cos x + 3 \sin x \end{pmatrix}.$$

In particular,

$$\frac{\partial f}{\partial Y}\begin{pmatrix} \frac{\pi}{4} \\ \cdot\frac{\pi}{6} \end{pmatrix} = \begin{pmatrix} \dfrac{1}{2} + \dfrac{3\pi\sqrt{3}}{8} \\ \dfrac{\pi\sqrt{2}}{12} + \dfrac{3\sqrt{2}}{2} \end{pmatrix}.$$

EXAMPLE 2. A real-valued function g is defined by

$$g\begin{pmatrix} x \\ y \end{pmatrix} = xy^2 e^{2x}, \qquad \begin{cases} -\infty < x < \infty. \\ -\infty < y < \infty. \end{cases}$$

We take $Y = \begin{pmatrix} a \\ b \end{pmatrix}$. Then, if $X = \begin{pmatrix} x \\ y \end{pmatrix}$,

$$\frac{\partial g}{\partial Y}\begin{pmatrix} x \\ y \end{pmatrix} = (d_X g)\, Y = (y^2 e^{2x}(1 + 2x) \quad 2xy e^{2x})\begin{pmatrix} a \\ b \end{pmatrix}$$

$$= y e^{2x}(ay + 2axy + 2bx).$$

For a real-valued function f, the derivative with respect to a vector is a natural generalization of the partial derivative. If the domain space of f is $\mathfrak{R}^n$ and

$$E_j = \begin{pmatrix} 0 \\ \vdots \\ 1 \\ \vdots \\ 0 \end{pmatrix}$$

is the n-dimensional column vector consisting of all zeros except that the jth coordinate is equal to 1, then

$$\frac{\partial f}{\partial E_j} X = \lim_{t \to 0} \frac{f(X + tE_j) - fX}{t} = \frac{\partial f}{\partial x_j} X.$$

Notice in Example 2 that

$$\frac{\partial g}{\partial Y} = \begin{cases} \dfrac{\partial g}{\partial x} & \text{if } a = 1 \text{ and } b = 0. \\[2ex] \dfrac{\partial g}{\partial y} & \text{if } a = 0 \text{ and } b = 1. \end{cases}$$

For each vector U in $\mathfrak{R}^n$ of length $|U| = 1$, we define the **directional derivative of f in the direction of** U to be the function $\partial f/\partial U$. The reason for the name "directional derivative" is that in a euclidean space there is a natural way to associate a vector to each direction, namely, take the unit vector (vector of length 1) in that direction. The value $(\partial f/\partial U)X$ is then regarded as a standard measure of the rate of change of the values of f in the direction of U.

EXAMPLE 3. The domain space of the function

$$f(x, y, z) = xyz + e^{2x+y}$$

is assumed to be euclidean 3-dimensional space. Find the directional derivative of f in the direction of

$$U = \begin{pmatrix} 1/2 \\ 1/2 \\ \sqrt{2}/2 \end{pmatrix}.$$

Setting

$$X = \begin{pmatrix} x \\ y \\ z \end{pmatrix}$$

and using Theorem 6.1, we obtain

$$\frac{\partial f}{\partial U} X = (d_X f) U = (yz + 2e^{2x+y} \quad xz + e^{2x+y} \quad xy) \begin{pmatrix} 1/2 \\ 1/2 \\ \sqrt{2}/2 \end{pmatrix}$$

$$= \frac{yz + xz + \sqrt{2}\, xy}{2} + \frac{3e^{2x+y}}{2}.$$

It follows that the directional derivative of f in the direction of U has at the origin

$$\begin{pmatrix} x \\ y \\ z \end{pmatrix} = \begin{pmatrix} 0 \\ 0 \\ 0 \end{pmatrix}$$

the value

$$\frac{\partial f}{\partial U} \begin{pmatrix} 0 \\ 0 \\ 0 \end{pmatrix} = \frac{3}{2}.$$

Let $\mathfrak{R}^2 \xrightarrow{f} \mathfrak{R}$ be a function whose graph is a surface in 3-dimensional euclidean space, and let U be a unit vector in $\mathfrak{R}^2$, i.e., $|U| = 1$. An example is shown in Figure 30. The value of the directional derivative $\partial f/\partial U$ at $X = (x, y)$ is by definition

$$\frac{\partial f}{\partial U} X = \lim_{t \to 0} \frac{f(X + tU) - fX}{t}.$$

The distance between the points $X + tU$ and X is given by

$$|(X + tU) - X| = |tU| = |t|.$$

Hence, the ratio

$$\frac{f(X + tU) - fX}{t}$$

is the slope of the line through the points $f(X + tU)$ and fX. It follows that the limit, $(\partial f/\partial U)X$, of the ratio is the slope of the tangent line at (X, fX) to the curve formed by the intersection of the graph of f with the plane that contains X and $X + U$, and is parallel to the z-axis. This curve is drawn with a dotted line in the figure. The angle γ shown in Figure 30 therefore satisfies the equation

$$\tan \gamma = \frac{\partial f}{\partial U} X.$$

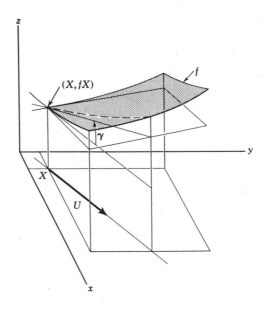

FIGURE 30

The situation here is a generalization of that illustrated in Figure 20 of Section 3. If we choose $U = (1, 0)$, the angle γ becomes the angle α in the earlier figure and

$$\frac{\partial f}{\partial U} = \frac{\partial f}{\partial x}.$$

On the other hand, if we take $V = (0, 1)$, then γ is the angle β in Figure 20, and

$$\frac{\partial f}{\partial V} = \frac{\partial f}{\partial y}.$$

The mean-value theorem for real-valued functions of a real variable can be extended to real-valued functions of a vector variable as follows.

6.2 Theorem. Let $\mathcal{R}^n \xrightarrow{f} \mathcal{R}$ be differentiable on an open set containing the segment S joining two vectors X and Y in $\mathfrak{R}^n$. Then there is a point X_0 on S such that

$$fY - fX = (d_{X_0} f)(Y - X)$$

$$= \frac{\partial f}{\partial(Y - X)} X_0.$$

Proof. Consider the function $g(t) = f(t(Y - X) + X)$, defined for $0 \leq t \leq 1$. If we set $X(t) = t(Y - X) + X$, then

$$g(a + h) - g(a) = f((a + h)(Y - X) + X) - f(a(Y - X) + X)$$

$$= (d_{X(a)} f) h(Y - X) + R,$$

where $\lim\limits_{h \to 0} \dfrac{R}{h} = 0$. Dividing by h, we get

$$\frac{g(a + h) - g(a)}{h} = (d_{X(a)} f)(Y - X) + \frac{R}{h},$$

whence

$$\frac{dg}{dt}(a) = \lim_{h \to 0} \frac{g(a + h) - g(a)}{h} = (d_{X(a)} f)(Y - X).$$

By the mean-value theorem for functions of one variable,

$$\frac{g(1) - g(0)}{1 - 0} = fY - fX = \frac{dg}{dt}(a),$$

for some a satisfying $0 < a < 1$. If we define X_0 to be $X(a)$, we obtain the first equation of the theorem. The second then follows by Theorem 6.1.

It is not hard to find a real-valued function of two variables and a point X at which $\partial f/\partial x$ exists and $\partial f/\partial y$ does not. Thus $(\partial f/\partial Y)X$ may be defined for some vectors Y and not for others. However, if a function f has a differential $d_X f$ at a point X, then $(\partial f/\partial Y)X$ is defined for every vector Y in the domain space of f (see Theorem 6.1). One might guess that if $(\partial f/\partial Y)X$ exists for every Y in the domain space of f, then conversely the differential $d_X f$ must exist. The following example shows that this is false. Let f be defined by

$$f(x, y) = \begin{cases} \dfrac{x|y|}{\sqrt{x^2 + y^2}}, & \text{if } x^2 + y^2 \neq 0. \\ 0, & \text{if } x^2 + y^2 = 0. \end{cases}$$

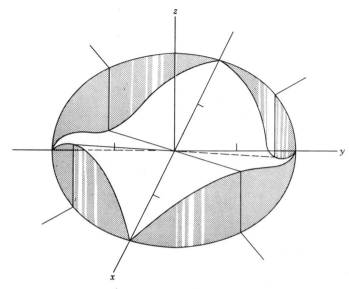

FIGURE 31

The graph of f is shown in Figure 31. We shall prove that $(\partial f/\partial Y)(0, 0)$ exists for every vector $Y = (a, b)$, but that f is not differentiable (has no differential) at $(0, 0)$.

First of all, if $Y = (0, 0)$, then $(\partial f/\partial Y)(0, 0) = 0$. So in what follows we assume that $a^2 + b^2 > 0$. Consider the straight line defined parametrically by

$$X(t) = t \begin{pmatrix} a \\ b \\ \dfrac{a\,|\,b\,|}{\sqrt{a^2 + b^2}} \end{pmatrix}, \qquad -\infty < t < \infty. \tag{1}$$

This line lies in the graph of f, that is, it follows at once from the definition of f that

$$f(at, bt) = \frac{a\,|\,b\,|\,t}{\sqrt{a^2 + b^2}}, \qquad -\infty < t < \infty.$$

Hence, by the definition of the derivative of f with respect to a vector, we have

$$\frac{\partial f}{\partial Y}(0, 0) = \lim_{t \to 0} \frac{f(at, bt) - f(0, 0)}{t} = \frac{a\,|\,b\,|}{\sqrt{a^2 + b^2}}.$$

Thus $(\partial f/\partial Y)(0, 0)$ exists for every vector $Y = (a, b)$. It remains to show that f is not differentiable at $(0, 0)$. Suppose it is. Then the graph of f has a tangent plane $\mathcal{P}$ at $(0, 0, 0)$. We have shown that, for every nonzero $Y = (a, b)$, the line defined by Equation (1) lies in the graph of f. It follows (see Section 5, Exercise 16) that these lines lie also in $\mathcal{P}$. In particular, the plane $\mathcal{P}$ contains the lines

$$X(t) = t\begin{pmatrix} 1 \\ 0 \\ 0 \end{pmatrix}, \qquad \text{for } Y = \begin{pmatrix} 1 \\ 0 \end{pmatrix},$$

$$X(t) = t\begin{pmatrix} 0 \\ 1 \\ 0 \end{pmatrix}, \qquad \text{for } Y = \begin{pmatrix} 0 \\ 1 \end{pmatrix},$$

and $$X(t) = t\begin{pmatrix} \sqrt{2} \\ \sqrt{2} \\ 1 \end{pmatrix}, \qquad \text{for } Y = \begin{pmatrix} \sqrt{2} \\ \sqrt{2} \end{pmatrix}.$$

But this implies that the 2-dimensional subspace $\mathcal{P}$ contains the three linearly independent vectors

$$\begin{pmatrix} 1 \\ 0 \\ 0 \end{pmatrix}, \quad \begin{pmatrix} 0 \\ 1 \\ 0 \end{pmatrix}, \quad \begin{pmatrix} \sqrt{2} \\ \sqrt{2} \\ 1 \end{pmatrix}.$$

This is impossible, and therefore the plane $\mathcal{P}$ cannot exist.

EXERCISES

1. Find the value at X of the derivative of each of the following functions with respect to the vector Y.

(a) $f \begin{pmatrix} u \\ v \end{pmatrix} = \begin{pmatrix} u + v \\ u - v \\ u^2 - v^2 \end{pmatrix}$, $X = \begin{pmatrix} 0 \\ 2 \end{pmatrix}$, and $Y = \begin{pmatrix} -1 \\ 1 \end{pmatrix}$.

$$\left[Ans. \begin{pmatrix} 0 \\ -2 \\ -4 \end{pmatrix} \right].$$

(b) $f \begin{pmatrix} x \\ y \end{pmatrix} = \begin{pmatrix} x^2 + y + 1 \\ 2xy \\ x^2 - 2y^2 \end{pmatrix}$, $X = \begin{pmatrix} x \\ y \end{pmatrix}$, and $Y = \begin{pmatrix} 1 \\ 1 \end{pmatrix}$.

(c) $T(x, y, z) = x^2y \, e^{x+y+2z}$, $X = \begin{pmatrix} 1 \\ 0 \\ 1 \end{pmatrix}$, and $Y = \begin{pmatrix} a \\ b \\ c \end{pmatrix}$.

(d) $f(x, y)$, $X = (x, y)$, and $Y = (\cos \alpha, \sin \alpha)$. (Assume that f is real-valued.)

2. For each of the following functions defined on 3-dimensional euclidean space, find the directional derivative in the direction of the unit vector U at the point X.

(a) $f \begin{pmatrix} x \\ y \\ z \end{pmatrix} = \begin{pmatrix} e^{x+y} + \sinh xz \\ x^2 + y^2 \end{pmatrix}$, $U = \frac{1}{\sqrt{3}} \begin{pmatrix} 1 \\ 1 \\ 1 \end{pmatrix}$, and $X = \begin{pmatrix} 1 \\ 0 \\ 1 \end{pmatrix}$.

(b) $h \begin{pmatrix} x \\ y \\ z \end{pmatrix} = xyz + e^{x^2+y^2+z^2}$, $X = \begin{pmatrix} 1 \\ 0 \\ 0 \end{pmatrix}$,

$$U = \begin{pmatrix} \cos \alpha \sin \beta \\ \sin \alpha \sin \beta \\ \cos \beta \end{pmatrix}.$$

3. For each of the following real-valued functions defined on euclidean space, find the directional derivative at X in the direction indicated.

(a) $f(x, y) = x^2 - y^2$ at $X = (1, 1)$ and in the direction

$$\left(\frac{1}{\sqrt{5}}, \frac{2}{\sqrt{5}}\right). \qquad\qquad \left[Ans. \ \frac{-2}{\sqrt{5}}.\right]$$

(b) $f(x, y) = e^x \sin y$ at $X = (1, 0)$ and in the direction $(\cos \alpha, \sin \alpha)$.

(c) $f(x, y)$ at $X = (x, y)$ and in the direction $(\cos \alpha, \sin \alpha)$.

(d) $f(x, y) = e^{x|y}$ at $X = (1, 1)$ in the direction of the curve defined by

$$g(t) = (t^2, t^3) \text{ at } g(2) \text{ for } t \text{ increasing.}$$

4. Show, using Theorem 6.1, that if $\mathcal{R}^n \xrightarrow{f} \mathcal{R}$ is differentiable and

$$Y = \begin{pmatrix} y_1 \\ \cdot \\ \cdot \\ \cdot \\ y_n \end{pmatrix},$$

then

$$\frac{\partial f}{\partial Y} X = \sum_{j=1}^{n} y_j \frac{\partial f}{\partial x_j} X.$$

5. Show, using Theorem 6.1, that if f is differentiable and a is a real number, then

$$\frac{\partial f}{\partial a Y} = a \frac{\partial f}{\partial Y}.$$

6. Show that if f is differentiable, then

$$\frac{\partial f}{\partial (Y + Z)} = \frac{\partial f}{\partial Y} + \frac{\partial f}{\partial Z}.$$

7. Find the absolute value of the directional derivative at $(1, 1, 0)$ of the function $f(x, y, z) = x^2 + ye^z$ in the direction of the tangent line at $g(0)$ to the curve in 3-dimensional euclidean space defined parametrically by $g(t) = (3t^2 + t + 1, 2t, t^2)$.

8. Find the directional derivative at $(1, 0, 0)$ of the function $f(x, y, z) = x^2 + ye^z$ in the direction of increasing t along the curve in euclidean $\mathcal{R}^3$ defined by $g(t) = (t^2 - t + 2, t, t + 2)$ at $g(0)$. $\qquad [Ans. -1/\sqrt{3}.]$

9. Find the absolute value of the directional derivative at $(1, 0, 1)$ of the function $f(x, y, z) = 4x^2y + y^2z$ in the direction of the perpendicular at $(1, 1, 1)$ to the surface in euclidean 3-space defined implicitly by $x^2 + 2y^2 + z^2 = 4$. $\qquad [Ans. \ 8/\sqrt{6}.]$

10. (a) Show that the vector $(y_1 z_2 - y_2 z_1, z_1 x_2 - z_2 x_1, x_1 y_2 - x_2 y_1)$ is perpendicular to (x_1, y_1, z_1) and (x_2, y_2, z_2).

(b) Find the absolute value of the directional derivative at $(1, 2, 1)$ of the function $f(x, y, z) = x^3 + y^2 + z$ in the direction of the perpendicular at $(1, 2, 1)$ to the surface defined parametrically by

$$(x, y, z) = (u^2 v, u + v, u). \qquad\qquad [Ans.\ 2/\sqrt{3}.]$$

11. The two euclidean unit vectors in $\mathfrak{R}$ are just the numbers 1 and -1. Show that for a real-valued function $f(x)$, the directional derivatives $\partial f/\partial 1$ and $\partial f/\partial(-1)$ are simply

$$\frac{\partial f}{\partial 1}\,(x) = f'(x) \quad \text{and} \quad \frac{\partial f}{\partial(-1)}\,(x) = -f'(x).$$

12. Give an example of a real-valued function $f(x, y)$, a point $X_0 = (x_0, y_0)$, and vectors Y_1, Y_2 in $\mathfrak{R}^2$ such that $(\partial f/\partial Y_1)\,X_0$ is defined, but $(\partial f/\partial Y_2)\,X_0$ is not. *Hint*: A possible choice for f is the function

$$f(x, y) = \begin{cases} xy \sin \dfrac{1}{x}, & \text{if } x \neq 0. \\[2mm] 0, & \text{if } x = 0. \end{cases}$$

7. THE CHAIN RULE

If two functions f and g are so related that the range space of f is the same as the domain space of g we may form the **composite function** $g \circ f$ by first applying f and then g. Thus,

$$(g \circ f)X = g(fX)$$

for every vector X such that X is in the domain of f and fX is in the domain of g. The domain spaces and range spaces of the functions f, g, and $g \circ f$ are related as shown in the diagram. The domain of $g \circ f$ consists of those

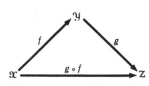

vectors X that are carried by f into the domain of g. It is conceivable that there are no such vectors X, i.e., that the intersection of the range of f with the domain of g is empty. If this happens, the composition $g \circ f$ is not defined. An abstract picture of the composition of two functions is shown in Figure 32.

EXAMPLE 1. The functions $\mathfrak{R}^2 \xrightarrow{f} \mathfrak{R}$ and $\mathfrak{R} \xrightarrow{g} \mathfrak{R}^3$ are defined by

$$f\begin{pmatrix} x \\ y \end{pmatrix} = [\ln (x + y)]^2, \qquad g(t) = \begin{pmatrix} \arcsin t \\ t^2 \\ t^3 \end{pmatrix}.$$

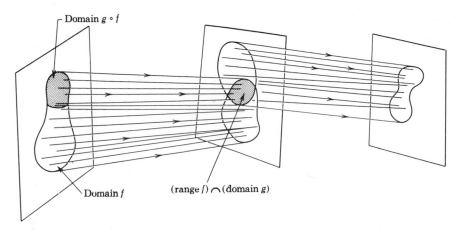

FIGURE 32

The domain of f consists of all vectors $\begin{pmatrix} x \\ y \end{pmatrix}$ such that $0 < x + y$, and the range of f is the set of all real numbers t such that $0 \leq t$. The domain of g is the interval $-1 \leq t \leq 1$. The intersection of the last two sets is the interval $0 \leq t \leq 1$. It follows that the domain of the composite function $g \bigcirc f$ is the set of all points

$$\begin{pmatrix} x \\ y \end{pmatrix}$$

such that

$$0 \leq [\ln (x + y)]^2 \leq 1$$

or, equivalently, such that $e^{-1} \leq x + y \leq e$; see Figure 33. Composing the formulas that define f and g, we obtain

$$(g \circ f) \begin{pmatrix} x \\ y \end{pmatrix} = \begin{pmatrix} \arcsin [\ln (x + y)]^2 \\ [\ln (x + y)]^4 \\ [\ln (x + y)]^6 \end{pmatrix}, \qquad \frac{1}{e} \leq x + y \leq e.$$

The purpose of this section is the determination of the differential of $g \bigcirc f$ in terms of the differentials of f and g. Suppose $\mathfrak{R}^n \xrightarrow{f} \mathfrak{R}^m$ is differentiable at X_0 and $\mathfrak{R}^m \xrightarrow{g} \mathfrak{R}^p$ is differentiable at Y_0. Since the range space $\mathfrak{R}^m$ of $d_{X_0}f$ is the domain of $d_{Y_0}g$, the composite function $(d_{Y_0}g) \bigcirc (d_{X_0}f)$

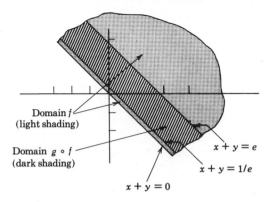

Domain f
(light shading)

Domain $g \circ f$
(dark shading)

$x + y = e$

$x + y = 1/e$

$x + y = 0$

FIGURE 33

is defined, and is a linear transformation with domain $\mathfrak{R}^n$ and range space. $\mathfrak{R}^p$. The chain rule asserts that if $Y_0 = fX_0$, this composite linear transformation is precisely the differential of $g \circ f$ at X_0. That is, *the differential of a composition is the composition of the differentials.*

7.1 Theorem. The chain rule. If $\mathfrak{R}^n \xrightarrow{f} \mathfrak{R}^m$ is differentiable at X_0 and $\mathfrak{R}^m \xrightarrow{g} \mathfrak{R}^p$ is differentiable at $Y_0 = fX_0$, then $g \circ f$ is differentiable at X_0 and

$$d_{X_0}(g \circ f) = (d_{Y_0}g) \circ (d_{X_0}f).$$

Proof. The first thing to prove is that X_0 is an interior point of the domain of $g \circ f$. Since g is differentiable at Y_0, the point Y_0 is by definition an interior point of the domain of g. Hence, there exists a positive real number δ' such that a point Y is in the domain of g whenever $|Y - Y_0| < \delta'$. The function f, being differentiable at X_0, is also continuous there (see Exercise 11, Section 4). Furthermore, X_0 is by definition an interior point of the domain of f. It follows that there exists a positive number δ such that if $|X - X_0| < \delta$, then X is in the domain of f and

$$|fX - Y_0| = |fX - fX_0| < \delta'.$$

But δ' has been chosen just so that if the last inequality holds, then fX is in the domain of g. Thus any point X in $\mathfrak{R}^n$ that satisfies $|X - X_0| < \delta$ lies in the domain of the composite function $g \circ f$, and the vector X_0 is therefore an interior point of that domain.

It remains to prove that the composite linear transformation $(d_{Y_0}g) \circ (d_{X_0}f)$ satisfies the criterion for being the differential of

$g \circ f$, that is, we must prove that if

$$R(X) = (g \circ f)X - (g \circ f)X_0 - (d_{Y_0}g) \circ (d_{X_0}f)(X - X_0),$$

then

$$\lim_{X \to X_0} \frac{R(X)}{|X - X_0|} = 0.$$

Since $d_{X_0}f$ and $d_{Y_0}g$ exist, there are remainder functions R_1 and R_2 such that

$$\lim_{X \to X_0} \frac{R_1(X)}{|X - X_0|} = 0 \quad \text{and} \quad \lim_{Y \to Y_0} \frac{R_2(Y)}{|Y - Y_0|} = 0, \tag{1}$$

and such that

$$fX - fX_0 = (d_{X_0}f)(X - X_0) + R_1(X)$$

$$gY - gY_0 = (d_{Y_0}g)(Y - Y_0) + R_2(Y).$$

Using the f-equation to substitute into the g-equation, we get

$$(g \circ f)X - (g \circ f)X_0$$

$$= (d_{Y_0}g)((d_{X_0}f)(X - X_0) + R_1(X)) + R_2(fX).$$

The linearity of $d_{Y_0}g$ and the definition of $R(X)$ imply that

$$R(X) = (d_{Y_0}g)R_1(X) + R_2(fX).$$

We shall collect some estimates for the things on the right side of the last equation. Since X_0 and Y_0 are interior points of the domains of f and g, we can assume X and Y restricted to neighborhoods of X_0 and Y_0 on which f and g are defined. Let ϵ be an arbitrary positive number. By the second equation in (1) there is a $\delta' > 0$ such that

$$|R_2(Y)| < \epsilon |Y - Y_0|, \quad \text{whenever } |Y - Y_0| < \delta'. \tag{2}$$

By the first equation in (1) and the fact that f is continuous at X_0 we can choose a single $\delta > 0$ such that

$$|R_1(X)| < \epsilon |X - X_0|, \quad \text{whenever } |X - X_0| < \delta, \tag{3}$$

and such that

$$|fX - fX_0| < \delta', \quad \text{whenever } |X - X_0| < \delta. \tag{4}$$

Finally, by Theorem 2.6 there is a number $k > 0$ such that

$$|(d_{Y_0}g)Y| < k|Y| \quad \text{and} \quad |(d_{X_0}f)(X - X_0)| \le k|X - X_0|. \tag{5}$$

Now using the first inequality in (5), and inequalities (2) and (4), we get

$$| R(X) | \leq k | R_1(X) | + \epsilon | fX - fX_0 |, \qquad \text{whenever } | X - X_0 | < \delta.$$

By the definition of R_1,

$$| R(X) | \leq k | R_1(X) | + \epsilon | (d_{X_0} f)(X - X_0) + R_1(X) |$$

$$\leq (k + \epsilon) | R_1(X) | + \epsilon | (d_{X_0} f)(X - X_0) |.$$

Using (3) and the second inequality in (5), we get

$$| R(X) | \leq (2k\epsilon + \epsilon^2) | X - X_0 |, \qquad \text{for } | X - X_0 | < \delta.$$

Since ϵ is arbitrary,

$$\lim_{X \to X_0} \frac{R(X)}{| X - X_0 |} = 0,$$

and the proof is complete.

EXAMPLE 2. Let f and g be the vector functions defined in Example 1, viz.

$$f\begin{pmatrix} x \\ y \end{pmatrix} = [\ln (x + y)]^2, \qquad g(t) = \begin{pmatrix} \arcsin t \\ t^2 \\ t^3 \end{pmatrix}.$$

Using the chain rule, we shall compute the matrix of the differential $d_{X_0}(g \circ f)$ at

$$X_0 = \begin{pmatrix} 1 \\ 1 \end{pmatrix}.$$

The matrix of $d_{X_0} f$ is the Jacobian matrix

$$\left(\frac{2 \ln (x + y)}{x + y} \quad \frac{2 \ln (x + y)}{x + y} \right)_{x=y=1} = (\ln 2 \quad \ln 2).$$

The point $Y_0 = fX_0$ is the real number $t_0 = (\ln 2)^2$. The Jacobian matrix of g at t_0 is

$$\begin{pmatrix} (1 - t_0^2)^{-1/2} \\ 2t_0 \\ 3t_0^2 \end{pmatrix} = \begin{pmatrix} [1 - (\ln 2)^4]^{-1/2} \\ 2(\ln 2)^2 \\ 3(\ln 2)^4 \end{pmatrix}.$$

According to the chain rule, $d_{x_0}(g \circ f) = (d_{t_0}g) \circ (d_{x_0}f)$. The matrix of the composition of two linear transformations is the product of their respective matrices. Hence the matrix of $d_{x_0}(g \circ f)$ is

$$
\begin{pmatrix}
\dfrac{1}{\sqrt{1-(\ln 2)^4}} \\[2mm]
2(\ln 2)^2 \\[2mm]
3(\ln 2)^4
\end{pmatrix}
(\ln 2 \quad \ln 2) =
\begin{pmatrix}
\dfrac{\ln 2}{\sqrt{1-(\ln 2)^4}} & \dfrac{\ln 2}{\sqrt{1-(\ln 2)^4}} \\[2mm]
2(\ln 2)^3 & 2(\ln 2)^3 \\[2mm]
3(\ln 2)^5 & 3(\ln 2)^5
\end{pmatrix}.
$$

The same result can be obtained by computing directly the partial derivatives of the matrix of $d_{x_0}(g \circ f)$.

It is common practice in calculus to denote a function by the same symbol as a typical element of its range. Thus the derivative of a function $\Re \xrightarrow{f} \Re$ is more often than otherwise denoted, in conjunction with the equation $y = f(x)$, by dy/dx. Similarly, the partial derivatives of a function $\Re^3 \xrightarrow{f} \Re$ are commonly written as

$$
\frac{\partial w}{\partial x}, \quad \frac{\partial w}{\partial y}, \quad \text{and} \quad \frac{\partial w}{\partial z}
$$

along with the explanatory equation $w = f(x, y, z)$. For example, if $w = xy^2e^{x+3z}$, then

$$
\frac{\partial w}{\partial x} = y^2e^{x+3z} + xy^2e^{x+3z},
$$

$$
\frac{\partial w}{\partial y} = 2xye^{x+3z},
$$

$$
\frac{\partial w}{\partial z} = 3xy^2e^{x+3z}.
$$

This notation has the disadvantage that because it does not contain specific reference to the function being differentiated it obscures the fact that *functions are the only mathematical objects that have derivatives and differentials*. On the other hand, it is notationally convenient and is, moreover, the traditional language of calculus. To illustrate its convenience, suppose that the functions g and f are given by

$$
w = g(x, y, z), \quad x = f_1(s, t), \quad y = f_2(s, t), \quad z = f_3(s, t).
$$

Then, by the chain rule

$$
\left(\begin{array}{cc} \dfrac{\partial w}{\partial s} & \dfrac{\partial w}{\partial t} \end{array}\right) = \left(\begin{array}{ccc} \dfrac{\partial g}{\partial x} & \dfrac{\partial g}{\partial y} & \dfrac{\partial g}{\partial z} \end{array}\right) \begin{vmatrix} \dfrac{\partial x}{\partial s} & \dfrac{\partial x}{\partial i} \\[2mm] \dfrac{\partial y}{\partial s} & \dfrac{\partial y}{\partial i} \\[2mm] \dfrac{\partial z}{\partial s} & \dfrac{\partial z}{\partial t} \end{vmatrix}.
$$

Matrix multiplication yields

$$
\left.\begin{aligned}
\frac{\partial w}{\partial s} &= \frac{\partial g}{\partial x}\frac{\partial x}{\partial s} + \frac{\partial g}{\partial y}\frac{\partial y}{\partial s} + \frac{\partial g}{\partial z}\frac{\partial z}{\partial s} \\[3mm]
\frac{\partial w}{\partial t} &= \frac{\partial g}{\partial x}\frac{\partial x}{\partial t} + \frac{\partial g}{\partial y}\frac{\partial y}{\partial t} + \frac{\partial g}{\partial z}\frac{\partial z}{\partial t}
\end{aligned}\right\} \tag{6}
$$

A slightly different looking application of the chain rule is obtained if the domain space of f is 1-dimensional, that is, if f is a function of one variable. Consider, for example,

$$
w = g(u, v), \qquad \begin{pmatrix} u \\ v \end{pmatrix} = f(t) = \begin{pmatrix} f_1(t) \\ f_2(t) \end{pmatrix}.
$$

The composition $g \circ f$ is in this case a real-valued function of one variable. Its differential is defined by the 1-by-1 matrix whose entry is the derivative

$$
\frac{d(g \circ f)}{dt} = \frac{dw}{dt}.
$$

The differentials of g and f are defined respectively by the Jacobian matrices

$$
\left(\begin{array}{cc} \dfrac{\partial w}{\partial u} & \dfrac{\partial w}{\partial v} \end{array}\right) \quad \text{and} \quad \begin{pmatrix} \dfrac{du}{dt} \\[3mm] \dfrac{dv}{dt} \end{pmatrix}.
$$

Hence, the chain rule implies that

$$
\frac{dw}{dt} = \left(\begin{array}{cc} \dfrac{\partial w}{\partial u} & \dfrac{\partial w}{\partial v} \end{array}\right) \begin{pmatrix} \dfrac{du}{dt} \\[3mm] \dfrac{dv}{dt} \end{pmatrix} = \frac{\partial w}{\partial u}\frac{du}{dt} + \frac{\partial w}{\partial v}\frac{dv}{dt}. \tag{7}
$$

Finally, let us suppose that both f and g are real-valued functions of one variable. This is the situation encountered in one-variable calculus.

The differentials of f at t, of g at $s = f(t)$, and of $g \circ f$ at t are represented by the three 1-by-1 Jacobian matrices $(f'(t))$, $(g'(s))$, and $((g \circ f)'(t))$ respectively. The chain rule implies that

7.2
$$(g \circ f)'(t) = g'(s)f'(t).$$

If the functions are presented in the form

$$x = g(s), \qquad s = f(t),$$

the more explicit formula (7.2) can be written as the famous equation

$$\frac{dx}{dt} = \frac{dx}{ds}\frac{ds}{dt}. \tag{8}$$

EXAMPLE 3. Given that

$$\begin{cases} x = u^2 + v^3, \\ y = e^{uv}, \end{cases} \quad \text{and} \quad \begin{cases} u = t + 1, \\ v = e^t, \end{cases}$$

find dx/dt and dy/dt at $t = 0$. Let $\Re \xrightarrow{f} \Re^2$ and $\Re^2 \xrightarrow{g} \Re^2$ be the functions defined by

$$f(t) = \begin{pmatrix} t + 1 \\ e^t \end{pmatrix} = \begin{pmatrix} u \\ v \end{pmatrix}, \qquad -\infty < t < \infty,$$

$$g\begin{pmatrix} u \\ v \end{pmatrix} = \begin{pmatrix} u^2 + v^3 \\ e^{uv} \end{pmatrix} = \begin{pmatrix} x \\ y \end{pmatrix}, \qquad \begin{vmatrix} -\infty < u < \infty. \\ -\infty < v < \infty. \end{vmatrix}$$

The differential of f at t is defined by the 2-by-1 Jacobian matrix

$$\begin{pmatrix} \dfrac{du}{dt} \\ \dfrac{dv}{dt} \end{pmatrix} = \begin{pmatrix} 1 \\ e^t \end{pmatrix}.$$

The matrix of the differential of g at $\begin{pmatrix} u \\ v \end{pmatrix}$ is

$$\begin{pmatrix} \dfrac{\partial x}{\partial u} & \dfrac{\partial x}{\partial v} \\ \dfrac{\partial y}{\partial u} & \dfrac{\partial y}{\partial v} \end{pmatrix} = \begin{pmatrix} 2u & 3v^2 \\ ve^{uv} & ue^{uv} \end{pmatrix}.$$

The dependence of x and y on t is given by

$$\begin{pmatrix} x \\ y \end{pmatrix} = (g \circ f)t, \qquad -\infty < t < \infty.$$

Hence, the two derivatives dx/dt and dy/dt are the entries in the Jacobian matrix that defines the differential of the composite function $g \circ f$. The chain rule $d_t(g \circ f) = (d_{\binom{u}{v}}g) \circ (d_t f)$ therefore implies that

$$\begin{pmatrix} \dfrac{dx}{dt} \\[2mm] \dfrac{dy}{dt} \end{pmatrix} = \begin{pmatrix} \dfrac{\partial x}{\partial u} & \dfrac{\partial x}{\partial v} \\[2mm] \dfrac{\partial y}{\partial u} & \dfrac{\partial y}{\partial v} \end{pmatrix} \begin{pmatrix} \dfrac{du}{dt} \\[2mm] \dfrac{dv}{dt} \end{pmatrix}.$$

That is,

$$\left. \begin{aligned} \frac{dx}{dt} &= \frac{\partial x}{\partial u}\frac{du}{dt} + \frac{\partial x}{\partial v}\frac{dv}{dt} = 2u + 3v^2 e^t \\[2mm] \frac{dy}{dt} &= \frac{\partial y}{\partial u}\frac{du}{dt} + \frac{\partial y}{\partial v}\frac{dv}{dt} = ve^{uv} + ue^{uv+t} \end{aligned} \right\} \qquad (9)$$

If $t = 0$, then $\begin{pmatrix} u \\ v \end{pmatrix} = f(0) = \begin{pmatrix} 1 \\ 1 \end{pmatrix}$ and we get $u = v = 1$. It follows that

$$\frac{dx}{dt}(0) = 2 + 3 = 5,$$

$$\frac{dy}{dt}(0) = e + e = 2e.$$

The definition of matrix multiplication gives the derivative formulas that result from applications of the chain rule a formal pattern that is easy to memorize. The pattern is particularly in evidence when the coordinate functions are denoted by real variables as in formulas (6), (7), (8), and (9). All formulas of the general form

$$\dots \frac{\partial z}{\partial x}\frac{\partial x}{\partial t} + \frac{\partial z}{\partial y}\frac{\partial y}{\partial t} + \dots$$

have the disadvantage, however, that they do not contain explicit reference to the points at which the various derivatives are evaluated. It is, of course, essential to know this information. It can be found by going to the formula

$$dx(g \circ f) = (d_{fx}g) \circ (d_x f).$$

It follows that derivatives appearing in the matrix that defines $d_x f$ are evaluated at X, and those in the matrix representing $d_{fx}g$ are evaluated at fX. This is the reason for setting $t = 0$ and $u = v = 1$ in formula (9) to obtain the final answers in Example 3.

EXAMPLE 4. Let

$$z = x^y \quad \text{and} \quad \begin{cases} x = f(u, v). \\ \\ y = g(u, v). \end{cases}$$

Suppose that when $u = 1$ and $v = 2$, we have

$$\frac{\partial x}{\partial u} = -1, \qquad \frac{\partial x}{\partial v} = 3, \qquad \frac{\partial y}{\partial u} = 5, \qquad \frac{\partial y}{\partial v} = 0.$$

Suppose also that $f(1, 2) = 2$ and $g(1, 2) = -2$. What is $(\partial z/\partial u)(1, 2)$? The chain rule implies that

$$.\frac{\partial z}{\partial u} = \frac{\partial z}{\partial x}\frac{\partial x}{\partial u} + \frac{\partial z}{\partial y}\frac{\partial y}{\partial u}. \tag{10}$$

When $u = 1$ and $v = 2$, we are given that $x = f(1, 2) = 2$ and $y = g(1, 2) = -2$. Hence

$$\frac{\partial z}{\partial x}(2, -2) = yx^{y-1}\,|_{x=2,y=-2} = (-2)(2^{-3}) = -\frac{1}{4},$$

$$\frac{\partial z}{\partial y}(2, -2) = x^y \ln x\,|_{x=2,y=-2} = \frac{1}{4}\ln 2.$$

In order to obtain $\partial z/\partial u$ at $(u, v) = (1, 2)$, it is necessary to know at what points to evaluate the partial derivatives that appear in Equation (10). In greater detail, the chain rule implies that

$$\frac{\partial z}{\partial u}(1, 2) = \frac{\partial z}{\partial x}(2, -2)\frac{\partial x}{\partial u}(1, 2) + \frac{\partial z}{\partial y}(2, -2)\frac{\partial y}{\partial u}(1, 2).$$

Hence

$$\frac{\partial z}{\partial u}(1, 2) = \left(-\frac{1}{4}\right)(-1) + \left(\frac{1}{4}\ln 2\right)5 = \frac{1}{4}(1 + 5\ln 2).$$

EXAMPLE 5. If $w = f(ax^2 + bxy + cy^2)$ and $y = x^2 + x + 1$, find $dw/dx(-1)$. We shall solve the problem in two ways. The first solution relies on formulas that follow from the chain rule (like (6), (7), (8), and (9)). Set

$$z = ax^2 + bxy + cy^2.$$

Then, $w = f(z)$ and

$$\frac{dz}{dx} = \frac{\partial z}{\partial x} + \frac{\partial z}{\partial y}\frac{dy}{dx}.$$

Hence, $\qquad \dfrac{dw}{dx} = \dfrac{df}{dz}\dfrac{dz}{dx} = \dfrac{df}{dz}\left(\dfrac{\partial z}{\partial x} + \dfrac{\partial z}{\partial y}\dfrac{dy}{dx}\right)$

$$= f'(z)\,(2ax + by + (bx + 2cy)\,(2x + 1)).$$

If $x = -1$, then $y = 1$ and so $z = a - b + c$. Thus,

$$\frac{dw}{dx}(-1) = f'(a - b + c)(-2a + 2b - 2c).$$

The second solution is by direct application of the chain rule. If we define functions $\Re \xrightarrow{h} \Re^2$ and $\Re^2 \xrightarrow{g} \Re$ by

$$h(x) = \begin{pmatrix} x \\ x^2 + x + 1 \end{pmatrix},$$

$$g\begin{pmatrix} x \\ y \end{pmatrix} = ax^2 + bxy + cy^2,$$

then the function whose derivative is denoted by dw/dx in the statement of the problem is the composite function $f \circ (g \circ h)$. By the chain rule,

$$d_{-1}(g \circ h) = (d_{h(-1)}g) \circ (d_{-1}h).$$

Since $h(-1) = \begin{pmatrix} -1 \\ 1 \end{pmatrix}$, the 1-by-1 matrix of $d_{-1}(g \circ h)$ is

$$(2ax + by \quad bx + 2cy)_{x=-1,y=1} \begin{pmatrix} 1 \\ 2x + 1 \end{pmatrix}_{x=-1}$$

$$= (-2a + b \quad -b + 2c)\begin{pmatrix} 1 \\ -1 \end{pmatrix} = -2a + 2b - 2c.$$

Again by the chain rule,

$$d_{-1}(f \circ (g \circ h)) = (d_{z_0} f) \circ d_{-1}(g \circ h),$$

where $z_0 = g(h(-1)) = a - b + c$. Each of the differentials in the above equation is defined by a 1-by-1 matrix. We obtain

$$\frac{dw}{dx}(-1) = \frac{d(f \circ (g \circ h))}{dx}(-1)$$

$$= f'(z_0)(-2a + 2b - 2c).$$

The Jacobian matrix of a function $\mathfrak{R}^n \xrightarrow{f} \mathfrak{R}^n$ at a point X is a square matrix. Its determinant is called **the Jacobian determinant of f at** X. An important corollary of the chain rule and the product rule for determinants (see Chapter 1, Section 17) is

7.3 Theorem. If $\mathfrak{R}^n \xrightarrow{f} \mathfrak{R}^n$ is differentiable at X_0 and $\mathfrak{R}^n \xrightarrow{g} \mathfrak{R}^n$ is differentiable at $Y_0 = fX_0$, then the Jacobian determinant of $g \circ f$ at X_0 is the product of the Jacobian determinant of f at X_0 and that of g at Y_0.

If f is defined by

$$f\begin{pmatrix} x_1 \\ \cdot \\ \cdot \\ \cdot \\ x_n \end{pmatrix} = \begin{pmatrix} f_1(x_1, \ldots, x_n) \\ \cdot \\ \cdot \\ \cdot \\ f_n(x_1, \ldots, x_n) \end{pmatrix} = \begin{pmatrix} y_1 \\ \cdot \\ \cdot \\ \cdot \\ y_n \end{pmatrix},$$

then the Jacobian determinant of f is denoted by

$$\frac{\partial(f_1, \ldots, f_n)}{\partial(x_1, \ldots, x_n)},$$

or equivalently

$$\frac{\partial(y_1, \ldots, y_n)}{\partial(x_1, \ldots, x_n)}.$$

The Jacobian determinant of f is a function of the variable X, and its value at $X_0 = (a_1, \ldots, a_n)$ will be denoted by

$$\frac{\partial(y_1, \ldots, y_n)}{\partial(x_1, \ldots, x_n)} X_0 = \frac{\partial(y_1, \ldots, y_n)}{\partial(x_1, \ldots, x_n)}(a_1, \ldots, a_n).$$

EXAMPLE 6. Let

$$f\begin{pmatrix} r \\ \theta \end{pmatrix} = \begin{pmatrix} r\cos\theta \\ r\sin\theta \end{pmatrix} = \begin{pmatrix} x \\ y \end{pmatrix} \quad \text{and} \quad g\begin{pmatrix} x \\ y \end{pmatrix} = \begin{pmatrix} x^2 - y^2 \\ 2xy \end{pmatrix} = \begin{pmatrix} w \\ z \end{pmatrix}.$$

Then,

$$\frac{\partial(x, y)}{\partial(r, \theta)} = \det\begin{pmatrix} \cos\theta & -r\sin\theta \\ \sin\theta & r\cos\theta \end{pmatrix} = r(\cos^2\theta + \sin^2\theta) = r,$$

and

$$\frac{\partial(w, z)}{\partial(x, y)} = \det\begin{pmatrix} 2x & -2y \\ 2y & 2x \end{pmatrix} = 4(x^2 + y^2).$$

The Jacobian determinant of the composite function $g \circ f$ is denoted in this case by $\partial(w, z)/\partial(r, \theta)$. If

$$\begin{pmatrix} x_0 \\ y_0 \end{pmatrix} = \begin{pmatrix} r_0\cos\theta_0 \\ r_0\sin\theta_0 \end{pmatrix},$$

Theorem 7.3 implies that

$$\frac{\partial(w, z)}{\partial(r, \theta)}(r_0, \theta_0) = \frac{\partial(w, z)}{\partial(x, y)}(x_0, y_0)\frac{\partial(x, y)}{\partial(r, \theta)}(r_0, \theta_0)$$

$$= 4(x_0^2 + y_0^2)r_0 = 4r_0^3.$$

EXERCISES

1. Given that

$$f\begin{pmatrix} x \\ y \end{pmatrix} = \begin{pmatrix} x^2 + xy + 1 \\ y^2 + 2 \end{pmatrix}, \quad g\begin{pmatrix} u \\ v \end{pmatrix} = \begin{pmatrix} u + v \\ 2u \\ v^2 \end{pmatrix},$$

find the matrix of the differential of the composite function $g \circ f$ at

$$X_0 = \begin{pmatrix} 1 \\ 1 \end{pmatrix}. \qquad \left[Ans. \begin{pmatrix} 3 & 3 \\ 6 & 2 \\ 0 & 12 \end{pmatrix} \right].$$

2. Let

$$f(t) = \begin{pmatrix} t \\ t+1 \\ t^2 \end{pmatrix} = \begin{pmatrix} x \\ y \\ z \end{pmatrix}$$

and

$$g \begin{pmatrix} x \\ y \\ z \end{pmatrix} = \begin{pmatrix} x + 2y + z^2 \\ x^2 - y \end{pmatrix} = \begin{pmatrix} u \\ v \end{pmatrix}.$$

(a) Find the Jacobian matrix of $g \circ f$ at $t = a$. $\left[Ans. \begin{pmatrix} 3 + 4a^3 \\ 2a - 1 \end{pmatrix}. \right]$

(b) Find du/dt in terms of the derivatives of x, y, z, and the partial derivatives of u.

3. Consider the curve defined parametrically by

$$f(t) = \begin{pmatrix} t \\ t^2 - 4 \\ e^{t-2} \end{pmatrix}, \qquad -\infty < t < \infty$$

Let g be a real-valued differentiable function with domain $\mathfrak{R}^3$. If

$$X_0 = \begin{pmatrix} 2 \\ 0 \\ 1 \end{pmatrix}$$

and

$$\frac{\partial g}{\partial x} X_0 = 4, \qquad \frac{\partial g}{\partial y} X_0 = 2, \qquad \frac{\partial g}{\partial z} X_0 = 2,$$

find $d/dt(g \circ f)$ at $t = 2$. $[Ans. \ 14.]$

4. Consider the functions

$$f \begin{pmatrix} u \\ v \end{pmatrix} = \begin{pmatrix} u + v \\ u - v \\ u^2 - v^2 \end{pmatrix} = \begin{pmatrix} x \\ y \\ z \end{pmatrix}$$

and

$$F(x, y, z) = x^2 + y^2 + z^2 = w.$$

(a) Find the matrix that defines the differential of $F \circ f$ at $\begin{pmatrix} a \\ b \end{pmatrix}$.

(b) Find $\dfrac{\partial w}{\partial u}$ and $\dfrac{\partial w}{\partial v}$.

5. Let $u = f(x, y)$. Make the change of variables $x = r \cos \theta$, $y = r \sin \theta$. Given that

$$\frac{\partial f}{\partial x} = x^2 + 2xy - y^2 \quad \text{and} \quad \frac{\partial f}{\partial y} = x^2 - 2xy + 2,$$

find $\dfrac{\partial f}{\partial \theta}$ when $r = 2$ and $\theta = \dfrac{\pi}{2}$.   [Ans. 8.]

6. If $w = \sqrt{x^2 + y^2 + z^2}$ and

$$\begin{pmatrix} x \\ y \\ z \end{pmatrix} = \begin{pmatrix} r \cos \theta \\ r \sin \theta \\ r \end{pmatrix},$$

find $\partial w / \partial r$ and $\partial w / \partial \theta$ using the chain rule. Check the result by direct substitution.

7. Vector functions f and g are defined by

$$f\begin{pmatrix} u \\ v \end{pmatrix} = \begin{pmatrix} u \cos v \\ u \sin v \end{pmatrix}, \qquad \begin{cases} 0 < u < \infty, \\ -\pi/2 < v < \pi/2, \end{cases}$$

$$g\begin{pmatrix} x \\ y \end{pmatrix} = \begin{pmatrix} \sqrt{x^2 + y^2} \\ \arctan \dfrac{y}{x} \end{pmatrix}, \qquad 0 < x < \infty.$$

(a) Find the Jacobian matrix of $g \circ f$ at $\begin{pmatrix} u \\ v \end{pmatrix}$.

(b) Find the Jacobian matrix of $f \circ g$ at $\begin{pmatrix} x \\ y \end{pmatrix}$.

(c) Are the following statements true or false?
    (1) domain of f = domain of $g \circ f$.
    (2) domain of g = domain of $f \circ g$.

8. A function I is called an **identity function** if $IX = X$ for all X in the domain of I.

(a) Show that if differentiable vector functions f and g are so related that the composite function $g \bigcirc f$ is an identity function, then the transformation $(d_{fX}g) \bigcirc (d_X f)$ is also an identity function for X in the domain of $g \bigcirc f$.

(b) How does this exercise apply to the preceding one?

9. If F and f are differentiable vector functions whose composition $f \bigcirc F$ is defined, show that

$$\frac{\partial f \bigcirc F}{\partial Y} X = \left(\frac{\partial f}{\partial (d_X F Y)} \bigcirc F \right) X$$

for every vector Y in the domain space of F and every vector X in the domain of $f \bigcirc F$.

10. Let X_1 be a tangent vector at X_0 to a curve defined parametrically by a differentiable vector function f. If X_0 is in the domain of a differentiable vector function F, prove that, if $d_{X_0}F \neq 0$, then $(d_{X_0}F)X_1$ is a tangent vector at FX_0 to the curve defined parametrically by $F \bigcirc f$.

11. The convention of denoting coordinate functions by real variables has its pitfalls. Resolve the following paradox: Let $w = f(x, y, z)$ and $z = g(x, y)$. By the chain rule

$$\frac{\partial w}{\partial x} = \frac{\partial w}{\partial x}\frac{\partial x}{\partial x} + \frac{\partial w}{\partial y}\frac{\partial y}{\partial x} + \frac{\partial w}{\partial z}\frac{\partial z}{\partial x}.$$

The quantities x and y are unrelated so that $\partial y/\partial x = 0$. Clearly $\partial x/\partial x = 1$. Hence,

$$\frac{\partial w}{\partial x} = \frac{\partial w}{\partial x} + \frac{\partial w}{\partial z}\frac{\partial z}{\partial x},$$

and so

$$0 = \frac{\partial w}{\partial z}\frac{\partial z}{\partial x}.$$

In particular, take $w = 2x + y + 3z$ and $z = 5x + y + 18$. Then

$$\frac{\partial w}{\partial z} = 3 \quad \text{and} \quad \frac{\partial z}{\partial x} = 5.$$

It follows that

$$0 = 15.$$

12. If $y = f(x - at) + g(x + at)$ where a is constant and f and g are twice differentiable, show that

$$a^2 \frac{\partial^2 y}{\partial x^2} = \frac{\partial^2 y}{\partial t^2}. \qquad \text{(Wave equation)}$$

13. Show that if $z = f(x, y)$ and $\begin{pmatrix} x \\ y \end{pmatrix} = \begin{pmatrix} r \cos \theta \\ r \sin \theta \end{pmatrix}$, then

$$\frac{\partial^2 z}{\partial x^2} + \frac{\partial^2 z}{\partial y^2} = \frac{\partial^2 z}{\partial r^2} + \frac{1}{r^2} \frac{\partial^2 z}{\partial \theta^2} + \frac{1}{r} \frac{\partial z}{\partial r}$$

14. If $z = f(x, y)$ is differentiable and $\begin{pmatrix} x \\ y \end{pmatrix} = \begin{pmatrix} r \cos \theta \\ r \sin \theta \end{pmatrix}$, show that

$$\left(\frac{\partial z}{\partial x}\right)^2 + \left(\frac{\partial z}{\partial y}\right)^2 = \left(\frac{\partial z}{\partial r}\right)^2 + \frac{1}{r^2} \left(\frac{\partial z}{\partial \theta}\right)^2.$$

15. If $f(tx, ty) = t^n f(x, y)$ for some integer n, and for all x, y, and t, show that

$$x \frac{\partial f}{\partial x} + y \frac{\partial f}{\partial y} = nf(x, y).$$

16. Show that for a differentiable real-valued function $g(x, y)$,

$$\frac{dg(x, x)}{dx} (a) = \frac{\partial g}{\partial x} (a, a) + \frac{\partial g}{\partial y} (a, a).$$

Using the function $f(x) = (x, x)$, show that this result is equivalent to the statement

$$d_x(g \circ f) = (d_{f(x)}g) \circ (d_x f).$$

Apply the equation to the function $g(x, y) = x^y$.

17. (a) If

$$w = f(x, y, z, t), \qquad x = g(u, z, t), \quad \text{and} \quad z = h(u, t),$$

write a formula for $\partial w / \partial t$, where by this symbol is meant the rate of change of w with respect to t, and where all the interrelations of w, x, z, t are taken into account.

(b) If

$$f(x, y, z, t) = 2xy + 3z + t^2,$$

$$g(u, z, t) = ut \sin z,$$

$$h(u, t) = 2u + t,$$

evaluate the above $\partial w / \partial t$ at the point $u = 1$, $t = 2$, $y = 3$, by using the formula you derived in part (a) and also by substituting in the functions for x and z and then differentiating.

18. Consider a real-valued function $f(x, y)$ such that

$$f_x(2, 1) = 3, \qquad f_y(2, 1) = -2, \qquad f_{xx}(2, 1) = 0,$$

$$f_{xy}(2, 1) = f_{yx}(2, 1) = 1, \qquad f_{yy}(2, 1) = 2.$$

Let $\mathcal{R}^2 \xrightarrow{g} \mathcal{R}^2$ be defined by

$$g(u, v) = (u + v, uv).$$

Find $\dfrac{\partial^2 (f \bigcirc g)}{\partial v\, \partial u}$ at $(1, 1)$.   [*Ans.* 2.]

19. Calculate the Jacobian determinants of the following functions at the points indicated.

(a) $f\begin{pmatrix} u \\ v \end{pmatrix} = \begin{pmatrix} u^2 + 2uv + 3v \\ u - v \end{pmatrix} = \begin{pmatrix} x \\ y \end{pmatrix}$, at $U_0 = \begin{pmatrix} 0 \\ 2 \end{pmatrix}$.   [*Ans.* -7.]

(b) $g\begin{pmatrix} x \\ y \end{pmatrix} = \begin{pmatrix} x^2 - y^2 \\ 2xy \end{pmatrix} = \begin{pmatrix} z \\ w \end{pmatrix}$, at $X_0 = \begin{pmatrix} 6 \\ -2 \end{pmatrix}$.   [*Ans.* 160.]

(c) $A\begin{pmatrix} x \\ y \end{pmatrix} = \begin{pmatrix} a & b \\ c & d \end{pmatrix}\begin{pmatrix} x \\ y \end{pmatrix}$, at an arbitrary $\begin{pmatrix} x \\ y \end{pmatrix}$.

(d) An affine transformation $\mathcal{R}^n \xrightarrow{A} \mathcal{R}^n$, $AX = LX + Y_0$, at an arbitrary X_0.

(e) $T\begin{pmatrix} r \\ \phi \\ \theta \end{pmatrix} = \begin{pmatrix} r \cos \theta \sin \phi \\ r \sin \theta \sin \phi \\ r \cos \phi \end{pmatrix}$, at $\begin{pmatrix} r \\ \phi \\ \theta \end{pmatrix}$.

20. Using the functions f and g in Exercises 19(a) and (b), compute the Jacobian determinant of the composite function $g \bigcirc f$ at $\begin{pmatrix} 0 \\ 2 \end{pmatrix}$.

[*Ans.* -1120.]

21. In terms of functions $\mathcal{R}^2 \xrightarrow{f} \mathcal{R}^2$ and $\mathcal{R}^2 \xrightarrow{g} \mathcal{R}^2$, what do the following equations say and how do they follow from Theorem 7.3?

(a) $\dfrac{\partial(x, y)}{\partial(u, v)} \dfrac{\partial(u, v)}{\partial(r, \theta)} = \dfrac{\partial(x, y)}{\partial(r, \theta)}$.   (b) $\dfrac{\partial(x, y)}{\partial(u, v)} \dfrac{\partial(u, v)}{\partial(x, y)} = 1$.

8. INVERSE FUNCTIONS

Let f be any function whatever. If there exists a function f^{-1} with the property

$$f^{-1}Y = X \quad \text{if and only if} \quad fX = Y,$$

then f^{-1} is called the **inverse function** of f. It follows that the domain of f^{-1} is the range of f and that the range of f^{-1} is the domain of f. Some familiar examples of functions and their inverses are

$$\begin{cases} f(x) = x^2, & x \geq 0. \\ f^{-1}(y) = \sqrt{y}, & y \geq 0. \end{cases}$$

$$\begin{cases} f(x) = e^x, & -\infty < x < \infty. \\ f^{-1}(y) = \ln y, & y > 0. \end{cases}$$

$$\begin{cases} f(x) = \sin x, & -\frac{\pi}{2} \leq x \leq \frac{\pi}{2}. \\ f^{-1}(y) = \arcsin y, & -1 \leq y \leq 1. \end{cases}$$

The inverse function f^{-1} should not be confused with the reciprocal $1/f$. For example, if $f(x) = x^2$, then $f^{-1}(2) = \sqrt{2}$, whereas $(f(2))^{-1} = 1/f(2) = \frac{1}{4}$.

We recall that a function is one-one if each element in the range is the image of precisely one element in the domain. A fact that is used repeatedly and is easy to prove is the following.

8.1 Theorem. A function f has an inverse if and only if it is one-one.

In connection with this remark notice that the function f defined by

$$f(x) = x^2, \quad -\infty < x < \infty,$$

is not one-one and does not have an inverse. In order for the inverse function to be defined, we can restrict the domain of f to be the non-negative real numbers.

The inverse function L^{-1} of every invertible linear transformation $\mathfrak{X} \xrightarrow{L} \mathfrak{Y}$ is itself linear. That is,

$$L^{-1}(aY_1 + bY_2) = aL^{-1}Y_1 + bL^{-1}Y_2,$$

whenever Y_1 and Y_2 are in the range of L. If the dimension of $\mathfrak{X}$ is less than that of $\mathfrak{Y}$, the range of L is a proper subspace of $\mathfrak{Y}$. In this case, L^{-1} is not defined on all of $\mathfrak{Y}$. On the other hand, if $\mathfrak{X}$ and $\mathfrak{Y}$ have the same dimension, the domain of L^{-1} is all of $\mathfrak{Y}$. Thus the inverse function of every one-one linear transformation $\mathfrak{R}^n \xrightarrow{L} \mathfrak{R}^n$ is a linear transformation $\mathfrak{R}^n \xrightarrow{L^{-1}} \mathfrak{R}^n$.

EXAMPLE 1. Consider the affine transformation $\mathfrak{R}^3 \xrightarrow{A} \mathfrak{R}^3$ defined by

$$A \begin{pmatrix} x \\ y \\ z \end{pmatrix} = \begin{pmatrix} 4 & 0 & 5 \\ 0 & 1 & -6 \\ 3 & 0 & 4 \end{pmatrix} \begin{pmatrix} x - 1 \\ y - 0 \\ z - 1 \end{pmatrix} + \begin{pmatrix} 1 \\ 5 \\ 2 \end{pmatrix}.$$

It is obvious that any affine transformation $AX = L(X - X_0) + Y_0$ is one-one if and only if the linear transformation L is one-one also. In this example,

$$X_0 = \begin{pmatrix} 1 \\ 0 \\ 1 \end{pmatrix} \quad \text{and} \quad LX = \begin{pmatrix} 4 & 0 & 5 \\ 0 & 1 & -6 \\ 3 & 0 & 4 \end{pmatrix} \begin{pmatrix} x \\ y \\ z \end{pmatrix}.$$

The inverse matrix of

$$\begin{pmatrix} 4 & 0 & 5 \\ 0 & 1 & -6 \\ 3 & 0 & 4 \end{pmatrix}$$

can be computed to be

$$\begin{pmatrix} 4 & 0 & -5 \\ -18 & 1 & 24 \\ -3 & 0 & 4 \end{pmatrix}.$$

It follows that L, and therefore A, has an inverse. In fact, if $AX = Y$ then

$$AX = L(X - X_0) + Y_0,$$

and

$$A^{-1}Y = L^{-1}(Y - Y_0) + X_0. \tag{1}$$

That this is the correct expression for A^{-1} may be checked by substituting AX for Y. We get

$$A^{-1}AX = L^{-1}(L(X - X_0)) + X_0 = X.$$

Hence

$$A^{-1} \begin{pmatrix} u \\ v \\ w \end{pmatrix} = \begin{pmatrix} 4 & 0 & -5 \\ -18 & 1 & 24 \\ -3 & 0 & 4 \end{pmatrix} \begin{pmatrix} u - 1 \\ v - 5 \\ w - 2 \end{pmatrix} + \begin{pmatrix} 1 \\ 0 \\ 1 \end{pmatrix}.$$

Obviously this method will enable us to find the inverse of any affine transformation $\mathfrak{R}^n \xrightarrow{A} \mathfrak{R}^n$ if the inverse exists.

The principal purpose of this section is the study of inverses of non-linear vector functions. Given a function $\mathfrak{R}^n \xrightarrow{f} \mathfrak{R}^n$ one may ask (1) Does it have an inverse? and (2) If it does, what are its properties? In general it is not easy to answer these questions just by looking at the function. For example, consider

$$f\begin{pmatrix} x \\ y \end{pmatrix} = \begin{pmatrix} x^4 y + x \\ x + y^3 \end{pmatrix}.$$

On the other hand, we do know how to tell whether or not an affine transformation has an inverse and, what is more, how to compute it explicitly when it does exist. Furthermore, if f is differentiable at a point X_0, it can be approximated near that point by an affine transformation A. For this reason, one might conjecture that if the domain of f is restricted to points close to X_0, then f will have an inverse if A does. In addition, one might guess that A^{-1} is the approximating affine transformation to f^{-1} near fX_0. Except for details, these statements are correct and are the content of the inverse function theorem.

8.2 The inverse function theorem. Let $\mathfrak{R}^n \xrightarrow{f} \mathfrak{R}^n$ be a continuously differentiable function such that $d_{X_0} f$ has an inverse. Then there is an open set N containing X_0 such that f, when restricted to N, has a continuously differentiable inverse f^{-1}. The image set fN is open. In addition,

$$d_{Y_0} f^{-1} = (d_{X_0} f)^{-1}, \qquad \text{where } Y_0 = fX_0.$$

That is, the differential of the inverse function at Y_0 is the inverse of the differential of f at X_0.

The existence of f^{-1} is proved in Appendix II. Once the existence has been established, we can write $f^{-1} \circ f = I$, where $\mathfrak{R}^n \xrightarrow{I} \mathfrak{R}^n$ is the identity transformation on the neighborhood N. Then by the chain rule we have, since $d_{X_0} I = I$,

$$(d_{Y_0} f^{-1}) \circ (d_{X_0} f) = I, \quad \text{or} \quad d_{Y_0} f^{-1} = (d_{X_0} f)^{-1}.$$

For real-valued functions of one variable, the existence of an inverse function is not hard to prove. Let $\mathfrak{R} \xrightarrow{f} \mathfrak{R}$ satisfy the differentiability condition of the theorem, and suppose that $d_{x_0} f$ is one-one, that is, has an inverse. The matrix of $d_{x_0} f$ is $(f'(x_0))$ and the matrix of $(d_{x_0} f)^{-1}$ is $(1/f'(x_0))$. Since the inverse matrix exists whenever $f'(x_0) \neq 0$, the geometric meaning of the condition that $d_{x_0} f$ have an inverse is that the graph of f should not have a horizontal tangent. To be specific, suppose that $f'(x_0) > 0$. Since f' is continuous, we have $f'(x) > 0$ for every x in some interval $a < x < b$ that contains x_0, as shown in Figure 34. We contend

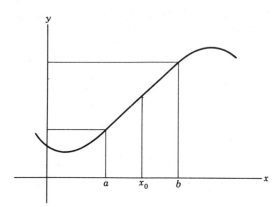

FIGURE 34

that f restricted to this interval is one-one. For suppose x_1 and x_2 are any two points in the interval such that $x_1 < x_2$. By the mean-value theorem it follows that

$$\frac{f(x_2) - f(x_1)}{x_2 - x_1} = f'(x_0),$$

for some x_0 in the interval $x_1 < x < x_2$. Since $f'(x_0) > 0$, and $x_2 - x_1 > 0$, we obtain

$$f(x_2) - f(x_1) > 0.$$

Thus, f is strictly increasing in the interval $a < x < b$, and our contention is proved. It follows that f restricted to this interval has an inverse. The other conclusions of the inverse function theorem can also be obtained in a straightforward way, for this special case.

EXAMPLE 2. Let f be the function defined by

$$f\begin{pmatrix} u \\ v \end{pmatrix} = \begin{pmatrix} x \\ y \end{pmatrix} = \begin{pmatrix} u^2 + v^2 \\ u \end{pmatrix}, \qquad v > 0.$$

At an arbitrary point

$$U = \begin{pmatrix} u \\ v \end{pmatrix}$$

in the domain of f, the matrix of $d_U f$ is

$$\begin{pmatrix} 2u & 2v \\ 1 & 0 \end{pmatrix}.$$

The inverse matrix is

$$\begin{pmatrix} 0 & 1 \\ \dfrac{1}{2v} & -\dfrac{u}{v} \end{pmatrix}.$$

The conclusion is that for some open set N containing the point

$$\begin{pmatrix} u \\ v \end{pmatrix}$$

with $v > 0$, there is an inverse function defined on the image set fN. For this particular example, f has an inverse as it stands, which we can compute explicitly. It is

$$f^{-1} \begin{pmatrix} x \\ y \end{pmatrix} = \begin{pmatrix} u \\ v \end{pmatrix} = \begin{pmatrix} y \\ \sqrt{x - y^2} \end{pmatrix}, \quad x > y^2.$$

At any point

$$X = \begin{pmatrix} x \\ y \end{pmatrix}$$

in the domain of f^{-1}, the matrix of $d_X f^{-1}$ is

$$\begin{pmatrix} 0 & 1 \\ \dfrac{1}{2\sqrt{x - y^2}} & \dfrac{-y}{\sqrt{x - y^2}} \end{pmatrix}.$$

For vectors X and U that correspond according to $X = fU$, i.e., for which $u = y$ and $v = \sqrt{x - y^2}$, we have indeed verified that $d_X f^{-1}$ has the same matrix as $(d_U f)^{-1}$.

EXAMPLE 3. Consider the function f defined by

$$f\begin{pmatrix} x \\ y \end{pmatrix} = \begin{pmatrix} x^3 - 2xy^2 \\ x + y \end{pmatrix}, \qquad \begin{cases} -\infty < x < \infty. \\ -\infty < y < \infty. \end{cases}$$

At the point

$$X_0 = \begin{pmatrix} 1 \\ -1 \end{pmatrix}$$

the differential $d_{X_0} f$ is defined by the Jacobian matrix

$$\begin{pmatrix} 3x^2 - 2y^2 & -4xy \\ 1 & 1 \end{pmatrix}_{x=1,\,y=-1} = \begin{pmatrix} 1 & 4 \\ 1 & 1 \end{pmatrix}.$$

The inverse of this matrix is

$$\begin{pmatrix} -\frac{1}{3} & \frac{4}{3} \\ \frac{1}{3} & -\frac{1}{3} \end{pmatrix},$$

and the fact that it exists implies that $d_{X_0} f$ is one-one. Since f is obviously continuously differentiable, we conclude from the inverse function theorem that in some open set containing X_0 the function f has an inverse f^{-1}. Moreover, if

$$Y_0 = fX_0 = \begin{pmatrix} -1 \\ 0 \end{pmatrix},$$

the matrix of the differential $d_{Y_0} f^{-1}$ is

$$\begin{pmatrix} -\frac{1}{3} & \frac{4}{3} \\ \frac{1}{3} & -\frac{1}{3} \end{pmatrix}.$$

Although it would be difficult to evaluate f^{-1} explicitly, it is easy to write down the affine transformation that approximates f^{-1} in the vicinity of the point Y_0. It is the inverse A^{-1} of the affine transformation A that approximates f near X_0. We have, either by the inverse function theorem, or by formula (1) of Example 1,

$$\begin{aligned} AX &= fX_0 + (d_{X_0} f)(X - X_0) \\ &= Y_0 + (d_{X_0} f)(X - X_0). \\ A^{-1} Y &= f^{-1} Y_0 + (d_{Y_0} f^{-1})(Y - Y_0) \\ &= X_0 + (d_{X_0} f)^{-1}(Y - Y_0). \end{aligned}$$

Hence, if we set $Y = \begin{pmatrix} u \\ v \end{pmatrix}$,

$$A^{-1}\begin{pmatrix} u \\ v \end{pmatrix} = \begin{pmatrix} 1 \\ -1 \end{pmatrix} + \begin{pmatrix} -\frac{1}{3} & \frac{4}{3} \\ \frac{1}{3} & -\frac{1}{3} \end{pmatrix}\begin{pmatrix} u + 1 \\ v - 0 \end{pmatrix}$$

$$= \begin{pmatrix} -\frac{1}{3} & \frac{4}{3} \\ \frac{1}{3} & -\frac{1}{3} \end{pmatrix}\begin{pmatrix} u \\ v \end{pmatrix} + \begin{pmatrix} \frac{2}{3} \\ -\frac{2}{3} \end{pmatrix}.$$

EXAMPLE 4. The equations

$$u = x^4 y + x, \qquad v = x + y^3$$

define a transformation from $\mathcal{R}^2$ to $\mathcal{R}^2$. The matrix of the differential of the transformation at $(x, y) = (1, 1)$ is

$$\begin{pmatrix} 4x^3y + 1 & x^4 \\ 1 & 3y^2 \end{pmatrix}_{(x,y)=(1,1)} = \begin{pmatrix} 5 & 1 \\ 1 & 3 \end{pmatrix}.$$

Since the columns of this matrix are independent, the differential has an inverse, and according to the inverse function theorem the transformation has an inverse also, in an open neighborhood of $(x, y) = (1, 1)$. The inverse transformation would be given by equations of the form

$$x = F(u, v), \qquad y = G(u, v).$$

The actual computation of F and G is difficult, but we can easily compute the partial derivatives of F and G with respect to u and v at the point $(u, v) = (2, 2)$ that corresponds to $(x, y) = (1, 1)$. These partial derivatives occur in the Jacobian matrix of F and G or, equivalently, in the inverse matrix of the differential of the given functions. We have

$$\begin{pmatrix} \dfrac{\partial F}{\partial u}(2, 2) & \dfrac{\partial F}{\partial v}(2, 2) \\ \dfrac{\partial G}{\partial u}(2, 2) & \dfrac{\partial G}{\partial v}(2, 2) \end{pmatrix} = \begin{pmatrix} 5 & 1 \\ 1 & 3 \end{pmatrix}^{-1} = \begin{pmatrix} \dfrac{3}{14} & -\dfrac{1}{14} \\ -\dfrac{1}{14} & \dfrac{5}{14} \end{pmatrix}.$$

Suppose $\mathcal{R}^n \xrightarrow{f} \mathcal{R}^n$ is a function for which the hypotheses of the inverse function theorem are satisfied at some point X_0. It is important to realize that the theorem does not settle the question of the existence of an inverse for the whole function f, but only for f restricted to some open set containing X_0. For example, the transformation

$$\begin{pmatrix} x \\ y \end{pmatrix} = \begin{pmatrix} u \cos v \\ u \sin v \end{pmatrix}, \quad 0 < u$$

has Jacobian matrix

$$\begin{pmatrix} \cos v & -u \sin v \\ \sin v & u \cos v \end{pmatrix}$$

with inverse matrix

$$\begin{pmatrix} \cos v & \sin v \\ -\dfrac{1}{u} \sin v & \dfrac{1}{u} \cos v \end{pmatrix}.$$

The inverse matrix exists for all (u, v) satisfying $u > 0$. However, the otherwise unrestricted transformation clearly has no inverse, for the same image point is obtained whenever v increases by 2π. Two corresponding regions are shown in Figure 35. If the transformation is restricted so that, for instance, $0 < v < 2\pi$, then it becomes one-one and has an inverse.

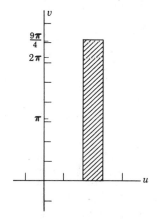
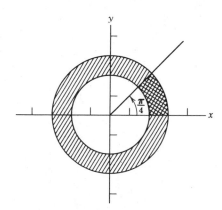

FIGURE 35

EXERCISES

1. Uniqueness of the inverse function. Prove, by assuming the contrary, that a function f cannot have two different inverse functions.

2. Prove that if f^{-1} is the inverse of f, then we have
   (1) domain of f^{-1} = range of f.
   (2) $(f^{-1} \circ f)X = X$, for every X in the domain of f.
   (3) range of f^{-1} = domain of f.
   (4) $(f \circ f^{-1})Y = Y$, for every Y in domain of f^{-1}.

3. Show that $(f^{-1})^{-1} = f$.

4. Which of the following functions have inverses?

(a) $y = \cosh x, -\infty < x < \infty$.

(b) $y = \cosh x, 0 \leq x < \infty$.

(c) $f(x) = \tan x,$ $\begin{cases} \dfrac{7}{4}\pi \leq x < \dfrac{11}{4}\pi. \\[2mm] x \neq \dfrac{10\pi}{4}. \end{cases}$

(d) $f(x) = \tan x, 0 \leq x \leq \pi/4$.

(e) $y = x^2 - 2x + 1, 1 \leq x < \infty$.

(f) $y = x^2 - 3x + 2, 0 \leq x < \infty$.

5. Compute A^{-1} for the following affine transformations:

(a) $A(x) = 7x + 2$.

(b) $A\begin{pmatrix} u \\ v \end{pmatrix} = \begin{pmatrix} 1 & 3 \\ 2 & 4 \end{pmatrix}\begin{pmatrix} u - 1 \\ v - 2 \end{pmatrix} + \begin{pmatrix} 3 \\ 4 \end{pmatrix}.$

$$\left[Ans.\ A^{-1}\begin{pmatrix} x \\ y \end{pmatrix} = \begin{pmatrix} -2 & \frac{3}{2} \\ 1 & -\frac{1}{2} \end{pmatrix}\begin{pmatrix} x - 3 \\ y - 4 \end{pmatrix} + \begin{pmatrix} 1 \\ 2 \end{pmatrix}. \right]$$

(c) $A\begin{pmatrix} x \\ y \\ z \end{pmatrix} = \begin{pmatrix} 3 & -1 & 2 \\ 3 & 0 & 1 \\ 2 & -1 & 2 \end{pmatrix}\begin{pmatrix} x \\ y \\ z \end{pmatrix} - \begin{pmatrix} 1 \\ 2 \\ 0 \end{pmatrix}.$

(d) $x = \quad u \qquad\quad - w + 1,$

$y = -4u + 2v + 3w + 3,$

$z = -3u + \quad v + 3w + 2.$

6. Using the inverse function theorem, show that the following functions have inverses when restricted to some open set containing x_0.

(a) $f(x) = \tan x, x_0 = \pi/6$.

(b) $y = x^2 - 3x + 2, x_0 = 4$.

(c) $y = x^3 - 7x + 6$, $x_0 = 4$.

(d) $f(x) = \int_{-\infty}^{x} e^{-t^2} dt$, $x_0 = 0$.

7. Let $f\begin{pmatrix} x \\ y \end{pmatrix} = \begin{pmatrix} x^2 - y^2 \\ 2xy \end{pmatrix}$.

(a) Show that for every point X_0 except

$$X_0 = \begin{pmatrix} 0 \\ 0 \end{pmatrix},$$

the restriction of f to some open set containing X_0 has an inverse.

(b) Show that with domain unrestricted, f has no inverse.

(c) If f^{-1} is the inverse of f in a neighborhood of the point $\begin{pmatrix} 1 \\ 2 \end{pmatrix}$, compute

the affine transformation that approximates f^{-1} close to

$$f\begin{pmatrix} 1 \\ 2 \end{pmatrix} = \begin{pmatrix} -3 \\ 4 \end{pmatrix}. \qquad \left[Ans. \begin{pmatrix} \frac{1}{10} & \frac{1}{5} \\ -\frac{1}{5} & \frac{1}{10} \end{pmatrix} \begin{pmatrix} u \\ v \end{pmatrix} + \begin{pmatrix} \frac{1}{2} \\ 1 \end{pmatrix}. \right]$$

8. Find the affine transformation that best approximates the inverse of the function

$$f\begin{pmatrix} x \\ y \end{pmatrix} = \begin{pmatrix} x^3 + 2xy + y^2 \\ x^2 + y \end{pmatrix}$$

near the point $f\begin{pmatrix} 1 \\ 1 \end{pmatrix}$. Notice that to find the precise inverse would be

difficult.

$$\left[Ans. \begin{pmatrix} -\frac{1}{3} & \frac{4}{3} \\ \frac{2}{3} & -\frac{5}{3} \end{pmatrix} \begin{pmatrix} u \\ v \end{pmatrix} + \begin{pmatrix} -\frac{1}{3} \\ \frac{5}{3} \end{pmatrix}. \right]$$

9. (a) Let T be defined by

$$\begin{pmatrix} x \\ y \end{pmatrix} = T\begin{pmatrix} r \\ \theta \end{pmatrix} = \begin{pmatrix} r \cos \theta \\ r \sin \theta \end{pmatrix}, \qquad \begin{cases} 0 < r. \\ 0 \leq \theta < 2\pi. \end{cases}$$

Find $d_U T$ and its inverse for those points

$$U = \begin{pmatrix} r \\ \theta \end{pmatrix}$$

for which they exist.

(b) Compute an explicit representation for T^{-1}, and compare $d_X T^{-1}$ with $(d_U T)^{-1}$ at corresponding points.

(c) Let S be defined by

$$\begin{pmatrix} x \\ y \\ z \end{pmatrix} = S \begin{pmatrix} r \\ \phi \\ \theta \end{pmatrix} = \begin{pmatrix} r \sin \phi \cos \theta \\ r \sin \phi \sin \theta \\ r \cos \phi \end{pmatrix}, \qquad \begin{cases} 0 \le r. \\ 0 \le \phi \le \pi/2. \\ 0 \le \theta < 2\pi. \end{cases}$$

Find $d_U S$ and its inverse for those points

$$U = \begin{pmatrix} r \\ \phi \\ \theta \end{pmatrix}$$

for which they exist.

(d) Compute an explicit representation for S^{-1}.

10. Suppose that the function T defined by

$$\begin{pmatrix} u \\ v \end{pmatrix} = T \begin{pmatrix} x \\ y \end{pmatrix} = \begin{pmatrix} f(x, y) \\ g(x, y) \end{pmatrix}$$

has a differentiable inverse function S defined by

$$\begin{pmatrix} x \\ y \end{pmatrix} = S \begin{pmatrix} u \\ v \end{pmatrix} = \begin{pmatrix} h(u, v) \\ k(u, v) \end{pmatrix}.$$

If $f(1, 2) = 3$, $g(1, 2) = 4$, and $d_{(1,2)} T$ is defined by

$$\begin{pmatrix} 3 & 5 \\ 4 & 7 \end{pmatrix}, \text{ find } \frac{\partial h}{\partial v} (3, 4). \qquad\qquad [Ans. -5.]$$

11. If

$$\begin{cases} x = u + v + w, \\ y = u^2 + v^2 + w^2, \\ z = u^3 + v^3 + w^3, \end{cases}$$

compute $\partial v/\partial y$ at the image of $(u, v, w) = (1, 2, -1)$, namely $(x, y, z) = (2, 6, 8)$. $\qquad\qquad [Ans. 0.]$

12. Let

$$f\begin{pmatrix} u \\ v \end{pmatrix} = \begin{pmatrix} u^2 + u^2v + 10v \\ u + v^3 \end{pmatrix}.$$

(a) Show that f has an inverse f^{-1} in the vicinity of the point $\begin{pmatrix} 1 \\ 1 \end{pmatrix}$.

(b) Find the approximate value of $f^{-1} \begin{pmatrix} 11.8 \\ 2.2 \end{pmatrix}$.

13. Does $f(t) = \begin{pmatrix} t \\ t \\ t \end{pmatrix}$ have an inverse?

14. Show that the differentiable function

$$F(x, y, z) = \begin{pmatrix} f(x, y, z) \\ g(x, y, z) \\ f(x, y, z) + g(x, y, z) \end{pmatrix}$$

can never have a differentiable inverse.

15. Although the condition that the differential $d_{x_0} f$ have an inverse is needed for the proof of the inverse function theorem, it is perfectly possible for this condition to fail even though an inverse exists. Verify this fact with the example $f(x) = x^3$.

16. The inverse function theorem is the correct modification of the simple, but false, assertion that if $d_x f$ has an inverse, then f has an inverse. The converse—namely, if f has an inverse, then $d_x f$ has an inverse—is also false (see Exercise 15). It too, however, is almost true. Using the chain rule prove the corrected form: *If f is differentiable and has a differentiable inverse, then $d_x f$ is one-one.*

17. Consider the function $\mathcal{R} \xrightarrow{f} \mathcal{R}$ defined by

$$f(x) = \begin{cases} \dfrac{x}{2} + x^2 \sin \dfrac{1}{x}, & \text{if } x \neq 0. \\ 0, & \text{if } x = 0. \end{cases}$$

Show that $d_0 f$ is one-one but that f has no inverse in the vicinity of $x = 0$. What is wrong?

18. What is the inverse function of the linear transformation

$$L\begin{pmatrix} u \\ v \end{pmatrix} = \begin{pmatrix} u + v \\ u - v \\ u \end{pmatrix}?$$

19. The inverse function theorem can be generalized as follows:

Let $\mathcal{R}^n \overset{f}{\to} \mathcal{R}^m$, where $n < m$, be continuously differentiable. If $d_{X_0} f$ is one-one, there is an open set N containing X_0 such that f, restricted to N, has an inverse f^{-1}.

An important difference between this theorem and the inverse function theorem as we have stated it is that here the image fN is not an open subset of $\mathcal{R}^m$. One consequence of this is that f^{-1} is not differentiable at fX_0.

(a) If

$$f\begin{pmatrix} u \\ v \end{pmatrix} = \begin{pmatrix} u + v \\ (u + v)^2 \\ (u + v)^3 \end{pmatrix},$$

for what points (u_0, v_0) does f have an inverse in a neighborhood of (u_0, v_0)?

(b) Prove the generalized inverse function theorem. [*Hint*: Let the vectors $Y_1, \ldots, Y_n$ be a basis for the range of $d_{X_0} f$. Extend to a basis $Y_1, \ldots, Y_n, Y_{n+1}, \ldots, Y_m$ for all of $\mathcal{R}^m$, and define $\mathcal{R}^m \overset{g}{\to} \mathcal{R}^n$ by

$$g\left(\sum_{i=1}^m a_i Y_i \right) = (a_1, \ldots, a_n).$$

Show that $(g \circ f)$ and $d_{X_0}(g \circ f) = (d_{fX_0}g) \circ (d_{X_0}f)$ satisfy the conditions of the inverse function theorem.]

9. CURVILINEAR COORDINATES

It is sometimes useful to introduce coordinates in $\mathcal{R}^n$ different from the natural coordinates x_i that appear in the designation of a typical point $(x_1, \ldots, x_n)$. Specifically, to each point $(x_1, \ldots, x_n)$ there will be assigned a new n-tuple $(u_1, \ldots, u_n)$. Clearly, if we are to be able to switch back and forth from one set of coordinates to the other, the assignment described above must be one-one, that is, for each $(x_1, \ldots, x_n)$ there should be just one n-tuple $(u_1, \ldots, u_n)$ and *vice versa*. In practice the new coordinate assignment is often made for some specific subregion of $\mathcal{R}^n$ rather than for the whole space. The vector space of new coordinates $(u_1, \ldots, u_n)$

will be denoted by $\mathcal{U}^n$ to avoid confusion with $\mathcal{R}^n$, whose points $(x_1, \ldots, x_n)$ are being assigned the new coordinates.

EXAMPLE 1. *Polar coordinates in the plane.* Consider two copies of 2-dimensional space: the xy-plane, denoted by $\mathcal{R}^2$, and the $r\theta$-plane, denoted by $\mathcal{U}^2$. The function $\mathcal{U}^2 \xrightarrow{T} \mathcal{R}^2$ defined by

$$\begin{pmatrix} x \\ y \end{pmatrix} = T\begin{pmatrix} r \\ \theta \end{pmatrix} = \begin{pmatrix} r \cos \theta \\ r \sin \theta \end{pmatrix}, \qquad \begin{cases} 0 < r < \infty \\ -\infty < \theta < \infty \end{cases} \qquad (1)$$

has a simple geometric description. The image under T of a point $\begin{pmatrix} r \\ \theta \end{pmatrix}$ is the point

$$X = \begin{pmatrix} x \\ y \end{pmatrix}$$

whose distance from the origin is r and such that the angle from the positive x-axis to X in the counterclockwise direction is θ. See Figure 36.

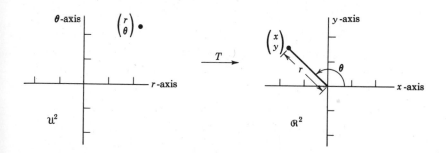

FIGURE 36

For any two points

$$\begin{pmatrix} r_1 \\ \theta_1 \end{pmatrix} \quad \text{and} \quad \begin{pmatrix} r_2 \\ \theta_2 \end{pmatrix}$$

in the domain of T, it is easy to prove that

$$T\begin{pmatrix} r_1 \\ \theta_1 \end{pmatrix} = T\begin{pmatrix} r_2 \\ \theta_2 \end{pmatrix}$$

if and only if $r_1 = r_2$ and $\theta_1 = \theta_2 + 2\pi m$ for some integer m. The range of T consists of all of $\mathcal{R}^2$ except for the origin. It follows that, for any point

$$X = \begin{pmatrix} x \\ y \end{pmatrix} \text{ in } \mathcal{R}^2 \text{ except } \begin{pmatrix} 0 \\ 0 \end{pmatrix},$$

there exist numbers r and θ, called **polar coordinates** of X, such that

$$T \begin{pmatrix} r \\ \theta \end{pmatrix} = X.$$

Furthermore, the polar coordinates of X are uniquely specified up to an integer multiple of 2π in the second coordinate.

From a slightly different point of view, the preceding paragraph says that T is not one-one, but that it becomes so if its domain is restricted to be a subset of a rectangular half-strip in the $r\theta$-plane defined by inequalities

$$0 < r < \infty, \qquad \theta_0 \leq \theta < \theta_0 + 2\pi.$$

So restricted, T has an inverse function. Solving the equations $x = r \cos \theta$, $y = r \sin \theta$ for r and θ, we obtain

$$r = \sqrt{x^2 + y^2}, \qquad \theta = \arctan \frac{y}{x}.$$

Unless the contrary is explicitly stated, any inverse trigonometric function is the principal branch of the corresponding multiple-valued function. Hence, the range of the function arctan is the interval $-\pi/2 < \theta < \pi/2$. It follows that the function defined by

$$\begin{pmatrix} r \\ \theta \end{pmatrix} = \begin{pmatrix} \sqrt{x^2 + y^2} \\ \arctan \dfrac{y}{x} \end{pmatrix}, \qquad x > 0,$$

is the inverse of the restriction of T to the region $0 < r < \infty$, $-\pi/2 < \theta < \pi/2$. Similarly, the function defined by

$$\begin{pmatrix} r \\ \theta \end{pmatrix} = \begin{pmatrix} \sqrt{x^2 + y^2} \\ \operatorname{arccot} \dfrac{x}{y} \end{pmatrix}, \qquad y > 0,$$

is the inverse to the restriction of T to $0 < r < \infty$, $0 < \theta < \pi$.

We have not defined polar coordinates for the origin of the xy-plane simply because

$$\begin{pmatrix} 0\cos\theta \\ 0\sin\theta \end{pmatrix} = \begin{pmatrix} 0 \\ 0 \end{pmatrix} \qquad \text{for all } \theta,$$

and so the one-oneness requirement is entirely lost. This fact causes no real difficulty. For example, the equation in rectangular coordinates of the lemniscate,

$$(x^2 + y^2)^2 = 2(x^2 - y^2), \tag{2}$$

becomes, upon introduction of polar coordinates,

$$r^2 = 2\cos 2\theta, \qquad r > 0. \tag{3}$$

The image under T of the set of pairs (r, θ) that satisfy Equation (3) is precisely the set of pairs (x, y) that satisfy Equation (2), except for the origin. We may simply fill in this one point. See Figure 37.

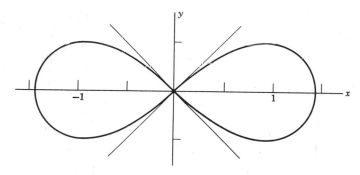

FIGURE 37

EXAMPLE 2. *Spherical coordinates in 3-dimensional space.* Consider the function $\mathcal{U}^3 \xrightarrow{T} \mathcal{R}^3$, defined by

$$\begin{pmatrix} x \\ y \\ z \end{pmatrix} = T\begin{pmatrix} r \\ \phi \\ \theta \end{pmatrix} = \begin{pmatrix} r\sin\phi\cos\theta \\ r\sin\phi\sin\theta \\ r\cos\phi \end{pmatrix}, \qquad \begin{cases} 0 < r < \infty \\ 0 < \phi < \pi \\ 0 \le \theta < 2\pi. \end{cases} \tag{4}$$

Here for simplicity we have restricted the domain of T from the outset so that it is one-one. Its range is all of $\mathcal{R}^3$ with the exception of the z-axis. Hence, it assigns **spherical coordinates** $(r, \phi, \theta) = T^{-1}(x, y, z)$ to every point of $\mathbb{R}^3$ except the z-axis. As with polar coordinates in the plane, the spherical coordinates (r, ϕ, θ) of a point $X = (x, y, z)$ have a simple geometric interpretation (see Figure 38): The number r is the distance from X to the origin. The coordinate ϕ is the angle in radians between the vector X and the positive z-axis. Finally, θ is the angle in radians from the positive x-axis to the projected image $(x, y, 0)$ of X on the xy-plane.

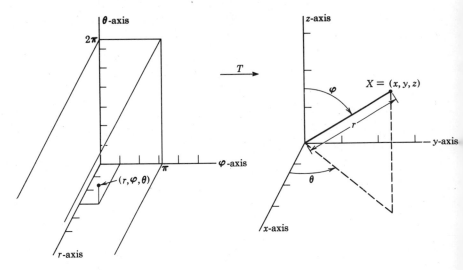

FIGURE 38

We can compute an explicit expression for the inverse function T^{-1} by solving the equations

$$x = r \sin \phi \cos \theta,$$

$$y = r \sin \phi \sin \theta,$$

$$z = r \cos \phi,$$

for r, θ, and ϕ. We get

$$\begin{pmatrix} r \\ \phi \\ \theta \end{pmatrix} = T^{-1} \begin{pmatrix} x \\ y \\ z \end{pmatrix} = \begin{pmatrix} \sqrt{x^2 + y^2 + z^2} \\ \arccos \dfrac{z}{\sqrt{x^2 + y^2 + z^2}} \\ \arccos \dfrac{x}{\sqrt{x^2 + y^2}} \end{pmatrix}, \qquad x^2 + y^2 > 0.$$

Since the range of *arccos* (the principal branch) is the interval $0 \le \theta \le \pi$, this function is actually the inverse of the function obtained by restricting the domain of T by the further condition $0 \le \theta \le \pi$. In order to get values of θ in the interval $\pi < \theta < 2\pi$, we may choose another branch of the inverse cosine.

Three surfaces in $\mathfrak{R}^3$ implicitly defined by spherical coordinate equations $r = 1$, $\phi = \pi/4$, and $\theta = \pi/3$, respectively, are shown in Figure 39.

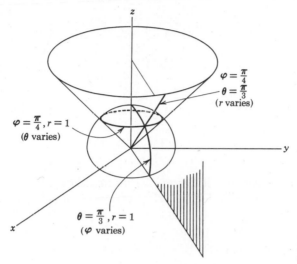

FIGURE 39

The corresponding rectangular coordinate equations derived from the above expressions for T^{-1} are

$$x^2 + y^2 + z^2 = 1, \qquad x^2 + y^2 > 0$$

$$z = \frac{\sqrt{2}}{2} \sqrt{x^2 + y^2 + z^2}, \qquad z > 0$$

$$y = \sqrt{3}\, x, \qquad x > 0,$$

respectively.

The name "curvilinear" is applied to coordinates for the reason that if all but one of the nonrectangular coordinates are held fixed, and the remaining one is varied, the coordinate transformation defines a curve in $\mathfrak{R}^n$. Thus in plane polar coordinates the coordinate curves are circles and straight lines as shown in Figure 40. For spherical coordinates, typical coordinate curves are the circle, semicircle, and half-line got as intersections of the spherical surfaces shown in Figure 39. The curves and surfaces got by varying one or more curvilinear coordinate variables play the same role that the natural coordinate lines and planes of $\mathfrak{R}^n$ do. For example, to say that a point in $\mathfrak{R}^3$ has rectangular coordinates $(x, y, z) =$

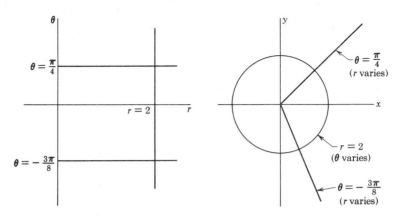

FIGURE 40

$(1, 2, 1)$ is to say that it lies at the intersection of the coordinate planes $x = 1$, $y = 2$, and $z = 1$. Similarly, to say that a point in $\mathfrak{R}^3$ has spherical coordinates $(r, \phi, \theta) = (1, \pi/4, \pi/3)$ is to say that it lies at the intersection of the surfaces shown in Figure 39.

Generalizing from the preceding examples, we see that a system of curvilinear coordinates in $\mathfrak{R}^n$ is determined by a function $\mathfrak{U}^n \xrightarrow{T} \mathfrak{R}^n$. It is assumed that for some open subset N in the domain of T, the restriction of T to N is one-one and therefore has an inverse T^{-1}. The **curvilinear coordinates**, determined by T and N, of a point X lying in the image set TN are

$$
\begin{pmatrix} u_1 \\ \cdot \\ \cdot \\ \cdot \\ u_n \end{pmatrix} = T^{-1} \begin{pmatrix} x_1 \\ \cdot \\ \cdot \\ \cdot \\ x_n \end{pmatrix}.
$$

It is convenient to impose fairly stringent regularity conditions on a coordinate transformation. Specifically, we shall assume that at every point U of N, T is continuously differentiable and $d_U T$ is one-one.

We have seen in the preceding section that under certain circumstances the fact that a transformation $\mathfrak{U}^n \xrightarrow{T} \mathfrak{R}^n$ is one-one is related to the fact that its differential $d_U T$ is one-one [see the inverse function theorem (Theorem 8.2)]. For the transformations (1) and (4) for polar and spherical coordinates this fact leads us to expect the Jacobian matrices

$$
\begin{pmatrix} \cos \theta & -r \sin \theta \\ \sin \theta & r \cos \theta \end{pmatrix} \tag{5}
$$

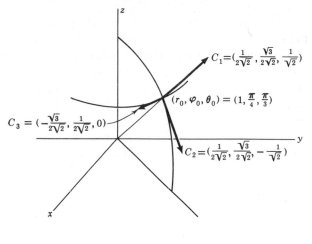

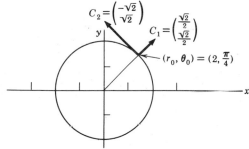

FIGURE 41

and

$$\begin{pmatrix} \sin\phi\cos\theta & r\cos\phi\cos\theta & -r\sin\phi\sin\theta \\ \\ \sin\phi\sin\theta & r\cos\phi\sin\theta & r\sin\phi\cos\theta \\ \\ \cos\phi & -r\sin\phi & 0 \end{pmatrix} \qquad (6)$$

to have inverses. The verification that they do in general have inverses is left as an exercise (see Exercise 6). Recall that the inverse function theorem does not imply that the polar and spherical coordinate transformations are one-one. The conclusion that can be drawn from that theorem is only that a transformation is one-one in a sufficiently small neighborhood of some point.

The matrices (5) and (6), and more generally the Jacobian matrices of differentiable coordinate transformations, have a simple geometric interpretation. Each column of the Jacobian is obtained by differentiation of the coordinate functions with respect to a single variable, while holding the other variables fixed. This means that the jth column of the matrix represents a tangent vector to the curvilinear coordinate curve for which the jth coordinate is allowed to vary. That is, if the coordinate transformation is given by $\mathfrak{U}^n \xrightarrow{T} \mathfrak{R}^n$, then the jth column of the matrix of the differential $d_{U_0}T$ is a tangent vector, which we shall denote by C_j, at $X_0 = TU_0$, to the curvilinear coordinate curve formed by allowing only the jth coordinate of U_0 to vary. Tangent vectors are shown (with their initial points translated to the point X_0) in Figure 41 for some polar and spherical coordinate curves. Since the coordinate curves lie in the cartesian space, the components of the tangent vectors $C_1, \ldots, C_n$ are rectangular components, not curvilinear components.

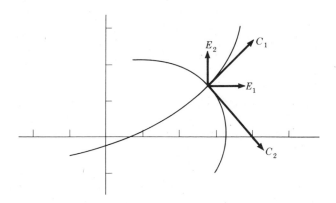

FIGURE 42

We shall show that the Jacobian matrix itself of a coordinate transformation can be interpreted as the matrix of a certain linear change of coordinates. To see this, consider curvilinear coordinates in $\mathfrak{R}^n$ given by $X = TU$ where U is the curvilinear coordinate variable. Fix a point X_0 having curvilinear coordinates U_0. At X_0 we can introduce a new origin and new unit vectors $E_1, \ldots, E_n$ with the same directions as the natural basis vectors for $\mathfrak{R}^n$. Then, the matrix of $d_{U_0}T$ is the matrix of the change of basis from the vectors $E_1, \ldots, E_n$ to the vectors $C_1, \ldots, C_n$ that are the tangent vectors to the curvilinear coordinate curves. Figure 42 illustrates the relation between the E_i and the C_i. Notice that the vectors $C_1, \ldots, C_n$ will be linearly independent if and only if $d_{U_0}T$ is one-one. This is one reason for our requirement that a coordinate transformation not only be one-one in a neighborhood of a point, but also that its differential be one-one.

EXAMPLE 3. *Cylindrical coordinates in* $\mathcal{R}^3$. The coordinate transformation is defined by

$$\begin{pmatrix} x \\ y \\ z \end{pmatrix} = \begin{pmatrix} r \cos \theta \\ r \sin \theta \\ z \end{pmatrix}, \qquad \begin{cases} 0 < r < \infty. \\ -\pi < \theta \leq \pi. \\ -\infty < z < \infty. \end{cases}$$

The Jacobian matrix is

$$\begin{pmatrix} \cos \theta & -r \sin \theta & 0 \\ \sin \theta & r \cos \theta & 0 \\ 0 & 0 & 1 \end{pmatrix}.$$

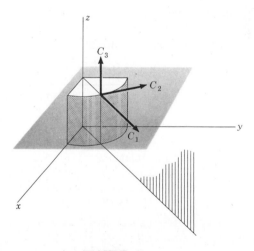

FIGURE 43

Curvilinear coordinate surfaces and tangent vectors to curvilinear coordinate curves are shown in Figure 43. Notice that the Jacobian determinant is

$$\frac{\partial(x, y, z)}{\partial(r, \theta, z)} = r.$$

EXAMPLE 4. *Spherical coordinates in* $\mathfrak{R}^n$. Let

$$x_1 = r \sin \theta_{n-1} \sin \theta_{n-2} \ldots \sin \theta_2 \sin \theta_1$$

$$x_2 = r \sin \theta_{n-1} \sin \theta_{n-2} \ldots \sin \theta_2 \cos \theta_1$$

$$x_3 = r \sin \theta_{n-1} \sin \theta_{n-2} \ldots \cos \theta_2$$

$$\cdot$$
$$\cdot$$
$$\cdot$$

$$x_{n-1} = r \sin \theta_{n-1} \cos \theta_{n-2}$$

$$x_n = r \cos \theta_{n-1}$$

where $0 < r$, $0 \leq \theta_1 < 2\pi$, $0 \leq \theta_i \leq \pi$ for $i = 2, \ldots, n - 1$. It will be noticed that in the interest of notational regularity the order of the variables has been chosen in the above equations in such a way that the polar coordinates of Example 1 and the 3-dimensional spherical coordinates of Example 2 do not immediately appear to be special cases. The discrepancy can be removed by an interchange of variables.

We compute the Jacobian determinant

$$J_n = \frac{\partial(x_1, \ldots, x_{n-1}, x_n)}{\partial(\theta_1, \ldots, \theta_{n-1}, r)}$$

of the above system. The particular order of variables in J_n has been chosen so that the sign in the final formula comes out to be $+1$. We first prove the following recurrence relation

$$J_{n+1} = r \sin^{n-1} \theta_n J_n$$

Denote the Jacobian matrix of the coordinate transformation by M_n. Its first $n - 1$ columns contain all the partial derivatives $\partial x_i / \partial \theta_i$, and form an n-by-$(n - 1)$ submatrix, which we call M_n^θ. The last column, denoted by M_n^r, contains the derivatives $\partial x_i / \partial r$. Thus we can write

$$M_n = (M_n^\theta \quad M_n^r)$$

The transformation equations for dimension $n + 1$ can be obtained from those for dimension n by multiplying the right-hand sides of the latter equations by $\sin \theta_n$, and adding an additional equation

$$x_{n+1} = r \cos \theta_n$$

Hence, the first $n - 1$ columns of the matrix M_{n+1} form the block

$$\begin{pmatrix} \sin\,\theta_n M_n^\theta \\ 0 \end{pmatrix}$$

The $(n + 1)$st column of M_{n+1} is just

$$M_{n+1}^r = \begin{pmatrix} \sin\,\theta_n M_n^r \\ \cos\,\theta_n \end{pmatrix}.$$

The nth column, that is, the column of derivatives with respect to θ_n, will have its first n coordinates equal to the column $r\,\cos\,\theta_n M_n^r$, and its $(n + 1)$st coordinate will be $-r\,\sin\,\theta_n$. We conclude that

$$M_{n+1} = \begin{pmatrix} \sin\,\theta_n M_n^\theta & r\,\cos\,\theta_n M_n^r & \sin\,\theta_n M_n^r \\ 0 & -r\,\sin\,\theta_n & \cos\,\theta_n \end{pmatrix}$$

To compute the determinant, we expand by the last row and get

$$\begin{aligned} J_{n+1} &= \det M_{n+1} \\ &= r\,\cos^2\,\theta_n\,\sin^{n-1}\,\theta_n J_n + r\,\sin^{n+1}\,\theta_n J_n \\ &= r\,\sin^{n-1}\,\theta_n J_n\,(\cos^2\,\theta_n + \sin^2\,\theta_n) \\ &= r\,\sin^{n-1}\,\theta_n J_n \end{aligned}$$

This proves the recurrence formula. Direct computation shows that

$$J_2 = \begin{vmatrix} r\,\cos\,\theta_1 & \sin\,\theta_1 \\ -r\,\sin\,\theta_1 & \cos\,\theta_1 \end{vmatrix} = r$$

Hence,

$$J_3 = r^2\,\sin\,\theta_2$$

$$J_4 = r^3\,\sin^2\,\theta_3\,\sin\,\theta_2$$

.

.

.

$$J_n = r^{n-1}\,\sin^{n-2}\,\theta_{n-1}\,\ldots\,\sin\,\theta_2$$

As noted above, a change in the order of the variables will produce a permutation of the rows or columns of the Jacobian matrix and a corresponding possible change in the sign of the determinant J_n. In a later chapter we shall use the formula for J_n to compute the volume of an n-dimensional ball in $\Re^n$.

We have seen that the vectors $C_1, \ldots, C_n$, tangent to coordinate curves, describe approximately the nature of a curvilinear coordinate system. The inner products of these vectors among themselves occur sufficiently often that there is a special notation for them:*

$$C_i \cdot C_j = g_{ij}, \qquad i, j = 1, \ldots, n.$$

Since $C_i \cdot C_j = C_j \cdot C_i$, we have $g_{ij} = g_{ji}$. If the vectors $C_1, \ldots, C_n$ are orthogonal, as is often the case in practice, then only the inner products $C_i \cdot C_i = g_{ii}$ will be different from zero. A number of important formulas can be expressed in curvilinear coordinates entirely in terms of the functions g_{ij} and without explicit reference to the particular curvilinear coordinate functions being used.

In the xy-plane suppose curvilinear coordinates are given by

$$\begin{pmatrix} x \\ y \end{pmatrix} = \begin{pmatrix} x(u, v) \\ y(u, v) \end{pmatrix}.$$

The Jacobian of the coordinate transformation is

$$\begin{pmatrix} \dfrac{\partial x}{\partial u} & \dfrac{\partial x}{\partial v} \\[2ex] \dfrac{\partial y}{\partial u} & \dfrac{\partial y}{\partial v} \end{pmatrix},$$

whence

$$g_{11} = \left(\frac{\partial x}{\partial u}\right)^2 + \left(\frac{\partial y}{\partial u}\right)^2,$$

$$g_{12} = g_{21} = \frac{\partial x}{\partial u}\frac{\partial x}{\partial v} + \frac{\partial y}{\partial u}\frac{\partial y}{\partial v},$$

$$g_{22} = \left(\frac{\partial x}{\partial v}\right)^2 + \left(\frac{\partial y}{\partial v}\right)^2.$$

Now suppose that

$$\begin{pmatrix} u(t) \\ v(t) \end{pmatrix}$$

* Other notations are often used. In particular, in two dimensions, $E = C_1 \cdot C_1$, $F = C_1 \cdot C_2 = C_2 \cdot C_1$, $G = C_2 \cdot C_2$ is customary.

is a differentiable function from an interval $[a, b]$ to $\mathcal{U}^2$. Then the equation

$$f(t) = \begin{pmatrix} x(u(t), v(t)) \\ y(u(t), v(t)) \end{pmatrix}, \qquad a \leq t \leq b,$$

is the parametric representation of a curve in $\mathcal{R}^2$. The tangent vector to the curve can be computed by the chain rule to be

$$\frac{df}{dt} = \begin{pmatrix} \dfrac{dx}{dt} \\[2mm] \dfrac{dy}{dt} \end{pmatrix} = \begin{pmatrix} \dfrac{\partial x}{\partial u}\dfrac{du}{dt} + \dfrac{\partial x}{\partial v}\dfrac{dv}{dt} \\[3mm] \dfrac{\partial y}{\partial u}\dfrac{du}{dt} + \dfrac{\partial y}{\partial v}\dfrac{dv}{dt} \end{pmatrix}.$$

The length of the tangent vector df/dt is then

$$\left| \frac{df}{dt} \right| = \left(\left(\frac{dx}{dt} \right)^2 + \left(\frac{dy}{dt} \right)^2 \right)^{1/2}$$

$$= \left(\left[\left(\frac{\partial x}{\partial u} \right)^2 + \left(\frac{\partial y}{\partial u} \right)^2 \right] \left(\frac{du}{dt} \right)^2 + 2 \left[\frac{\partial x}{\partial u}\frac{\partial x}{\partial v} + \frac{\partial y}{\partial u}\frac{\partial y}{\partial v} \right] \frac{du}{dt}\frac{dv}{dt} \right.$$

$$\left. + \left[\left(\frac{\partial x}{\partial v} \right)^2 + \left(\frac{\partial y}{\partial v} \right)^2 \right] \left(\frac{dv}{dt} \right)^2 \right)^{1/2}$$

$$= \left(g_{11} \left(\frac{du}{dt} \right)^2 + 2g_{12} \frac{du}{dt}\frac{dv}{dt} + g_{22} \left(\frac{dv}{dt} \right)^2 \right)^{1/2}.$$

A similar computation in $\mathcal{R}^n$ leads to the formula

$$\left| \frac{df}{dt} \right| = \left(\sum_{i,j=1}^{n} g_{ij} \frac{du_i}{dt}\frac{du_j}{dt} \right)^{1/2}, \tag{7}$$

where $f(t) = [x_1(u_1(t), \ldots, u_n(t)), \ldots, x_n(u_1(t), \ldots, u_n(t))]$.

Once the g_{ij} have been computed for the particular coordinate system, the above formula can be used for any differentiable curve by substituting in the components of the vector

$$\begin{pmatrix} \dfrac{du}{dt} \\[3mm] \dfrac{dv}{dt} \end{pmatrix}$$

To be more specific, suppose we are given plane polar coordinates

$$\begin{pmatrix} x \\ y \end{pmatrix} = \begin{pmatrix} r \cos \theta \\ r \sin \theta \end{pmatrix}.$$

The Jacobian matrix is

$$\begin{pmatrix} \cos \theta & -r \sin \theta \\ \sin \theta & r \cos \theta \end{pmatrix}.$$

Hence

$$g_{11} = 1, \qquad g_{12} = g_{21} = 0, \qquad g_{22} = r^2.$$

A curve $f(\theta) = \begin{pmatrix} r(\theta) \cos \theta \\ r(\theta) \sin \theta \end{pmatrix}$ has a tangent vector $df/d\theta$ of length

$$\left| \frac{df}{d\theta} \right| = \left(\left(\frac{dr}{d\theta} \right)^2 + r^2 \right)^{1/2}.$$

EXERCISES

1. Sketch the four curves given below in polar coordinates.

   (a) $r = \theta, 0 \le \theta \le \pi/2$.

   (b) $r(\sin \theta - \cos \theta) = \pi/2, \pi/2 \le \theta \le \pi$.

   (c) $r = \pi/2 \cos \theta, \pi \le \theta \le 3\pi/2$.

   (d) $r = t + 1, \theta = t^2, 0 \le t \le 1$.

2. In $\mathcal{R}^3$, sketch the curves and surfaces given below in spherical coordinates.

   (a) $r = 2, 0 \le \theta \le \pi/4, \pi/4 \le \phi \le \pi/2$.

   (b) $1 \le r \le 2, \theta = \pi/2, \phi = \pi/4$.

   (c) $0 \le r \le 1, 0 \le \theta \le \pi/2, \phi = \pi/4$.

   (d) $0 \le r \le 1, \theta = \pi/4, 0 \le \phi \le \pi/4$.

3. Use cylindrical coordinates in $\mathcal{R}^3$ to describe the region defined in rectangular coordinates by $0 \le x, x^2 + y^2 \le 1$.

4. Let (r, θ) be polar coordinates in $\mathcal{R}^2$. The equation

   $$\begin{pmatrix} r \\ \theta \end{pmatrix} = \begin{pmatrix} \sin t \\ t \end{pmatrix}, \qquad 0 \le t \le \frac{\pi}{2},$$

   describes a curve in $\mathcal{U}^2$. Sketch this curve, and sketch its image in $\mathcal{R}^2$ under the polar coordinate transformation.

5. Let (r, ϕ, θ) be spherical coordinates in $\mathcal{R}^3$. The equation

$$\begin{pmatrix} r \\ \phi \\ \theta \end{pmatrix} = \begin{pmatrix} 1 \\ t \\ t \end{pmatrix}$$

determines a curve in $\mathcal{R}^3$ (as well as in the $r\phi\theta$-space $\mathcal{U}^3$). Sketch the curve in $\mathcal{R}^3$. [*Suggestion*: The curve lies on a sphere.]

6. Prove that the Jacobian matrices (5) and (6) of the polar and spherical coordinate transformations given in Examples 2 and 3 have inverses.

7. The equations

$$\left.\begin{array}{l} x = ar \sin \phi \cos \theta \\[2mm] y = br \sin \phi \sin \theta \\[2mm] z = cr \cos \phi \end{array}\right\}, \qquad a, b, c > 0,$$

define spheroidal coordinates in $\mathcal{R}^3$. For $a = 1, b = c = 2$, sketch a typical example of each of the three kinds of coordinate surface.

8. Compute the cartesian components of the tangent vectors to the coordinate curves for the general spheroidal coordinates given in Exercise 7, when $a = b = 1, c = 2$, and $r = \frac{1}{2}, \phi = \theta = \pi/2$.

9. Let r, ϕ, and θ be spherical coordinates in $\mathcal{R}^3$. The equation

$$\begin{pmatrix} r \\ \phi \\ \theta \end{pmatrix} = \begin{pmatrix} 1 \\ t \\ t^2 \end{pmatrix}$$

determines a curve in $\mathcal{R}^3$. Compute the cartesian components of the tangent vector to the curve.

10. Prove that in the n-dimensional spherical coordinates of Example 4 in the text, the sphere $x_1^2 + x_2^2 + \ldots + x_n^2 = 1$ has the equation $r = 1$.

11. Let "elliptic" coordinates in the plane be determined by

$$\begin{pmatrix} x \\ y \end{pmatrix} = \begin{pmatrix} ar \cos \theta \\ br \sin \theta \end{pmatrix}, \qquad a > 0, b > 0.$$

(a) Compute the coefficients g_{ij} for this coordinate system.
(b) For what choices of a and b will it always be true that $g_{ij} = 0$ for $i \neq j$?

12. Verify the assertion made in the text that the jth column of the Jacobian matrix at U_0 of a coordinate transformation $\mathfrak{U}^n \overset{T}{\to} \mathfrak{R}^n$ is a tangent vector at $X_0 = TU_0$ to the curvilinear coordinate curve obtained by letting the jth coordinate of U_0 vary.

10. IMPLICITLY DEFINED FUNCTIONS

For any two functions $\mathfrak{R}^2 \overset{F}{\to} \mathfrak{R}$ and $\mathfrak{R} \overset{f}{\to} \mathfrak{R}$, **the equation**

$$F(x, y) = 0 \tag{1}$$

defines f implicitly if $F(x, f(x)) = 0$ for every x in the domain of f. The zero on the right-hand side of Equation (1) can be replaced by any constant c. But since $F(x, y) = c$ is equivalent to $G(x, y) = F(x, y) - c = 0$, it is customary to absorb such a constant into the function F.

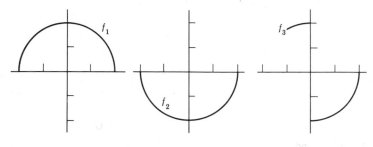

FIGURE 44

EXAMPLE 1. Let $F(x, y) = x^2 + y^2 - 1$. Then the condition that $F(x, f(x)) = x^2 + (f(x))^2 - 1 = 0$, for every x in the domain of f, is satisfied by each of the following choices for f.

$$f_1(x) = \sqrt{1 - x^2}, \quad -1 \le x \le 1.$$

$$f_2(x) = -\sqrt{1 - x^2}, \quad -1 \le x \le 1.$$

$$f_3(x) = \begin{cases} \sqrt{1 - x^2}, & -\tfrac{1}{2} \le x < 0. \\ -\sqrt{1 - x^2}, & 0 \le x \le 1. \end{cases}$$

Their graphs are shown in Figure 44. It follows from the definition of an implicitly defined function that all three functions f_1, f_2, f_3 are defined implicitly by the equation $x^2 + y^2 - 1 = 0$.

Consider a function $\mathfrak{R}^{n+m} \overset{F}{\to} \mathfrak{R}^m$. An arbitrary element in $\mathfrak{R}^{n+m}$ can be written as $(x_1, \ldots, x_n, y_1, \ldots, y_m)$ or as a pair (X, Y) where $X =$

$(x_1, \ldots, x_n)$ and $Y = (y_1, \ldots, y_m)$. In this way F can be thought of either as a function of the two vector variables, X in $\mathfrak{R}^n$ and Y in $\mathfrak{R}^m$, or else as a function of the single vector variable (X, Y) in $\mathfrak{R}^{n+m}$. **The function $\mathfrak{R}^n \xrightarrow{f} \mathfrak{R}^m$ is defined implicitly by the equation**

$$F(X, Y) = 0$$

if $F(X, fX) = 0$ for every X in the domain of f.

EXAMPLE 2. The equations

$$x + y + z - 1 = 0$$
$$2x \quad\quad + z + 2 = 0 \tag{2}$$

determine y and z as functions of x. We get

$$y = x + 3, \quad\quad z = -2x - 2.$$

In terms of a function $\mathfrak{R}^3 \xrightarrow{F} \mathfrak{R}^2$, Equations (2) can be written

$$F\left(x, \begin{pmatrix} y \\ z \end{pmatrix}\right) = \begin{pmatrix} x + y + z - 1 \\ 2x \quad\quad + z + 2 \end{pmatrix} = \begin{pmatrix} 0 \\ 0 \end{pmatrix}$$

$$= \begin{pmatrix} 1 \\ 2 \end{pmatrix} x + \begin{pmatrix} 1 & 1 \\ 0 & 1 \end{pmatrix} \begin{pmatrix} y \\ z \end{pmatrix} + \begin{pmatrix} -1 \\ 2 \end{pmatrix} = \begin{pmatrix} 0 \\ 0 \end{pmatrix}.$$

The implicitly defined function $\mathfrak{R} \xrightarrow{f} \mathfrak{R}^2$ is

$$f(x) = \begin{pmatrix} y \\ z \end{pmatrix} = \begin{pmatrix} x + 3 \\ -2x - 2 \end{pmatrix}.$$

Although Example 1 shows that an implicitly defined function need not be continuous, we shall be primarily concerned in this section with functions that are not only continuous but also differentiable. The *implicit function theorem* appearing at the end of this section gives conditions for the existence of a differentiable f defined by an equation $F(X, fX) = 0$. Before discussing this theorem, however, we consider the problem of finding the differential $d_X f$ when it is known that f exists. Suppose the functions $\mathfrak{R}^2 \xrightarrow{F} \mathfrak{R}$ and $\mathfrak{R} \xrightarrow{f} \mathfrak{R}$ are differentiable and that

$$F(x, f(x)) = 0, \quad\quad \text{for every } x \text{ in the domain of } f.$$

Then the chain rule applied to $F(x, f(x))$ yields

$$\frac{\partial F}{\partial x}(x, f(x)) + \frac{\partial F}{\partial y}(x, f(x)) f'(x) = 0.$$

Hence,

10.1 $$f'(x) = -\frac{\dfrac{\partial F}{\partial x}(x, f(x))}{\dfrac{\partial F}{\partial y}(x, f(x))}, \qquad \text{if } \frac{\partial F}{\partial y}(x, f(x)) \neq 0.$$

For vector-valued functions a similar computation is possible.

EXAMPLE 3. Given the equations

$$x^2 + y^2 + z^2 - 5 = 0, \qquad xyz + 2 = 0, \tag{3}$$

suppose that x and y are differentiable functions of z, that is, the function defined implicitly by Equations (3) is of the form

$$\begin{pmatrix} x \\ y \end{pmatrix} = f(z).$$

To compute dx/dz and dy/dz, we apply the chain rule to the given equations to get

$$2x \frac{dx}{dz} + 2y \frac{dy}{dz} + 2z = 0,$$

$$yz \frac{dx}{dz} + xz \frac{dy}{dz} + xy = 0.$$

These new equations can be solved for $\dfrac{dx}{dz}$ and $\dfrac{dy}{dz}$. The solution is

$$\begin{pmatrix} \dfrac{dx}{dz} \\ \dfrac{dy}{dz} \end{pmatrix} = \begin{pmatrix} \dfrac{x(y^2 - z^2)}{z(x^2 - y^2)} \\ \dfrac{y(z^2 - x^2)}{z(x^2 - y^2)} \end{pmatrix},$$

which is the matrix of $d_z f$. Notice that the corresponding values for x and y have to be known to make the formula completely explicit. That is, from the information given so far there is no possible way of evaluating $(dx/dz)(1)$.

On the other hand, given the point $(x, y, z) = (1, -2, 1)$, we have $(dx/dz)(1) = -1$. The reason is that, just as in Example 1, there is more than one function f defined implicitly by Equations (3). By specifying a particular point on its graph, we determine f uniquely in the vicinity of the point.

EXAMPLE 4. Consider

$$xu + yv + zw = 1,$$

$$x + y + z + u + v + w = 0,$$

$$xy + zuv + w = 1.$$

Suppose that each of x, y, and z is a function of u, v, and w. To find the partial derivatives of x, y, and z with respect to w, we differentiate the three equations using the chain rule.

$$u \frac{\partial x}{\partial w} + v \frac{\partial y}{\partial w} + w \frac{\partial z}{\partial w} + z = 0,$$

$$\frac{\partial x}{\partial w} + \frac{\partial y}{\partial w} + \frac{\partial z}{\partial w} + 1 = 0,$$

$$y \frac{\partial x}{\partial w} + x \frac{\partial y}{\partial w} + uv \frac{\partial z}{\partial w} + 1 = 0.$$

Then,

$$\frac{\partial x}{\partial w} = \frac{uv^2 + xz + w - zuv - xw - v}{u^2v + vy + wx - yw - ux - uv^2}.$$

Similarly we could solve for $\partial y/\partial w$ and $\partial z/\partial w$. To find partials with respect to u, differentiate the original equations with respect to u and solve for $\partial x/\partial u$, $\partial y/\partial u$, and $\partial z/\partial u$. Partials with respect to v are found by the same method.

The computation indicated in Example 4 leads to the nine entries in the matrix of the differential of an implicitly defined vector function. In order for the computation to work smoothly it is good to have the number of given equations equal the number of implicitly defined coordinate functions. To get some insight into the reason for this requirement, suppose we are given a differentiable vector function

$$F(u, v, x, y) = \begin{pmatrix} F_1(u, v, x, y) \\ F_2(u, v, x, y) \end{pmatrix}$$

and that the equations

$$F_1(u, v, x, y) = 0, \qquad F_2(u, v, x, y) = 0 \tag{4}$$

implicitly define a differentiable function

$$\begin{pmatrix} x \\ y \end{pmatrix} = f\begin{pmatrix} u \\ v \end{pmatrix}.$$

Differentiating Equations (4) with respect to u and v by means of the chain rule we get

$$\frac{\partial F_1}{\partial u} + \frac{\partial F_1}{\partial x}\frac{\partial x}{\partial u} + \frac{\partial F_1}{\partial y}\frac{\partial y}{\partial u} = 0, \qquad \frac{\partial F_1}{\partial v} + \frac{\partial F_1}{\partial x}\frac{\partial x}{\partial v} + \frac{\partial F_1}{\partial y}\frac{\partial y}{\partial v} = 0,$$

$$\frac{\partial F_2}{\partial u} + \frac{\partial F_2}{\partial x}\frac{\partial x}{\partial u} + \frac{\partial F_2}{\partial y}\frac{\partial y}{\partial u} = 0, \qquad \frac{\partial F_2}{\partial v} + \frac{\partial F_2}{\partial x}\frac{\partial x}{\partial v} + \frac{\partial F_2}{\partial y}\frac{\partial y}{\partial v} = 0.$$

These equations can be written in matrix form as follows:

$$\begin{pmatrix} \dfrac{\partial F_1}{\partial u} & \dfrac{\partial F_1}{\partial v} \\[2ex] \dfrac{\partial F_2}{\partial u} & \dfrac{\partial F_2}{\partial v} \end{pmatrix} + \begin{pmatrix} \dfrac{\partial F_1}{\partial x} & \dfrac{\partial F_1}{\partial y} \\[2ex] \dfrac{\partial F_2}{\partial x} & \dfrac{\partial F_2}{\partial y} \end{pmatrix}\begin{pmatrix} \dfrac{\partial x}{\partial u} & \dfrac{\partial x}{\partial v} \\[2ex] \dfrac{\partial y}{\partial u} & \dfrac{\partial y}{\partial v} \end{pmatrix} = 0. \tag{5}$$

The last matrix on the right is the matrix of the differential of f at $\begin{pmatrix} u \\ v \end{pmatrix}$.

Solving for it, we get

$$\begin{pmatrix} \dfrac{\partial x}{\partial u} & \dfrac{\partial x}{\partial v} \\[2ex] \dfrac{\partial y}{\partial u} & \dfrac{\partial y}{\partial v} \end{pmatrix} = -\begin{pmatrix} \dfrac{\partial F_1}{\partial x} & \dfrac{\partial F_1}{\partial y} \\[2ex] \dfrac{\partial F_2}{\partial x} & \dfrac{\partial F_2}{\partial y} \end{pmatrix}^{-1}\begin{pmatrix} \dfrac{\partial F_1}{\partial u} & \dfrac{\partial F_1}{\partial v} \\[2ex] \dfrac{\partial F_2}{\partial u} & \dfrac{\partial F_2}{\partial v} \end{pmatrix}. \tag{6}$$

In order to be able to solve Equation (5) uniquely for the matrix of $d_{\binom{u}{v}} f$, it is essential that the inverse matrix that appears in Equation (6) exist. This implies in particular that the number of equations originally given equals the number of variables implicitly determined, or equivalently, that the range spaces of F and f must have the same dimension.

The analogue of Equation (6) holds for an arbitrary number of co-ordinate functions F_i and is proved in exactly the same way. We can summarize the result in the following generalization of 10.1.

10.2 Theorem. If $\mathfrak{R}^{n+m} \xrightarrow{F} \mathfrak{R}^m$ and $\mathfrak{R}^n \xrightarrow{f} \mathfrak{R}^m$, are differentiable, and $Y = fX$, satisfies $F(X, Y) = 0$, then

$$d_X f = -(d_Y F)^{-1} \circ (d_X F)$$

provided $d_Y F$ has an inverse. The differential $d_Y F$ is computed with X held fixed and $d_X F$ is computed with Y held fixed.

We have seen that in order to be able to solve for a unique $d_X f$, it is necessary that $d_Y F$ have an inverse. It is natural that the same condition occur in the next theorem, which treats the question of whether or not there exists a function f defined implicitly by $F(X, Y) = 0$. Thus far we have been concerned only with the computation (using the chain rule) of $d_X f$ given that f exists. The implicit function theorem states that if certain conditions on F are satisfied, then it is theoretically possible to solve the equation $F(X, Y) = 0$ for Y in terms of X.

10.3 Implicit function theorem. Let $\mathfrak{R}^{n+m} \xrightarrow{F} \mathfrak{R}^m$, be a continuously differentiable function. Suppose that for some X_0 in $\mathfrak{R}^n$ and Y_0 in $\mathfrak{R}^m$

   (i) $F(X_0, Y_0) = 0$,
   (ii) $d_{Y_0} F$ has an inverse.

Then there exists a unique differentiable function $\mathfrak{R}^n \xrightarrow{f} \mathfrak{R}^m$ defined on some neighborhood N, of X_0 such that $fX_0 = Y_0$ and $F(X, fX) = 0$, for all X in N.

Proof. The proof consists in reducing the theorem to an application of the inverse function theorem. For that purpose we extend F to a function $\mathfrak{R}^{n+m} \xrightarrow{H} \mathfrak{R}^{n+m}$ by setting $H(X, Y) = (X, F(X, Y))$. In terms of the coordinate functions $F_1, \ldots, F_m$ of F, the coordinate functions of H are given by

$$H_1(X, Y) \quad = \quad x_1,$$

$$H_2(X, Y) \quad = \quad x_2,$$

$$\cdot$$
$$\cdot$$
$$\cdot$$

$$H_n(X, Y) \quad = \quad x_n,$$

$$H_{n+1}(X, Y) = F_1(x_1, \ldots, x_n, y_1, \ldots, y_m),$$

$$\cdot$$
$$\cdot$$
$$\cdot$$

$$H_{n+m}(X, Y) = F_m(x_1, \ldots, x_n, y_1, \ldots, y_m).$$

The Jacobian matrix of H at (X_0, Y_0) is

$$
\begin{pmatrix}
1 & 0 & \cdots & 0 & 0 & \cdots & 0 \\
0 & 1 & \cdots & 0 & 0 & \cdots & 0 \\
\vdots & & \ddots & & & \ddots & \\
0 & 0 & & 1 & 0 & & 0 \\
\dfrac{\partial F_1}{\partial x_1} & \dfrac{\partial F_1}{\partial x_2} & \cdots & \dfrac{\partial F_1}{\partial x_n} & \dfrac{\partial F_1}{\partial y_1} & \cdots & \dfrac{\partial F_1}{\partial y_m} \\
\vdots & & & & & & \\
\dfrac{\partial F_m}{\partial x_1} & \dfrac{\partial F_m}{\partial x_2} & \cdots & \dfrac{\partial F_m}{\partial x_n} & \dfrac{\partial F_m}{\partial y_1} & \cdots & \dfrac{\partial F_m}{\partial y_m}
\end{pmatrix}
$$

where all the partial derivatives are evaluated at (X_0, Y_0). By assumption (ii), the m columns on the right of the matrix are independent. Since they are also independent of the n independent columns on the left, all columns of the matrix are independent, and therefore, the differential of H at (X_0, Y_0) has an inverse.

The transformation H is certainly continuously differentiable, so we can apply the inverse function theorem at the point (X_0, Y_0) to get a function H^{-1} that is inverse to H from some open set N' in $\mathfrak{R}^{n+m}$ containing $H(X_0, Y_0)$ to an open set about (X_0, Y_0). Since $H(X_0, Y_0) = (X_0, F(X_0, Y_0)) = (X_0, 0)$, the set N of all points X in $\mathfrak{R}^n$ such that $(X, 0)$ is in N' is an open set (see Exercise 14) and contains X_0.

Let G_1 be the function that selects the first n variables of a point in $\mathfrak{R}^{n+m}$, and G_2 the function that selects the last m variables. Thus, $G_1(X, Y) = X$ and $G_2(X, Y) = Y$. Since $H(X, Y) = (X, F(X, Y))$, the function H is the identity on X. The same must therefore be true of H^{-1}. Hence,

$$G_1 = G_1 \circ H^{-1}.$$

We define f by

$$fX = G_2 H^{-1}(X, 0), \qquad \text{for every } X \text{ in } N.$$

Then

$$H^{-1}(X, 0) = (G_1 H^{-1}(X, 0), G_2 H^{-1}(X, 0)) = (X, fX).$$

Applying H to both sides, we get

$$(X, 0) = H(X, fX) = (X, F(X, fX)),$$

for every X in N. The two parts of the first and last pairs must be equal. Hence,

$$0 = F(X, fX), \qquad \text{for every } X \text{ in } N.$$

Finally, f being the composition of two differentiable functions, is itself differentiable by the chain rule.

The function f is the only differentiable function implicitly defined in a neighborhood of X_0 for which $fX_0 = Y_0$. For suppose there were two functions, f and $\bar{f}$ satisfying $F(X, \bar{f}X) = F(X, fX) = 0$ near X_0. By applying H to both sides of the following two equations, one can check that they are valid.

$$H^{-1}(X, F(X, fX)) = (X, fX),$$
$$H^{-1}(X, F(X, \bar{f}X)) = (X, \bar{f}X).$$

But since the left-hand sides are both just $H^{-1}(X, 0)$, the right-hand sides are equal, and $\bar{f}X = fX$.

EXAMPLE 5. The equation $x^3y + y^3x - 2 = 0$ defines $y = f(x)$ implicitly in a neighborhood of $x = 1$ if $f(1) = 1$. As a function of y, $x^3y + y^3x - 2$ has Jacobian $(1 + 3y^2)$ at $x = 1$, and the latter is invertible at $y = 1$, that is,

$$1 + 3y^2 \big|_{y=1} = 4 \neq 0.$$

The solution can be computed by standard methods to be

$$y = \sqrt[3]{\frac{1}{x} + \frac{1}{x}\sqrt{\frac{x^{10} + 27}{27}}} + \sqrt[3]{\frac{1}{x} - \frac{1}{x}\sqrt{\frac{x^{10} + 27}{27}}} .*$$

EXAMPLE 6. The equations

$$z^3x + w^2y^3 + 2xy = 0, \qquad xyzw - 1 = 0 \tag{7}$$

can be written in the form $F(X, Y) = 0$ where $X = \begin{pmatrix} x \\ y \end{pmatrix}$, $Y = \begin{pmatrix} z \\ w \end{pmatrix}$, and

$$F(X, Y) = \begin{pmatrix} z^3x + w^2y^3 + 2xy \\ xyzw - 1 \end{pmatrix}.$$

---

*See R. S. Burington, *Mathematical Tables and Formulas*, Handbook Publishers, Inc., 1956, p. 8.

Let $X_0 = \begin{pmatrix} -1 \\ -1 \end{pmatrix}$ and $Y_0 = \begin{pmatrix} 1 \\ 1 \end{pmatrix}$. Then

$$F(X_0, Y) = \begin{pmatrix} -z^3 - w^2 + 2 \\ zw - 1 \end{pmatrix}$$

and the matrix of $d_{Y_0}F$ is

$$\begin{pmatrix} -3z^2 & -2w \\ w & z \end{pmatrix}_{\left(\begin{smallmatrix} z \\ w \end{smallmatrix}\right) = \left(\begin{smallmatrix} 1 \\ 1 \end{smallmatrix}\right)} = \begin{pmatrix} -3 & -2 \\ 1 & 1 \end{pmatrix}.$$

The inverse exists and is the matrix

$$\begin{pmatrix} -1 & -2 \\ 1 & 3 \end{pmatrix}.$$

It is then a consequence of the implicit function theorem that Equations (7) implicitly define a function f in an open set about X_0 such that $fX_0 = Y_0$. That is, we have

$$\begin{pmatrix} z \\ w \end{pmatrix} = f\begin{pmatrix} x \\ y \end{pmatrix}$$

and so each of z and w is a function of x and y near

$$\begin{pmatrix} -1 \\ -1 \end{pmatrix}.$$

EXERCISES

1. Consider the equation $(x - 2)^3 y + xe^{y-1} = 0$
   (a) Is y defined implicitly as a function of x in a neighborhood of $(x, y) = (1, 1)$?
   (b) In a neighborhood of $(0, 0)$?
   (c) In a neighborhood of $(2, 1)$?

2. The point $(x, y, t) = (0, 1, -1)$ satisfies the equations

$$xyt + \sin xyt = 0, \qquad x + y + t = 0.$$

Are x and y defined implicitly as functions of t in a neighborhood of $(0, 1, -1)$?

3. If
$$x^2 y + yz = 0, \qquad xyz + 1 = 0,$$

find $\dfrac{dx}{dz}$ and $\dfrac{dy}{dz}$ at $(x, y, z) = (1, 1, -1)$. $\qquad \left[Ans. \ \dfrac{dx}{dz} = -\dfrac{1}{2}, \ \dfrac{dy}{dz} = \dfrac{3}{2}. \right]$

4. If Exercise 3 is expressed in the general vector notation of Theorem 10.2, what are F, X, Y, $d_X F$, and $d_Y F$?

5. If
$$x + y - \quad u - v = 0,$$
$$x - y + 2u + v = 0,$$

find $\dfrac{\partial x}{\partial u}$ and $\dfrac{\partial y}{\partial u}$

(a) by solving for x and y in terms of u and v,
(b) by implicit differentiation.

6. If Exercise 5 is expressed in the vector notation of Theorem 10.2 what is the matrix of $d_X f$?

7. If $x^2 + yu + xv + w = 0$, $x + y + uvw + 1 = 0$, then, regarding x and y as functions of u, v, and w, find

$\dfrac{\partial x}{\partial u}$ and $\dfrac{\partial y}{\partial u}$ at $(x, y, u, v, w) = (1, -1, 1, 1, -1)$.

$$\left[Ans. \ \frac{\partial x}{\partial u} = 0, \ \frac{\partial y}{\partial u} = 1. \right]$$

8. The equations $2x^3 y + yx^2 + t^2 = 0$, $x + y + t - 1 = 0$ implicitly define a curve
$$f(t) = \begin{pmatrix} x(t) \\ y(t) \end{pmatrix}$$

which satisfies
$$f(1) = \begin{pmatrix} -1 \\ 1 \end{pmatrix}.$$

Find the tangent line to f at $t = 1$. $\qquad \left[Ans. \ t \begin{pmatrix} -\frac{3}{5} \\ -\frac{2}{5} \end{pmatrix} + \begin{pmatrix} -1 \\ 1 \end{pmatrix}. \right]$

9. (a) Show that the equation $x^2/4 + y^2 + z^2/9 - 1 = 0$ defines z implicitly as a function $z = f(x, y)$ near the point $x = 1$, $y = \sqrt{11}/6$, $z = 2$.
(b) The graph of the function f is a surface. Find its tangent plane at $(1, \sqrt{11}/6, 2)$.

10. Suppose the equation $F(x, y, z) = 0$ implicitly defines $z = f(x, y)$ and that $z_0 = f(x_0, y_0)$. Suppose further that the surface that is the graph of $z = f(x, y)$ has a tangent plane at (x_0, y_0). Show that

$$(x - x_0) \frac{\partial F}{\partial x} (x_0, y_0, z_0) + (y - y_0) \frac{\partial F}{\partial y} (x_0, y_0, z_0)$$

$$+ (z - z_0) \frac{\partial F}{\partial z} (x_0, y_0, z_0) = 0$$

is the equation for this tangent plane.

11. The equations

$$2x + y + 2z + u - v - 1 = 0,$$
$$xy + z - u + 2v - 1 = 0,$$
$$yz + xz + u^2 + v = 0,$$

near $(x, y, z, u, v) = (1, 1, -1, 1, 1)$ define x, y, and z as functions of u and v.

(a) Find the matrix of the differential of the implicitly defined function

$$\begin{pmatrix} x \\ y \\ z \end{pmatrix} = \begin{pmatrix} x(u, v) \\ y(u, v) \\ z(u, v) \end{pmatrix} = f\begin{pmatrix} u \\ v \end{pmatrix} \qquad \text{at } (u, v) = (1, 1).$$

(b) The function f parametrically defines a surface in the (x, y, z) space. Find the tangent plane to it at the point $(1, 1, -1)$.

12. The implicit function theorem states that under certain conditions the implicitly defined function f is unique. In Example 1 of this section what conditions are violated to allow more than one f?

13. Requirement (ii) in the implicit function theorem that $d_{Y_0}F$ have an inverse is not a necessary condition for the equation $F(X, Y) = 0$ to define a unique differentiable function f such that $fX_0 = Y_0$. Show this by taking $F(x, y) = x^9 - y^3$ and $(x_0, y_0) = (0, 0)$.

14. Show that if N' is an open subset of $\mathfrak{R}^{n+m}$ containing the point (X_0, Y_0), then the subset N of all X in $\mathfrak{R}^n$ such that (X, Y_0) is in N' is an open subset of $\mathfrak{R}^n$.

3

Real-valued Functions

1. EXTREME VALUES

A real-valued function f has an **absolute maximum value** at X_0 if, for all X in the domain of f,

$$fX \leq fX_0$$

and an **absolute minimum value** if

$$fX_0 \leq fX.$$

The number fX_0 is called a **local maximum value** or a **local minimum value** if there is a neighborhood N of X_0 such that, respectively,

$$fX \leq fX_0 \quad \text{or} \quad fX_0 \leq fX,$$

for all X in N. A maximum or minimum value of f is called an **extreme value**. A point X_0 at which an extreme value occurs is called an **extreme point**.

EXAMPLE 1. Consider the function $f(x, y) = x^2 + y^2$ whose domain is the set of points (x, y) that lie inside or on the ellipse $x^2 + 2y^2 = 1$. The graph of f is shown in Figure 1. Suppose that f has an extreme value (i.e., maximum or minimum) at a point (x_0, y_0) in the interior of the ellipse. Then, obviously both functions f_1 and f_2 defined by

$$f_1(x) = f(x, y_0), \qquad f_2(y) = f(x_0, y)$$

must also have extreme values at x_0 and y_0 respectively. Applying the familiar criterion for functions of one variable, we have

$$f_1'(x_0) = f_2'(y_0) = 0.$$

Since

$$f_1'(x_0) = \frac{\partial f}{\partial x}(x_0, y_0)$$

and

$$f_2'(y_0) = \frac{\partial f}{\partial y}(x_0, y_0),$$

a necessary condition for f to have an extreme value at (x_0, y_0) is

$$\frac{\partial f}{\partial x}(x_0, y_0) = \frac{\partial f}{\partial y}(x_0, y_0) = 0.$$

In this example,

$$\frac{\partial f}{\partial x}(x, y) = 2x \quad \text{and} \quad \frac{\partial f}{\partial y}(x, y) = 2y,$$

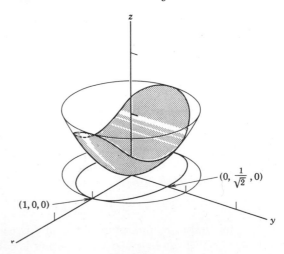

FIGURE 1

and so the only extreme value of f in the interior of the ellipse occurs at $(x_0, y_0) = (0, 0)$. It is obvious from the graph of f, shown in Figure 1, that this value is a minimum. The ellipse itself can be defined parametrically by the function

$$g(t) = (x, y) = \left(\cos t, \frac{1}{\sqrt{2}} \sin t\right), \qquad 0 \le t < 2\pi.$$

Thus, the values of f on the ellipse are given as the values of the composition $(f \circ g)$. Any extreme values of f on the ellipse will be extreme for $(f \circ g)$. The latter is a real-valued function of one variable, and we treat it in the usual way—that is, by setting its derivative equal to zero. By the chain rule, we obtain

$$\frac{d}{dt}(f \circ g) = \left(2 \cos t \quad \frac{2}{\sqrt{2}} \sin t\right) \begin{pmatrix} -\sin t \\ \frac{1}{\sqrt{2}} \cos t \end{pmatrix}$$

$$= -2 \cos t \sin t + \sin t \cos t$$

$$= -\frac{1}{2} \sin 2t.$$

Extreme values therefore may occur at $t = 0$, $\pi/2$, π, and $3\pi/2$. The corresponding values of (x, y) are $(1, 0)$, $(0, 1/\sqrt{2})$, $(-1, 0)$, and $(0, -1/\sqrt{2})$, and those of f are 1, $\frac{1}{2}$, 1, and $\frac{1}{2}$ respectively. We see that the absolute minimum of f is 0 at $(0, 0)$ and that the absolute maximum of f occurs at the two points $(1, 0)$ and $(-1, 0)$. Notice that the two extreme values of $(f \circ g)$ which occur at $t = \pi/2$ and $3\pi/2$ are not extreme for f, as can be seen by looking at Figure 1.

The methods used in the preceding example are valid in any number of dimensions. The next theorem is the principal criterion used in this extension.

1.1 Theorem. If a differentiable function $\mathfrak{R}^n \xrightarrow{f} \mathfrak{R}$ has a local extreme value at a point X_0 interior to its domain, then $d_{X_0}f = 0$.

Proof. Suppose f has a local minimum at X_0. For any Y in $\mathfrak{R}^n$, there is an $\epsilon > 0$ such that if $-\epsilon < t < \epsilon$, then $fX_0 \leq f(X_0 + tY)$. Hence, for $0 < t < \epsilon$,

$$0 \leq \frac{f(X_0 + tY) - fX_0}{t},$$

$$0 \leq \frac{f(X_0 - tY) - fX_0}{t}.$$

It follows by Theorem 6.1 of Chapter 2 that

$$\frac{\partial f}{d Y} X_0 = (d_{X_0} f) \, Y.$$

Therefore,

$$0 \leq \lim_{t \to 0+} \frac{f(X_0 + tY) - fX_0}{t} = (d_{X_0} f) \, Y,$$

$$0 \leq \lim_{t \to 0+} \frac{f(X_0 - tY) - fX_0}{t} = (d_{X_0} f)(-Y) = -(d_{X_0} f) \, Y.$$

We conclude that $(d_{X_0} f) \, Y = 0$. Because Y is arbitrary, $d_{X_0} f = 0$. The argument for a maximum value is entirely analogous.

The above result is what we should expect. Recall that

$$\frac{\partial f}{\partial Y} X_0 = d_{X_0} f Y$$

measures the rate of change of f in the direction of Y. At an extreme point in the interior of the domain of f, this rate should be zero in every direction. The importance of the theorem is that of all the interior points X of the domain of f we need to look for extreme points only among those for which $d_X f = 0$. Points X for which $d_X f = 0$ are called **critical points** of f.

In practice we are often given a function f that is differentiable on an open set and want to find the extreme points of f when it is restricted to some subset S of the domain of f. In the next example the following two remarks are illustrated: (1) *a point X such that $d_X f = 0$ is not necessarily an extreme point for f*; (2) *f may have an extreme point X when restricted to a set S without having $d_X f = 0$.*

EXAMPLE 2. Let $f(x, y, z) = xyz$ in the region defined by $|x| \leq 1$, $|y| \leq 1$, $|z| \leq 1$. Thus the domain of f is the cube with each edge of length 2 illustrated in Figure 2. The condition for critical points, $d_x f = 0$, is equivalent to

$$
\begin{pmatrix} yz \\ xz \\ xy \end{pmatrix} = \begin{pmatrix} 0 \\ 0 \\ 0 \end{pmatrix}.
$$

The solutions of this equation are the points satisfying $x = y = 0$ or $x = z = 0$ or $y = z = 0$, in other words, the coordinate axes. Since f

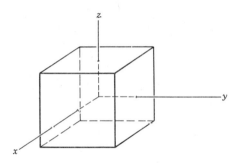

FIGURE 2

has the value zero at any one of its critical points, and since f has both positive and negative values in the neighborhood of any one of these points, no critical point can be an extreme point. Furthermore, a little thought shows that f has maximum value 1 and minimum value -1. These values occur at the corners of the cube, none of which is a critical point.

The problem of finding the extreme values of a function f on the boundary of a subregion R of $\mathfrak{R}^n$ is one in which f has been restricted to a set S of lower dimension than that of R. Then, as we have seen in Example 2, it is not sufficient just to examine the critical points of f as a function on R. More generally, we may be interested in f when it is restricted to a lower-dimensional set S that is not necessarily the boundary of any region at all.

EXAMPLE 3. The function $f(x, y, z) = y^2 - z - x$ has a differential defined by the matrix

$$(-1 \quad 2y \quad -1),$$

so f has no critical points as a function defined on $\mathbb{R}^3$. Suppose, however, that f is restricted to the curve S defined parametrically by

$$\begin{pmatrix} x \\ y \\ z \end{pmatrix} = \begin{pmatrix} t \\ t^2 \\ t^3 \end{pmatrix}, \quad -\infty < t < \infty.$$

On S, f takes the values $F(t) = f(t, t^2, t^3) = t^4 - t^3 - t$ while t varies over $(-\infty, \infty)$. We have

$$F'(t) = 4t^3 - 3t^2 - 1 = (t - 1)(4t^2 + t + 1).$$

Then $F'(t)$ is zero only at $t = 1$. Furthermore, since $F''(t) = 12t^2 - 6t$, we have $F''(1) > 0$. It follows that the point

$$\begin{pmatrix} 1 \\ 1 \\ 1 \end{pmatrix}$$

is a relative minimum for f restricted to the curve S. The minimum value of f on S is -1, and there are no other extreme values.

EXAMPLE 4. Suppose the function $f(x, y, z) = x + y + z$ is restricted to the intersection of the two surfaces

$$x^2 + y^2 = 1, \quad z = 2$$

shown in Figure 3. The curve C of intersection can be parametrized by

$$\begin{pmatrix} x \\ y \\ z \end{pmatrix} = \begin{pmatrix} \cos t \\ \sin t \\ 2 \end{pmatrix}, \quad 0 \le t < 2\pi.$$

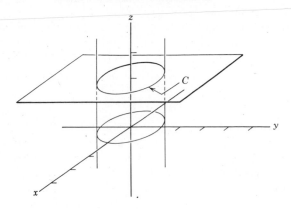

FIGURE 3

The function f on C takes the value $F(t) = \cos t + \sin t + 2$. We have $F'(t) = -\sin t + \cos t$, so $F'(t) = 0$ at $t = \pi/4$ and $t = 5\pi/4$. Since $F''(\pi/4) < 0$ and $F''(5\pi/4) > 0$,

$$f(\sqrt{2}/2, \sqrt{2}/2, 2) = \sqrt{2} + 2$$

is the maximum and

$$f(-\sqrt{2}/2, -\sqrt{2}/2, 2) = -\sqrt{2} + 2$$

is the minimum value for f on C.

The solution of the previous problem depended on our being able to find a concrete parametric representation for the curve of intersection of the cylinder $x^2 + y^2 - 1 = 0$ and the plane $z - 2 = 0$. When a concrete parametrization is not readily available, we can still sometimes apply the method of **Lagrange multipliers** to be described below. The method consists in verifying the pure existence of a parametric representation and then deriving necessary conditions for there to be an extreme point for a function f when restricted to the parametrized curve or surface.

1.2 Theorem. Lagrange multiplier method. Let the function $\mathcal{R}^n \xrightarrow{G} \mathcal{R}^m$, $n > m$, be continuously differentiable and have coordinate functions $G_1, G_2, \ldots, G_m$. Suppose the equations

$$G_1(x_1, \ldots, x_n) = 0$$

$$G_2(x_1, \ldots, x_n) = 0$$

$$\vdots \qquad \qquad \vdots$$

$$G_m(x_1, \ldots, x_n) = 0$$

implicitly define a surface S in $\mathcal{R}^n$, and that at a point X_0 of S the matrix of $d_{X_0}G$ has some m columns linearly independent.

If X_0 is an extreme point of a differentiable function $\mathcal{R}^n \xrightarrow{f} \mathcal{R}$, when restricted to S, then X_0 is a critical point of the function

$$f + \lambda_1 G_1 + \ldots + \lambda_m G_m$$

for some constants $\lambda_1, \ldots, \lambda_m$.

Proof. The implicit function theorem ensures that there is a parametric representation for S in a neighborhood of X_0. For suppose that for some choice of m variables, say $x_1, \ldots, x_m$, the columns of the matrix

$$\begin{pmatrix} \dfrac{\partial G_1}{\partial x_1} & \dfrac{\partial G_1}{\partial x_2} & \cdots & \dfrac{\partial G_1}{\partial x_m} \\ & & & \\ \cdot & & \cdot \\ \cdot & & \cdot \\ \cdot & & \cdot \\ & & & \\ \dfrac{\partial G_m}{\partial x_1} & \dfrac{\partial G_m}{\partial x_2} & \cdots & \dfrac{\partial G_m}{\partial x_m} \end{pmatrix}_{X_0} \tag{1}$$

are independent. Then the matrix has an inverse. Writing $X_0 = (a_1, \ldots, a_n)$, we set $U_0 = (a_1, \ldots, a_m)$ and $V_0 = (a_{m+1}, \ldots, a_n)$, and conclude that $d_{U_0}G$ is one-one. By the implicit function theorem, there is a differentiable function $\mathcal{R}^{n-m} \xrightarrow{h} \mathcal{R}^m$ defined on a neighborhood N of V_0 such that $hV_0 = U_0$ and $G(hV, V) = 0$ for all V in N. The function $\mathcal{R}^{n-m} \xrightarrow{H} \mathcal{R}^n$ defined by

$$HV = (hV, V), \qquad \text{for all } V \text{ in } N,$$

is a parametric representation of a part of S containing $X_0 = HV_0$. The surface S has a tangent $\mathfrak{I}$ of dimension $n - m$ at X_0, because the Jacobian of H at V_0 is

$$\begin{pmatrix} \dfrac{\partial h_1}{\partial x_{m+1}} & \dfrac{\partial h_1}{\partial x_{m+2}} & \cdots & \dfrac{\partial h_1}{\partial x_n} \\ \cdots & & & \\ \dfrac{\partial h_m}{\partial x_{m+1}} & & \cdots & \dfrac{\partial h_m}{\partial x_n} \\ 1 & 0 & \cdots & 0 \\ 0 & 1 & \cdots & 0 \\ \cdots & & & \\ 0 & 0 & \cdots & 1 \end{pmatrix}_{V_0}$$

where $h_1, \ldots, h_m$ are the coordinate functions of h, and the columns of this matrix are clearly independent.

Now compose H with f. Since X_0 is an extreme point of f in S, the point V_0 is an extreme point of $f \circ H$. Hence,

$$d_{V_0}(f \circ H) = d_{X_0}f \circ d_{V_0}H = 0. \tag{2}$$

Because G is constantly zero on S,

$$d_{V_0}(G \circ H) = d_{X_0}G \circ d_{V_0}H = 0. \tag{3}$$

Looking at (2) and (3) together, we see that $d_{X_0}f$ and $d_{X_0}G$ are both zero on the range of $d_{V_0}H$, which set is the tangent $\mathfrak{I}$. Thus the matrix

$$\begin{pmatrix} \dfrac{\partial f}{\partial x_1} & \cdots & \dfrac{\partial f}{\partial x_n} \\[2mm] \dfrac{\partial G_1}{\partial x_1} & \cdots & \dfrac{\partial G_1}{\partial x_n} \\[2mm] \cdot & & \\ \cdot & & \\ \cdot & & \\ \dfrac{\partial G_m}{\partial x_1} & \cdots & \dfrac{\partial G_m}{\partial x_n} \end{pmatrix}_{X_0}$$

defines a linear transformation $\mathfrak{R}^n \xrightarrow{L} \mathfrak{R}^{m+1}$ that is identically zero on $\mathfrak{I}$. Since the dimension of $\mathfrak{I}$ is $n - m$, we have

$$n - m \leq \text{dimension of kernel of } L.$$

It is always true (see Theorem 10.6 of Chapter 1) that

$$n = \text{dimension of kernel of } L + \text{dimension of range of } L,$$

so

$$n \geq n - m + \text{dimension of range of } L,$$

that is,

$$m \geq \text{dimension of range of } L.$$

Then there is a linear functional $\mathfrak{R}^{m+1} \xrightarrow{\Lambda} \mathfrak{R}$ such that Λ is zero on the range of L, but not identically zero on $\mathfrak{R}^{m+1}$. In other words, there is a nonzero Λ such that $\Lambda \circ L = 0$. In matrix form $\Lambda = (\lambda_0, \lambda_1, \ldots, \lambda_m)$ and

$$(\lambda_0, \lambda_1, \ldots, \lambda_m) \begin{pmatrix} \dfrac{\partial f}{\partial x_1} & \cdots & \dfrac{\partial f}{\partial x_n} \\[2mm] \dfrac{\partial G_1}{\partial x_1} & & \dfrac{\partial G_1}{\partial x_n} \\[2mm] \cdot & & \cdot \\ \cdot & & \cdot \\ \cdot & & \cdot \\ \dfrac{\partial G_m}{\partial x_1} & \cdots & \dfrac{\partial G_m}{\partial x_n} \end{pmatrix}_{X_0} = 0 \tag{4}$$

It cannot happen that $\lambda_0 = 0$, for then the rows of (1) are dependent, contradicting the fact that (1) has an inverse. Taking $\lambda_0 = 1$ (if $\lambda_0 \neq 1$, divide through by λ_0), the condition (4) becomes

$$\begin{pmatrix} \dfrac{\partial f}{\partial x_1} \\[2mm] \cdot \\ \cdot \\ \cdot \\ \dfrac{\partial f}{\partial x_n} \end{pmatrix}_{X_0} + \lambda_1 \begin{pmatrix} \dfrac{\partial G_1}{\partial x_1} \\[2mm] \cdot \\ \cdot \\ \dfrac{\partial G_1}{\partial x_n} \end{pmatrix}_{X_0} + \ldots + \lambda_m \begin{pmatrix} \dfrac{\partial G_m}{\partial x_1} \\[2mm] \cdot \\ \cdot \\ \dfrac{\partial G_m}{\partial x_n} \end{pmatrix}_{X_0} = 0,$$

or $d_{X_0}(f + \lambda_1 G_1 + \ldots + \lambda_m G_m) = 0$. This completes the proof.

In applying the theorem it is important to verify that some m columns of $d_X G$ are independent for X in S. Points for which this condition fails must be examined separately in looking for extreme points. All extreme points X_0 for which the condition is satisfied are such that there are constants $\lambda_1, \ldots, \lambda_n$ for which

$$f + \lambda_1 G_1 + \ldots + \lambda_m G_m$$

has X_0 as a critical point, or in other words,

$$d_{X_0}(f + \lambda_1 G_1 + \ldots + \lambda_m G_m) = 0. \tag{5}$$

EXAMPLE 5. The problem of Example 4 is that of finding the extreme points of $f(x, y, z) = x + y + z$ subject to the conditions

$$x^2 + y^2 - 1 = 0, \qquad z - 2 = 0. \tag{6}$$

We write down

$$(x + y + z) + \lambda_1(x^2 + y^2 - 1) + \lambda_2(z - 2).$$

The critical points of this function occur when

$$1 + 2\lambda_1 x = 0, \qquad 1 + 2\lambda_1 y = 0, \qquad 1 + \lambda_2 = 0.$$

In addition, we must satisfy Equations (6). Solving for λ_1 and λ_2, as well as x, y, and z, we get

$$\lambda_2 = -1, \quad \lambda_1 = \pm\frac{1}{\sqrt{2}}, \quad x = y = \pm\frac{1}{\sqrt{2}}, \quad z = 2.$$

That is, the critical points are

$$\left(\frac{1}{\sqrt{2}}, \frac{1}{\sqrt{2}}, 2\right) \quad \text{and} \quad \left(-\frac{1}{\sqrt{2}}, -\frac{1}{\sqrt{2}}, 2\right).$$

As in Example 4, we easily see that f has its maximum value, $\sqrt{2} + 2$, at the first of these points and its minimum value, $-\sqrt{2} + 2$, at the other. Notice that while the λ's are not needed in the final answer, it is necessary to consider all values of the λ's for which the equations can be satisfied.

EXAMPLE 6. Find the maximum value of $f(x, y, z) = x - y + z$, subject to the condition $x^2 + y^2 + z^2 = 1$. The function

$$x - y + z + \lambda(x^2 + y^2 + z^2 - 1)$$

has critical points satisfying

$$1 + 2\lambda x = 0, \qquad -1 + 2\lambda y = 0, \qquad 1 + 2\lambda z = 0.$$

and $$x^2 + y^2 + z^2 = 1.$$

The solutions of these equations are

$$\lambda = \pm\sqrt{3}/2, \qquad x = -y = z = \pm 1/\sqrt{3}.$$

The maximum of f occurs at $\left(\frac{1}{\sqrt{3}}, -\frac{1}{\sqrt{3}}, \frac{1}{\sqrt{3}}\right)$. The maximum value is $\sqrt{3}$.

EXAMPLE 7. Let $g(x_1, x_2, \ldots, x_n) = 0$ implicitly define a surface S in $\mathcal{R}^n$ and let $A = (a_1, a_2, \ldots, a_n)$ be a fixed point. Minimizing the distance from S to A is the same thing as minimizing the square of the distance. Thus P, the nearest point to A on S, must be among the critical points of

$$\sum_{k=1}^{n} (x_k - a_k)^2 + \lambda g(x_1, \ldots, x_n)$$

for some λ. The critical points satisfy, in addition to $g(x_1, \ldots, x_n) = 0$, the equations

$$2(x_1 - a_1) + \lambda \frac{\partial g}{\partial x_1} (x_1, \ldots, x_n) = 0$$

$$\cdot$$
$$\cdot$$
$$\cdot$$

$$2(x_n - a_n) + \lambda \frac{\partial g}{\partial x_n} (x_1, \ldots, x_n) = 0.$$

In vector form these equations reduce at the critical point P to

$$\begin{pmatrix} p_1 - a_1 \\ \cdot \\ \cdot \\ \cdot \\ p_n - a_n \end{pmatrix} = -\frac{\lambda}{2} \begin{pmatrix} \dfrac{\partial g}{\partial x_1} P \\ \cdot \\ \cdot \\ \cdot \\ \dfrac{\partial g}{\partial x_n} P \end{pmatrix},$$

where $P = (p_1, \ldots, p_n)$. The vector P–A on the left is then parallel to the normal vector to S at P, which appears on the right side of the equation. In other words, P–A is perpendicular to S. A two-dimensional example is illustrated in Figure 4.

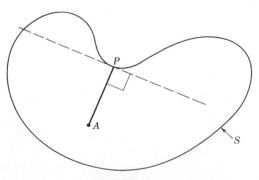

FIGURE 4

If f is a differentiable real-valued function, $\mathfrak{R}^n \xrightarrow{f} \mathfrak{R}$, then the vector

$$\left(\frac{\partial f}{\partial x_1} X, \ldots, \frac{\partial f}{\partial x_n} X\right) = \text{grad}_X f$$

is called the **gradient vector** of f at X. Making use of euclidean length in $\mathfrak{R}^n$, it follows that *the direction of the gradient vector of f at X is a direction of maximum rate of increase for f at X.* For, given a unit vector U,

$$\frac{\partial f}{\partial U} X = (d_X f) U = (\text{grad}_X f) \cdot U \leq |\text{grad}_X f|$$

by the Cauchy-Schwarz inequality. But

$$\frac{\partial f}{\partial U} X = |\text{grad}_X f|$$

when $U = (\text{grad}_X f)/|\text{grad}_X f|$. Thus the rate of increase is never greater than $|\text{grad}_X f|$ and is equal to it in the direction of the gradient.

In terms of the gradient the Lagrange condition (5) can be written

$$\text{grad}_{X_0} f + \lambda_1 \text{grad}_{X_0} G_1 + \ldots + \lambda_m \text{grad}_{X_0} G_m = 0. \tag{7}$$

Furthermore, for each $i = 1, \ldots, m$, the vector

$$\text{grad}_{X_0} G_i = \left(\frac{\partial G_i}{\partial x_1} X_0, \ldots, \frac{\partial G_i}{\partial x_n} X_0\right)$$

is perpendicular to the tangent to the surface S_i at X_0 determined by $G_i X = 0$. It follows that each vector $\text{grad}_{X_0} G_i$ is perpendicular to the tangent to S at X_0, because the tangent to S is the intersection of the tangents to the S_i. Since by (7), $\text{grad}_{X_0} f$ is a linear combination of the vectors $\text{grad}_{X_0} G_i$, the gradient of f itself is perpendicular to S. In other words, if X_0 is an extreme point of f restricted to S, the direction of greatest increase for f must be perpendicular to S.

EXAMPLE 8. The planes

$$x + y + z - 1 = 0 \quad \text{and} \quad x + y - z = 0$$

intersect in a line S as shown in Figure 5. Let $f(x, y) = xy$, and restrict f to S. Using the Lagrange method we consider

$$xy + \lambda(x + y + z - 1) + \mu(x + y - z).$$

Its critical points occur when

$$y + \lambda + \mu = 0, \qquad x + \lambda + \mu = 0, \qquad \lambda - \mu = 0.$$

The only point that satisfies these conditions, together with the condition that it lie on S, is $X_0 = (\frac{1}{4}, \frac{1}{4}, \frac{1}{2})$. We have $\mathrm{grad}_{X_0} f = (\frac{1}{4}, \frac{1}{4}, 0)$, which is perpendicular to S. The unit vector U in the direction of $\mathrm{grad}_{X_0} f$ is shown in Figure 5 with its initial point moved to X_0.

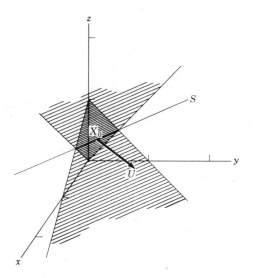

FIGURE 5

EXERCISES

1. Find the critical points of $x^2 + 4xy - y^2 - 8x - 6y$.   [*Ans.* (2, 1)]

2. Find the points at which the largest and smallest values are attained by the following functions.

(a) $x + y$ in the square with corners $\pm 1, \pm 1)$.
[*Ans.* Max. (1, 1), min (−1, −1).]

(b) $x + y + z$ in the region $x^2 + y^2 + z^2 \leq 1$.
[*Ans.* Max. $(1/\sqrt{3}, 1/\sqrt{3}, 1/\sqrt{3})$, min. $(-1/\sqrt{3}, -1/\sqrt{3}, -1/\sqrt{3})$.]

(c) $x^2 + 24xy + 8y^2$ in the region $x^2 + y^2 \leq 25$.
[*Ans.* Max. $\pm$ (3, 4), min. $\pm$ (4, −3).]

(d) $1/(x^2 + y^2)$ in the region $(x - 2)^2 + y^2 \leq 1$.
[*Ans.* Max (1, 0), min. (3, 0).]

(e) $x^2 + y^2 + (2\sqrt{2}/3)xy$ in the ellipse $x^2 + 2y^2 \leq 1$.
[*Ans.* Max. $(\pm 2/\sqrt{5}, \pm 1/\sqrt{10})$, min. (0, 0).]

3. Find the point on the curve

$$\begin{pmatrix} x \\ y \\ z \end{pmatrix} = \begin{pmatrix} \cos t \\ \sin t \\ \sin t/2 \end{pmatrix}$$

that is farthest from the origin.   [*Ans.* $(-1, 0, 1)$.]

4. Find the critical points of the following functions.

(a) $x + y \sin x$.   (b) $xy + xz$.   (c) $x^2 + y^2 + z^2 - 1$.

5. Find the maximum value of the function $x(y + z)$, given that $x^2 + y^2 = 1$ and $xz = 1$.   [*Ans.* 3/2.]

6. Find the minimum value of $x + y^2$, subject to the condition $2x^2 + y^2 = 1$.
                    [*Ans.* $-1/\sqrt{2}$.]

7. Let $f(x, y)$ and $g(x, y)$ be continuously differentiable, and suppose that, subject to the condition $g(x, y) = 0, f(x, y)$ attains its maximum value M at (x_0, y_0). Show that the level curve $f(x, y) = M$ is tangent to the curve $g(x, y) = 0$ at (x_0, y_0).

8. Find the dimension of the cube of largest volume that can be fitted inside a sphere of radius a.

9. A store buys sharp razor blades for a dollar a dozen and dull razor blades for fifty cents a dozen. Let s and d be the prices the store asks for the two kinds of blade, and assume that at these prices the demands per day will be

$$S = 20 + 5d - 6s,$$

$$D = \ \ 1 - 2d + 3s.$$

Assume also that the store owner refuses to pay to have any blades taken away and that he feels a moral obligation not to charge more than five dollars per dozen for any blades he sells. Under these conditions find the maximum profit per day and the prices to be charged to attain the maximum.

10. (a) Find the maximum value of $x^2 + xy + y^2 + yz + z^2$, subject to the condition $x^2 + y^2 + z^2 = 1$.   [*Ans.* $1 + 1/\sqrt{2}$.]

(b) Find the maximum value of the same function subject to the conditions $x^2 + y^2 + z^2 = 1$ and $ax + by + cz = 0$, where (a, b, c) is a point at which the maximum is attained in (a).
                    [*Ans.* 1.]

11. Consider a differentiable function $\Re^n \xrightarrow{f} \Re$ and a continuously differentiable function $\Re^n \xrightarrow{G} \Re^m$, $m < n$. Suppose the surface S defined by $GX = 0$ has a tangent $\mathfrak{I}$ of dimension $n - m$ at X_0, and that the function f restricted to S has an extreme value at X_0. Show that $\mathfrak{I}$ is parallel to the tangent to the surface defined explicitly by f at the point (X_0, fX_0).

12. (a) Find the points X_0 at which $f(x, y) = x^2 - y^2 - y$ attains its maximum on the circle $x^2 + y^2 = 1$. $[Ans.\ (\pm\sqrt{15}/4,\ -\tfrac{1}{4}).]$

(b) Find the directions in which f increases most rapidly at X_0. $[Ans.\ (\pm\sqrt{15}/2,\ -\tfrac{1}{2}).]$

13. The planes $x + y - z - 2w = 1$ and $x - y + z + w = 2$ intersect in a flat $\mathfrak{F}$ in $\Re^4$. Find the point on $\mathfrak{F}$ that is nearest to the origin. $[Ans.\ (\tfrac{27}{19},\ -\tfrac{7}{19},\ \tfrac{7}{19},\ -\tfrac{3}{19}).]$

14. Let $X_1, \ldots, X_N$ be points in $\Re^n$, and let

$$fX = \sum_{k=1}^{N} |\, X - X_k\,|^2.$$

Find the point at which f attains its minimum and find the minimum value.

15. Prove by solving an appropriate minimum problem that if $a_k > 0$, $k = 1, \ldots, n$, then

$$(a_1 \quad a_2 \quad \ldots \quad a_n)^{1/n} \le \frac{a_1 + a_2 + \ldots + a_n}{n}.$$

2. QUADRATIC POLYNOMIALS

Let $F(X, Y) = X \cdot Y$, be the euclidean dot product of two vectors X and Y in $\Re^n$. In addition to having the property $F(X, X) \ge 0$, the function F satisfies

$$F(X, Y) = F(Y, X) \tag{1}$$

$$F(X + X', Y) = F(X, Y) + F(X', Y) \tag{2}$$

$$F(aX, Y) = aF(X, Y) \tag{3}$$

where a is any real number. As a consequence of the definition of F, or of the above three properties, F is linear in the second variable also. Because of the symmetry property (1) and the linearity in both variables, a real-valued function F satisfying (1)–(3) for all pairs of vectors X and Y in $\Re^n$ is called a **symmetric bilinear function**. Such a function can be written in terms of coordinates as follows. Let $X = (x_1, \ldots, x_n)$ and $Y = (y_1, \ldots, y_n)$. Then,

$$X = \sum_{i=1}^{n} x_i E_i, \qquad Y = \sum_{j=1}^{n} y_j E_j,$$

where E_k, $k = 1, 2, \ldots, n$, are the natural basis vectors

$$\begin{pmatrix} 1 \\ 0 \\ \cdot \\ \cdot \\ \cdot \\ 0 \end{pmatrix}, \quad \begin{pmatrix} 0 \\ 1 \\ \cdot \\ \cdot \\ \cdot \\ 0 \end{pmatrix}, \quad \ldots, \quad \begin{pmatrix} 0 \\ 0 \\ \cdot \\ \cdot \\ \cdot \\ 1 \end{pmatrix},$$

of $\mathcal{R}^n$. We have from (2) and (3)

$$F(X, Y) = F\left(\sum_{1}^{n} x_i E_i, \sum_{1}^{n} y_j E_j \right) = \sum_{i=1}^{n} \sum_{j=1}^{n} F(E_i, E_j) x_i y_j$$

where, by (1), $F(E_i, E_j) = F(E_j, E_i)$. Conversely, an arbitrary choice of the numbers $F(E_i, E_j) = a_{ij}$, consistent with $a_{ij} = a_{ji}$, determines the most general symmetric bilinear function. In summary, symmetric bilinear functions are just those that in terms of coordinates have the form

$$F(X, Y) = \sum_{i,j=1}^{n} a_{ij} x_i y_j, \qquad a_{ij} = a_{ji}. \tag{4}$$

In particular, if $a_{ii} = 1$ and $a_{ij} = 0$ for $i \neq j$, we get our original example

$$X \cdot Y = \sum_{i=1}^{n} x_i y_i.$$

If F is a symmetric bilinear function on $\mathcal{R}^n$, the real-valued function of a single vector defined by

$$QX = F(X, X) \qquad \text{for all } X \text{ in } \mathcal{R}^n$$

is called a **homogeneous quadratic polynomial**, or sometimes a **quadratic form**. Thus, by definition, every Q is associated with some bilinear F, and *vice versa*. From (4) it follows that in coordinate form,

$$QX = \sum_{i,j=1}^{n} a_{ij} x_i x_j, \qquad a_{ij} = a_{ji}. \tag{5}$$

For example, if F is the euclidean dot product, we have associated with it the quadratic polynomial

$$X \cdot X = \sum_{i=1}^{n} x_i^2.$$

The word **homogeneous**, applied to a polynomial, refers to the fact that all terms have the same degree in the coordinate variables x_i. Throughout this section the phrase "quadratic polynomial" will be understood to mean "homogeneous quadratic polynomial."

Equation (4) can be written as a matrix product as follows:

$$F(X, Y) = (x_1 \quad x_2 \quad \ldots \quad x_n) \begin{pmatrix} a_{11} & a_{12} & \ldots & a_{1n} \\ a_{21} & & & \cdot \\ \ldots & & & \cdot \\ a_{n1} & & \ldots & a_{nn} \end{pmatrix} \begin{pmatrix} y_1 \\ y_2 \\ \cdot \\ \cdot \\ y_n \end{pmatrix}$$

or

$$F(X, Y) = X^t A Y = X \cdot A Y.$$

This follows immediately from the definition of matrix multiplication. The condition $a_{ij} = a_{ji}$ means that the matrix $A = (a_{ij})$ is symmetric about its principal diagonal.

In the matrix notation, (5) becomes

$$QX = X^t A X,$$

and we have as a familiar special case

$$QX = X^t I X = X \cdot X.$$

In case $a_{ij} = 0$ for $i \neq j$, A is a **diagonal** matrix and Q is said to be represented in **diagonal form**.

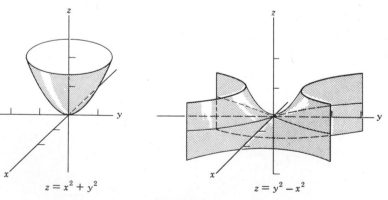

$$z = x^2 + y^2 \qquad\qquad z = y^2 - x^2$$

FIGURE 6

EXAMPLE 1. We give some examples of quadratic polynomials.

$$(x \quad y) \begin{pmatrix} 1 & 2 \\ 2 & 4 \end{pmatrix} \begin{pmatrix} x \\ y \end{pmatrix} = x^2 + 4xy + y^2,$$

$$(x \quad y \quad z) \begin{pmatrix} 1 & 0 & 1 \\ 0 & 1 & 0 \\ 1 & 0 & 1 \end{pmatrix} \begin{pmatrix} x \\ y \\ z \end{pmatrix} = x^2 + y^2 + z^2 + 2xz,$$

$$(x_1 \quad x_2 \quad x_3 \quad x_4) \begin{pmatrix} 1 & 0 & 0 & 0 \\ 0 & 2 & 0 & 0 \\ 0 & 0 & 3 & 0 \\ 0 & 0 & 0 & 4 \end{pmatrix} \begin{pmatrix} x_1 \\ x_2 \\ x_3 \\ x_4 \end{pmatrix} = x_1^2 + 2x_2^2 + 3x_3^2 + 4x_4^2.$$

A quadratic polynomial Q is called **positive definite** if $QX > 0$ except for $X = 0$. We remark that if Q is positive definite and F is its associated bilinear function, then F is an inner product in $\mathfrak{R}^n$. This is so because (1)–(3) together with the positive definiteness condition are the characteristic properties of an inner product.

EXAMPLE 2. The graphs of two quadratic polynomials are shown in Figure 6. The one on the left is positive definite. The other one is not; its graph is called a **hyperbolic paraboloid**.

EXAMPLE 3. The quadratic polynomial

$$Q_1(x, y, z) = (x - y - z)^2 = x^2 + y^2 + z^2 - 2xy - 2xz + 2yz$$

is non-negative. However, it is not positive definite because it is zero on the plane $x - y - z = 0$.

The polynomial

$$Q_2(x, y, z) = (x + y + z)^2 - (x - y - z)^2 = 4xy + 4xz$$

changes sign. In fact, Q_2 is negative on the plane $x + y + z = 0$ and positive on the plane $x - y - z = 0$, except along the line of intersection of the two planes, where Q_2 is zero.

The polynomial

$$Q_3(x, y, z) = x^2 + y^2$$

is non-negative, but not positive definite, because $Q_3(0, 0, z) = 0$ for arbitrary z.

In the examples just given, we have seen illustrations of the fact that if a quadratic polynomial can be written, say, in the diagonal form

$$Q(x, y, z) = a_1 x^2 + a_2 y^2 + a_3 z^2,$$

then Q is positive definite if and only if all the coefficients a_i are positive. Furthermore, in the event that some coefficients are negative or zero, it is possible to determine regions for which Q is positive or negative. In the next examples we consider one way in which a polynomial $Q(x, y)$ can be written in diagonal form.

EXAMPLE 4. In $\mathfrak{R}^2$ the most general symmetric bilinear function is got by choosing a, b, and c arbitrarily in

$$F((x, y), (x', y')) = (x \quad y) \begin{pmatrix} a & b \\ b & c \end{pmatrix} \begin{pmatrix} x' \\ y' \end{pmatrix}.$$

The general quadratic polynomial is then

$$Q(x, y) = ax^2 + 2bxy + cy^2.$$

To determine conditions under which Q is positive definite, notice first that we could not have both $a = 0$ and $c = 0$. For then $Q(x, y) = 2bxy$, and, if $b \neq 0$, this polynomial assumes both positive and negative values. Suppose then that $a \neq 0$. Completing the square, we have

$$Q(x, y) = \frac{1}{a} \left[a^2 \left(x + \frac{b}{a} y \right)^2 + (ac - b^2) y^2 \right]. \tag{6}$$

Similarly, if $c \neq 0$,

$$Q(x, y) = \frac{1}{c} \left[c^2 \left(y + \frac{b}{c} x \right)^2 + (ac - b^2) x^2 \right]. \tag{7}$$

We see directly that Q is positive definite if and only if $ac - b^2 > 0$ and either $a > 0$ or $c > 0$.

EXAMPLE 5. Having written Q in one of the above two forms (6) or (7), an obvious change of variable can be used to simplify the polynomial. To be specific, suppose $a \neq 0$ and that (6) holds. Letting

$$u = x + \frac{b}{a} y, \qquad v = 0x + y,$$

we can write Q in the form

$$au^2 + \frac{1}{a}(ac - b^2)v^2.$$

This transformation of coordinates corresponds to a change of basis in which the natural basis of $\mathfrak{R}^2$ is replaced by the basis

$$X_1 = (1, 0), \qquad X_2 = \left(-\frac{b}{a}, 1\right).$$

The coordinate relations between x, y and u, v can be written in matrix form as

$$\begin{pmatrix} u \\ v \end{pmatrix} = \begin{pmatrix} 1 & \dfrac{b}{a} \\ 0 & 1 \end{pmatrix}\begin{pmatrix} x \\ y \end{pmatrix}, \qquad \begin{pmatrix} x \\ y \end{pmatrix} = \begin{pmatrix} 1 & -\dfrac{b}{a} \\ 0 & 1 \end{pmatrix}\begin{pmatrix} u \\ v \end{pmatrix}.$$

In order to see concretely the geometric significance of the choice of new basis, we consider a numerical example. Let

$$QX = Q(x, y) = x^2 + 2xy + 3y^2.$$

Then $a = b = 1$ and $c = 3$. The new basis consists of the vectors $X_1 \cdot = (1, 0)$ and $X_2 = (-1, 1)$. With respect to the new coordinates

$$QX = u^2 + 2v^2,$$

where

$$\begin{pmatrix} u \\ v \end{pmatrix} = \begin{pmatrix} 1 & 1 \\ 0 & 1 \end{pmatrix}\begin{pmatrix} x \\ y \end{pmatrix}, \qquad \begin{pmatrix} x \\ y \end{pmatrix} = \begin{pmatrix} 1 & -1 \\ 0 & 1 \end{pmatrix}\begin{pmatrix} u \\ v \end{pmatrix}.$$

Clearly Q is positive definite. The vectors X_1 and X_2, together with the level curve $QX = 1$, are shown in Figure 7.

We have seen in Example 5 that a quadratic polynomial can be reduced to diagonal form by writing it in terms of the coordinates of an appropriately chosen basis. However, this was done with basis vectors that were not necessarily perpendicular. The next theorem shows that we can always find a diagonalizing basis consisting of perpendicular vectors of length 1.

restricted to the unit sphere of the subspace of $\mathfrak{R}^n$ perpendicular to $X_1, X_2, \ldots, X_{k-1}$.

The maximum value property of the basis vectors X_k can be used to compute them, as in the next example.

EXAMPLE 6. Suppose the quadratic polynomial

$$Q(x, y) = 3x^2 + 2xy + 3y^2$$

is expressed using the coordinates of the natural basis for $\mathfrak{R}^2$. We restrict Q to the unit circle

$$x^2 + y^2 - 1 = 0.$$

By Lagrange's theorem, (Theorem 1.2), Q will have its maximum at the critical points of

$$3x^2 + 2xy + 3y^2 - \lambda(x^2 + y^2 - 1),$$

for some λ. That is, for some λ, (x, y) must satisfy

$$(3 - \lambda)x + \qquad y = 0$$
$$x + (3 - \lambda)y = 0$$

in addition to $x^2 + y^2 = 1$. (λ has been replaced by $-\lambda$.) Nonzero solutions to these equations will exist only if the columns of the matrix

$$\begin{pmatrix} 3 - \lambda & 1 \\ 1 & 3 - \lambda \end{pmatrix}$$

are dependent. Since dependence is equivalent to

$$\begin{vmatrix} 3 - \lambda & 1 \\ 1 & 3 - \lambda \end{vmatrix} = 0,$$

we must have $(3 - \lambda)^2 - 1 = 0$ or $\lambda = 2, 4$. The corresponding solutions for (x, y) are

$$\lambda = 2: \qquad (x, y) = \left(\pm\frac{1}{\sqrt{2}}, \mp\frac{1}{\sqrt{2}}\right).$$

$$\lambda = 4: \qquad (x, y) = \left(\pm\frac{1}{\sqrt{2}}, \pm\frac{1}{\sqrt{2}}\right).$$

The maximum of Q occurs at $(\pm 1/\sqrt{2}, \pm 1/\sqrt{2})$, so we can choose $X_1 = (1/\sqrt{2}, 1/\sqrt{2})$. For X_2 we can take either of the two vectors $(\pm 1/\sqrt{2}, \mp 1/\sqrt{2})$. Let $X_2 = (-1/\sqrt{2}, 1/\sqrt{2})$.

The change of coordinate equation is then

$$\begin{pmatrix} x \\ y \end{pmatrix} = \begin{pmatrix} \dfrac{1}{\sqrt{2}} & \dfrac{-1}{\sqrt{2}} \\[2mm] \dfrac{1}{\sqrt{2}} & \dfrac{1}{\sqrt{2}} \end{pmatrix} \begin{pmatrix} u \\ v \end{pmatrix}.$$

In terms of the new variables we have

$$QX = 4u^2 + 2v^2.$$

In Figure 8, level curves of Q are shown in their relation to the new and to the original basis vectors.

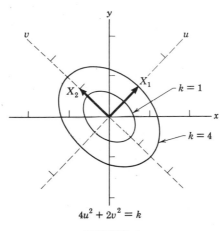

$$4u^2 + 2v^2 = k$$

FIGURE 8

For some purposes it is unnecessary to compute the orthonormal basis vectors X of Theorem 2.1 provided that the numbers λ can be found. For example, it is clear just from knowing the λ_k whether Q is positive definite or not. The following theorem enables us to compute, or estimate, the λ_k.

2.3 Theorem. Let Q be a quadratic polynomial in $\Re^n$ given by

$$QX = X^t A X,$$

where A is a symmetric matrix. Suppose that, with respect to the co-ordinates of the orthonormal basis $X_1, \ldots, X_n$, Q has the form

$$QX = \sum_{k=1}^{n} \lambda_k y_k^2, \tag{8}$$

where $QX_k = \lambda_k$. Then the numbers λ_k are the roots of the equation

$$\det (A - \lambda I) = 0. \tag{9}$$

Although the existence of the basis vectors, $X_1, \ldots, X_k$ has been proved in Theorem 2.1, it is not necessary to know what they are in order to find the λ_k. The λ_k can be computed by solving Equation (9). Equation (9) is called the **characteristic equation** of Q and the roots λ_k are called **characteristic roots** or **eigenvalues**. The next theorem provides another method for computing the basis vectors $X_1, \ldots, X_n$.

2.4 Theorem. Let $Z_1, \ldots, Z_n$ be any orthonormal basis such that, for each $k = 1, \ldots, n$, Z_k satisfies the matrix equation

$$(A - \lambda_k I)Z_k = 0. \tag{10}$$

Then, with respect to this basis, Q has the diagonal form (8).

Vectors Z_k that satisfy Equation (10) are called **characteristic vectors corresponding to λ_k**.

Proof (of Theorem 2.3). Suppose that the orthonormal basis vectors $X_1, \ldots, X_n$ that diagonalize Q are

$$X_1 = \begin{pmatrix} b_{11} \\ \cdot \\ \cdot \\ \cdot \\ b_{n1} \end{pmatrix}, \quad X_2 = \begin{pmatrix} b_{12} \\ \cdot \\ \cdot \\ \cdot \\ b_{n2} \end{pmatrix}, \quad \ldots, \quad X_n = \begin{pmatrix} b_{1n} \\ \cdot \\ \cdot \\ \cdot \\ b_{nn} \end{pmatrix}.$$

Let B be the n by n matrix with columns $X_1, \ldots, X_n$. According to Chapter 1, Section 11, coordinates of the same point are related by the equation $X = BY$, where

$$X = \begin{pmatrix} x_1 \\ \cdot \\ \cdot \\ \cdot \\ x_n \end{pmatrix} \quad \text{and} \quad Y = \begin{pmatrix} y_1 \\ \cdot \\ \cdot \\ \cdot \\ y_n \end{pmatrix},$$

where $y_1, \ldots, y_n$ are the coordinates with respect to $X_1, \ldots, X_n$. Then substituting BY for X gives

$$\begin{aligned} QX &= (BY)^t A (BY) \\ &= Y^t (B^t A B) Y \\ &= Y^t \Lambda Y. \end{aligned}$$

By the choice of the columns of B, the matrix $\Lambda = B^t A B$ is a diagonal matrix with diagonal entries $\lambda_1, \ldots, \lambda_k$. Furthermore, since the columns of B are the coordinates of perpendicular unit vectors with respect to an orthonormal basis, we have directly, by matrix multiplication, $B^tB = I$. In other words, $B^t = B^{-1}$. Then $\Lambda = B^{-1}AB$. Subtracting λI from both sides of this equation and factoring the right-hand member, we get

$$\Lambda - \lambda I = B^{-1}AB - \lambda I$$
$$= B^{-1}(A - \lambda I)B.$$

But $\Lambda - \lambda I$ is a diagonal matrix with diagonal entries $\lambda_k - \lambda$, so

$$(\lambda_1 - \lambda)(\lambda_2 - \lambda) \ldots (\lambda_n - \lambda) = \det (\Lambda - \lambda I)$$
$$= \det B^{-1} \det (A - \lambda I) \det B$$
$$= \det (A - \lambda I).$$

This shows that the roots of $\det (A - \lambda I) = 0$ are $\lambda_1, \ldots, \lambda_n$.

Proof (of Theorem 2.4). Let $Z_1, \ldots, Z_n$ be an orthonormal basis satisfying $AZ_k = \lambda_k Z_k$, for $k = 1, 2, \ldots, n$. Let C be the matrix with columns $Z_1, Z_2, \ldots, Z_n$. The equation

$$X = CZ$$

gives the relation between the coordinates of the basis $Z_1, \ldots, Z_n$ in $\mathfrak{R}^n$ and the natural coordinates. Then

$$QX = X^tAX = (CZ)^tA(CZ) = Z^t(C^tAC)Z.$$

All we have to do is verify that the matrix C^tAC is diagonal with diagonal entries $\lambda_1, \ldots, \lambda_n$. Schematically, we write

$$C^tAC = \begin{pmatrix} Z_1^t \\ \cdot \\ \cdot \\ \cdot \\ Z_n^t \end{pmatrix} A(Z_1 \ \ldots \ Z_n)$$

$$= \begin{pmatrix} Z_1^t \\ \cdot \\ \cdot \\ \cdot \\ Z_n^t \end{pmatrix} (AZ_1 \ \ldots \ AZ_n)$$

$$= \begin{pmatrix} Z_1^t \\ \cdot \\ \cdot \\ \cdot \\ Z_n^t \end{pmatrix} (\lambda_1 Z_1 \ \ldots \ \lambda_n Z_n).$$

Using the fact that

$$Z_i^t Z_j = Z_i \cdot Z_j = \begin{cases} 1, & \text{if } i = j, \\ 0, & \text{if } i \neq j, \end{cases}$$

we get

$$C^t A C = \begin{pmatrix} \lambda_1 & 0 & \cdots & 0 \\ 0 & \lambda_2 & & \vdots \\ \vdots & & & \vdots \\ 0 & & \cdots & \lambda_n \end{pmatrix}.$$

This completes the proof.

EXAMPLE 7. Let $Q(x, y, z) = xy + yz + zx$. The matrix of Q is

$$\begin{pmatrix} 0 & \tfrac{1}{2} & \tfrac{1}{2} \\ \tfrac{1}{2} & 0 & \tfrac{1}{2} \\ \tfrac{1}{2} & \tfrac{1}{2} & 0 \end{pmatrix}$$

and the characteristic equation is

$$\begin{vmatrix} -\lambda & \tfrac{1}{2} & \tfrac{1}{2} \\ \tfrac{1}{2} & -\lambda & \tfrac{1}{2} \\ \tfrac{1}{2} & \tfrac{1}{2} & -\lambda \end{vmatrix} = 0$$

or

$$-\lambda^3 + \tfrac{3}{4}\lambda + \tfrac{1}{4} = 0.$$

The characteristic roots are $\lambda = 1, -\tfrac{1}{2}, -\tfrac{1}{2}$. So there is an orthonormal system of coordinates (u, v, w) with respect to which Q has the form

$$u^2 - \tfrac{1}{2}v^2 - \tfrac{1}{2}w^2.$$

To find the related basis vectors we look for the unit vector solutions of the equations

$$\begin{pmatrix} -\lambda & \tfrac{1}{2} & \tfrac{1}{2} \\ \tfrac{1}{2} & -\lambda & \tfrac{1}{2} \\ \tfrac{1}{2} & \tfrac{1}{2} & -\lambda \end{pmatrix} \begin{pmatrix} x \\ y \\ z \end{pmatrix} = 0,$$

with $\lambda = 1$ and $\lambda = -\tfrac{1}{2}$. With $\lambda = 1$ we get $x = y = z$ for a solution, so we can choose $X_1 = (1/\sqrt{3}, 1/\sqrt{3}, 1/\sqrt{3})$. When $\lambda = -\tfrac{1}{2}$, the matrix equation simply requires that the two remaining basis vectors lie in the plane $x + y + z = 0$, perpendicular to X_1. Then X_2 and X_3 can be chosen to be arbitrary perpendicular vectors in that plane, for example,

$$\left(\frac{1}{\sqrt{2}}, -\frac{1}{\sqrt{2}}, 0 \right) \quad \text{and} \quad \left(\frac{1}{\sqrt{6}}, \frac{1}{\sqrt{6}}, -\frac{2}{\sqrt{6}} \right).$$

A level surface of a quadratic polynomial is called a **quadratic surface**. Since every quadratic polynomial can be diagonalized with respect to some orthonormal basis, it is sufficient to be able to picture the level surfaces of some standard quadratic polynomials in order to be able to picture a more general quadratic surface. For reference we give some illustrations of quadratic surfaces in $\mathfrak{R}^3$ (see Figure 9).

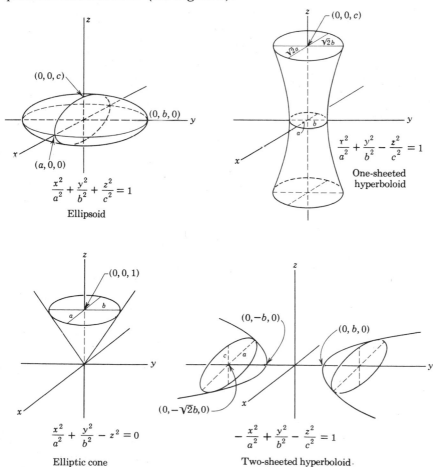

FIGURE 9

EXAMPLE 8. The quadratic polynomial $xy + yz$ can be represented by a symmetric matrix as

$$xy + yz = (x \quad y \quad z) \begin{pmatrix} 0 & \frac{1}{2} & 0 \\ \frac{1}{2} & 0 & \frac{1}{2} \\ 0 & \frac{1}{2} & 0 \end{pmatrix} \begin{pmatrix} x \\ y \\ z \end{pmatrix}.$$

The characteristic equation is $-\lambda^3 + \frac{1}{2}\lambda = 0$, and this equation has roots $\lambda = 1/\sqrt{2},\ 0,\ -1/\sqrt{2}$. The corresponding characteristic vector equations, together with their unit vector solutions, are as follows:

$$\lambda = \frac{1}{\sqrt{2}}: \quad \begin{vmatrix} -\dfrac{1}{\sqrt{2}} & \dfrac{1}{2} & 0 \\ \dfrac{1}{2} & -\dfrac{1}{\sqrt{2}} & \dfrac{1}{2} \\ 0 & \dfrac{1}{2} & -\dfrac{1}{\sqrt{2}} \end{vmatrix} \begin{pmatrix} x \\ y \\ z \end{pmatrix} = 0, \qquad (x, y, z) = \pm\left(\frac{1}{2}, \frac{1}{\sqrt{2}}, \frac{1}{2}\right)$$

$$\lambda = 0: \quad \begin{vmatrix} 0 & \dfrac{1}{2} & 0 \\ \dfrac{1}{2} & 0 & \dfrac{1}{2} \\ 0 & \dfrac{1}{2} & 0 \end{vmatrix} \begin{pmatrix} x \\ y \\ z \end{pmatrix} = 0, \qquad (x, y, z) = \pm\left(\frac{1}{\sqrt{2}}, 0, -\frac{1}{\sqrt{2}}\right)$$

$$\lambda = -\frac{1}{\sqrt{2}}: \quad \begin{vmatrix} \dfrac{1}{\sqrt{2}} & \dfrac{1}{2} & 0 \\ \dfrac{1}{2} & \dfrac{1}{\sqrt{2}} & \dfrac{1}{2} \\ 0 & \dfrac{1}{2} & \dfrac{1}{\sqrt{2}} \end{vmatrix} \begin{pmatrix} x \\ y \\ z \end{pmatrix} = 0, \qquad (x, y, z) = \pm\left(\frac{1}{2}, -\frac{1}{\sqrt{2}}, \frac{1}{2}\right)$$

We choose the diagonalizing basis

$$X_1 = \left(\frac{1}{2}, \frac{1}{\sqrt{2}}, \frac{1}{2}\right), \qquad X_2 = \left(\frac{1}{\sqrt{2}}, 0, -\frac{1}{\sqrt{2}}\right), \qquad X_3 = \left(\frac{1}{2}, -\frac{1}{\sqrt{2}}, \frac{1}{2}\right).$$

If u, v, and w are the coordinates with respect to the new basis, then the polynomial will have the form $(1/\sqrt{2})u^2 - (1/\sqrt{2})w^2$. The level surface

$$\frac{1}{\sqrt{2}}\,u^2 - \frac{1}{\sqrt{2}}\,w^2 = 1$$

is the hyperbolic cylinder one sheet of which is shown in Figure 10.

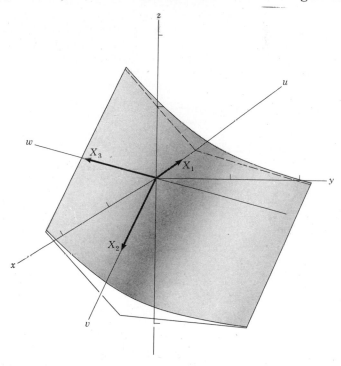

FIGURE 10

Homogeneous polynomials of degree $N > 2$ can be defined in very much the same way as quadratic polynomials. We can start with a real-valued function $F(X_1, \ldots, X_N)$ that is symmetric in its N vector variables, and linear in each of them, and defined for every N vectors $X_1, \ldots, X_N$. Then

$$PX = F(X, X, \ldots, X)$$

will be a polynomial of degree N. Alternatively, we can consider functions of $X = (x_1, x_2, \ldots, x_n)$ having the form

$$PX = \sum_{i_1, \cdots, i_N=1}^{n} a_{i_1 \ldots i_N} x_{i_1} \ldots x_{i_N},$$

where the coefficients $a_{i_1...i_N}$ are symmetric in the subscripts. In both cases we get the same class of functions. The symmetry condition on the coefficients or on F is a convenience, and if it were not assumed, it could be obtained simply by averaging the nonsymmetric coefficients. The details are left as an exercise (Exercise 12).

EXERCISES

1. By changing coordinates, write each of the following quadratic polynomials as a sum of squares. In each problem exhibit an orthonormal basis that does the job, and write the coordinate transformation.
   (a) $3x^2 + 2\sqrt{2}\, xy + 4y^2$.

   $$\left[Ans.\ QX = 2u^2 + 5v^2;\ X_1 = \left(\frac{\sqrt{2}}{\sqrt{3}}, -\frac{1}{\sqrt{3}}\right),\ X_2 = \left(\frac{1}{\sqrt{3}}, \frac{\sqrt{2}}{\sqrt{3}}\right). \right]$$

   (b) $3x^2 + 2\sqrt{3}\, xy + 5y^2$.

   $$\left[Ans.\ QX = 2u^2 + 6v^2;\ X_1 = \left(-\frac{\sqrt{3}}{2}, \frac{1}{2}\right),\ X_2 = \left(\frac{1}{2}, \frac{\sqrt{3}}{2}\right). \right]$$

   (c)
   $$(x\ \ y) \begin{pmatrix} 2 & 2 \\ 2 & 5 \end{pmatrix} \begin{pmatrix} x \\ y \end{pmatrix}.$$

   (d) $2x^2 - 5xy + 2y^2 - 2xz - 4z^2 - 2yz$.

   $$\left[Ans.\ QX = \frac{9}{2}u^2 - \frac{9}{2}v^2 + 0w^2;\ X_1 = \begin{pmatrix} \dfrac{1}{\sqrt{2}} \\[2mm] -\dfrac{1}{\sqrt{2}} \\[2mm] 0 \end{pmatrix},\ X_2 = \begin{pmatrix} \dfrac{1}{3\sqrt{2}} \\[2mm] \dfrac{1}{3\sqrt{2}} \\[2mm] \dfrac{4}{3\sqrt{2}} \end{pmatrix},\ X_3 = \begin{pmatrix} \dfrac{2}{3} \\[2mm] \dfrac{2}{3} \\[2mm] -\dfrac{1}{3} \end{pmatrix}. \right]$$

   (e)
   $$(x\ \ y\ \ z) \begin{pmatrix} -1 & 2 & 0 \\ 2 & 0 & 2 \\ 0 & 2 & 1 \end{pmatrix} \begin{pmatrix} x \\ y \\ z \end{pmatrix}.$$

2. (a) For each polynomial Q in Exercise 1, find the maximum of Q when Q is restricted to the unit sphere, $|X| = 1$, of the euclidean space on which Q is defined. [*Hint.* See Theorem 2.2.]

   (b) Find the maximum of the polynomial in 1(a), restricted to the circle $x^2 + y^2 = 3$ [*Ans.* 15].

3. Classify the following quadratic polynomials as positive definite, negative definite, or neither. Give reasons. (Q is **negative definite** if $Q < 0$ except for $Q0 = 0$.)

(a) $2x^2 - 7xy + 5y^2$.   [*Ans.* Neither.]

(b) $2x^2 - 3xy + 5y^2$.   [*Ans.* Positive definite.]

(c) $-x^2 + 2xy - 6y^2$.   [*Ans.* Negative definite.]

(d) $3x^2 + xy + 3y^2 + 5z^2$.   [*Ans.* Positive definite.]

(e) $(x \quad y \quad z) \begin{pmatrix} 1 & 3 & 0 \\ 3 & 1 & 1 \\ 0 & 1 & 3 \end{pmatrix} \begin{pmatrix} x \\ y \\ z \end{pmatrix}$.

[*Ans.* Neither.]

4. Prove that $x^2 + y^2 + z^2 - xy - xz - yz$ is not positive definite, but becomes so when restricted to the plane $x + y + z = 0$.

5. Sketch the level curves $QX = 1$ and $QX = 0$ for each of the following polynomials in $\mathcal{R}^2$.

(a) xy.   (b) $x^2 + xy + y^2$.   (c) $x^2 + xy - 2y^2$.

6. Sketch the level surfaces $QX = 1$ and $QX = 0$ for the following polynomials in $\mathcal{R}^3$.

(a) $x^2 - xy + y^2 + z^2$.   (b) $x^2 + xy$.   (c) $x^2 - 2xy + y^2 - z^2$.

7. Show that every quadratic polynomial Q satisfies

$$Q(aX) = a^2 QX,$$

for every real number a.

8. Let Q be an arbitrary quadratic polynomial on $\mathcal{R}^n$, and F its associated symmetric bilinear function. Prove that

$$F(X, Y) = \tfrac{1}{2}[Q(X + Y) - QX - QY],$$

for all vectors X and Y in $\mathcal{R}^n$. This equation proves that F is uniquely determined by Q.

9. Prove that every quadratic polynomial Q on $\mathcal{R}^n$ is a continuous function.

10. Let Q be an arbitrary quadratic polynomial on $\mathcal{R}^n$, and F its associated symmetric bilinear function, that is $QX = F(X, X)$. Prove that Q is a differentiable vector function, more explicitly, that

$$(d_X Q) Y = 2F(X, Y).$$

11. Prove that every quadratic polynomial Q is a continuously differentiable function.

12. What follows illustrates the fact that the condition of symmetry on a bilinear function can be obtained by averaging out the nonsymmetry. Let F be a real-valued function defined for all pairs of vectors X and Y and linear in each variable (we do *not* assume symmetry). Show that the function F' defined by

$$F'(X, Y) = \tfrac{1}{2}(F(X, Y) + F(Y, X))$$

is a symmetric bilinear function on $\mathfrak{X}$. Show that $F'(X, X) = F(X, X)$, and hence that F' and F define the same quadratic polynomial.

13. Let Q be a quadratic polynomial on $\mathfrak{R}^n$. Prove that there exists a basis $(X_1, \ldots, X_n)$ for $\mathfrak{R}^n$ such that, for any vector $X = y_1 X_1 + \ldots + y_n X_n$,

$$QX = \sum_{i=1}^{n} \lambda_i y_i^2, \qquad \text{with } \lambda_i = 0, 1, \text{ or } -1.$$

14. Prove that if Q is a positive-definite quadratic polynomial on $\mathfrak{R}^n$, there exists a positive real number m such that

$$QX \geq m \mid X \mid^2, \qquad \text{for all } X \text{ in } \mathfrak{R}^n.$$

[*Suggestion.* Diagonalize Q.] A corollary is that the values of Q on the unit sphere $\mid X \mid = 1$ are bounded away from zero.

15. Let Q be a positive-definite quadratic polynomial in $\mathfrak{R}^2$ and let λ_1 and λ_2 be its characteristic roots. Show that $\lambda_1^{-1/2}$ and $\lambda_2^{-1/2}$ are the lengths of the principal axes of the ellipse $QX = 1$.

16. Verify that if $a \neq 0$ and $ab - f^2 \neq 0$

$$(x \quad y \quad z) \begin{pmatrix} a & f & e \\ f & b & d \\ e & d & c \end{pmatrix} \begin{pmatrix} x \\ y \\ z \end{pmatrix} = a\left(x + \frac{f}{a}y + \frac{e}{a}z\right)^2$$

$$+ \frac{\begin{vmatrix} a & f \\ f & b \end{vmatrix}}{a}\left(y + \frac{\begin{vmatrix} a & f \\ e & d \end{vmatrix}}{\begin{vmatrix} a & f \\ f & b \end{vmatrix}}z\right)^2 + \frac{\begin{vmatrix} a & f & e \\ f & b & d \\ e & d & c \end{vmatrix}}{\begin{vmatrix} a & f \\ f & b \end{vmatrix}}z^2.$$

Conclude that the above polynomial is positive definite if and only if the three determinants are positive:

$$\begin{array}{c|c|c} a & f & e \\ \hline f & b & d \\ \hline e & d & c \end{array}.$$

What is the condition for negative definiteness? The criterion can be extended to quadratic polynomials in $\mathfrak{R}^n$. See R. M. Thrall and L. Tornheim, *Vector Spaces and Matrices*, Wiley, 1957, p. 170.

17. Show that the linear transformation $\mathfrak{R}^n \xrightarrow{L} \mathfrak{R}^n$ determined by a symmetric matrix A has the property that

$$LX \cdot Y = X \cdot LY$$

for all X and Y in $\mathfrak{R}^n$. Conversely, show that if this equation is satisfied, then A is a symmetric matrix

18. A transformation $\mathfrak{R}^n \xrightarrow{L} \mathfrak{R}^n$ for which the equation in Exercise 17 holds is called a symmetric transformation. Show that for a given symmetric transformation there is an orthonormal basis such that with respect to this basis the matrix of the transformation is diagonal.

19. (a) Give a geometric description of the action on $\mathfrak{R}^3$ of the symmetric transformations with matrices

$$\begin{pmatrix} \lambda_1 & 0 & 0 \\ 0 & 1 & 0 \\ 0 & 0 & 1 \end{pmatrix}, \quad \begin{pmatrix} 1 & 0 & 0 \\ 0 & \lambda_2 & 0 \\ 0 & 0 & 1 \end{pmatrix} \quad \text{and} \quad \begin{pmatrix} 1 & 0 & 0 \\ 0 & 1 & 0 \\ 0 & 0 & \lambda_3 \end{pmatrix}.$$

(b) Use the result of Exercise 18 to give a geometric description of the action of a symmetric transformation in $\mathfrak{R}^3$.

20. The proof of Theorem 2.1 works just as well when the euclidean inner product is replaced by an arbitrary one. Use this fact to prove the following theorem. If Q_1 and Q_2 are quadratic polynomials in $\mathfrak{R}^n$, and Q_1 is positive definite, then there is an orthonormal basis for $\mathfrak{R}^n$ with respect to which Q_1 and Q_2 both have diagonal form.

21. Prove the converse of Theorem 2.4, namely, that if $X_1, \ldots, X_n$ is an orthonormal diagonalizing basis for $QX = X^t A X$, then $(A - \lambda_k I) X_k = 0$, where $\lambda_k = Q X_k$.

3. TAYLOR EXPANSIONS

We begin by reviewing the definition and the simplest properties of the Taylor expansion for functions of one variable. If $f(x)$ has an Nth derivative at x_0, its **Taylor expansion of degree N about x_0** is the polynomial

$$f(x_0) + \frac{1}{1!} f'(x_0)(x - x_0) + \frac{1}{2!} f''(x_0)(x - x_0)^2$$

$$+ \ldots + \frac{1}{N!} f^{(N)}(x_0)(x - x_0)^N.$$

The relation between f and its Taylor expansion can be expressed conveniently by the following **integral remainder formula**.

3.1 Theorem. If f has a continuous Nth derivative in a neighborhood of x_0, then in that neighborhood

$$f(x) = f(x_0) + \frac{1}{1!} f'(x_0)(x - x_0) + \ldots + \frac{1}{N!} f^{(N)}(x_0)(x - x_0)^N + R_N,$$

(1)

where

$$R_N = \frac{1}{(N-1)!} \int_{x_0}^{x} (x - t)^{N-1} [f^{(N)}(t) - f^{(N)}(x_0)] \, dt.$$

Proof. The remainder can be written as the difference

$$R_N = \frac{1}{(N-1)!} \int_{x_0}^{x} (x - t)^{N-1} f^{(N)}(t) \, dt - \frac{f^{(N)}(x_0)}{(N-1)!} \int_{x_0}^{x} (x - t)^{N-1} \, dt.$$

The second of these integrals is directly computed to be

$$\frac{1}{N!} f^{(N)}(x_0)(x - x_0)^N,$$

which is just the last term of the Taylor expansion. The first integral can be integrated by parts to give

$$\frac{1}{(N-2)!} \int_{x_0}^{x} (x - t)^{N-2} [f^{(N-1)}(t) - f^{(N-1)}(x_0)] \, dt = R_{N-1}.$$

We therefore obtain

$$R_N = -\frac{1}{N!} f^{(N)}(x_0)(x - x_0)^N + R_{N-1}.$$

If we substitute the preceding equation into (1), we get (1) back again with N replaced by $N - 1$. The induction is completed by noticing that for $N = 1$, Equation (1) is just

$$f(x) = f(x_0) + f'(x_0)(x - x_0) + \int_{x_0}^{x} [f'(t) - f'(x_0)] \, dt,$$

and that this is a valid equation.

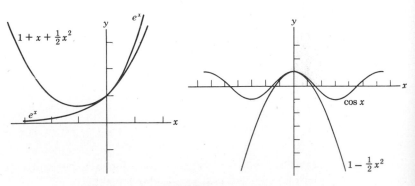

FIGURE 11

It follows from the remainder formula that a polynomial of degree N is equal to its Taylor expansion of degree N. For if f is of degree N, $f^{(N)}$ is a constant function and so the remainder is identically zero. We list some common examples. It is only in the first one that we have equality. The expansions are all about $x = 0$.

$$(1 + x)^N = \sum_{k=0}^{N} \binom{N}{k} x^k,$$

$$\frac{1}{(1 - x)^M} : \quad \sum_{k=0}^{N} \binom{M + k - 1}{M - 1} x^k,$$

$$e^x : \quad 1 + \frac{1}{1!} x + \frac{1}{2!} x^2 + \ldots + \frac{1}{N!} x^N,$$

$$\log (1 - x) : \quad -x - \frac{1}{2} x^2 - \frac{1}{3} x^3 - \ldots - \frac{1}{N} x^N,$$

$$\cos x : \quad 1 - \frac{x^2}{2!} + \frac{x^4}{4!} - \ldots + (-1)^k \frac{x^{2k}}{(2k)!},$$

$$\sin x : \quad x - \frac{x^3}{3!} + \frac{x^5}{5!} - \ldots + (-1)^k \frac{x^{2k+1}}{(2k + 1)!}.$$

(2)

Figure 11 shows the graphical relationship between the functions e^x and $\cos x$, and their 2nd-degree Taylor expansions.

For a function $f(x, y)$ of two variables having continuous Nth-order partial derivatives in a neighborhood of (x_0, y_0), the **Taylor expansion of degree N about** (x_0, y_0) is the polynomial

$$f(x_0, y_0) + \frac{1}{1!} ((x - x_0)f_x(x_0, y_0) + (y - y_0)f_y(x_0, y_0))$$

$$+ \frac{1}{2!} ((x - x_0)^2 f_{xx}(x_0, y_0) + 2(x - x_0)(y - y_0)f_{xy}(x_0, y_0)$$

$$+ (y - y_0)^2 f_{yy}(x_0, y_0))$$

(3)

$$\cdot$$
$$\cdot$$
$$\cdot$$

$$+ \frac{1}{N!} \sum_{k=0}^{N} \binom{N}{k} (x - x_0)^k (y - y_0)^{N-k} f_{x^k y^{N-k}}(x_0, y_0).$$

EXAMPLE 1. Let $f(x, y) = \sqrt{1 + x^2 + y^2}$. To expand about $(0, 0)$ through the second degree, we compute

$$f_x(0, 0) = f_y(0, 0) = 0,$$

$$f_{xx}(0, 0) = f_{yy}(0, 0) = 1 \quad \text{and} \quad f_{xy}(0, 0) = 0$$

Then Formula (3) reduces to the second-degree polynomial $1 + \frac{1}{2}(x^2 + y^2)$. The graphs of f and its 2nd-degree Taylor expansion are shown in Figure 12.

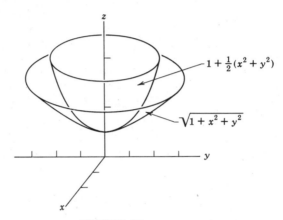

FIGURE 12

To simplify the writing of the terms of the Taylor expansion, we can use the following notation. The differential operator

$$\left(x \frac{\partial}{\partial x} + y \frac{\partial}{\partial y} \right)$$

applied to f and evaluated at $X_0 = (x_0, y_0)$ is by definition the first-degree polynomial

$$(d_{X_0} f) \begin{pmatrix} x \\ y \end{pmatrix} = \left(x \frac{\partial}{\partial x} + y \frac{\partial}{\partial y} \right) f \bigg|_{X_0} = x \frac{\partial f}{\partial x} X_0 + y \frac{\partial f}{\partial y} X_0.$$

Differentials of order k, $k > 1$, can also be defined. They are homogeneous polynomials of degree k. If f has the required derivatives, the definition is

$$(d_{X_0}^k f) \begin{pmatrix} x \\ y \end{pmatrix} = \left(x \frac{\partial}{\partial x} + y \frac{\partial}{\partial y} \right)^k f \bigg|_{X_0}$$

$$= \sum_{j=0}^{k} \binom{k}{j} x^j y^{k-j} \frac{\partial^k f}{\partial x^j \, \partial y^{k-j}} X_0.$$

Here the operator

$$\left(x \frac{\partial}{\partial x} + y \frac{\partial}{\partial y} \right)^k$$

has been multiplied out according to the binomial expansion. The operator is applied to f, and the partial derivatives are then evaluated at $X_0 = (x_0, y_0)$. Notice that x and y are the only variables that appear in the preceding equation, since

$$\binom{k}{j} \frac{\partial^k f}{\partial x^j \, \partial y^{k-j}} X_0$$

is a constant for a fixed X_0. The Nth-degree Taylor expansion of f at X_0 can now be written

$$f(x_0, y_0) + \frac{1}{1!} \, (d_{X_0} f) \begin{pmatrix} x - x_0 \\ y - y_0 \end{pmatrix} + \ldots + \frac{1}{N!} \, (d_{X_0}^N f) \begin{pmatrix} x - x_0 \\ y - y_0 \end{pmatrix}.$$

EXAMPLE 2. If $f(x, y) = x^2 e^y$ then the differential of order 3 at $(1, 1)$ evaluated at $(x - 1, y - 1)$ is the polynomial

$$(d^3{}_{(1,1)} f) \begin{pmatrix} x - 1 \\ y - 1 \end{pmatrix} = \left((x - 1) \frac{\partial}{\partial x} + (y - 1) \frac{\partial}{\partial y} \right)^3_{(1,1)}$$

$$= (x - 1)^3 \frac{\partial^3 f}{\partial x^3} (1, 1) + 3 (x - 1)^2 (y - 1) \frac{\partial^3 f}{\partial x^2 \, \partial y} (1, 1)$$

$$+ 3 (x - 1) (y - 1)^2 \frac{\partial^3 f}{\partial x \, \partial y^2} (1, 1) + (y - 1)^3 \frac{\partial^3 f}{\partial y^3} (1, 1).$$

EXAMPLE 3. When the polynomial $(x_1 + x_2 + \ldots + x_n)^N$ is multiplied out, each term will consist of a constant times a factor of the form $x_1^{k_1} x_2^{k_2} \ldots x_n^{k_n}$ where the non-negative integers k_i satisfy $k_1 + \ldots + k_n = N$. The **multinomial expansion** has the form

$$(x_1 + \ldots + x_n)^N = \sum_{k_1 + \ldots + k_n = N} \binom{N}{k_1 \ldots k_n} x_1^{k_1} \ldots x_n^{k_n}.$$

The **multinomial coefficients** can be computed to be

$$\binom{N}{k_1 \ldots k_n} = \frac{N!}{k_1! \ldots k_n!}.$$

This computation will be done later using Taylor's theorem (Theorem 3.2). The coefficients can also be computed by counting.*

For a function of n variables, the kth-**order differential at** $X_0 = (a_1, \ldots, a_n)$ is defined to be the following polynomial in $X = (x_1, \ldots, x_n)$:

$$(d_{X_0}^k f) X = \left(x_1 \frac{\partial}{\partial x_1} + \ldots + x_n \frac{\partial}{\partial x_n} \right)^k_{X_0} f$$

$$= \sum_{k_1 + \cdots + k_n = k} \binom{k}{k_1 \ldots k_n} x_1^{k_1} \ldots x_n^{k_n} \frac{\partial^k f}{\partial x_1^{k_1} \ldots \partial x_n^{k_n}} (a_1, \ldots, a_n).$$

In terms of differentials the Taylor expansion about X_0 is

$$f X_0 + \frac{1}{1!} (d_{X_0} f)(X - X_0) + \frac{1}{2!} (d_{X_0}^2 f)(X - X_0)$$

$$+ \ldots + \frac{1}{N!} (d_{X_0}^N f)(X - X_0).$$

The function $d_{X_0} f$ is exactly the same as the differential defined in Section 4 of Chapter 2. For completeness we can also define the zeroth differential by

$$(d_{X_0}^0 f) X = f X_0.$$

EXAMPLE 4. The second-degree Taylor expansion of $e^{x_1 + \cdots + x_n}$ about $X = 0$ is

$$1 + \frac{1}{1!} \left(x_1 \frac{\partial}{\partial x_1} + \ldots + x_n \frac{\partial}{\partial x_n} \right)_0 f + \frac{1}{2!} \left(x_1 \frac{\partial}{\partial x_1} + \ldots + x_n \frac{\partial}{\partial x_n} \right)^2_0 f$$

$$= 1 + \frac{1}{1!} (x_1 + \ldots + x_n) + \frac{1}{2!} (x_1^2 + 2x_1 x_2 + \ldots + x_2^2 + \ldots + x_n^2).$$

According to the preceding paragraphs the Taylor expansion of a function f is defined in such a way that the coefficients of the polynomial can be computed in a routine manner from the derivatives of f. The Taylor expansion is important because it provides a polynomial approximation to f near X_0 that exhibits in a simple way many of the characteristics of f near X_0. Furthermore, as higher-degree terms are included in the ex-

---

* See Kemeny, Snell, Thompson, *Finite Mathematics*, Prentice-Hall, 1957, p. 107.

pansion, the approximation gets better. Consider first the one-variable case. The expansion

$$f(x_0) + \frac{1}{1!} f'(x_0)(x - x_0) = f(x_0) + d_{x_0} f(x - x_0)$$

is the affine approximation to f provided by $d_{x_0} f$. In other words, as x approaches x_0,

$$f(x) - f(x_0) - f'(x_0)(x - x_0)$$

tends to zero faster than $x - x_0$.

Having found a first-degree approximation, we now ask for one of the 2nd degree. Indeed, the next theorem shows that the desired approximation is the 2nd-degree Taylor expansion and that as x approaches x_0,

$$f(x) - f(x_0) - \frac{1}{1!} f'(x_0)(x - x_0) - \frac{1}{2!} f''(x_0)(x - x_0)^2$$

tends to zero faster than $(x - x_0)^2$. For a function of two variables, the first-degree Taylor expansion can be written

$$f(x_0, y_0) + \frac{1}{1!} \left(\frac{\partial f}{\partial x}(x_0, y_0)(x - x_0) + \frac{\partial f}{\partial y}(x_0, y_0)(y - y_0) \right)$$

$$= f(x_0, y_0) + (d_{\binom{x_0}{y_0}} f) \binom{x - x_0}{y - y_0}$$

and so is just the affine approximation to f provided by the differential. We shall see that to find a second-degree approximation of a similar kind we need to take the second-degree Taylor expansion. The complete statement follows.

3.2 Taylor's theorem. Let $\mathfrak{R}^n \xrightarrow{f} \mathfrak{R}$ have all derivatives of order N continuous in a neighborhood of X_0. Let $T_N(X - X_0)$ be the Nth-degree Taylor expansion of f about X_0. That is,

$$T_N(X - X_0) = fX_0 + (d_{X_0} f)(X - X_0) + \ldots + \frac{1}{N!} (d_{X_0}^N f)(X - X_0).$$

Then

$$\lim_{X \to X_0} \frac{(fX - T_N(X - X_0))}{|X - X_0|^N} = 0, \tag{4}$$

and T_N is the only Nth-degree polynomial having this property.

Proof. Let $Y = X - X_0$ and define

$$F(t) = f(X_0 + t(X - X_0)) = f(X_0 + tY).$$

Then for $k = 0, 1, \ldots, N$, we can apply the chain rule to get

$$F^{(k)}(t) = (d^k_{X_0+tY}f)\,Y. \tag{5}$$

To see this, notice that for $k = 0$ the formula is true by definition. Assuming it to hold for some $k < N$, we have

$$F^{(k+1)}(t) = \frac{d}{dt}\,(d^k_{X_0+tY}f)\,Y$$

$$= \frac{d}{dt}\left(y_1\frac{\partial}{\partial x_1} + \ldots + y_n\frac{\partial}{\partial x_n}\right)^k_{X_0+tY} f$$

$$= d_{X_0+tY}\left[\left(y_1\frac{\partial}{\partial x_1} + \ldots + y_n\frac{\partial}{\partial x_n}\right)^k f\right]Y$$

$$= \left(y_1\frac{\partial}{\partial x_1} + \ldots + y_n\frac{\partial}{\partial x_n}\right)^{k+1}_{X_0+tY} f$$

$$= (d^{k+1}_{X_0+tY}f)\,Y.$$

This completes the proof of Equation (5) by induction. In particular,

$$F^{(k)}(0) = (d^k_{X_0}f)\,Y.$$

From Equation (1) we obtain

$$F(1) - F(0) - \frac{1}{1!}F'(0) - \ldots - \frac{1}{N!}F^{(N)}(0)$$

$$= \frac{1}{(N-1)!}\int_0^1 (1-t)^{N-1}[F^{(N)}(t) - F^{(N)}(0)]\,dt.$$

In terms of f, this is

$$fX - T_N(X - X_0) = fX - fX_0 - \frac{1}{1!}(d_{X_0}f)\,Y - \ldots - \frac{1}{N!}(d^N_{X_0}f)\,Y$$

$$= \frac{1}{(N-1)!}\int_0^1 (1-t)^{N-1}$$

$$\cdot\,[(d^N_{X_0+tY}f)\,Y - (d^N_{X_0}f)\,Y]\,dt.$$

We now estimate this difference.

$$|fX - T_N Y| \leq \frac{1}{(N-1)!} \max_{0 \leq t \leq 1} |(d^N_{X_0+tY}f)Y - (d^N_{X_0}f)Y|$$

$$\leq \max_{0 \leq t \leq 1} \left| \left(y_1 \frac{\partial}{\partial x_1} + \ldots + y_n \frac{\partial}{\partial x_n}\right)^N_{X_0+tY} f \right.$$

$$\left. - \left(y_1 \frac{\partial}{\partial x_1} + \ldots + y_n \frac{\partial}{\partial x_n}\right)^N_{X_0} f \right|$$

$$= \max_{0 \leq t \leq 1} \left| \sum_{k_1+\ldots+k_n=N} \binom{N}{k_1 \ldots k_n} y_1^{k_1} \ldots y_n^{k_n} \right.$$

$$\left. \cdot \left(\frac{\partial^N f}{\partial x_1^{k_1} \ldots \partial x_n^{k_n}}(X_0 + tY) - \frac{\partial^N f}{\partial x_1^{k_1} \ldots \partial x_n^{k_n}}(X_0) \right) \right|.$$

Then, since $|y_i| \leq |Y|$, we have

$$\frac{|y_1^{k_1} \ldots y_n^{k_n}|}{|Y|^N} \leq 1,$$

and so

$$\frac{|fX - T_N Y|}{|Y|^N} \leq \sum_{k_1+\ldots+k_n=N} \binom{N}{k_1 \ldots k_n} \cdot$$

$$\max_{0 \leq t \leq 1} \left| \frac{\partial^N f}{\partial x_1^{k_1} \ldots \partial x_n^{k_n}}(X_0 + tY) - \frac{\partial^N f}{\partial x_1^{k_1} \ldots \partial x_n^{k_n}}(X_0) \right|. \qquad (6)$$

By assumption the derivatives of f through order N are continuous functions at X_0. Then as Y tends to zero, each term in the last sum tends to zero, which proves Equation (4). The inequality (6) shows that if f is a polynomial of degree N, then it equals its Nth-degree Taylor expansion. For then all the terms on the right are zero.

The proof that T_N is the only Nth-degree polynomial satisfying Equation (4) is very similar to the proof that the differential is unique, given in Section 4, Chapter 2. Let T_N and T_N' be two such polynomials. By (4),

$$\lim_{Y \to 0} \frac{T_N Y - T_N' Y}{|Y|^N} = 0.$$

Suppose that $T_N - T_N'$ were not identically zero, and let

$$P_k Y + R Y = T_N Y - T_N' Y,$$

where P_k is the polynomial consisting of the terms of lowest degree (say k) that actually occur in $T_N - T'_N$. Then, there is a vector Y_0 such that $P_k Y_0 \neq 0$. On the other hand, since $k \leq N$

$$0 = \lim_{t \to 0} \frac{T_N(tY_0) - T'_N(tY_0)}{|tY_0|^k}$$

$$= \lim_{t \to 0} \frac{P_k(tY_0) + R(tY_0)}{|tY_0|^k}$$

$$= \frac{P_k Y_0}{|Y_0|^k} + \lim_{t \to 0} \frac{R(tY_0)}{|t|^k |Y_0|^k}.$$

However, because all the terms of R have degree greater than k, the last limit is zero. But then $P_k Y_0 = 0$, which is a contradiction.

As we have remarked above, Equation (6) shows that a polynomial of degree N is equal to its Nth-degree Taylor expansion about an arbitrary point X_0.

EXAMPLE 5. The polynomial $x^2y + x^3 + y^3$ can be written as a polynomial in $(x - 1)$ and $(y + 1)$ by computing its Taylor expansion about $(1, -1)$. The result is

$$x^2y + x^3 + y^3 = -1 + \frac{1}{1!} \left((x - 1) + 4(y + 1) \right)$$

$$+ \frac{1}{2!} \left(4(x - 1)^2 + 4(x - 1)(y + 1) - 6(y + 1)^2 \right)$$

$$+ \frac{1}{3!} \left(6(x - 1)^3 + 6(x - 1)^2(y + 1) + 6(y + 1)^3 \right)$$

$$= -1 + (x - 1) + 4(y + 1) + 2(x - 1)^2$$
$$+ 2(x - 1)(y + 1) - 3(y + 1)^2 + (x - 1)^3$$
$$+ (x - 1)^2(y + 1) + (y + 1)^3.$$

EXAMPLE 6. The infinite series expansion $e^t = 1 + t + (1/2!)t^2 + \ldots$ is valid for all t. Letting $t = x + y$ we get

$$e^{x+y} = 1 + \frac{1}{1!}(x + y) + \frac{1}{2!}(x^2 + 2xy + y^2) + \ldots, \qquad \text{for all } x \text{ and } y.$$

It follows that

$$1 + \frac{1}{1!}\,(x + y) + \frac{1}{2!}\,(x^2 + 2xy + y^2)$$

is the 2nd-degree Taylor expansion of e^{x+y}. For the remainder, $(1/3!)\,(x + y)^3 + \ldots\,$, tends to zero when it is divided by $(\sqrt{x^2 + y^2})^2$ and (x, y) tends to $(0, 0)$. According to Taylor's theorem, there is only one polynomial of degree two having this property.

EXAMPLE 7. Let $f(x, y) = e^{xy} \sin\,(x + y)$. Since

$$e^{xy} = 1 + xy + \frac{1}{2!}\,x^2y^2 + R_1$$

$$\text{and} \quad \sin\,(x + y) = (x + y) - \frac{1}{3!}\,(x + y)^3 + R_2,$$

we can multiply the expansions together, putting into the remainder all terms of degree greater than three. The result is

$$f(x, y) = e^{xy} \sin\,(x + y) = (x + y) + x^2y + xy^2 - \frac{1}{3!}\,(x + y)^3 + R,$$

where $R/|\,(x, y)\,|^3$ tends to zero as (x, y) tends to $(0, 0)$. In other words, we have found the third-degree Taylor expansion of $e^{xy} \sin\,(x + y)$ about $(0, 0)$. In standard form the expansion looks like

$$f(x, y) = e^{xy} \sin\,(x + y) = \frac{1}{1!}\,(x + y)$$

$$+ \frac{1}{3!}\,(-x^3 + 3x^2y + 3xy^2 - y^3) + R.$$

We can conclude that

$$\frac{\partial^3 f}{\partial y^3}\,(0, 0) = \frac{\partial^3 f}{\partial x^3}\,(0, 0) = -1,$$

$$\frac{\partial^3 f}{\partial x\,\partial y^2}\,(0, 0) = \frac{\partial^3 f}{\partial x^2\,\partial y}\,(0, 0) = 1.$$

EXAMPLE 8. The functions e^x and $\cos x$ have second-degree expansions about $x = 0$

$$e^x = 1 + x + \frac{x^2}{2} + R(x), \quad \cos x = 1 - \frac{x^2}{2} + R'(x).$$

12. Compute the 2nd-degree Taylor expansion of $\exp(-x_1^2 - x_2^2 - \ldots - x_n^2)$ about $(x_1, x_2, \ldots, x_n) = (0, 0 \ldots 0)$.

13. Prove that the Taylor expansion of degree N of a polynomial of degree K, $K \geq N$, consists of the terms of the polynomial that are of degree less than or equal to N.

14. Compute the differentials $(d_{X_0}^k f) Y$ for arbitrary Y.

(a) $k = 2$, $X_0 = (1, 2)$, $f(x, y) = x^3 y + 3x^2 + 2xy^3$.
$$[Ans.\ 18x^2 + 54xy + 24y^2.]$$

(b) $k = 1$, $X_0 = (a, b, c)$, $f(x, y, z) = 1/(x + y + z + 1)$.

(c) $k = 2$, $X_0 = (0, 0, 0)$, $f(x, y, z) = 1/(x + y + z + 1)$.
$$[Ans.\ 2(x + y + z)^2.]$$

(d) $k = 4$, $X_0 = (0, 0, 0)$, $f(x, y, z) = x^3 + 3xy^2 + 4xy^3 + 6x^2 y^3 + 7y^5$.
$$[Ans.\ 96xy^3.]$$

15. Find the second differential of $\sin(x_1 + x_2 + \ldots + x_n)$ at

$$(x_1, x_2, \ldots, x_n) = (0, 0, \ldots, 0). \qquad [Ans.\ 0.]$$

4. APPLICATIONS OF TAYLOR EXPANSIONS TO MAXIMA AND MINIMA

The tangent $\mathfrak{I}$ to the graph of a function $\mathfrak{R}^n \xrightarrow{f} \mathfrak{R}$ at a point (X_0, fX_0) is found by computing the first-degree Taylor expansion of f about X_0. We now consider the question of whether or not the graph of f crosses $\mathfrak{I}$ at (X_0, fX_0). The possibilities for a function of one variable are shown in Figure 13.

Consider first a very much simplified situation in which f is equal to its second-degree Taylor expansion. That is, assume that

$$fX = fX_0 + (d_{X_0} f)(X - X_0) + \tfrac{1}{2}(d_{X_0}^2 f)(X - X_0).$$

The first two terms of the expansion constitute the best affine approximation to f near X_0, and the graph of $fX_0 + (d_{X_0} f)(X - X_0)$ is the tangent

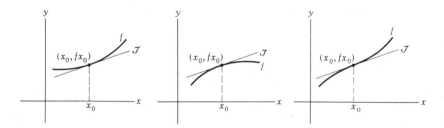

FIGURE 13

ꭍ to the graph of f at $P_0 = (X_0, fX_0)$. It is clear that if $(d^2_{X_0} f)(X - X_0)$ is positive for all X in $\mathfrak{R}^n$ except $X = X_0$, then

$$fX > fX_0 + (d_{X_0} f)(X - X_0), \quad \text{for } X \neq X_0,$$

which implies that the graph of f lies above the tangent ꭍ. Similarly, if $(d^2_{X_0} f)(X - X_0)$ is negative except for $X = X_0$, the graph of f lies below ꭍ. On the other hand, if $(d^2_{X_0} f)(X - X_0)$ changes sign at X_0, then the graph of f will cross ꭍ at P_0.

To say that the quadratic polynomial $Q(X - X_0) = (d^2_{X_0} f)(X - X_0)$ changes sign at X_0 means that there are points X_1 and X_2 arbitrarily close to X_0 such that

$$Q(X_1 - X_0) > 0 \quad \text{and} \quad Q(X_2 - X_0) < 0. \tag{1}$$

The phrase "arbitrarily close" is superfluous, because every homogeneous quadratic polynomial Q has the property

$$Q(tX) = t^2 QX. \tag{2}$$

It follows that if (1) holds for two vectors X_1 and X_2, not necessarily close to X_0, then (1) also holds for $t(X_1 - X_0) + X_0$ and $t(X_2 - X_0) + X_0$, for any $t \neq 0$. By choosing t small enough, we can bring the latter vectors as close to X_0 as we like.

EXAMPLE 1. The function

$$f(x, y) = 2x^2 - xy - 3y^2 - 3x + 7y$$

equals its second-degree Taylor expansion. It has one critical point at $X_0 = (1, 1)$, and the tangent plane ꭍ at $(1, 1, 2)$ is therefore horizontal. The second differential is given by

$$(d^2_{X_0} f) \begin{pmatrix} x - 1 \\ y - 1 \end{pmatrix} = 4(x - 1)^2 - 2(x - 1)(y - 1) - 6(y - 1)^2.$$

Trying $X_1 = (2, 1)$ and $X_2 = (1, 2)$, we obtain

$$(d^2_{X_0} f)(X_1 - X_0) = 4 > 0,$$

$$(d^2_{X_0} f)(X_2 - X_0) = -6 < 0.$$

We conclude that the graph of f crosses the tangent plane ꭍ at $(1, 1, 2)$ and, consequently, that f has neither a local maximum nor minimum at X_0.

The assumption that f equals its second-degree Taylor expansion is too strong to be of much practical value. However, the next theorem shows that under more general hypothesis, the sign of the second differential still determines whether or not f crosses its tangent. The quadratic polynomial

$(d_{X_0}^2 f)(X - X_0)$ is always zero at $X = X_0$. If it is positive except at that one point, it is said to be **positive definite**, and if it is negative except at that one point, it is said to be **negative definite**.

4.1 Theorem. Let $\mathfrak{R}^n \xrightarrow{f} \mathfrak{R}$ have all its second partial derivatives continuous in a neighborhood of X_0, and denote the tangent to the graph of f at $P_0 = (X_0, fX_0)$ by $\mathfrak{J}$.

>   (i) If $(d_{X_0}^2 f)(X - X_0)$ is positive definite, then f lies above $\mathfrak{J}$ in some neighborhood of X_0.
>   (ii) If $(d_{X_0}^2 f)(X - X_0)$ is negative definite, then f lies below $\mathfrak{J}$ in some neighborhood of X_0.
>   (iii) If $(d_{X_0}^2 f)(X - X_0)$ assumes both positive and negative values, then f crosses the tangent $\mathfrak{J}$ at P_0.

Notice that all possible cases are not covered by (i), (ii), and (iii). It may happen, for example, that the second differential is zero somewhere other than at X_0, but that it still does not change sign.

Proof (of 4.1). By Taylor's theorem we have

$$fX - fX_0 - (d_{X_0} f)(X - X_0) = \tfrac{1}{2}(d_{X_0}^2 f)(X - X_0) + R, \qquad (3)$$

where
$$\lim_{X \to X_0} \frac{R}{|X - X_0|^2} = 0.$$

Under assumption (i), we must show that

$$\tfrac{1}{2}(d_{X_0}^2 f)(X - X_0) + R > 0$$

in some neighborhood of X_0, excluding X_0 itself. The homogeneity of the quadratic polynomial $d_{X_0}^2 f$ (see Equation (2)) implies that

$$\frac{(d_{X_0}^2 f)(X - X_0)}{|X - X_0|^2} = (d_{X_0}^2 f)\left(\frac{X - X_0}{|X - X_0|}\right).$$

Since $d_{X_0}^2 f$ is positive definite, its values for unit vectors are bounded away from zero by a constant $m > 0$. (See Exercise 14, Section 2). Now choose $\delta > 0$ so that, for $0 < |X - X_0| < \delta$,

$$\frac{|R|}{|X - X_0|^2} \leq \frac{m}{4}.$$

It follows that

$$\frac{1}{2}(d_{X_0}^2 f)(X - X_0) + R \geq \frac{m}{2}|X - X_0|^2 - \frac{m}{4}|X - X_0|^2 > 0$$

which, according to Equation (3), is what we wanted to show.

The proof of (ii) is practically the same as the proof just given. To prove (iii), suppose that $(d_{X_0}^2 f)(X_1 - X_0) > 0$ and $(d_{X_0}^2 f)(X_2 - X_0) < 0$. Set

$$X_i(t) = t(X_i - X_0) + X_0, \qquad i = 1, 2, \quad -\infty < t < \infty.$$

Using the homogeneity property of the polynomial $d_{X_0}^2 f$, and also of the norm, we obtain, for any $t \ne 0$,

$$fX_i(t) - fX_0 - (d_{X_0} f)(X_i(t) - X_0)$$

$$= t^2 \left[\frac{1}{2} (d_{X_0}^2 f)(X_i - X_0) + |X_i - X_0|^2 \frac{R}{|X_i(t) - X_0|^2} \right]. \qquad (4)$$

Since

$$\lim_{t \to 0} \frac{R}{|X_i(t) - X_0|^2} = 0,$$

it follows that, for any nonzero t sufficiently small, the left-hand side of Equation (4) is positive if $i = 1$ and negative if $i = 2$. In other words, the graph of f lies both above and below the tangent $\mathfrak{I}$ for some values of X arbitrarily close to X_0. This completes the proof.

EXAMPLE 2. The function

$$f(x, y) = (x^2 + y^2)e^{x^2 - y^2}$$

has its critical points at $(0, 0)$, $(0, 1)$, and $(0, -1)$. This implies that the tangents at these points are horizontal planes. The second-degree Taylor expansions at the three points are, respectively,

$$f(0, 0) + \frac{1}{2} (d_{(0,0)}^2 f)\begin{pmatrix} x \\ y \end{pmatrix} = x^2 + y^2,$$

$$f(0, 1) + \frac{1}{2} (d_{(0,1)}^2 f)\begin{pmatrix} x \\ y - 1 \end{pmatrix} = \frac{1}{e} [1 + 2x^2 - 2(y - 1)^2],$$

$$f(0, -1) + \frac{1}{2} (d_{(0,-1)}^2 f)\begin{pmatrix} x \\ y + 1 \end{pmatrix} = \frac{1}{e} [1 + 2x^2 - 2(y + 1)^2].$$

Clearly, $d_{(0,0)}^2 f$ is positive definite, while $d_{(0,1)}^2 f$ and $d_{(0,-1)}^2 f$ assume both positive and negative values arbitrarily close to their respective critical points. We conclude that f has a local minimum value at $(0, 0)$ and neither a maximum nor a minimum at the points $(0, 1)$ and $(0, -1)$. The graph of f and the horizontal tangent planes at $(0, 0, 0)$ and $(0, 1, 1/e)$ are shown in Figure 14.

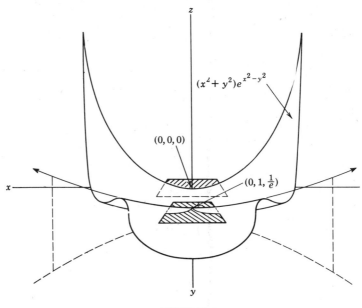

$$(x^2 + y^2)e^{x^2 - y^2}$$

$(0, 0, 0)$

$(0, 1, \frac{1}{e})$

FIGURE 14

EXAMPLE 3. The function

$$f(x, y, z) = x \sin z + z \sin y$$

has a critical point at $X_0 = (-1, \pi/2, 0)$. The second differential at X_0 is

$$(d^2_{X_0}f) \begin{pmatrix} x + 1 \\ y - \dfrac{\pi}{2} \\ z \end{pmatrix} = 2z(x + 1).$$

Since $d^2_{X_0}f$ has both positive and negative values, the function f has neither a local maximum nor minimum at X_0.

EXAMPLE 4. If $f(x) = x \sin^3 x$, the first four terms of the Taylor expansion at $x = 0$ are identically zero, while

$$(d^4_0 f)x = 24x^4.$$

The criteria of Theorem 3.1 do not cover this example. However, a similar proof would show that f behaves like its Taylor expansion in the matter of crossing its tangent. The conclusion is that $x \sin^3 x$ has a local minimum at $x = 0$.

For distinguishing among the critical points of a function those that are maximum points or minimum points, a detailed examination of the polynomial $(d_{X_0}^2 f)(X - X_0)$ is not necessary. It is enough to know that this quadratic approximation is positive or negative definite. In addition to the criteria of Section 2, we list here for reference a simple test for quadratic polynomials in two or three variables. (See Section 2, Example 4 and Exercise 16.)

The polynomial

$$ax^2 + 2bxy + cy^2 = (x \quad y) \begin{pmatrix} a & b \\ b & c \end{pmatrix} \begin{pmatrix} x \\ y \end{pmatrix}$$

is positive definite if and only if

$$a > 0 \quad and \quad \begin{vmatrix} a & b \\ b & c \end{vmatrix} > 0$$

and is negative definite if and only if

$$a < 0 \quad and \quad \begin{vmatrix} a & b \\ b & c \end{vmatrix} > 0.$$

The character of the polynomial

$$ax^2 + by^2 + cz^2 + 2dyz + 2exz + 2fxy = (x \quad y \quad z) \begin{pmatrix} a & f & e \\ f & b & d \\ e & d & c \end{pmatrix} \begin{pmatrix} x \\ y \\ z \end{pmatrix}$$

depends on the sign of the three determinants

$$a, \quad \begin{vmatrix} a & f \\ f & b \end{vmatrix}, \quad \begin{vmatrix} a & f & e \\ f & b & d \\ e & d & c \end{vmatrix}.$$

The polynomial is positive definite if and only if all three determinants are positive, and is negative definite if and only if the middle one is positive and the other two are negative.

EXAMPLE 5. The function $f(x, y, z) = x^2 + y^2 + z^2 + xy$ has critical points only when

$$f_x = 2x + y = 0,$$

$$f_y = 2y + x = 0,$$

$$f_z = 2z \qquad = 0,$$

so the only critical point occurs at $(0, 0, 0)$. Since $d_X^2 f = f$, we can test f itself for positive definiteness. We have

$$a = 1, \qquad \begin{vmatrix} a & f \\ f & b \end{vmatrix} = \begin{vmatrix} 1 & \frac{1}{2} \\ \frac{1}{2} & 1 \end{vmatrix} = \tfrac{3}{4}, \qquad \begin{vmatrix} a & f & e \\ f & b & d \\ e & d & c \end{vmatrix} = \begin{vmatrix} 1 & \frac{1}{2} & 0 \\ \frac{1}{2} & 1 & 0 \\ 0 & 0 & 1 \end{vmatrix} = \tfrac{3}{4}.$$

Thus f is positive definite, and, as a result, f has minimum value 0 at $(0, 0, 0)$.

EXERCISES

1. Find all the critical points of the following functions:

   (a) $(x + y)e^{-xy}$. $\qquad\qquad\qquad$ [*Ans.* $(\pm 1/\sqrt{2}, \pm 1/\sqrt{2})$.]

   (b) $xy + xz$. $\qquad\qquad\qquad\qquad$ [*Ans.* $(0, y, -y)$, any y.]

   (c) $(x^2 + y^2) \ln (x^2 + y^2)$.

   (d) $\cos (x^2 + y^2 + z^2)$.

   (e) $x^2 + y^2 + z^2$.

2. Compute the second-degree Taylor expansion of the function in exercise 1(a) at each of its critical points.

3. Classify the critical points in 1(a), 1(b), and 1(e) as maximum, minimum, or neither.

4. In each of the following consider the tangent to the graph of the function at the point indicated. Decide whether the function lies above or below the tangent near the indicated point, or whether it crosses there.

   (a) $x^2 \sin x$ at $x = 1$. $\qquad\qquad\qquad\qquad$ [*Ans.* Lies above.]

   (b) $1/(x - y)$ at $(x, y) = (2, 1)$.

   (c) $x^4 + y^4$ at $(0, 0)$.

   (d) $e^{z+w} - x^2 - y^2$ at $(0, 0, 0, 0)$. $\qquad\qquad$ [*Ans.* Crosses.]

5. Locate all the critical points X_0 of each of the following functions and by looking at $d_{X_0}^2 f$ decide whether the function has a local maximum, or a local minimum, or neither at X_0. If examination of the 2nd differential fails to give any information, consider the next highest term of the Taylor expansion that does give information.

   (a) $\sin x \cos x$.

   (b) $x^2 y^2$. $\qquad\qquad\qquad\qquad\qquad$ [*Ans.* $x = 0$ or $y = 0$, min.]

(c) $x^2 + 4xy - y^2 - 8x - 6y$.

(d) $x^2 - xy - y^2 + 5y - 1$. $[Ans.\ (1, 2),\ \text{neither}.]$

(e) $x^2 + 2y^2 - x$.

(f) $x \sin y$.

(g) $x^4 + y^4$. $[Ans.\ (0, 0),\ \text{min}.]$

(h) $(x - y)^4$.

(i) $\exp(-x_1^2 - x_2^2 - \ldots - x_n^2)$.

4

Integral Calculus

1. ITERATED INTEGRALS

This chapter is devoted to the study of the integral of real-valued functions with domains in n-dimensional euclidean space. In the present section we introduce the iterated integral, based on the ordinary definite integral,

$$\int_a^b f(x) \ dx,$$

of a real-valued function of one real variable. We begin with $n = 2$, that is, with the iterated integral of functions $\mathfrak{R}^2 \xrightarrow{f} \mathfrak{R}$.

Suppose $f(x, y)$ is a function defined on a rectangle $a \le x \le b$, $c \le y \le d$. By

$$\int_c^d f(x, y) \ dy$$

355

is meant simply the definite integral of the function of one variable obtained by holding x fixed; for example

$$\int_0^2 x^3 y^2 \, dy = \frac{x^3 y^3}{3}\Bigg]_{y=0}^{y=2} = \frac{8}{3} x^3.$$

As this example shows, if the integral exists, it depends on x. Thus, we may set

$$F(x) = \int_c^d f(x, y) \, dy$$

and form the **iterated integral**

$$\int_a^b F(x) \, dx = \int_a^b \left[\int_c^d f(x, y) \, dy \right] dx.$$

A common notational convention, which we shall adopt, is to omit the brackets and write the iterated integral as

$$\int_a^b dx \int_c^d f(x, y) \, dy.$$

This notation has the advantage of emphasizing which variable goes with which integral sign, namely, x with $\int_a^b$ and y with $\int_c^d$.

EXAMPLE 1. Consider $f(x, y) = x^2 + y$, defined on the rectangular region $0 \le x \le 1, 1 \le y \le 2$.

$$\int_0^1 dx \int_1^2 (x^2 + y) \, dy = \int_0^1 \left[x^2 y + \frac{y^2}{2} \right]_{y=1}^{y=2} dx$$

$$= \int_0^1 \left[(2x^2 + 2) - \left(x^2 + \frac{1}{2} \right) \right] dx$$

$$= \int_0^1 \left(x^2 + \frac{3}{2} \right) dx = \frac{1}{3} + \frac{3}{2} = \frac{11}{6}.$$

To interpret this example geometrically, look at the surface defined by $z = x^2 + y$ shown in Figure 1. For each x in the interval between 0 and 1, the integral

$$\int_1^2 (x^2 + y) \, dy = x^2 + \frac{3}{2}$$

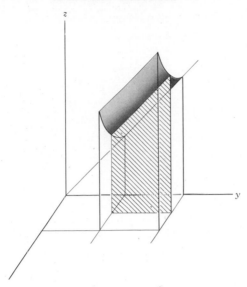

FIGURE 1

is the area of the shaded cross section. It is natural to interpret the definite integral of an area-valued function as volume. Thus it is reasonable to regard the iterated integral

$$\int_0^1 dx \int_1^2 (x^2 + y)\, dy = \frac{11}{6}$$

as the volume of the 3-dimensional region lying below the surface and above the rectangle $0 \le x \le 1, 1 \le y \le 2$.

EXAMPLE 2. We can perform the integration in Example 1 in the opposite order.

$$\int_1^2 dy \int_0^1 (x^2 + y)\, dx = \int_1^2 \left[\frac{x^3}{3} + yx\right]_{x=0}^{x=1} dy$$

$$= \int_1^2 \left(\frac{1}{3} + y\right) dy = \frac{y}{3} + \frac{y^2}{2}\bigg]_1^2$$

$$= \left(\frac{2}{3} + 2\right) - \left(\frac{1}{3} + \frac{1}{2}\right) = \frac{11}{6}.$$

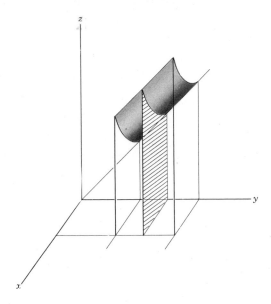

FIGURE 2

This time

$$\int_0^1 (x^2 + y) \, dx = \frac{1}{3} + y$$

is the area of a cross section parallel to the xz-plane. See Figure 2. The second integral again gives the volume of the 3-dimensional region lying below the surface $z = x^2 + y$ and above the rectangle $0 \le x \le 1, 1 \le y \le 2$. It is not surprising, therefore, that the two iterated integrals of Examples 1 and 2 are equal.

It is important to be able to integrate over subsets of the plane that are more general than rectangles. In such problems the limits in the first integration will depend on the remaining variable.

EXAMPLE 3. Consider the iterated integral

$$\int_0^1 dx \int_0^{1-x^2} (x + y) \, dy = \int_0^1 \left[xy + \frac{y^2}{2} \right]_0^{1-x^2} dx$$

$$= \int_0^1 \left(x(1 - x^2) + \frac{(1 - x^2)^2}{2} \right) dx$$

$$= \int_0^1 \left(x - x^3 + \frac{1 - 2x^2 + x^4}{2} \right) dx = \frac{31}{60}.$$

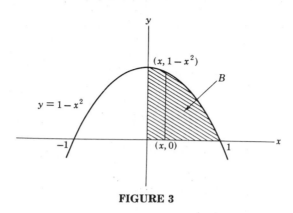

FIGURE 3

For each x between 0 and 1, the number y is between $y = 0$ and $y = 1 - x^2$. In other words the point (x, y) runs along the line segment joining $(x, 0)$ and $(x, 1 - x^2)$. As x varies between 0 and 1, this line segment sweeps out the shaded region B as shown in Figure 3. The integrand $f(x, y) = x + y$ has a graph (see Figure 4), and the iterated integral is the volume under the graph and above the region B.

Suppose we are given an iterated integral over a plane region B in which the integrand is the constant function f defined by $f(x, y) = 1$, for all (x, y) in B. The integral may then be interpreted either as the volume

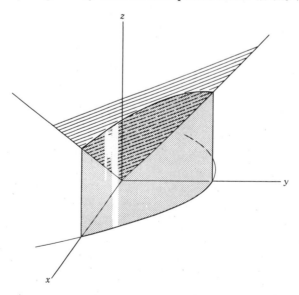

FIGURE 4

of the slab of unit thickness and with base B or simply as the area of B. For example,

$$\int_0^1 dx \int_0^{1-x^2} dy = \frac{2}{3}$$

is the area of the region B shown in Figure 3.

EXAMPLE 4. Let f be defined by $f(x, y) = x^2y + xy^2$ over the region bounded by $y = |x|$, $y = 0$, $x = -1$, and $x = 1$. See Figure 5. The two

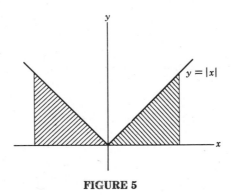

FIGURE 5

iterated integrals over the region are

$$\int_{-1}^1 dx \int_0^{|x|} (x^2y + xy^2) \, dy$$

and

$$\int_0^1 dy \left[\int_{-1}^{-y} (x^2y + xy^2) \, dx + \int_y^1 (x^2y + xy^2) \, dx \right].$$

The second integral breaks into two pieces because for fixed y between 0 and 1 the integration with respect to x is carried out over two separate intervals. Computation of the integral is straightforward. We get

$$\int_0^1 \left[\frac{x^3y}{3} + \frac{x^2y^2}{2} \right]_{-1}^{-y} + \left[\frac{x^3y}{3} + \frac{x^2y^2}{2} \right]_y^1 dy$$

$$= \int_0^1 \frac{2}{3} (y - y^4) \, dy = \frac{1}{3} - \frac{2}{15} = \frac{1}{5}.$$

The iterated integral in the other order is

$$\int_{-1}^{1}\left[\frac{x^2y^2}{2} + \frac{xy^3}{3}\right]_0^{|x|} dx = \int_{-1}^{1}\left(\frac{x^4}{2} + \frac{x\,|\,x\,|^3}{3}\right) dx$$

$$= \int_{-1}^{1}\frac{x^4}{2}\,dx + \int_{-1}^{1}\frac{x\,|\,x\,|^3}{3}\,dx.$$

The functions $x^4/2$ and $x\,|\,x\,|^3/3$ are even and odd, respectively.* It follows that

$$\int_{-1}^{1}\frac{x^4}{2}\,dx + \int_{-1}^{1}\frac{x\,|\,x\,|^3}{3}\,dx = \int_{0}^{1} x^4\,dx = \frac{1}{5}.$$

The theorem which states that, under quite general hypotheses, the value of an iterated integral is independent of the order of integration will be proved in the next section. At present the concrete evidence in support of this contention consists of two examples (see Examples 1, 2, and 4). On the other hand, the interpretation of the iterated integral as volume provides a very convincing argument: the two iterated integrals are each equal to the volume under the surface and above the region of integration. The argument fails to be a proof for two reasons. The first is that the notion of volume under a surface makes sense only for non-negative functions, whereas the lack of dependence of iterated integration on order has nothing to do with the sign of the integrand. A more serious objection, however, is the fact that our present notion of volume is a purely intuitive one introduced as an aid in understanding the iterated integral. Our argument based on volume will achieve the status of a proof only after the two iterated integrals are shown to be equal to a clearly defined mathematical object. The double integral is such an object, and in the next section it will be defined independently of the iterated integral. By means of the double integral the notion of the volume under a non-negative surface will be given a precise definition.

Iterated integrals for functions defined on subsets of dimension greater than two can also be computed by repeated 1-dimensional integration.

* See, for example, Cogan, Norman, and Thompson, *Calculus of Functions of One Argument*, Prentice-Hall, 1960, p. 61.

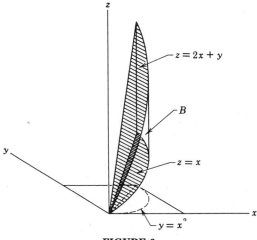

FIGURE 6

EXAMPLE 5.

$$\int_0^1 dx \int_{x^2}^x dy \int_x^{2x+y} (x + y + 2z)\, dz = \int_0^1 dx \int_{x^2}^x (4x^2 + 6xy + 2y^2)\, dy$$

$$= \int_0^1 \left(\frac{23}{3} x^3 - 4x^4 - 3x^5 - \frac{2x^6}{3} \right) dx$$

$$= \frac{23}{12} - \frac{4}{5} - \frac{1}{2} - \frac{2}{21}.$$

It is not possible to give a complete interpretation of this integral by drawing a picture. However, the region of integration B can be drawn and is shown in Figure 6. It is bounded on the top by the surface $z = 2x + y$ and on the bottom by $z = x$. On the sides it is bounded by the surfaces obtained by projecting the curves $y = x^2$ and $y = x$ parallel to the z-axis. With the same limits of integration the integral

$$\int_0^1 dx \int_{x^2}^x dy \int_x^{2x+y} dz$$

is the volume of B. For fixed x and y the first integral,

$$\int_x^{2x+y} dz,$$

is the length of the vertical segment joining the point (x, y, x) to the point $(x, y, 2x + y)$. For fixed x, the integral

$$\int_{x^2}^x dy \int_x^{2x+y} dz$$

is the area of a cross section parallel to the yz-plane. Finally, the triply iterated integral is the volume.

EXAMPLE 6. The n-fold iterated integral

$$\int_0^1 dx_1 \int_0^{x_1} dx_2 \ldots \int_0^{x_{n-1}} dx_n$$

can be thought of as the volume of the region in n-dimensional euclidean space defined by the inequalities

$$0 \le x_n \le x_{n-1} \le \ldots \le x_2 \le x_1 \le 1.$$

To get some idea of what this region is like, consider the cases $n = 1$, $n = 2$, and $n = 3$. For $n = 1$, the integral

$$\int_0^1 dx_1 = 1$$

is simply the length of the unit interval $0 \le x_1 \le 1$. If $n = 2$, we have $0 \le x_2 \le x_1 \le 1$. The region of integration is the intersection of the regions $0 \le x_2$, $x_2 \le x_1$, and $x_1 \le 1$ shown in Figure 7. For $n = 3$, we have simultaneously $0 \le x_3$, $x_3 \le x_2$, $x_2 \le x_1$, and $x_1 \le 1$. See Figure 8. If we denote the n-fold integral by I_n, then $I_1 = 1$, $I_2 = \frac{1}{2}$, and $I_3 = \frac{1}{6}$. These numbers can be obtained either by direct computation or by observing that they are the length, area, and volume, respectively, of the regions of integration. Direct evaluation of I_n is straightforward:

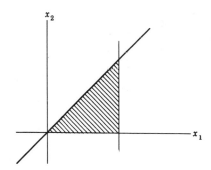

FIGURE 7

$$I_n = \int_0^1 dx_1 \int_0^{x_1} dx_2 \ldots \int_0^{x_{n-1}} dx_n$$

$$= \int_0^1 dx_1 \int_0^{x_1} dx_2 \ldots \int_0^{x_{n-2}} x_{n-1} \, dx_{n-1}$$

$$= \int_0^1 dx_1 \int_0^{x_1} dx_2 \ldots \int_0^{x_{n-3}} \frac{x_{n-2}^2}{2} \, dx_{n-2}$$

$$= \int_0^1 dx_1 \int_0^{x_1} dx_2 \ldots \int_0^{x_{n-4}} \frac{x_{n-3}^3}{3!} \, dx_{n-3}$$

$$= \ldots = \int_0^1 \frac{x_1^{n-1}}{(n-1)!} \, dx_1 = \frac{1}{n!}$$

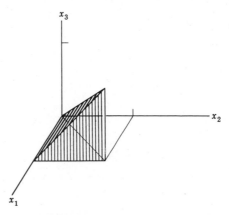

FIGURE 8

EXERCISES

Evaluate the following iterated integrals and sketch the region of integration for each.

1. $\displaystyle\int_{-1}^{0} dx \int_{1}^{2} (x^2y^2 + xy^3)\, dy.$

2. $\displaystyle\int_{0}^{2} dy \int_{1}^{3} |x - 2|\sin y\, dx.$ $\qquad\qquad$ $\left[Ans.\ 1 - \cos 2.\right]$

3. $\displaystyle\int_{1}^{0} dx \int_{2}^{0} (x + y^2)\, dy.$

4. $\displaystyle\int_{0}^{\pi/2} dy \int_{-y}^{y} \sin x\, dx.$ $\qquad\qquad$ $\left[Ans.\ 0.\right]$

5. $\displaystyle\int_{-2}^{1} dy \int_{0}^{y^2} (x^2 + y)\, dx.$

6. $\displaystyle\int_{-1}^{1} dx \int_{0}^{|x|} dy.$ $\qquad\qquad$ $\left[Ans.\ 1.\right]$

7. $\displaystyle\int_{0}^{1} dx \int_{0}^{\sqrt{1-x^2}} dy.$

8. $\displaystyle\int_{1}^{-1} dx \int_{x}^{2x} e^{x+y}\, dy.$

9. $\displaystyle\int_{0}^{\pi/2} dy \int_{0}^{\cos y} x \sin y\, dx.$

10. $\displaystyle\int_1^2 dx \int_{x^2}^{x^3} x \, dy.$ [*Ans.* 49/20.]

11. $\displaystyle\int_0^1 dz \int_0^z dy \int_0^y dx.$

12. $\displaystyle\int_0^2 dx \int_1^x dy \int_2^{x+y-1} y \, dz.$ [*Ans.* 2/3.]

13. $\displaystyle\int_1^2 dy \int_0^1 dx \int_x^y dz.$

14. $\displaystyle\int_{-1}^1 dx \int_0^{|x|} dy \int_0^1 (x + y + z) \, dz.$ [*Ans.* 5/6.]

15. $\displaystyle\int_0^\pi \sin x \, dx \int_0^1 dy \int_0^2 (x + y + z) \, dz.$

16. Evaluate the integral $\displaystyle\int_0^1 dx \int_{-x}^x dy \int_{-x-y}^{x+y} dz \int_{-z}^x dw.$

17. Sketch the subset B defined by $0 \le x \le 1, 0 \le y \le x$, and write down the integral over B in each of the two possible orders of $f(x, y) = x \sin y$. Evaluate both integrals.

18. Sketch the region defined by $x \ge 0$, $x^2 + y^2 \le 2$, and $x^2 + y^2 \ge 1$. Write down the integral over the region in each of the two possible orders of $f(x, y) = x^2$. Evaluate both integrals.   [*Ans.* $3\pi/8$.]

19. Consider two real-valued functions $c(x)$ and $d(x)$ of a real variable x. Suppose that for all x in the interval $a \le x \le b$, we have $c(x) \le d(x)$.

    (a) Make a sketch of two such functions and of the subset B of the xy-plane consisting of all (x, y) such that $a \le x \le b$ and $c(x) \le y \le d(x)$.

    (b) Express the area of B as an iterated integral.

    (c) Set up the iterated integral of $f(x, y)$ over B.

20. Sketch the subset B of $\mathfrak{R}^3$, defined by $0 \le x \le 1, 0 \le y \le 1 + x$ and $0 \le z \le 2$. Write down the iterated integral with order of integration z, then y, and then x, of the function $f(x, y, z) = x^2 + z$ over the subset B. Compute the integral.   [*Ans.* 25/6.]

21. Sketch the region defined by $0 \le x \le 1$, $x^2 \le y \le \sqrt{x}$ and $1 \le z \le x + y$ and evaluate the iterated integral, in some order, of $f(x, y, z) = x + y + z$ over the region.

22. Let f be defined by $f(x, y, z) = 1$ on the hemisphere bounded by the plane $z = 0$ and the surface $z = \sqrt{1 - x^2 - y^2}$. Evaluate an iterated integral of f in some order over the region. $[Ans.\ 2\pi/3.]$

23. Let f be defined by $f(x_1, \ldots, x_n) = x_1 x_2 \ldots x_n$ on the cube $0 \leq x_1 \leq 1$, $0 \leq x_2 \leq 1, \ldots, 0 \leq x_n \leq 1$. Evaluate

$$\int_0^1 dx_1 \int_0^1 dx_2 \ldots \int_0^1 x_1 x_2 \ldots x_n \, dx_n.$$

24. Show that if in the integral

$$\int_{a_1}^{b_1} dx_1 \int_{a_2}^{b_2} dx_2 \ldots \int_{a_n}^{b_n} f(x_1, \ldots, x_n) \, dx_n$$

the order of the limits of integration is interchanged on an even number of integral signs, then the value of the integral is unchanged. If the limits are interchanged on an odd number of integral signs then the whole iterated integral changes sign.

25. Evaluate

$$\int_0^1 dx_1 \int_0^1 dx_2 \ldots \int_0^1 dx_{n-1} \int_0^{x_1} (x_1 + x_2) \, dx_n.$$

26. Prove that

$$\int_0^x dx_1 \int_0^{x_1} dx_2 \ldots \int_0^{x_{n-1}} f(x_n) \, dx_n = \frac{1}{(n-1)!} \int_0^x (x - t)^{n-1} f(t) \, dt.$$

2. MULTIPLE INTEGRALS

Multiple integrals are closely related to the iterated integrals of the preceding section, but they are not the same things. One-dimensional integrals are associated with the idea of area under a curve. Similarly, multiple integrals can be used to define volume.

We first consider some simple sets in $\mathfrak{R}^n$. A **closed coordinate rectangle** is a subset of $\mathfrak{R}^n$ consisting of all points $X = (x_1, \ldots, x_n)$ that satisfy a set of inequalities

$$a_i \leq x_i \leq b_i, \qquad i = 1, \ldots, n. \tag{1}$$

If in Formula (1) some of the symbols "$\leq$" are replaced by "$<$," the resulting set is still called a **coordinate rectangle**. In particular, if all the inequalities are of the form $a_i < x_i < b_i$, the set is open and is called an **open coordinate rectangle**. A coordinate rectangle has its edges parallel to the coordinate axes. Throughout this section the word "rectangle" will be understood to mean "coordinate rectangle." Rectangles in $\mathfrak{R}^2$ and $\mathfrak{R}^3$ are illustrated in Figure 9. A rectangle in $\mathfrak{R}$ is just an interval.

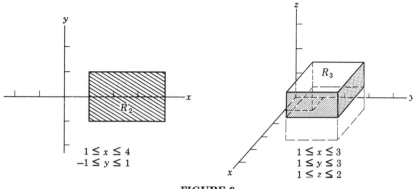

$$1 \leq x \leq 4$$
$$-1 \leq y \leq 1$$

$$1 \leq x \leq 3$$
$$1 \leq y \leq 3$$
$$1 \leq z \leq 2$$

FIGURE 9

Let R be a rectangle (open, closed, or neither) defined by Formula (1) with replacement of any symbols "$\leq$" by "$<$" permitted. The **volume** or **content** of R, written $V(R)$, is defined by

$$V(R) = (b_1 - a_1)(b_2 - a_2) \ldots (b_n - a_n). \qquad (2)$$

In the examples shown in Figure 9, $V(R_2) = (4 - 1)(1 - (-1)) = 6$ and $V(R_3) = (3 - 1)(3 - 1)(2 - 1) = 4$. If, for some i in Formula (1), $a_i = b_i$, then R is called **degenerate** and $V(R) = 0$. For rectangles in $\mathfrak{R}^2$, content is the same thing as area, and we often write $A(R)$ instead of $V(R)$ in recognition of this fact.

A subset B of $\mathfrak{R}^n$ is called **bounded** if there is a real number k such that $|X| < k$ for all X in B. A finite set of $(n - 1)$-dimensional planes in $\mathfrak{R}^n$ (lines in $\mathfrak{R}^2$) parallel to the coordinate planes will be called a **grid**. As illustrated in Figure 10, a grid separates $\mathfrak{R}^n$ into a finite number of closed, bounded rectangles $R_1, \ldots, R_r$ and a finite number of unbounded regions.

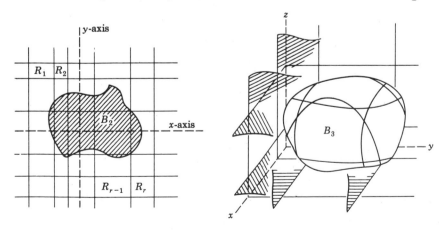

FIGURE 10

EXAMPLE 1. Evaluate the multiple integral

$$\int_B (2x + y) \ dx \ dy,$$

where B is the rectangle $0 \le x < 1$, $0 \le y \le 2$. The existence of the integral is ensured by Theorem 2.1. For this reason, any sequence of Riemann sums with mesh tending to zero may be used to evaluate it. For each $n = 1, 2, \ldots$, consider the grid G_n consisting of the lines $x = i/n$,

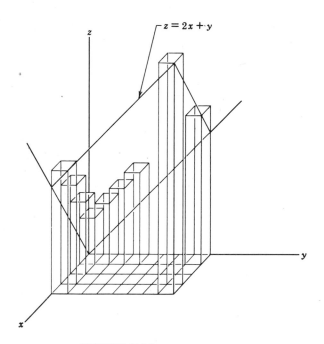

FIGURE 11(a)

$i = 0, \ldots, n$, and $y = j/n$, $j = 0, \ldots, 2n$. (See Figure 11(b).) The mesh of G_n is $1/n$, and the area of each of the rectangles R_{ij} is $1/n^2$. Setting

$$X_{ij} = (x_i, y_j) = \left(\frac{i}{n}, \frac{j}{n}\right),$$

we form the Riemann sum

$$\sum_{i=1}^{n} \sum_{j=1}^{2n} (2x_i + y_j) A(R_{ij}) = \sum_{i=1}^{n} \sum_{j=1}^{2n} \left(\frac{2i}{n} + \frac{j}{n} \right) \frac{1}{n^2}$$

$$= \frac{1}{n^3} \left(4n \sum_{i=1}^{n} i + n \sum_{j=1}^{2n} j \right)$$

$$= \frac{1}{n^2} \left(4 \frac{n^2 + n}{2} + \frac{4n^2 + 2n}{2} \right)$$

$$= \frac{4n^2 + 3n}{n^2} = 4 + \frac{3}{n}.$$

Hence,

$$\int_B (2x + y) \, dx \, dy = \lim_{n \to \infty} \left(4 + \frac{3}{n} \right) = 4.$$

A direct evaluation of a multiple integral will be very arduous for most functions we wish to integrate. Fortunately, in many instances the multiple integral can be easily evaluated by repeated application of ordinary 1-dimensional integration instead of by finding the limits of Riemann sums. The pertinent theorem, which we prove at the end of this section, is the following.

2.2 Theorem. Let B be a subset of $\Re^n$ such that the iterated integral

$$\int dx_1 \int dx_2 \ldots \int f \, dx_n$$

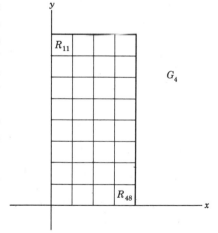

FIGURE 11(b)

exists over B. If, in addition, the multiple integral

$$\int_B f \, dV$$

exists, then the two integrals are equal.

Since the argument used to prove Theorem 2.2 applies equally well to any order of iterated integration we have as an immediate corollary

2.3 Theorem. If $\int_B f\, dV$ exists and iterated integrals exist for some orders of integration, then all of these integrals are equal.

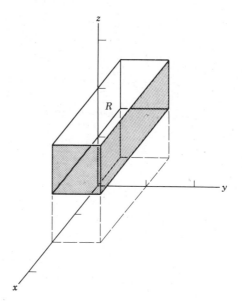

FIGURE 12

EXAMPLE 2. Evaluate $\int_B (2x + y)\, dx\, dy$, where B is the rectangle $0 \le x \le 1, 0 \le y \le 2$. This is the same integral that occurs in Example 1. Theorem 2.2 is applicable, and we obtain

$$\int_B (2x + y)\, dx\, dy = \int_0^1 dx \int_0^2 (2x + y)\, dy$$

$$= \int_0^1 (4x + 2)\, dx$$

$$= 2x^2 + 2x\big]_0^1 = 4.$$

EXAMPLE 3. Let R be the 3-dimensional rectangle defined by $-1 \le x \le 2, 0 \le y \le 1, 1 \le z \le 2$, and shown in Figure 12. Consider

$f(x, y, z) = xyz$. Then

$$\int_R f \, dV = \int_R xyz \, dx \, dy \, dz$$

$$= \int_{-1}^{2} dx \int_0^1 dy \int_1^2 xyz \, dz = \int_{-1}^2 x \, dx \int_0^1 y \, dy \int_1^2 z \, dz$$

$$= \left(\tfrac{3}{2}\right)\left(\tfrac{1}{2}\right)\left(\tfrac{3}{2}\right) = \tfrac{9}{8}.$$

EXAMPLE 4. Let $f(x, y, z) = xyz$, and let the subset B of $\mathfrak{R}^3$ be defined by $x^2 + y^2 + z^2 \leq 4$, $y \geq 0$, $z \geq 0$. B is the interior and boundary of one quarter of the spherical ball of radius 2 with center at the origin, shown in Figure 13. The integral $\int_B f \, dV$ equals the triple iterated integral of the function $f(x, y, z) = xyz$ over B.

For fixed x and y, the variable z runs from 0 to $\sqrt{4 - x^2 - y^2}$, which are the limits of the first integration with respect to z. The result of this integration is a function of x and y which next must be integrated over the 2-dimensional subset obtained by projecting B on the xy-plane, that is, over the region $x^2 + y^2 \leq 4$, $y \geq 0$. For fixed x, the variable y runs from 0 to $\sqrt{4 - x^2}$; hence, these are the limits on the integration with respect to y. Finally, x runs from -2 to 2, so we conclude that

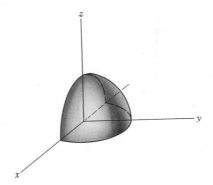

FIGURE 13

$$\int_B f \, dV = \int_{-2}^2 dx \int_0^{\sqrt{4-x^2}} dy \int_0^{\sqrt{4-x^2-y^2}} xyz \, dz.$$

Then

$$\int_B f \, dV = \frac{1}{2} \int_{-2}^2 x \, dx \int_0^{\sqrt{4-x^2}} y(4 - x^2 - y^2) \, dy$$

$$= \frac{1}{2} \int_{-2}^2 x \left(2(4 - x^2) - \frac{x^2}{2}(4 - x^2) - \frac{(4 - x^2)^2}{4}\right) dx.$$

The last integrand is an odd function and for that reason the integral has value zero.

If the constant function 1 is integrable over a subset B of $\Re^n$, the **content**, or **volume**, of B is denoted by $V(B)$ and defined by

$$V(B) = \int_B 1 \, dV = \int_B dV.$$

For sets B in $\Re^2$, we write $A(B)$, for area, instead of $V(B)$. It follows from the last part of Theorem 2.1 that the content of a continuously differentiable k-dimensional $(k < n)$ curve or surface S is zero, for

$$V(S) = \int_S dV = 0.$$

For some sets B, the integral $\int_B dV$ does not exist. If this happens, the content of B is not defined (see Exercise 21). Notice that for rectangles R, $V(R)$ has been defined twice: first as the product of the lengths of mutually perpendicular edges and second as an integral. That the two definitions agree follows immediately from Theorems 2.1 and 2.6.

EXAMPLE 5. Let B be the region in $\Re^2$ under the curve $y = f(x)$ from $x = a$ to $x = b$, where f is a non-negative function. Assuming the existence of the following integrals, we obtain, using the iterated integral theorem (Theorem 2.2),

$$A(B) = \int_B dA = \int_a^b dx \int_0^{f(x)} dy = \int_a^b f(x) \, dx.$$

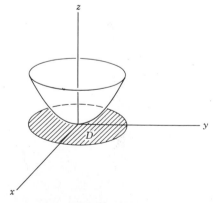

FIGURE 14

Hence, the above definition of content is consistent with the usual one for the area under the graph of a non-negative integrable function of one variable. If f is integrable over B and also non-negative on B, we could similarly show that the volume under the graph of f and above the set B is the double integral $\int_B f \, dA$.

EXAMPLE 6. The volume above the disc D defined by $x^2 + y^2 \leq 1$ and under the graph of $f(x, y) = x^2 + y^2$ (see Figure 14) is equal to

$$\int_D (x^2 + y^2)\, dx\, dy = \int_{-1}^{1} dx \int_{-\sqrt{1-x^2}}^{\sqrt{1-x^2}} (x^2 + y^2)\, dy$$

$$= 2\int_{-1}^{1} \left(x^2\sqrt{1 - x^2} + \frac{1}{3}(1 - x^2)\sqrt{1 - x^2} \right) dx$$

$$= \frac{4}{3}\int_{0}^{1} (\sqrt{1 - x^2} + 2x^2\sqrt{1 - x^2})\, dx$$

$$= \frac{4}{3}\left(\frac{\pi}{4} + \frac{\pi}{8} \right) = \frac{\pi}{2}.$$

EXAMPLE 7. Find the volume of the region B in $\mathcal{R}^3$ bounded by the

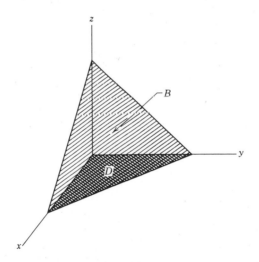

FIGURE 15

four planes $x = 0,\ y = 0,\ z = 0$, and $x + y + z = 1$, shown in Figure 15.

$$V(B) = \int_B dV = \int_{0}^{1} dx \int_{0}^{1-x} dy \int_{0}^{1-x-y} dz = \frac{1}{6}.$$

The volume of the region B can be computed directly as a double integral. The projection of B on the xy-plane is the triangle D bounded by the lines $x = 0,\ y = 0,\ x + y = 1$. The set B itself can be described as the region under the graph of the function $f(x, y) = 1 - x - y$ and above D. Hence, according to the remark at the end of Example 5,

$$V(B) = \int_D f \, dA = \int_0^1 dx \int_0^{1-x} (1 - x - y) \, dy = \frac{1}{6}.$$

Notice that what we have called the content of a subset of $\mathfrak{R}^n$ is more properly called its **n-dimensional content**. For example, the square defined by the inequalities $0 \leq x \leq 2, 0 \leq y \leq 2$ in $\mathfrak{R}^2$ has 2-dimensional content 4, whereas the square defined in $\mathfrak{R}^3$ by $0 \leq x \leq 2, 0 \leq y \leq 2, z = 0$, and which looks the same, has 3-dimensional content 0. Thus the content of a set depends on the dimension of the containing euclidean space with respect to which it is being measured, as well as on the shape of the set itself. Having already indicated that 2-dimensional content is called area, we remark that 1-dimensional content is length.

Some characteristic properties of the Riemann integral are summarized in the following four theorems.

2.4 Theorem. Linearity. If f and g are integrable over B and a and b are any two real numbers, then $af + bg$ is integrable over B and

$$\int_B (af + bg) \, dV = a \int_B f \, dV + b \int_B g \, dV.$$

2.5 Theorem. Positivity. If f is non-negative and integrable over B, then

$$\int_B f \, dV \geq 0.$$

2.6 Theorem. If R is a rectangle, then $\int_R dV = V(R)$ (where the content $V(R)$ is defined by Equation (2)).

2.7 Theorem. If B is a subset of a bounded set C, then $\int_B f \, dV$ exists if and only if $\int_C f_B \, dV$ exists. Whenever both integrals exist, they are equal.

Proof of 2.4. Let $\epsilon > 0$ be given, and choose $\delta > 0$ so that if S_1 and S_2 are any two Riemann sums for f_B and g_B, respectively, and whose grids have mesh less than δ, then

$$\left| a \right| \left| S_1 - \int_B f \, dV \right| < \frac{\epsilon}{2} \quad \text{and} \quad \left| b \right| \left| S_2 - \int_B g \, dV \right| < \frac{\epsilon}{2}.$$

Let S be any Riemann sum for $(af + bg)_B$ whose grid has mesh less than δ. Then

$$S = \sum_i ((af + bg)_B X_i) V(R_i)$$

$$= a \sum_i (f_B X_i) V(R_i) + b \sum_i (g_B X_i) V(R_i)$$

$$= a\, S_1 + b\, S_2.$$

Hence,

$$\left| S - a \int_B f\, dV - b \int_B g\, dV \right.$$

$$= \left| aS_1 - a \int_B f\, dV + bS_2 - b \int_B g\, dV \right|$$

$$\leq |a| \left| S_1 - \int_B f\, dV \right| + |b| \left| S_2 - \int_B g\, dV \right|$$

$$< \frac{\epsilon}{2} + \frac{\epsilon}{2} = \epsilon.$$

Thus

$$\lim_{m(G) \to 0} \sum_i ((af + bg)_B X_i) V(R_i) = a \int_B f\, dV + b \int_B g\, dV,$$

and the proof is complete.

Proof of 2.5. Since all the Riemann sums are non-negative, the limit must also be non-negative.

Proof of 2.6. This follows immediately from Theorems 2.1 and 2.2.

Proof of 2.7. The existence and the value of the integral $\int_B f\, dV$ depend only on the function f_B. Similarly, $\int_C f_B\, dV$ is defined with respect to $(f_B)_C$ which is equal to f_B.

Many of the important properties of the integral can be derived directly from the preceding four theorems, without reference to the original definition. The next two theorems are given as examples.

2.8 Theorem. If f and g are integrable over B and $f \leq g$ on B, then

$$\int_B f\, dV \leq \int_B g\, dV.$$

Proof. The function $g - f$ is non-negative and, by Theorem 2.4, is integrable over B. Hence, by Theorems 2.4 and 2.5,

$$0 \leq \int_B (g - f) \, dV = \int_B g \, dV - \int_B f \, dV,$$

from which the conclusion follows.

The second theorem establishes the analogue of the equation

$$\int_a^c f(x) \, dx = \int_a^b f(x) \, dx + \int_b^c f(x) \, dx$$

that holds for functions of one variable.

2.9 Theorem. If f is integrable over each of two disjoint sets B_1 and B_2, then f is integrable over their union and

$$\int_{B_1 \cup B_2} f \, dV = \int_{B_1} f \, dV + \int_{B_2} f \, dV.$$

Proof. By Theorem 2.7,

$$\int_{B_1} f \, dV + \int_{B_2} f \, dV = \int_{B_1 \cup B_2} f_{B_1} \, dV + \int_{B_1 \cup B_2} f_{B_2} \, dV.$$

Since B_1 and B_2 are disjoint, $f_{B_1 \cup B_2} = f_{B_1} + f_{B_2}$. Hence, by Theorem 2.4, $f_{B_1 \cup B_2}$ is integrable over $B_1 \cup B_2$, and

$$\int_{B_1 \cup B_2} f_{B_1} \, dV + \int_{B_1 \cup B_2} f_{B_2} \, dV = \int_{B_1 \cup B_2} f_{B_1 \cup B_2} \, dV.$$

Finally, by Theorem 2.7 again, f is integrable over $B_1 \cup B_2$ and

$$\int_{B_1 \cup B_2} f_{B_1 \cup B_2} \, dV = \int_{B_1 \cup B_2} f \, dV.$$

This completes the proof.

The next theorem will show that for functions f and regions B for which $\int_B f \, dV$ exists, the value of the integral is completely determined by the properties stated in the four theorems 2.4–2.7.

2.10 Theorem. Suppose I is a function that assigns to certain functions $\Re^n \overset{f}{\to} \Re$, and sets B a real number $I_B f$, and which satisfies the conditions:

(a) If $I_B f$ and $I_B g$ are defined and a and b are real numbers, then $I_B(af + bg)$ is defined and

$$I_B(af + bg) = aI_B f + bI_B g.$$

(b) If f is non-negative and $I_B f$ is defined, then $I_B f \geq 0$.

(c) If R is a rectangle, then $I_R 1 = V(R)$ (as defined by Equation (2)).

(d) If B is contained in a bounded set C, then $I_B f$ is defined if and only if $I_C f_B$ is defined. Whenever both exist, they are equal.

Then, if $I_B f$ and $\int_B f \, dV$ both exist, they are equal.

Proof. Suppose $\int_B f \, dV < I_B f$. Set

$$\epsilon = I_B f - \int_B f \, dV,$$

and choose $\delta > 0$ so that if S is any Riemann sum for f_B whose grid has mesh less than δ, then

$$\left| \int_B f \, dV - S \right| < \frac{\epsilon}{2}.$$

Let G be an arbitrary grid that covers B and has mesh less than δ, and denote the closed bounded rectangles formed by G by $R_1, \ldots, R_r$. Set

$$C = R_1 \cup \ldots \cup R_r,$$

$$\bar{f}_i = \text{supremum of } f_B \text{ in } R_i.*$$

Consider the function g defined by

$$g = \sum_{i=1}^{r} \bar{f}_i \, \chi_{Ri}.$$

The function χ_{Ri} is the characteristic function of R_i. It is defined by

$$\chi_{Ri}(X) = \begin{cases} 1, & \text{if } X \text{ is in } R_i. \\ 0, & \text{otherwise.} \end{cases}$$

It follows immediately from (c), (d), and (a) that $I_C g$ is defined and that

$$I_C g = \sum_{i=1}^{r} \bar{f}_i V(R_i).$$

The definition of **supremum** implies that there exists a Riemann sum

---

* The **supremum** of a set S of real numbers is discussed at the beginning of Appendix II.

for f_B on the grid G that is arbitrarily close to $I_C g$. Hence,

$$\left| \int_B f \, dV - I_C g \right| \leq \frac{\epsilon}{2},$$

and so

$$I_C g < I_B f. \tag{4}$$

By (d), $I_B f = I_C f_B$. Moreover the function g has been constructed so that $f_B \leq g$. It follows from (b) (as extended in Theorem 2.8) that

$$I_B f = I_C f_B \leq I_C g. \tag{5}$$

The inequalities (4) and (5) are contradictory, so we conclude that

$$\int_B f \, dV \geq I_B f.$$

By an entirely analogous argument using the notion of **infimum** instead of **supremum**, we can obtain

$$\int_B f \, dV \leq I_B f,$$

and this completes the proof.

For an application of Theorem 2.10, take the functions $\mathfrak{R}^2 \xrightarrow{f} \mathfrak{R}$ and sets B for which the iterated integral $\int dx \int f \, dy$ over B is defined. Let

$$I_B f = \int_{(\text{over } B)} dx \int f \, dy.$$

Verification of the conditions of Theorem 2.10 is straightforward and reduces to a knowledge of the corresponding properties of the definite integral for functions of one variable. For example, for integration over intervals,

$$\int_\alpha^\beta (af + bg) \, dx = a \int_\alpha^\beta f \, dx + b \int_\alpha^\beta g \, dx.$$

$$\int_\alpha^\beta f \, dx \geq 0 \qquad\qquad \text{if } f \geq 0.$$

$$\int_\alpha^\beta dx = \beta - \alpha.$$

$$\int_\gamma^\delta f \, dx = \int_\alpha^\beta f_{[\gamma, \delta]} \, dx \qquad \text{if } \alpha \leq \gamma \leq \delta \leq \beta \text{ and } [\gamma, \ \delta] \text{ is the interval } \gamma \leq x \leq \delta.$$

It follows immediately from Theorem 2.10 that if both the iterated integral and the double integral of f exist over B, then they are equal. This proves Theorem 2.2 for two variables. The general case is no harder.

A second application of Theorem 2.10 has to do with the Lebesgue integral, named after Henri Lebesgue (1875–1941). The Lebesgue integral is a generalization of the Riemann integral in that it is defined for a larger class of functions f and sets B. The Lebesgue integral also has the characteristic properties of Theorem 2.10. It follows that if a function has both Riemann and Lebesgue integrals, the two integrals are equal.

EXERCISES

1. Make a drawing of the set B and compute $\int_B f \, dA$, where

   (a) $f(x, y) = x^2 + 3y^2$ and B is the disc $x^2 + y^2 \leq 1$.   [$Ans.\ \pi.$]

   (b) $f(x, y) = 1/(x + y)$ and B is region bounded by the lines $y = x$, $x = 1$, $x = 2$, $y = 0$.   [$Ans.\ \text{Log } 2.$]

   (c) $f(x, y) = x \sin xy$ and B is the rectangle $0 \leq x \leq \pi$, $0 \leq y \leq 1$.   [$Ans.\ \pi.$]

   (d) $f(x, y) = x^2 - y^2$ and B consists of all (x, y) such that $0 \leq x \leq 1$ and $x^2 - y^2 \geq 0$.   [$Ans.\ \frac{1}{3}.$]

   (e) $f(x, y) = 1$, for all (x, y), and B is defined by $x^2 - y^2 \leq 1$, $|y| \leq 1$.
   [$Ans.\ 2\sqrt{2} + \log (\sqrt{2} + 1)/(\sqrt{2} - 1).$]

2. Using the definition of the double integral as a limit of Riemann sums,

   compute $\int_B f(x, y) \, dx \, dy$, where

   (a) $f(x, y) = x + 4y$ and B is the rectangle $0 \leq x \leq 2$, $0 \leq y \leq 1$.
   [$Ans.\ 6.$]

   (b) $f(x, y) = 3x^2 + 2y$ and B is the rectangle $0 \leq x \leq 2$, $0 \leq y \leq 1$.
   [$Ans.\ 10.$]

   (c) $f(x, y) = x + 4y$ and B is the triangular region bounded by the lines $x = 0$, $y = 0$, $x + y = 2$.   [$Ans.\ \frac{20}{3}.$]

   (d) $f(x, y) = 2x + 1$ and B is the region defined by $0 \leq x \leq 1$, $0 \leq y \leq x^2$.
   [$Ans.\ \frac{5}{6}.$]

   The following formulas will be useful in doing this problem:

   $$\sum_{i=1}^{n} i = \frac{n(n + 1)}{2},$$

   $$\sum_{i=1}^{n} i^2 = \frac{n(n + 1)(2n + 1)}{6},$$

   $$\sum_{i=1}^{n} i^3 = \left(\sum_{i=1}^{n} i\right)^2.$$

3. Find the volume under the graph of f and above the set B, where

(a) $f(x, y) = x + y^2$ and B is the rectangle with corners $(1, 1)$, $(1, 3)$, $(2, 3)$, and $(2, 1)$. $\qquad$ $\left[Ans. \frac{35}{3}.\right]$

(b) $f(x, y) = x + y + 2$ and B is the region bounded by the curves $y^2 = x$ and $x = 2$. $\qquad$ $\left[Ans. \frac{128}{15}\sqrt{2}.\right]$

(c) $f(x, y) = x^2$ and B consists of all (x, y) such that $x \geq 0$, $x^2 + y^2 \leq 2$, $x^2 + y^2 \geq 1$. $\qquad$ $\left[Ans. 3\pi/8.\right]$

(d) $f(x, y) = |x + y|$ and B is the disc $x^2 + y^2 \leq 1$. $\qquad$ $\left[Ans. 4\sqrt{2}/3.\right]$

4. Find by integration, the area of the subset of $\mathcal{R}^2$ bounded by the curve $x^2 - 2x + 4y^2 - 8y + 1 = 0$. $\qquad$ $\left[Ans. 2\pi.\right]$

5. Find by integration the area of a parallelogram with corners $(0, 0)$, (x_1, y_1), (x_2, y_2), $(x_1 + x_2, y_1 + y_2)$. $\qquad$ $\left[Ans. |x_1y_2 - x_2y_1|.\right]$

6. Consider the rectangles

$$B_1 \quad \text{defined by } 0 < x \leq 1, 0 \leq y < 1$$

$$B_2 \quad \text{defined by } 1 \leq x \leq 2, -1 \leq y \leq 1$$

and the function

$$f(x, y) = \begin{cases} 2x - y, & \text{if } x < 1. \\ x^2 + y, & \text{if } x \geq 1. \end{cases}$$

Compute $\displaystyle\int_{B_1 \cup B_2} f(x, y) \, dx \, dy$. $\qquad$ $\left[Ans. \frac{31}{6}.\right]$

7. Compute $\displaystyle\int_B f \, dA$, where

$$f(x, y) = \begin{cases} x + xy, & \text{if } x \leq y \\ xy + y^2, & \text{if } x > y \end{cases}$$

and B is the disc $(x - 1)^2 + (y - 1)^2 \leq 1$. $\qquad$ $\left[Ans. \pi/8 - \sqrt{2}/3.\right]$

8. Consider the function $f(x, y, z) = xy$ and the subset B of $\mathcal{R}^3$ defined by the inequalities $0 \leq x \leq 2$, $-1 \leq y \leq x^2$, $1 \leq z \leq y$. Compute

$$\int_B f \, dV.$$ $\qquad$ $\left[Ans. 7.\right]$

9. Given that $f(x, y, z) = xyz$ and that

$$\int_B f(x, y, z) \, dx \, dy \, dz = \int_0^2 dx \int_0^x dy \int_0^{x+y} xyz \, dz,$$

sketch the region B and evaluate the integral. $\qquad$ $\left[Ans. \frac{68}{9}.\right]$

10. Compute the multiple integral of $f(x, y, z, w) = xyzw$ over the 4-dimensional rectangle

$$0 \leq x \leq 1, \quad -1 \leq y \leq 2, \quad 1 \leq z \leq 2, \quad 2 \leq w \leq 3.$$
$$\left[Ans. \tfrac{45}{16}.\right]$$

11. Sketch the region B in $\mathfrak{R}^3$ bounded by the surface $z = 4 - 4x^2 - y^2$ and the xy-plane. Set up the volume of B as a triple integral and also as a double integral. Compute the volume. $\left[Ans.\ 4\pi.\right]$

12. Sketch the region B in $\mathfrak{R}^3$ bounded by the surface $z = 4x^2 + y^2$ and the plane $z = 4x + 3$. Compute the volume $V(B)$. $\left[Ans.\ 4\pi.\right]$

13. Write an expression for the volume of the ball $x^2 + y^2 + z^2 \leq a^2$,
(a) as a triple integral.
(b) as a double integral.

14. Sketch in $\mathfrak{R}^3$ the two cylindrical solids defined by $x^2 + z^2 \leq 1$ and $y^2 + z^2 \leq 1$ respectively. Find the volume of their intersection.
$$\left[Ans.\ \tfrac{16}{3}.\right]$$

15. The 4-dimensional ball B of radius 1 and with center at the origin is the subset of $\mathfrak{R}^4$ defined by $x_1^2 + x_2^2 + x_3^2 + x_4^2 \leq 1$. Set up an expression for the volume $V(B)$ as a four-fold iterated integral.

16. Show that if the following integrals are defined, then

$$\int_{B_1 \cup B_2} f\, dV = \int_{B_1} f\, dV + \int_{B_2} f\, dV - \int_{B_1 \cap B_2} f\, dV.$$

17. (a) Denote by $[x]$ the algebraically greatest integer that is less than or equal to x, e.g. $[\tfrac{3}{2}] = 1$, $[\pi] = 3$, $[-7.5] = -8$. Draw the curve $y = [x]$.
(b) Let $f(x, y) = [x]$ and let B be the triangular region bounded by the curves $x + y = 3$, $x = 0$, $y = 0$. Evaluate

$$\int_B f(x, y)\ dx\ dy.$$
$$\left[Ans.\ \tfrac{5}{2}.\right]$$

(c) Let $f(x, y) = [x + y]$ and let B be the region in part (b). Evaluate

$$\int_B f(x, y)\ dx\ dy.$$
$$\left[Ans.\ \tfrac{13}{2}.\right]$$

18. (See Theorem 2.9.) Tell whether the following statement is true or false: If f is integrable over the union of two disjoint subsets B_1 and B_2 of $\mathfrak{R}^2$, then f is integrable over each of B_1 and B_2.

19. Show that the set $\mathfrak{R}_B$ of Riemann integrable functions over a given set B is a vector space and that the transformation $L(f) = \int_B f\, dA$, for any f in $\mathfrak{R}_B$, is a linear functional on $\mathfrak{R}_B$.

20. Let B be the rectangle $0 \le x \le 1$ and $0 \le y \le 1$. Prove that the vector space $\mathcal{R}_B$ defined in Exercise 19 is not finite dimensional. [*Hint.* Consider the functions $c_1, c_2, \ldots$, where c_n is the characteristic function of the rectangle $0 \le x \le 1$ and $0 \le y \le 1 - 1/n$.]

21. Let R be the rectangle $0 \le x \le 1$ and $0 \le y \le 1$, and consider the function

$$f(x, y) = \begin{cases} 1, & \text{if } x \text{ is a rational number.} \\ 0, & \text{otherwise.} \end{cases}$$

Prove that f is not Riemann integrable over R. It follows that the subset B of R consisting of all (x, y) such that x is a rational number has no content or area, that is, $\int_B dA$ does not exist.

22. Let the sequence of functions $f_1, f_2, \ldots$ be defined on the interval $[0, 1]$ by

$$f_m(x) = \begin{cases} 1, & \text{if } x = k/2^m, \text{ for some integer } k \text{ in } 0 \le k \le 2^m. \\ 0, & \text{otherwise.} \end{cases}$$

(a) Show that $\lim_{m \to \infty} f_m(x)$ exists for all x in $[0, 1]$ ($[0, 1]$ is the set of all x such that $0 \le x \le 1$) but that the limit function is not Riemann integrable over $[0, 1]$.

(b) Show that each function f_m is Riemann integrable over $[0, 1]$. Evaluate

$$\int_0^1 f_m(x) \, dx.$$

23. Prove that the union of the edges of a rectangle in 2-dimensional space is a set of zero area.

24. Let B be the subset of $\mathcal{R}^2$ consisting of all points (x, y) such that $0 \le y \le 1$, $x = 0, 1, \frac{1}{2}, \frac{1}{3}, \ldots, 1/n, \ldots$. What is the area of B?

25. On the rectangle $0 \le x \le 1$ and $0 \le y \le 1$, let $f(x, y) = 1$, if x is rational and $f(x, y) = 2y$, if x is irrational. Show that

$$\int_0^1 dx \int_0^1 f(x, y) \, dy = 1,$$

but that f is not Riemann integrable over the rectangle.

26. Prove that

$$\int_0^1 dy \int_1^\infty (e^{-xy} - 2e^{-2xy}) \, dx \ne \int_1^\infty dx \int_0^1 (e^{-xy} - 2e^{-2xy}) \, dy.$$

3. CHANGE OF VARIABLE IN MULTIPLE INTEGRALS

The change-of-variable formula for 1-dimensional integrals is

$$\int_{\phi(a)}^{\phi(b)} f(x)\ dx = \int_{a}^{b} f(\phi(u))\phi'(u)\ du \tag{1}$$

For example, taking $\phi(u) = \sin u$, we obtain

$$\int_{0}^{1} \sqrt{1 - x^2}\ dx = \int_{0}^{\pi/2} \cos^2 u\ du = \frac{\pi}{4}.$$

In this section Equation (1) will be extended to dimensions higher than one. In n-dimensional space a change of variable is effected by a function $\mathfrak{R}^n \xrightarrow{T} \mathfrak{R}^n$. In what follows it will usually be more convenient to consider the domain space and range space of T as distinct. We therefore regard T as a transformation from one copy of $\mathfrak{R}^n$, which we label $\mathfrak{U}^n$, to another copy, which we continue to label $\mathfrak{R}^n$, writing typically $TU = X$ where U is in $\mathfrak{U}^n$ and X is in $\mathfrak{R}^n$. The statement of the n-dimensional change-of-variable theorem follows.

3.1 Theorem. Let $\mathfrak{U}^n \xrightarrow{T} \mathfrak{R}^n$ be a continuously differentiable transformation. Let R be a set in $\mathfrak{U}^n$ having a boundary consisting of finitely many pieces of smooth surface. Suppose that R and its boundary are contained in the interior of the domain of T and that

(a) T is one-one on R.
(b) J, the Jacobian determinant of T, is different from zero on R.

Then, if the function f is bounded and continuous on TR (the image of R under T) we have

$$\int_{TR} f\ dV = \int_{R} (f \bigcirc T)\ |\ J\ |\ dV.$$

Either (a) or (b) is allowed to fail on a set of zero content.

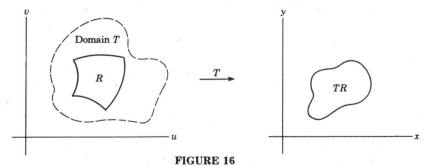

FIGURE 16

The proof is in the Appendix. Before showing why the formula works we give some examples of its application. Notice that the factor ϕ' that occurs in Equation (1) has been replaced in higher dimensions by $|J|$, the absolute value of the Jacobian determinant of T. Aside from the computation of J, the application of the transformation formula is a matter of finding the geometric relationship between the subset R and its image TR for various transformations T.

EXAMPLE 1. The integral $\int_P (x + y)\ dx\ dy$, in which P is the parallelo-

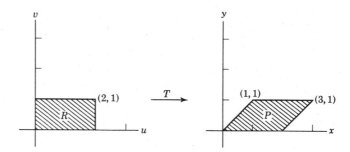

FIGURE 17

gram shown in Figure 17, can be transformed into an integral over a rectangle. This is done by means of the transformation

$$\begin{pmatrix} x \\ y \end{pmatrix} = T \begin{pmatrix} u \\ v \end{pmatrix} = \begin{pmatrix} u + v \\ v \end{pmatrix}.$$

The Jacobian determinant of T is

$$J = \begin{vmatrix} 1 & 1 \\ 0 & 1 \end{vmatrix} = 1.$$

By the change-of-variable theorem,

$$\int_P (x + y)\ dx\ dy = \int_R [(u + v) + v]1\ du\ dv$$

$$= \int_0^2 du \int_0^1 (u + 2v)\ dv = 4.$$

The transformation T is clearly one-one, because it is a linear transformation with nonzero determinant. Notice that the region of integration in the given integral is in the range of the transformation rather than in its domain.

EXAMPLE 2. The transformation

$$\begin{pmatrix} x \\ y \end{pmatrix} = \begin{pmatrix} u \cos v \\ u \sin v \end{pmatrix}$$

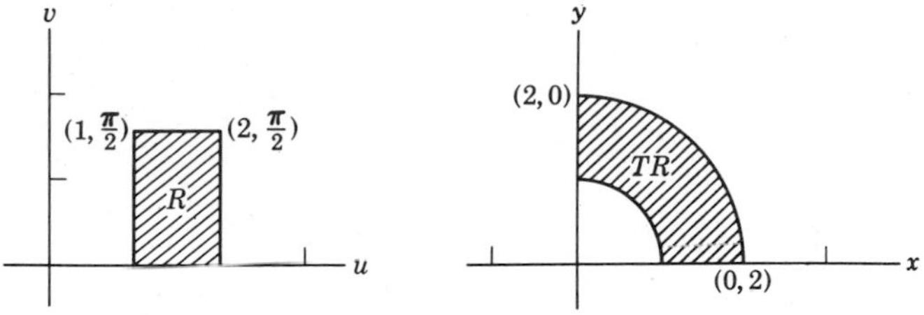

FIGURE 18

makes correspond the regions shown in Figure 18. The Jacobian is

$$J = \begin{vmatrix} \cos v & -u \sin v \\ \sin v & u \cos v \end{vmatrix} = u.$$

The transformation is one one between R and TR. This can be seen geometrically because of the interpretation of v and u as angle and radius respectively, or directly from the relations

$$u = \sqrt{x^2 + y^2}, \qquad \cos v = \frac{x}{\sqrt{x^2 + y^2}},$$

together with the fact that $\cos v$ is one-one for $0 \leq v \leq \pi/2$. Given the integral of $x^2 + y^2$ over TR, we can transform as follows:

$$\int_{TR} (x^2 + y^2)\, dA = \int_R u^2 \cdot u\, dA = \int_1^2 u^3\, du \int_0^{\pi/2} dv = \frac{15\pi}{8}.$$

EXAMPLE 3. Let B be the subset of 3-dimensional space $\mathfrak{R}^3$ defined by the inequalities

$$x^2 + y^2 + z^2 \leq 1, \qquad \begin{cases} x \geq 0. \\ y \geq 0. \\ z \geq 0. \end{cases}$$

To transform the integral $\int_B (x^2 + y^2)\ dx\ dy\ dz$, we can define T by

$$\begin{pmatrix} x \\ y \\ z \end{pmatrix} = T \begin{pmatrix} u \\ v \\ w \end{pmatrix} = \begin{pmatrix} u \sin v \cos w \\ u \sin v \sin w \\ u \cos v \end{pmatrix}.$$

Restricting $\begin{pmatrix} u \\ v \\ w \end{pmatrix}$ to the rectangle R defined by

$$\begin{cases} 0 \le u \le 1, \\ 0 \le v \le \pi/2, \\ 0 \le w \le \pi/2, \end{cases}$$

we get $TR = B$. The corresponding regions are shown in Figure 19. Since

$$u = \sqrt{x^2 + y^2 + z^2},$$

$$\cos v = \frac{z}{\sqrt{x^2 + y^2 + z^2}},$$

$$\cos w = \frac{x}{\sqrt{x^2 + y^2}},$$

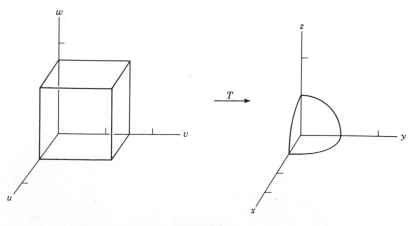

FIGURE 19

we conclude that the transformation T is one-one from R to B except on the boundary planes $u = 0$ and $v = 0$. The Jacobian determinant is

$$J = \begin{vmatrix} \sin v \cos w & u \cos v \cos w & -u \sin v \sin w \\ \sin v \sin w & u \cos v \sin w & u \sin v \cos w \\ \cos v & -u \sin v & 0 \end{vmatrix}$$

$$= u^2 \sin v.$$

The transformed integral is

$$\int_B (x^2 + y^2) \, dx \, dy \, dz = \int_R (u^2 \sin^2 v \cos^2 w + u^2 \sin^2 v \sin^2 w)$$

$$u^2 \sin v \, du \, dv \, dw$$

$$= \int_0^1 u^4 \, du \int_0^{\pi/2} \sin^3 v \, dv \int_0^{\pi/2} dw$$

$$= \frac{1}{5} \cdot \frac{2}{3} \cdot \frac{\pi}{2} = \frac{\pi}{15}.$$

Notice that values of u and v appear in the transformed integral for which the Jacobian $u^2 \sin v$ is zero, that is, for $u = 0$ and $v = 0$. We have already remarked that the transformation fails to be one-one for points satisfying these conditions. However, the set of points on which this failure occurs has zero content, so the change-of-variable theorem still applies. Of course, the value of neither integral is affected by including or excluding these points.

EXAMPLE 4. Let a function $\mathfrak{U}^2 \xrightarrow{T} \mathfrak{R}^2$ be defined by

$$\begin{pmatrix} x \\ y \end{pmatrix} = T\begin{pmatrix} u \\ v \end{pmatrix} = \begin{pmatrix} u^2 - v \\ u + v^2 \end{pmatrix}.$$

The unit square R_{uv} defined by the inequalities $0 \le u \le 1, 0 \le v \le 1$ is carried by T onto the subset R_{xy} shown in Figure 20. Corresponding pieces of the boundaries are indicated in the picture. The image of each of the four line segments that comprise the boundary of R_{uv} is computed as follows:

(a) If $u = 0$ and $0 \le v \le 1$, then $x = -v$ and $y = v^2$. That is, $y = x^2$ and $-1 \le x \le 0$.

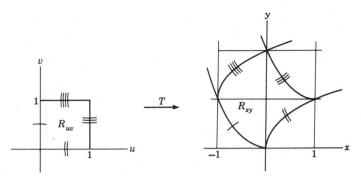

FIGURE 20

(b) If $v = 0$ and $0 \le u \le 1$, then $x = u^2$ and $y = u$. That is, $x = y^2$ and $0 \le y \le 1$.

(c) If $u = 1$ and $0 \le v \le 1$, then $x = 1 - v$ and $y = 1 + v^2$. That is, $y - 1 = (x - 1)^2$ and $0 \le x \le 1$.

(d) If $v = 1$ and $0 \le u \le 1$, then $x = u^2 - 1$ and $y = u + 1$. That is, $(y - 1)^2 = x + 1$ and $1 \le y \le 2$.

It is not hard to verify that T is one-one on R_{uv}. For suppose

$$T \begin{pmatrix} u_1 \\ v_1 \end{pmatrix} = T \begin{pmatrix} u_2 \\ v_2 \end{pmatrix}.$$

Then

$$u_1^2 - v_1 = u_2^2 - v_2,$$

$$u_1 + v_1^2 = u_2 + v_2^2.$$

Obviously, if $u_1 = u_2$, then $v_1 = v_2$. Suppose $u_1 < u_2$. This implies

$$0 < u_2^2 - u_1^2 = v_2 - v_1,$$

$$0 < u_2 - u_1 = v_1^2 - v_2^2.$$

Hence, $v_1 < v_2$ whereas $v_2^2 < v_1^2$. This is impossible if both v_1 and v_2 are non-negative; so the one-oneness of T on R_{uv} is established. The Jacobian determinant of T is

$$J = \begin{vmatrix} 2u & -1 \\ 1 & 2v \end{vmatrix} = 4uv + 1,$$

and we therefore have as an application of the change-of-variable theorem

$$\int_{R_{xy}} x \, dx \, dy = \int_{R_{uv}} (u^2 - v)(4uv + 1) \, du \, dv$$

$$= \int_0^1 dv \int_0^1 (4u^3v - 4uv^2 + u^2 - v) \, du$$

$$= \int_0^1 \left(-2v^2 + \frac{1}{3}\right) dv = -\frac{1}{3}.$$

To understand why the change-of-variable formula works for a continuously differentiable vector function T, we need to know what effect T has on volume. We use the affine approximation to T that replaces TU near U_0 by $TU_0 + (d_{U_0}T)(U - U_0)$. The way in which T alters volume will be reflected in the way in which $d_{U_0}T$ alters volume. In fact, translation of a subset by the vector TU_0 leaves its volume unchanged, and the differential $d_{U_0}T$, being a linear transformation, changes volume in a particularly simple way. Indeed, under a linear transformation volumes get multiplied by a constant factor, and the factor of proportionality is just the absolute value of the determinant of the transformation. For suppose T is taken to be a linear transformation, and f is the constant function 1, that is, $fU = 1$ for all U in $\mathfrak{U}^n$. The change-of-variable theorem (Theorem 3.1) then implies

3.2 Theorem. If $\mathfrak{U}^n \xrightarrow{T} \mathfrak{R}^n$ is a linear transformation, then

$$V(TR) = \int_{TR} dV = \int_R |J| \, dV = |J| \, V(R).$$

The last step is valid because, for a linear transformation, the Jacobian determinant of the transformation is constant. Then $|J|$ can be taken outside the integral.

EXAMPLE 5. The transformation from $\mathfrak{U}$ to $\mathfrak{R}$ given by $x = 3u$ is linear. It is therefore its own differential (see Chapter 2, Section 4, Exercise 9) and has Jacobian determinant $J = 3$. It is clear from Figure 21 that lengths get multiplied by 3 under this transformation.

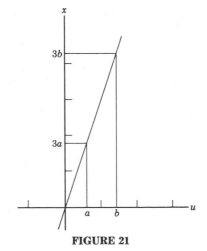

FIGURE 21

EXAMPLE 6. The transformation T from $\mathfrak{U}^2$ to $\mathfrak{R}^2$ given by

$$T\begin{pmatrix} u \\ v \end{pmatrix} = \begin{pmatrix} u^2 \\ u + v \end{pmatrix}$$

has as its differential at $U_0 = \begin{pmatrix} u_0 \\ v_0 \end{pmatrix} = \begin{pmatrix} 1 \\ 1 \end{pmatrix}$ the linear transformation

$$(d_{U_0}T)\begin{pmatrix} u \\ v \end{pmatrix} = \begin{pmatrix} 2u_0 & 0 \\ 1 & 1 \end{pmatrix}\begin{pmatrix} u \\ v \end{pmatrix} = \begin{pmatrix} 2 & 0 \\ 1 & 1 \end{pmatrix}\begin{pmatrix} u \\ v \end{pmatrix}.$$

Near

$$U_0 = \begin{pmatrix} 1 \\ 1 \end{pmatrix}$$

the function T is approximated by the affine transformation

$$A\begin{pmatrix} u \\ v \end{pmatrix} = T\begin{pmatrix} 1 \\ 1 \end{pmatrix} + (d_{U_0}T)\begin{pmatrix} u - 1 \\ v - 1 \end{pmatrix}$$

$$= \begin{pmatrix} 1 \\ 2 \end{pmatrix} + \begin{pmatrix} 2 & 0 \\ 1 & 1 \end{pmatrix}\begin{pmatrix} u - 1 \\ v - 1 \end{pmatrix} = \begin{pmatrix} 2u - 1 \\ u + v \end{pmatrix}.$$

The square R in the uv-plane in Figure 22 is carried by T onto the curved figure on the right. The affine approximation A carries R onto the parallelogram outlined with dashes. Notice that the area of the parallelogram is roughly equal to that of the curved figure. The exact area of the parallelo-

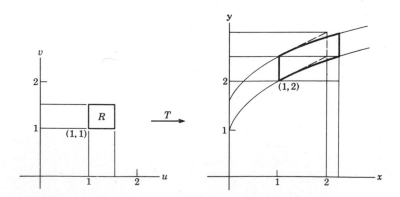

FIGURE 22

gram is easily computed to be $\frac{1}{2}$, twice the area of R. The important point is that the affine approximation to T doubles the area of the square, while T itself approximately doubles that area. The magnification factor, 2, is given by the Jacobian determinant of T at $U_0 = \begin{pmatrix} 1 \\ 1 \end{pmatrix}$. In fact

$$J = \begin{vmatrix} 2 & 0 \\ 1 & 1 \end{vmatrix} = 2.$$

To find the exact area of the image TR, we use the change-of-variable theorem. Since u is positive on R, the transformation T is one-one there. The inverse function is given explicitly by

$$T^{-1}\begin{pmatrix} x \\ y \end{pmatrix} = \begin{pmatrix} \sqrt{x} \\ y - \sqrt{x} \end{pmatrix},$$

so T is one-one. Moreover, the Jacobian determinant $J = 2u$ is positive on R. Hence,

$$A(TR) = \int_{TR} dA = \int_R |J|\, dA$$

$$= \int_1^{3/2} dv \int_1^{3/2} 2u\, du = \frac{1}{2} u^2 \Big]_1^{3/2} = \frac{5}{8}.$$

To understand the change-of-variable theorem itself, let T be a continuously differentiable transformation and consider the corresponding regions R and TR. A 2-dimensional example is illustrated in Figure 23. Decompose R into regions R_i by means of coordinate lines. Denoting

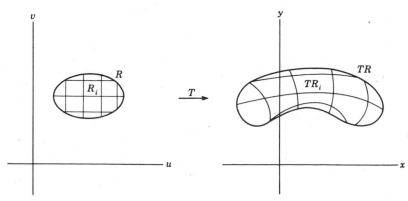

FIGURE 23

approximate equality by the symbol $\approx$, we have

$$\int_{TR} f \, dV = \sum_i \int_{TR_i} f \, dV \approx \sum_i f_i V(TR_i), \tag{3}$$

where the number f_i is a value assumed by the function f in TR_i. We assume that $f_i V(TR_i)$ is a reasonable approximation to $\int_{TR_i} f \, dV$. Next, approximate $V(TR_i)$ by $|J_i| V(R_i)$, where J_i is a value assumed by the Jacobian determinant of T in R_i. Thus we are led to the approximation

$$\sum_i f_i V(TR_i) \approx \sum_i f_i |J_i| V(R_i). \tag{4}$$

But the number f_i is equally well a value of $f \circ T$ in R_i, which we can write $(f \circ T)_i$, getting from Formulas (3) and (4)

$$\int_{TR} f \, dV \approx \sum_i (f \circ T)_i |J_i| V(R_i).$$

Finally, the last sum can be used to approximate $\int_R (f \circ T) |J| \, dV$. To make this argument precise is difficult, so the proof given in the Appendix follows other lines.

The above discussion shows that the Jacobian determinant can be interpreted as an approximate local magnification factor for volume. A one-one continuously differentiable transformation, looked at as a co-ordinate change, leads to another slightly different interpretation of J.

EXAMPLE 7. Polar coordinate curves in $\mathfrak{R}^2$ bound regions like S in Figure 24. Since the Jacobian determinant of the polar coordinate transformation

$$\begin{pmatrix} x \\ y \end{pmatrix} = \begin{pmatrix} r \cos \theta \\ r \sin \theta \end{pmatrix} = T \begin{pmatrix} r \\ \theta \end{pmatrix}$$

is

$$J = \begin{vmatrix} \cos \theta & -r \sin \theta \\ \sin \theta & r \cos \theta \end{vmatrix} = r,$$

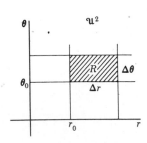 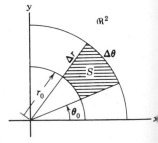

FIGURE 24

we expect an approximation to the shaded area $S = TR$ in the xy-plane to be $r_0 \, \Delta r \, \Delta\theta$. Computation of the exact area of S, using the change-of-variable theorem, gives

$$\int_S dA = \int_R r \, dA = \int_{r_0}^{r_0 + \Delta r} r \, dr \int_{\theta_0}^{\theta_0 + \Delta\theta} d\theta$$

$$= (\tfrac{1}{2}(r_0 + \Delta r)^2 - \tfrac{1}{2}r_0^2) \, \Delta\theta$$

$$= r_0 \, \Delta r \, \Delta\theta + \tfrac{1}{2}(\Delta r)^2 \, \Delta\theta$$

$$\approx r_0 \, \Delta r \, \Delta\theta \qquad \text{(for small } \Delta r, \, \Delta\theta \text{).}$$

Thus the significance of J in this case is that $J \, \Delta r \, \Delta\theta$ is an approximation to the area of a polar coordinate "rectangle," or region bounded by polar coordinate curves, with Δr and $\Delta\theta$ as the difference between pairs of values of r and θ.

EXAMPLE 8. Spherical coordinates are introduced in $\mathfrak{R}^3$ by means of the transformation

$$\begin{pmatrix} x \\ y \\ z \end{pmatrix} = \begin{pmatrix} r \sin \phi \cos \theta \\ r \sin \phi \sin \theta \\ r \cos \phi \end{pmatrix}.$$

Except for a notational change, the same transformation is considered in Example 3. The Jacobian determinant is $J = r^2 \sin \phi$. This suggests the approximation $r^2 \sin \phi \, \Delta r \, \Delta\phi \, \Delta\theta$ for the volume of the spherical coordinate "cube" C shown in Figure 25. The spherical ball with center at the origin

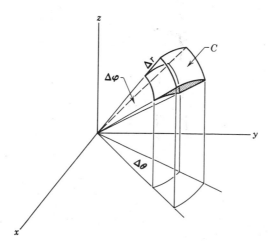

FIGURE 25

and radius 1 is in $\mathfrak{R}^3$ defined by $x^2 + y^2 + z^2 \leq 1$ and is denoted below by B_{xyz}. With respect to polar coordinates, the same ball is defined by the inequalities

$$0 \leq r \leq 1, \qquad 0 \leq \phi \leq \pi, \qquad 0 \leq \theta \leq 2\pi,$$

and is denoted below by $B_{r\phi\theta}$. Using the change-of-variable theorem, we compute the volume of the ball to be

$$V(B_{xyz}) = \int_{B_{xyz}} dx\, dy\, dz = \int_{B_{r\phi\theta}} r^2 \sin \phi\, dr\, d\phi\, d\theta$$

$$= \int_0^1 r^2\, dr \int_0^\pi \sin \phi\, d\phi \int_0^{2\pi} d\theta$$

$$= \frac{1}{3}(1+1)2\pi = \frac{4\pi}{3}.$$

Notice (as in Example 3) that both conditions (a) and (b) of Theorem 3.1 fail to hold on $B_{r\phi\theta}$. However, except on a subset of $B_{r\phi\theta}$ having zero volume the Jacobian $J = r^2 \sin \phi$ is positive and the coordinate transformation is one-one. The change-of-variable formula is therefore applicable.

EXAMPLE 9. We shall compute the volume of an n-dimensional spherical ball. The computation involves a knowledge of elementary formulas for the Γ-function, which we assume. Spherical coordinates in $\mathfrak{R}^n$ are defined by the transformation

$$x_1 = r \sin \theta_{n-1} \sin \theta_{n-2} \ldots \sin \theta_2 \sin \theta_1$$

$$x_2 = r \sin \theta_{n-1} \sin \theta_{n-2} \ldots \sin \theta_2 \cos \theta_1$$

$$x_3 = r \sin \theta_{n-1} \sin \theta_{n-2} \ldots \cos \theta_2$$

$$\cdot$$
$$\cdot$$
$$\cdot$$

$$x_{n-1} = r \sin \theta_{n-1} \cos \theta_{n-2}$$

$$x_n = r \cos \theta_{n-1}.$$

Then,

$$|J| = r^{n-1} |\sin^{n-2} \theta_{n-1} \sin^{n-3} \theta_{n-2} \ldots \sin^2 \theta_3 \sin \theta_2|.$$

(See Example 4, Section 9, Chapter 2). The n-dimensional spherical ball of radius a will be denoted by B_a. It is defined by the inequality $x_1^2 + \ldots + x_n^2 \leq a^2$. Then

$$V(B_a) = 2^n V(O_a),$$

where O_a is the part of the ball that lies in the first orthant of $\Re^n$, that is, the orthant for which $0 \leq \theta_i \leq \pi/2$, $i = 1, 2, \ldots, n - 1$. Applying the change-of-variable theorem, we obtain

$$V(B_a) = 2^n \int_{O_a} dx_1 \ldots dx_n$$

$$= 2^n \int_0^a r^{n-1} dr \int_0^{\pi/2} \sin^{n-2} \theta_{n-1} d\theta_{n-1} \ldots \int_0^{\pi/2} \sin \theta_2 d\theta_2 \int_0^{\pi/2} d\theta_1$$

$$= \frac{2^n a^n}{n} \int_0^{\pi/2} \sin^{n-2} \theta \, d\theta \ldots \int_0^{\pi/2} d\theta.$$

Now

$$\int_0^{\pi/2} \sin^N \theta \, d\theta = \int_0^1 \frac{x^N}{\sqrt{1 - x^2}} \, dx = \frac{1}{2} \int_0^1 x^{N/2 - 1/2} (1 - x)^{-1/2} \, dx$$

$$= \frac{1}{2} \frac{\Gamma\left(\frac{N}{2} + \frac{1}{2}\right)\Gamma\left(\frac{1}{2}\right)}{\Gamma\left(\frac{N}{2} + 1\right)} = \frac{\sqrt{\pi}}{2} \frac{\Gamma\left(\frac{N+1}{2}\right)}{\Gamma\left(\frac{N+2}{2}\right)}.$$

(See Burington's Tables, #367.) Then

$$V(B_a) = \frac{2^n a^n}{n} \left(\frac{\sqrt{\pi}}{2}\right)^{n-2} \frac{\Gamma\left(\frac{n-1}{2}\right)}{\Gamma\left(\frac{n}{2}\right)} \cdot \frac{\Gamma\left(\frac{n-2}{2}\right)}{\Gamma\left(\frac{n-1}{2}\right)} \cdot \ldots \cdot \frac{\Gamma(1)}{\Gamma\left(\frac{3}{2}\right)} \cdot \frac{\pi}{2}$$

$$= \frac{2a^n (\sqrt{\pi})^n}{n\Gamma\left(\frac{n}{2}\right)}.$$

For $n = 2$ and $n = 3$ we get the familiar formulas

$$V(B_a) = \frac{a^2(\sqrt{\pi})^2}{\Gamma(1)} = \pi a^2, \qquad n = 2,$$

and

$$V(B_a) = \frac{2a^3(\sqrt{\pi})^3}{3\Gamma\left(\frac{3}{2}\right)} = \frac{4}{3}\pi a^3, \qquad n = 3.*$$

* For an alternative method of computation see R. Courant, *Differential and Integral Calculus*, Interscience, 1936, vol. 2, p. 302.

EXERCISES

In applying the change-of-variable theorem, it is frequently hard to verify hypothesis (a), i.e., that T is one-one on R. A useful theorem is the following.* Let $\mathfrak{U}^2 \xrightarrow{T} \mathfrak{R}^2$ be a transformation and R a subset of the domain of T so that, with the exception of condition (a), the premises of Theorem 3.1 are satisfied. If the boundary of R is a simple, closed curve and T is one-one on the boundary, then T is one-one on all of R.

1. Let

$$\begin{pmatrix} x \\ y \end{pmatrix} = T \begin{pmatrix} u \\ v \end{pmatrix} = \begin{pmatrix} u^2 - v^2 \\ 2uv \end{pmatrix}.$$

(a) Sketch the image under T of the square in $\mathfrak{U}^2$ with vertices at $(1, 1)$, $(1, \frac{3}{2})$, $(\frac{3}{2}, 1)$, $(\frac{3}{2}, \frac{3}{2})$.

(b) Sketch the image under $d_{\binom{1}{1}} T$ of the square in part (a).

(c) Sketch the translate of the image found in part (b) by the vector

$$T \begin{pmatrix} 1 \\ 1 \end{pmatrix} - (d_{\binom{1}{1}} T) \begin{pmatrix} 1 \\ 1 \end{pmatrix}.$$

Verify that this is the image of the square under the affine approxima-

tion to T at $\begin{pmatrix} 1 \\ 1 \end{pmatrix}$.

(d) Find the area of the region sketched in (c).   [*Ans.* 2.]
(e) Find the area of the region sketched in (a).   [*Ans.* $\frac{19}{6}$.]

2. Let

$$\begin{pmatrix} x \\ y \end{pmatrix} = T \begin{pmatrix} u \\ v \end{pmatrix} = \begin{pmatrix} u \cos v \\ u \sin v \end{pmatrix}.$$

(a) Sketch the image under T of the square S with vertices at $(0, 0)$, $(0, \pi/2)$, $(\pi/2, 0)$, and $(\pi/2, \pi/2)$.

(b) Sketch the image under $d_{\binom{\pi/2}{0}} T$ of the square S. What is the area of the image?

(c) Sketch the image of S under the affine approximation to T at $(\pi/4, \pi/4)$. What is the area of the image?

(d) What is the area of the region sketched in (a)?

3. (a) If $x = \phi(u) = u^3$ find $d_0\phi$ and $d_1\phi$.

(b) What is the length of the image of the interval $[0, 1]$ under each of the transformations $d_0\phi$ and $d_1\phi$?

* See D. V. Widder, *Advanced Calculus*, 2nd ed., Prentice-Hall, 1961, p. 244.

4. Let

$$T\begin{pmatrix} u \\ v \end{pmatrix} = \begin{pmatrix} u \cos v \\ u \sin v \end{pmatrix}.$$

Show that $d_{\binom{u}{v}} T$ transforms a rectangle of area A into a region having area uA.

5. Compute the area of the image of the rectangle in the uv-plane with vertices at $(0, 0)$, $(0, 1)$, $(2, 0)$ and $(2, 1)$ under the transformation

$$\begin{pmatrix} x \\ y \end{pmatrix} = \begin{pmatrix} 2 & 3 \\ 2 & 1 \end{pmatrix}\begin{pmatrix} u \\ v \end{pmatrix}.$$ $[Ans. 8.]$

6. Consider the transformation T defined by

$$\begin{pmatrix} x \\ y \end{pmatrix} = T\begin{pmatrix} u \\ v \end{pmatrix} = \begin{pmatrix} u^2 - v^2 \\ 2uv \end{pmatrix}.$$

Let R_{uv} be the quarter of the unit disc lying in the first quadrant, i.e., $u^2 + v^2 \leq 1, u \geq 0, v \geq 0$.

(a) Sketch the image region $R_{xy} = TR_{uv}$.

(b) Compute $\displaystyle\int_{R_{xy}} \frac{dx\,dy}{\sqrt{x^2 + y^2}}$. $[Ans. \pi.]$

7. Let the transformation from the uv-plane to the xy-plane be defined by $x = u + v, y = u^2 - v$. Let R_{uv} be the region bounded by (1) u-axis, (2) v-axis, (3) the line $u + v = 2$.

(a) Find and sketch the image region R_{xy}.

(b) Compute the integral

$$\int_{R_{xy}} \frac{dx\,dy}{\sqrt{1 + 4x + 4y}}.$$ $[Ans. 2.]$

8. Let a transformation of the uv-plane to the xy-plane be given by

$$x = u, \qquad y = v(1 + u^2)$$

and let R_{uv} be the rectangular region given by $0 \leq u \leq 3$ and $0 \leq v \leq 2$.

(a) Find and sketch the image region R_{xy}.

(b) Find $\dfrac{\partial(x, y)}{\partial(u, v)}$.

(c) Transform $\int_{R_{xy}} x\,dx\,dy$ to an integral over R_{uv} and compute either one of them. $[Ans. \frac{99}{2}.]$

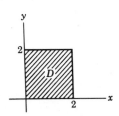

9. The transformation $u = x^2 - y^2$, $v = 2xy$ maps the region D (see sketch) onto a region R in the uv-plane and is one-one on D.

(a) Find R.

(b) Compute $\int_R 1 \ du \ dv$ by integrating directly over R, then by using the transformation formulas to integrate over D. $\left[Ans. \ \frac{128}{3}.\right]$

(c) Compute $\int_R v \ du \ dv$ both directly and by using the change-of-variable theorem. $\left[Ans. \ 128.\right]$

10. Let a transformation from the xy-plane to the uv-plane be given by

$$u = x$$

$$v = y(1 + 2x).$$

(a) What happens to horizontal lines in the xy-plane?

(b) If D is the rectangular region

$$0 \le x \le 3$$

$$1 \le y \le 3,$$

find the image region R of D.

(c) Find

$$\int_R du \ dv, \qquad \int_R v \ dv \ du \quad \text{and} \quad \int_R u \ dv \ du$$

by direct integration, then by reducing them to integrals over D.

[Ans. 24, 228, 45.]

11. Compute the area bounded by the polar coordinate curves $\theta = 0$, $\theta = \pi/4$, and $r = \theta^2$. $\left[Ans. \ \pi^5/2^{10} \cdot 10.\right]$

12. Find the area bounded by the lemniscate $(x^2 + y^2)^2 = 2a^2(x^2 - y^2)$ by changing to polar coordinates. $\left[Ans. \ 2a^2.\right]$

13. Compute the volume of the ellipsoid

$$\frac{x^2}{a^2} + \frac{y^2}{b^2} + \frac{z^2}{c^2} \le 1.$$

[Use the transformation

$$\begin{pmatrix} x \\ y \\ z \end{pmatrix} = \begin{pmatrix} au \\ bv \\ cw \end{pmatrix}$$

to transform the sphere $u^2 + v^2 + w^2 \le 1$ onto the ellipsoid. Assume the volume of the sphere to be known.]

14. Evaluate the integral of $f(x, y, z) = a$ over the hemisphere $x^2 + y^2 + z^2 \leq 1$, $x \geq 0$ by changing to spherical coordinates. $[Ans. \frac{2}{3}\pi a.]$

15. (a) Compute the Jacobian of the cylindrical coordinate transformation

$$\begin{pmatrix} x \\ y \\ z \end{pmatrix} = \begin{pmatrix} r\cos\theta \\ r\sin\theta \\ z \end{pmatrix}.$$

(b) Use cylindrical coordinates to compute

$$\int_{x^2+y^2\leq 1, 0\leq z\leq 1.} x^2 \, dx \, dy \, dz.$$

16. Prove that the transformation

$$x_1 = u_1$$

$$x_2 = u_1 + u_2$$

$$x_3 = u_1 + u_2 + u_3$$

$$\cdot$$
$$\cdot$$
$$\cdot$$

$$x_n = u_1 + u_2 + \ldots + u_n$$

leaves volumes of corresponding regions unchanged.

17. Use n-dimensional spherical coordinates to compute the integral of $x_1^2 + x_2^2 + \ldots + x_n^2$ over the ball $x_1^2 + x_2^2 + \ldots + x_n^2 \leq a^2$.

4. ARC LENGTH

Once we have a definition of length for vectors, we can define the length of a curve. More precisely, we shall define the arc length of a curve C that is parametrically defined by a continuously differentiable function $\mathcal{R} \xrightarrow{f} \mathcal{R}^n$ with domain the closed interval $[a, b]$ of real numbers. Corresponding to any set of $N + 1$ numbers $\{t_k\}$ satisfying $a = t_0 < t_1 < \ldots < t_N = b$, there are points X_k on C such that $X_k = f(t_k)$. The straight-line distance between successive points is equal to $|X_k - X_{k-1}|$. Hence the sum

$$\sum_{k=1}^{N} |X_k - X_{k-1}| \qquad (1)$$

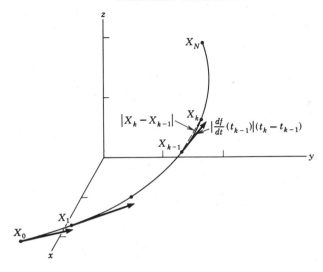

FIGURE 26

is an approximation to the arc length of C. Since

$$X_k - X_{k-1} = f(t_k) - f(t_{k-1}) = (d_{t_{k-1}}f)(t_k - t_{k-1}) + R,$$

where $\lim\limits_{t_k \to t_{k-1}} \dfrac{R}{|t_k - t_{k-1}|} = 0$, the length of the tangent vector,

$$(d_{t_{k-1}}f)(t_k - t_{k-1}) = (t_k - t_{k-1})\frac{df}{dt}(t_{k-1})$$

is an approximation to $|X_k - X_{k-1}|$. We can therefore also take the sum of the lengths of these vectors,

$$\sum_{k=1}^{N} \left| \frac{df}{dt}(t_{k-1}) \right| (t_k - t_{k-1}),$$

as an approximation to the length of C. Typical tangent vectors are shown in Figure 26 for a curve in $\mathfrak{R}^3$. The assumption that f is continuously differentiable means that the function $|df/dt|$ is continuous on $[a, b]$. Furthermore, the set of points $\{t_k\}$ constitutes a grid G covering the interval with mesh $m(G) = \max\limits_{1 \le k \le N} \{t_k - t_{k-1}\}$. It follows that, for every sequence of grids with mesh tending to zero,

$$\lim_{m(G) \to 0} \sum_{k=1}^{N} \left| \frac{df}{dt}(t_{k-1}) \right| (t_k - t_{k-1}) = \int_a^b \left| \frac{df}{dt} \right| dt.$$

For this reason, the **arc length** of C is defined to be

$$l(C) = \int_a^b \left| \frac{df}{dt} \right| dt, \tag{2}$$

whenever f is continuously differentiable.

A curve in $\Re^n$ will usually be given by coordinate functions. Thus if C is defined for $a \leq t \leq b$ by

$$f(t) = \begin{pmatrix} f_1(t) \\ \cdot \\ \cdot \\ \cdot \\ f_n(t) \end{pmatrix}, \quad \text{then} \quad \frac{df}{dt}(t) = \begin{pmatrix} \dfrac{df_1}{dt}(t) \\ \cdot \\ \cdot \\ \cdot \\ \dfrac{df_n}{dt}(t) \end{pmatrix},$$

and

$$l(C) = \int_a^b \sqrt{\left(\frac{df_1}{dt}\right)^2 + \ldots + \left(\frac{df_n}{dt}\right)^2} \, dt.$$

EXAMPLE 1. The curve in $\Re^3$ defined by

$$f(t) = \begin{pmatrix} t \\ \cos t \\ \sin t \end{pmatrix}, \quad 0 \leq t \leq 1,$$

has length

$$\int_0^1 \sqrt{1^2 + (-\sin t)^2 + (\cos t)^2} \, dt = \sqrt{2}.$$

EXAMPLE 2. The plane curve defined by

$$f(t) = \begin{pmatrix} t \\ |t| \end{pmatrix}, \quad -1 \leq t \leq 1,$$

is shown in Figure 27. Although this curve is not continuously differentiable, it can be split naturally into two continuously differentiable pieces and its arc length

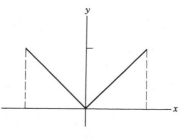

FIGURE 27

can still be defined to be

$$\int_{-1}^{1} \left| \frac{df}{dt} \right| dt = \int_{-1}^{0} \sqrt{1^2 + (-1)^2} \, dt + \int_{0}^{1} \sqrt{1^2 + 1^2} \, dt = 2\sqrt{2}.$$

EXAMPLE 3. The graph of $y = f(x)$, $a \leq x \leq b$, is a curve C defined parametrically by

$$\begin{pmatrix} x \\ y \end{pmatrix} = \begin{pmatrix} x \\ f(x) \end{pmatrix}, \qquad a \leq x \leq b.$$

If f' is continuous, the length of C is

$$l(C) = \int_{a}^{b} \sqrt{1 + (f')^2} \, dx.$$

If the natural coordinates $x_1, \ldots, x_n$ in $\mathfrak{R}^n$ are replaced by curvilinear coordinates $u_1, \ldots, u_n$, then a curve C in $\mathfrak{R}^n$ can be described by an equation of the form

$$\begin{pmatrix} u_1 \\ \cdot \\ \cdot \\ \cdot \\ u_n \end{pmatrix} = \begin{pmatrix} u_1(t) \\ \cdot \\ \cdot \\ \cdot \\ u_n(t) \end{pmatrix}, \qquad a \leq t \leq b,$$

where the curve itself is defined parametrically in $\mathfrak{R}^n$ by the function

$$f(t) = \begin{pmatrix} x_1(u_1(t), \ldots, u_n(t)) \\ \cdot \\ \cdot \\ \cdot \\ x_n(u_1(t), \ldots, u_n(t)) \end{pmatrix}, \qquad a \leq t \leq b.$$

According to Equation 7 of Section 9, Chapter 2, the length of the tangent vector $\dfrac{df}{dt}$ is

$$\left| \frac{df}{dt} \right| = \sqrt{\sum_{i,j=1}^{n} g_{ij} \frac{du_i}{dt} \frac{du_j}{dt}},$$

so

$$l(C) = \int_{a}^{b} \sqrt{\sum_{i,j=1}^{n} g_{ij} \frac{du_i}{dt} \frac{du_j}{dt}} \, dt. \tag{3}$$

EXAMPLE 4. If (r, ϕ, θ) are spherical coordinates in $\mathcal{R}^3$, the length of a curve C defined by an equation

$$\begin{pmatrix} r \\ \phi \\ \theta \end{pmatrix} = \begin{pmatrix} r(t) \\ \phi(t) \\ \theta(t) \end{pmatrix}, \qquad a \le t \le b,$$

can be computed from (3). The differential of the coordinate transformation

$$\begin{pmatrix} x \\ y \\ z \end{pmatrix} = \begin{pmatrix} r \sin \phi \cos \theta \\ r \sin \phi \sin \theta \\ r \cos \phi \end{pmatrix}$$

is defined by the matrix

$$\begin{pmatrix} \sin \phi \cos \theta & r \cos \phi \cos \theta & -r \sin \phi \sin \theta \\ \sin \phi \sin \theta & r \cos \phi \sin \theta & r \sin \phi \cos \theta \\ \cos \phi & -r \sin \phi & 0 \end{pmatrix}.$$

The function g_{ij} is the inner product of the ith and the jth column of the preceding matrix. Hence

$$\begin{pmatrix} g_{11} & g_{12} & g_{13} \\ g_{21} & g_{22} & g_{23} \\ g_{31} & g_{32} & g_{33} \end{pmatrix} = \begin{pmatrix} 1 & 0 & 0 \\ 0 & r^2 & 0 \\ 0 & 0 & r^2 \sin^2 \phi \end{pmatrix}.$$

And so Equation (2) yields

$$l(C) = \int_a^b \sqrt{\left(\frac{dr}{dt}\right)^2 + r^2 \left(\frac{d\phi}{dt}\right)^2 + r^2 \sin^2 \phi \left(\frac{d\theta}{dt}\right)^2}\, dt.$$

In particular, the curve λ defined by

$$\begin{pmatrix} r \\ \phi \\ \theta \end{pmatrix} = \begin{pmatrix} 1 \\ t \\ t \end{pmatrix}, \qquad 0 \le t \le \frac{\pi}{2}$$

has length

$$l(\lambda) = \int_0^{\pi/2} \sqrt{1 + \sin^2 t}\, dt.$$

This integral cannot be computed by means of an elementary indefinite integral. It can, however, be approximated by simple methods. Or it can be reduced to a standard elliptic integral as follows. Replacing t by $\pi/2 - \theta$, and using $\cos^2 \theta = 1 - \sin^2 \theta$, we get

$$\int_0^{\pi/2} \sqrt{1 + \sin^2 t}\, dt = \sqrt{2} \int_0^{\pi/2} \sqrt{1 - \tfrac{1}{2} \sin^2 \theta}\, d\theta.$$

The latter integral appears in a tabulation,* and we estimate

$$l(\lambda) \approx \sqrt{2}\,(1.35) \approx 1.91.$$

Arc length can also be defined for some curves that are not continuously differentiable in pieces.†

EXERCISES

1. Find the arc length of the curves

(a) $\begin{pmatrix} x \\ y \end{pmatrix} = \begin{pmatrix} t \\ \ln \cos t \end{pmatrix}$, $0 \le t \le 1$.   [*Ans.* ln (sec 1 + tan 1).]

(b) $\begin{pmatrix} x \\ y \end{pmatrix} = \begin{pmatrix} t^2 \\ \tfrac{2}{3}t^3 - \tfrac{1}{2}t \end{pmatrix}$, $0 \le t \le 2$.   [*Ans.* $\tfrac{19}{3}$.]

(c) $y = x^{3/2}$, $0 \le x \le 5$.

(d) $f(t) = \begin{pmatrix} 6t^2 \\ 4\sqrt{2}t^3 \\ 3t^4 \end{pmatrix}$, $-1 \le t \le 2$.   [*Ans.* 81.]

2. Suppose a curve C in $\Re^n$ is parametrically defined by two continuously differentiable functions,

$$f(t), \qquad a \le t \le b.$$

$$g(s), \qquad \alpha \le s \le \beta.$$

These functions are called **equivalent** parametrizations if there exists a continuously differentiable function ϕ such that

$$a = \phi(\alpha) \quad \text{and} \quad b = \phi(\beta).$$

$$(f \bigcirc \phi)(s) = g(s), \qquad \alpha \le s \le \beta.$$

$$\phi'(s) > 0, \qquad \alpha \le s \le \beta.$$

---

* See, for example, R. S. Burington, *Handbook of Mathematical Tables and Formulas*, Handbook Publishers, 1956, p. 279.

† See R. C. Buck, *Advanced Calculus*, McGraw-Hill, 1956, p. 258.

(a) Prove that equivalent parametrizations of C assign the same arc length to C.

(b) Show that

$$\begin{pmatrix} x \\ y \end{pmatrix} = \begin{pmatrix} \cos t \\ \sin t \end{pmatrix}, \qquad 0 \le t \le \frac{\pi}{2},$$

and

$$\begin{pmatrix} x \\ y \end{pmatrix} = \begin{pmatrix} \dfrac{1 - s^2}{1 + s^2} \\[2mm] \dfrac{2s}{1 + s^2} \end{pmatrix}, \qquad 0 \le s \le 1,$$

are equivalent parametrizations of a curve and verify that both give the same arc length.

3. If the curve $X = f(t)$ is thought of as having time as parameter, then it describes the motion of a point in $\mathfrak{R}^n$. The vector $(df/dt)(t)$ is called the **velocity** of the point at time t, and its length $|(df/dt)(t)|$ is the **speed**. The second derivative $(d^2f/dt^2)(t)$ is called the **acceleration** of the point at time t, and $|(d^2f/dt^2)(t)|$ is simply the magnitude of the acceleration. Sketch the velocity and acceleration vectors together with the curves at the indicated times.

(a) $\begin{pmatrix} x \\ y \end{pmatrix} = \begin{pmatrix} t \\ e^t \end{pmatrix}$ at $t = 0$.   (b) $\begin{pmatrix} x \\ y \\ z \end{pmatrix} = \begin{pmatrix} t \\ t^2 \\ t^3 \end{pmatrix}$ at $t = 0$.

4. If it should happen that for the curve C defined by

$$f(s), \qquad 0 \le s \le b, \qquad s = \int_0^s \left| \frac{df}{ds} \right| ds,$$

then C is said to be parametrized by arc length s.

(a) Show that the curve

$$\begin{pmatrix} x \\ y \end{pmatrix} = \begin{pmatrix} \cos s \\ \sin s \end{pmatrix}, \qquad 0 \le s \le 2\pi$$

is parametrized by arc length.

(b) Prove that if C is parametrized by arc length, then $\left| \dfrac{df}{ds} \right| = 1$.

(c) Sketch the velocity and acceleration vectors together with the curve

$$\begin{pmatrix} x \\ y \end{pmatrix} = \begin{pmatrix} \cos s \\ \sin s \end{pmatrix} \qquad \text{at} \quad s = \pi/2.$$

(d) Prove that if C is parametrized by arc length, then considered as a motion the speed is 1 and the velocity and acceleration vectors are perpendicular. To prove the second statement, use the fact that

$$\frac{d}{dt}(f \cdot g) = \left(\frac{df}{dt} \cdot g\right) + \left(f \cdot \frac{dg}{dt}\right).$$

5. (a) Find the formula for the arc length of a curve determined in plane polar coordinates by an equation of the form

$$\begin{pmatrix} r \\ \theta \end{pmatrix} = \begin{pmatrix} r(t) \\ \theta(t) \end{pmatrix}, \quad a \le t \le b.$$

(b) Compute the length of the curve $\begin{pmatrix} r \\ \theta \end{pmatrix} = \begin{pmatrix} 2t \\ t \end{pmatrix}$, $0 \le t \le 2$.

$$[Ans.\ 2\sqrt{5} + \log(2 + \sqrt{5}).]$$

(c) Sketch the curve.

6. (a) Set up the integral for the arc length of the ellipse

$$\begin{pmatrix} x \\ y \end{pmatrix} = \begin{pmatrix} a \cos t \\ b \sin t \end{pmatrix}, \quad 0 \le t \le 2\pi.$$

(b) Show that the computation of the integral of part (a) can be reduced to the computation of a standard elliptic integral of the form

$$\int_0^{\pi/2} \sqrt{1 - k^2 \sin^2 \theta}\ d\theta.$$

(c) Find an approximate value for the arc length of the ellipse in (a) with $a = 1$ and $b = 2$. $[Ans.\ 9.7.]$

7. An equation

$$\begin{pmatrix} u \\ v \end{pmatrix} = \begin{pmatrix} u(t) \\ v(t) \end{pmatrix}, \quad a \le t \le b,$$

determines a curve c on the conical surface in $\Re^3$

$$\begin{pmatrix} x \\ y \\ z \end{pmatrix} = \begin{pmatrix} u \cos v \sin \alpha \\ u \sin v \sin \alpha \\ u \cos \alpha \end{pmatrix}, \quad \begin{cases} 0 \le u \le \infty, \\ 0 \le v \le 2\pi, \end{cases}$$

where α is fixed, $0 < \alpha < \pi/2$. Find the general formula for the arc length of c.

8. Let c be a continuously differentiable curve with end-points P_1 and P_2. Let s be the straight-line segment $P_1 + t(P_2 - P_1)$, $0 \leq t \leq 1$, joining the end-points of c. Prove that $l(s) \leq l(c)$.

5. SURFACE AREA

Before defining surface area, we shall consider a special area problem, the solution to which will be a guide in making the general definition. Let $X_0 = (a_1, a_2, a_3)$ and $Y_0 = (b_1, b_2, b_3)$ be two vectors in $\mathfrak{R}^3$. The vectors X_0 and Y_0 span a parallelogram P as illustrated in Figure 28. The 2-

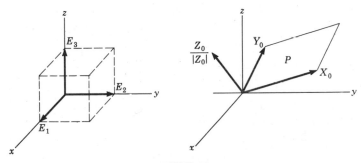

FIGURE 28

dimensional area of P is something that we have not yet defined, unless P happens to be in one of the coordinate planes, in which case $A(P)$ is the double integral over P of the function identically equal to 1 on P. In order to extend $A(P)$ in a way consistent with previously defined areas and volumes we can define the **area of** P to be the volume of the box of height 1 having P as its base. This definition applies just as well to the $(n-1)$-dimensional volume of a parallelogram spanned by $(n-1)$ vectors in $\mathfrak{R}^n$. We now derive a computational formula for $A(P)$.

5.1 Theorem. The 2-dimensional area of the parallelogram P spanned by

$$X_0 = \begin{pmatrix} a_1 \\ a_2 \\ a_3 \end{pmatrix} \quad \text{and} \quad Y_0 = \begin{pmatrix} b_1 \\ b_2 \\ b_3 \end{pmatrix}$$

is equal to

$$A(P) = \sqrt{ \begin{vmatrix} a_2 & b_2 \\ a_3 & b_3 \end{vmatrix}^2 + \begin{vmatrix} a_3 & b_3 \\ a_1 & b_1 \end{vmatrix}^2 + \begin{vmatrix} a_1 & b_1 \\ a_2 & b_2 \end{vmatrix}^2 } \tag{1}$$

Proof. The proof generalizes easily to a parallelogram in $\mathfrak{R}^n$. Direct computation shows that the right-hand side of the last equation is zero if and only if X_0 and Y_0 are linearly dependent (see Exercise 4). We therefore assume that X_0 and Y_0 are independent, for if not, both sides of Equation (1) are zero. The vector Z_0 with coordinates

$$(c_1,\ c_2,\ c_3) = \left(\begin{vmatrix} a_2 & b_2 \\ a_3 & b_3 \end{vmatrix},\ \begin{vmatrix} a_3 & b_3 \\ a_1 & b_1 \end{vmatrix},\ \begin{vmatrix} a_1 & b_1 \\ a_2 & b_2 \end{vmatrix} \right)$$

is not zero and is perpendicular to both X_0 and Y_0. For example,

$$X_0 \cdot Z_0 = a_1 \begin{vmatrix} a_2 & b_2 \\ a_3 & b_3 \end{vmatrix} + a_2 \begin{vmatrix} a_3 & b_3 \\ a_1 & b_1 \end{vmatrix} + a_3 \begin{vmatrix} a_1 & b_1 \\ a_2 & b_2 \end{vmatrix} = \begin{vmatrix} a_1 & a_1 & b_1 \\ a_2 & a_2 & b_2 \\ a_3 & a_3 & b_3 \end{vmatrix},$$

and the last determinant is zero because two columns are the same. Thus the box of height 1 having P as base is spanned by the vectors X_0, Y_0, and $Z_0/|Z_0|$. *Furthermore, the length of Z_0 is just the number that we wish to prove is equal to $A(P)$.* Now consider the linear transformation $\mathfrak{R}^3 \xrightarrow{L} \mathfrak{R}^3$ defined on the natural basis vectors E_1, E_2, E_3 so that

$$LE_1 = X_0, \qquad LE_2 = Y_0, \qquad LE_3 = Z_0/|Z_0|.$$

The matrix of L is

$$\begin{pmatrix} a_1 & b_1 & c_1/|Z_0| \\ a_2 & b_2 & c_2/|Z_0| \\ a_3 & b_3 & c_3/|Z_0| \end{pmatrix}.$$

Because of the linearity of L the interior of the box B spanned by E_1, E_2, and E_3 is transformed by L exactly onto the interior of the box LB whose volume we want to find. By Theorem 3.2, a corollary of the change-of-variable theorem, we get

$$V(LB) = |J| V(B) \tag{2}$$

where J is the determinant of the matrix of the transformation L. But $V(B) = 1$, and we can directly compute J to be

$$J = \frac{1}{|Z_0|} (c_1^2 + c_2^2 + c_3^2) = \frac{Z_0 \cdot Z_0}{|Z_0|} = |Z_0|.$$

Then, from Equation (2),

$$V(LB) = |Z_0|,$$

which proves Theorem 5.1, because $V(LB)$ is the area of P.

The formula just derived will now be used to justify the following definition of surface area. Let a surface S be defined parametrically by a continuously differentiable function.

$$f\begin{pmatrix} u \\ v \end{pmatrix} = \begin{pmatrix} x(u, v) \\ y(u, v) \\ z(u, v) \end{pmatrix},$$

where the domain of f is a bounded set M in $\mathfrak{R}^2$. The **area of** S is defined to be

$$A(S) = \int_M \sqrt{\left(\frac{\partial(y, z)}{\partial(u, v)}\right)^2 + \left(\frac{\partial(z, x)}{\partial(u, v)}\right)^2 + \left(\frac{\partial(x, y)}{\partial(u, v)}\right)^2} \, du \, dv \qquad (3)$$

We shall cut S into pieces and approximate the pieces with bits of tangent plane to S. To be specific, we cut S along coordinate curves determined by setting $u = $ constant and $v = $ constant. Then, corresponding to a point $U_0 = (u_0, v_0)$ in M, we have, passing through the point fU_0 on S, the curves given parametrically by

$$\begin{pmatrix} x \\ y \\ z \end{pmatrix} = \begin{pmatrix} x(u_0, t) \\ y(u_0, t) \\ z(u_0, t) \end{pmatrix} \quad \text{and} \quad \begin{pmatrix} x \\ y \\ z \end{pmatrix} = \begin{pmatrix} x(t, v_0) \\ y(t, v_0) \\ z(t, v_0) \end{pmatrix}.$$

Suppose also that two nearby coordinate curves pass through $f(U_0 + \Delta U)$, where $\Delta U = (\Delta u, \Delta v)$, $\Delta u > 0$, $\Delta v > 0$. Then all four coordinate curves together determine the edges of a region on S. The situation is illustrated in Figure 29. The tangent plane to S at fU_0 is defined parametrically by the affine approximation

$$X = fU_0 + (d_{U_0}f)(U - U_0).$$

If we set $U_1 = (u_0 + \Delta u, v_0)$ and $U_2 = (u_0, v_0 + \Delta v)$, we get as corresponding vectors in the tangent plane

$$C_1 = (d_{U_0}f)(U_1 - U_0) \quad \text{and} \quad C_2 = (d_{U_0}f)(U_2 - U_0).$$

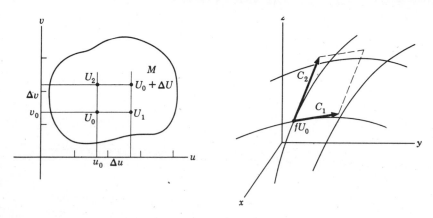

FIGURE 29

The vectors C_1 and C_2 are tangent to the coordinate curves $v = v_0$ and $u = u_0$ respectively. Since $U_1 - U_0 = (\Delta u, 0)$ and $U_2 - U_0 = (0, \Delta v)$, we have

$$C_1 = \begin{vmatrix} \dfrac{\partial x}{\partial u} U_0 \\[2ex] \dfrac{\partial y}{\partial u} U_0 \\[2ex] \dfrac{\partial z}{\partial u} U_0 \end{vmatrix} \Delta u \quad \text{and} \quad C_2 = \begin{vmatrix} \dfrac{\partial x}{\partial v} U_0 \\[2ex] \dfrac{\partial y}{\partial v} U_0 \\[2ex] \dfrac{\partial z}{\partial v} U_0 \end{vmatrix} \Delta v.$$

The vectors C_1 and C_2 span a parallelogram, and it is this parallelogram that we use to approximate the area of the piece of surface bounded by the four coordinate curves. By Equation (1), the area of the parallelogram spanned by C_1 and C_2 is

$$A_0 = \left[\begin{vmatrix} \dfrac{\partial y}{\partial u} & \dfrac{\partial y}{\partial v} \\[2ex] \dfrac{\partial z}{\partial u} & \dfrac{\partial z}{\partial v} \end{vmatrix}^2 + \begin{vmatrix} \dfrac{\partial z}{\partial u} & \dfrac{\partial z}{\partial v} \\[2ex] \dfrac{\partial x}{\partial u} & \dfrac{\partial x}{\partial v} \end{vmatrix}^2 + \begin{vmatrix} \dfrac{\partial x}{\partial u} & \dfrac{\partial x}{\partial v} \\[2ex] \dfrac{\partial y}{\partial u} & \dfrac{\partial y}{\partial v} \end{vmatrix}^2 \right]^{1/2} \Delta u\, \Delta v$$

$$= \sqrt{\left(\frac{\partial(y, z)}{\partial(u, v)} \right)^2 + \left(\frac{\partial(z, x)}{\partial(u, v)} \right)^2 + \left(\frac{\partial(x, y)}{\partial(u, v)} \right)^2}\ \Delta u\, \Delta v,$$

where all the partial derivatives are evaluated at U_0. Now cover the set M by a grid with points of intersection in M at $U_0, U_1, \ldots, U_N$. The image curves of the grid lines will cut S along curves that determine the edges of pieces of surface in S. The same kind of tangent approximation that was at fU_0 can be made at $fU_1, \ldots, fU_N$. The sum of the approximating areas is

$$\sum_{k=1}^{N} \sqrt{\left(\frac{\partial(y, z)}{\partial(u, v)} U_k\right)^2 + \left(\frac{\partial(z, x)}{\partial(u, v)} U_k\right)^2 + \left(\frac{\partial(x, y)}{\partial(u, v)} U_k\right)^2} \, \Delta u_k \, \Delta v_k.$$

Since the partial derivatives that occur in the sum are assumed to be continuous functions of U in M, the sum converges, as the mesh of the grid tends to zero, to the integral (3). We therefore define that integral to be the surface area.

EXAMPLE 1. Let

$$f\begin{pmatrix} u \\ v \end{pmatrix} = \begin{pmatrix} u \\ v \\ u + v \end{pmatrix} \quad \text{in } M: \ 0 \leq u \leq 1, 0 \leq v \leq 1.$$

The matrix of $d_{(u,v)} f$ is

$$\begin{pmatrix} 1 & 0 \\ 0 & 1 \\ 1 & 1 \end{pmatrix}.$$

And

$$A(S) = \int_M \sqrt{\begin{vmatrix} 0 & 1 \\ 1 & 1 \end{vmatrix}^2 + \begin{vmatrix} 1 & 1 \\ 1 & 0 \end{vmatrix}^2 + \begin{vmatrix} 1 & 0 \\ 0 & 1 \end{vmatrix}^2} \, du \, dv$$

$$= \int_0^1 du \int_0^1 \sqrt{3} \, dv = \sqrt{3}.$$

The area can be computed directly by noticing that S is a parallelogram spanned by the vectors $(1, 0, 1)$ and $(0, 1, 1)$. Then Equation (1) gives $A(S) = \sqrt{3}$. The sets M and S are shown in Figure 30.

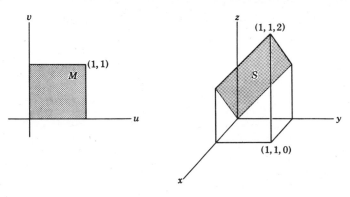

FIGURE 30

EXAMPLE 2. Let

$$f\begin{pmatrix} u \\ v \end{pmatrix} = \begin{pmatrix} u \cos v \\ u \sin v \\ v \end{pmatrix} \quad \text{with } M: \quad 0 \le u \le 1, 0 \le v \le 3\pi.$$

This surface has been discussed in Example 7, Section 1, and Example 1, Section 5, of Chapter 2. The matrix of $d_{(u,v)}f$ is

$$\begin{pmatrix} \cos v & -u \sin v \\ \sin v & u \cos v \\ 0 & 1 \end{pmatrix},$$

and

$$A(S) = \int_M \sqrt{\sin^2 v + \cos^2 v + u^2} \, du \, dv$$

$$= \int_0^1 \sqrt{1 + u^2} \, du \int_0^{3\pi} dv$$

$$= \frac{3}{2}\pi(\sqrt{2} + \ln(1 + \sqrt{2})).$$

A surface may be defined explicitly as the graph of a function $f(x, y)$ with (x, y) in some region R of $\Re^2$. We can change the representation into parametric form by writing

$$\begin{pmatrix} x \\ y \\ z \end{pmatrix} = \begin{pmatrix} x \\ y \\ f(x, y) \end{pmatrix} \qquad \text{with } (x, y) \text{ in } R.$$

The Jacobian matrix is

$$\begin{pmatrix} 1 & 0 \\ 0 & 1 \\ \dfrac{\partial f}{\partial x} & \dfrac{\partial f}{\partial y} \end{pmatrix}.$$

The area formula is therefore

$$A(S) = \int_R \sqrt{\begin{vmatrix} 1 & 0 \\ 0 & 1 \end{vmatrix}^2 + \begin{vmatrix} 0 & 1 \\ \dfrac{\partial f}{\partial x} & \dfrac{\partial f}{\partial y} \end{vmatrix}^2 + \begin{vmatrix} 1 & 0 \\ \dfrac{\partial f}{\partial x} & \dfrac{\partial f}{\partial y} \end{vmatrix}^2} \; dx \, dy.$$

$$= \int_R \sqrt{1 + \left(\frac{\partial f}{\partial x}\right)^2 + \left(\frac{\partial f}{\partial y}\right)^2} \; dx \, dy. \tag{4}$$

EXAMPLE 3. Let $z = x^2 + y^2$ define a surface S over the disc D: $x^2 + y^2 < 1$. Then, according to Equation (4),

$$A(S) = \int_D \sqrt{1 + (2x)^2 + (2y)^2} \; dx \, dy.$$

Introducing polar coordinates, we get

$$A(S) = \int_Q \sqrt{1 + 4r^2} \; r \, dr \, d\theta,$$

where Q is the rectangle in the $r\theta$-plane defined by $0 < r < 1, 0 \leq \theta < 2\pi$. Iterated integration shows that $A(S) = (\pi/6)(5^{3/2} - 1)$.

If a surface S is defined implicitly, then it may be difficult to find a parametric representation for S. However, according to the implicit function theorem there may be explicit representations of a restricted sort. For example, for the sphere $x^2 + y^2 + z^2 - 1 = 0$ we can write

$$z = \sqrt{1 - x^2 - y^2}, \qquad x^2 + y^2 \leq 1,$$

$$z = -\sqrt{1 - x^2 - y^2}, \qquad x^2 + y^2 \leq 1,$$

$$y = \sqrt{1 - x^2 - z^2}, \qquad x^2 + z^2 \leq 1.$$

If we confine our attention to pieces of implicitly defined surface that can be represented explicitly in this way, then Equation (4) can be used as in Example 3.

Sometimes it is convenient to have a formula for the area of an implicitly defined surface in terms of the given function. That is, suppose that $\mathfrak{R}^3 \xrightarrow{G} \mathfrak{R}$ is continuously differentiable and that

$$\frac{\partial G}{\partial z} (x_0, y_0, z_0) \neq 0.$$

Then in some open set N containing (x_0, y_0) there is a function $\mathfrak{R}^2 \xrightarrow{f} \mathfrak{R}$ satisfying

$$G(x, y, f(x, y)) = 0$$

for (x, y) in N. Equation (4) requires only that $\partial f/\partial x$ and $\partial f/\partial y$ be known, and these can be computed from G. We have

$$\frac{\partial f}{\partial x} = -\frac{\partial G}{\partial x} \bigg/ \frac{\partial G}{\partial z}, \qquad \frac{\partial f}{\partial y} = -\frac{\partial G}{\partial y} \bigg/ \frac{\partial G}{\partial z}.$$

Substitution into Equation (4) gives

$$A(S) = \int_N \frac{\sqrt{\left(\frac{\partial G}{\partial x}\right)^2 + \left(\frac{\partial G}{\partial y}\right)^2 + \left(\frac{\partial G}{\partial z}\right)^2}}{\left|\frac{\partial G}{\partial z}\right|} \, dx \, dy. \tag{5}$$

If we solve for x or y instead of z we get similar formulas with $\partial G/\partial x$ or $\partial G/\partial y$ in the denominator. To carry out the integration in Equation (5) it may still be necessary to eliminate z.

EXAMPLE 4. Let $G(x, y, z) = x^2 + y^2 + z^2 - 1$. Then $G = 0$ determines a sphere implicitly. The part of the sphere for which $x > 0$, $y > 0$, and

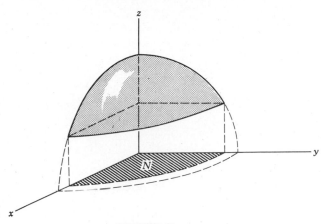

FIGURE 31

$z > \frac{1}{2}$ is shown in Figure 31. Since $\partial G/\partial x = 2x$, $\partial G/\partial y = 2y$, and $\partial G/\partial z = 2z$,

$$A(S) = \int_N \frac{\sqrt{4x^2 + 4y^2 + 4z^2}}{2z} \, dx \, dy = \int_N \frac{1}{z} \, dx \, dy,$$

where N is the region $0 < x$, $0 < y$, $x^2 + y^2 < \frac{3}{4}$. Changing to polar coordinates, we obtain

$$A(S) = \int_N \frac{1}{\sqrt{1 - x^2 - y^2}} \, dx \, dy = \int_0^{\pi/2} d\theta \int_0^{\sqrt{3/4}} \frac{1}{\sqrt{1 - r^2}} r \, dr$$
$$= \pi/4.$$

A surface can be defined parametrically by different functions, and a surface having two equivalent parametrizations will have the same area, whichever parametrization is used for the computation. Suppose a surface S is defined parametrically by

$$X = fU, \quad \text{for } U \text{ in } M, \text{ and}$$

$$X = gW, \quad \text{for } W \text{ in } N.$$

If there is a one-one transformation T continuously differentiable both ways between M and N such that

$$fU = g(TU), \quad \text{for } U \text{ in } M,$$

then f and g are **equivalent** parametrizations of S. Exercise 7 consists in showing that equivalent parametrizations lead to the same surface area.

EXAMPLE 5. The function

$$\begin{pmatrix} x \\ y \end{pmatrix} = \begin{pmatrix} u \cos v \\ u \sin v \end{pmatrix}, \qquad 0 \le u < 1,\, 0 \le v \le 3\pi,$$

has an image the disc of radius 1 about the origin in the xy-plane. The disc can also be represented by the function

$$z = 0, \qquad \text{for } x^2 + y^2 < 1.$$

These are inequivalent representations of the disc. The first function covers its image $1\frac{1}{2}$ times for a surface area of $3\pi/2$. The second function describes a simple disc of area π.

The integrand in the parametric surface area formula (3) consists of a square root of a sum of squares, just as does the corresponding expression in the arc-length formula. The terms to be squared consist in both cases of subdeterminants of the Jacobian matrix of the representation function. Side by side the formulas look like this:

Curve:

$$f(t) = \begin{pmatrix} x(t) \\ y(t) \\ z(t) \end{pmatrix}, \qquad d_t f\colon \begin{pmatrix} x'(t) \\ y'(t) \\ z'(t) \end{pmatrix},$$

$$l(C) = \int \sqrt{(x')^2 + (y')^2 + (z')^2}\, dt.$$

Surface:

$$f(u, v) = \begin{pmatrix} x(u, v) \\ y(u, v) \\ z(u, v) \end{pmatrix}, \qquad d_{(u,v)} f\colon \begin{pmatrix} \dfrac{\partial x}{\partial u} & \dfrac{\partial x}{\partial v} \\[2mm] \dfrac{\partial y}{\partial u} & \dfrac{\partial y}{\partial v} \\[2mm] \dfrac{\partial z}{\partial u} & \dfrac{\partial z}{\partial v} \end{pmatrix},$$

$$A(S) = \int \sqrt{\left(\frac{\partial(y, z)}{\partial(u, v)}\right)^2 + \left(\frac{\partial(z, x)}{\partial(u, v)}\right)^2 + \left(\frac{\partial(x, y)}{\partial(u, v)}\right)^2}\, du\, dv.$$

The arc-length formula extends to curves in $\mathfrak{R}^n$, and the surface-area formula can be extended also. We consider an $(n-1)$-dimensional surface given parametrically in $\mathfrak{R}^n$ by

$$X = fU = \begin{pmatrix} x_1(U) \\ x_2(U) \\ \cdot \\ \cdot \\ \cdot \\ x_n(U) \end{pmatrix},$$

where f is continuously differentiable in some subset M of $\mathfrak{R}^{n-1}$. The Jacobian matrix of f is

$$\begin{pmatrix} \dfrac{\partial x_1}{\partial u_1} & \cdots & \dfrac{\partial x_1}{\partial u_{n-1}} \\ \cdot \\ \cdot \\ \cdot \\ \dfrac{\partial x_n}{\partial u_1} & & \dfrac{\partial x_n}{\partial u_{n-1}} \end{pmatrix}$$

The area of S is defined to be

$$A(S)$$
$$= \int_M \sqrt{\left(\frac{\partial(x_2, \ldots, x_n)}{\partial(u_1, \ldots, u_{n-1})} \right)^2 + \ldots + \left(\frac{\partial(x_1, \ldots, x_{n-1})}{\partial(u_1, \ldots, u_{n-1})} \right)^2} \, du_1 \ldots du_{n-1},$$

in which all $(n-1)$-by-$(n-1)$ subdeterminants of the Jacobian are used, one row at a time being left out. The justification for this definition is that, as in the case of a two-dimensional surface, the integrand is the $(n-1)$-dimensional area of the parallelotope spanned by the tangent vectors $C_1, \ldots, C_{n-1}$, to the coordinate curves on S. Such a parallelotope consists of all vectors that are linear combinations

$$a_1 C_1 + \ldots + a_{n-1} C_{n-1}$$

with coefficients a_k satisfying $0 \leq a_k \leq 1$. (See Exercise 8.)

EXERCISES

1. Compute the surface area.

(a) $\begin{pmatrix} x \\ y \\ z \end{pmatrix} = \begin{pmatrix} u + v \\ 2u + 3v \\ u + 2v \end{pmatrix}$, $0 \leq u \leq 1$, $-1 \leq v \leq 1$. $\quad$ [Ans. $2\sqrt{3}$.]

(b) $\begin{pmatrix} x \\ y \\ z \end{pmatrix} = \begin{pmatrix} \cos u \sin v \\ \sin u \sin v \\ \cos v \end{pmatrix}$, $0 \leq u \leq 2\pi$, $0 \leq v \leq \pi/2$.

(c) $\begin{pmatrix} x \\ y \\ z \end{pmatrix} = \begin{pmatrix} u \cos v \\ u \sin v \\ v \end{pmatrix}$, $0 \leq u < 1$, $0 \leq v \leq 2\pi$.

[Ans. $\pi(\sqrt{2} + \log(1 + \sqrt{2}))$.]

(d) $\begin{pmatrix} x_1 \\ x_2 \\ x_3 \\ x_4 \end{pmatrix} = \begin{pmatrix} u + v \\ v + w \\ u + w \\ u + v + w \end{pmatrix}$, $u^2 + v^2 + w^2 \leq 1$. $\quad$ [Ans. $\frac{4}{3}\sqrt{7}\,\pi$.]

(e) $z = x^2 + y$, $0 \leq x \leq 1$, $0 \leq y \leq 1$.

[Ans. $\sqrt{\frac{3}{2}} + \frac{1}{2}\log(\sqrt{2} + \sqrt{3})$.]

(f) $w = x^2 + y^2 + z^2$, $x^2 + y^2 + z^2 \leq 1$.

[Ans. $(\pi/4)(9\sqrt{5} - \frac{1}{2}\log(2 + \sqrt{5}))$.]

(g) $x^2 + y^2 + z^2 + w^2 = a^2$.

2. Find the area of the part of the plane $x + 2y + z = 0$ that lies inside the cylinder $2x^2 + y^2 = 1$. $\quad$ [Ans. $\sqrt{3}\,\pi$.]

3. (a) Let (r, ϕ, θ) be spherical coordinates in $\mathcal{R}^3$. Prove that

$$\left| \frac{\partial(x, y, z)}{\partial(r, \phi, \theta)} (1, \phi_0, \theta_0) \right|$$

is the area spanned by the tangent vectors C_2 and C_3 to the ϕ and θ coordinate curves through $(1, \phi_0, \theta_0)$.

(b) Deduce from (a) by integration that the area of a sphere of radius a is $4\pi a^2$.

(c) Generalize the results of (a) and (b) to show that the area of an $(n - 1)$-dimensional sphere of radius a in $\mathscr{R}^n$ is

$$(2\pi^{n/2}a^{n-1}) \Big/ \Gamma\!\left(\frac{n}{2}\right).$$

4. Prove that

$$\begin{vmatrix} a_2 & b_2 \\ a_3 & b_3 \end{vmatrix}^2 + \begin{vmatrix} a_3 & b_3 \\ a_1 & b_1 \end{vmatrix}^2 + \begin{vmatrix} a_1 & b_1 \\ a_2 & b_2 \end{vmatrix}^2 = 0$$

if and only if the vectors

$$\begin{pmatrix} a_1 \\ a_2 \\ a_3 \end{pmatrix} \quad \text{and} \quad \begin{pmatrix} b_1 \\ b_2 \\ b_3 \end{pmatrix}$$

are linearly dependent. [*Suggestion.* Prove that

$$\begin{vmatrix} a & b \\ c & d \end{vmatrix} = 0$$

if and only if $\begin{pmatrix} a \\ c \end{pmatrix}$ and

$\begin{pmatrix} b \\ d \end{pmatrix}$ are dependent.]

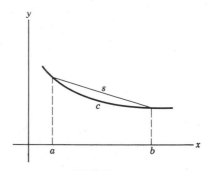

FIGURE 32

5. Let f be a real-valued continuously differentiable function of one variable, non-negative for $a \le x \le b$. The graph of f, rotated around the x-axis between a and b, generates a surface S in $\mathscr{R}^3$.

(a) Find a parametric representation for S in terms of f.

(b) Prove that $A(S) = 2\pi \displaystyle\int_a^b f(x) \sqrt{1 + (f'(x))^2} \, dx$.

(c) Figure 32 shows a line segment s joining two points on a plane curve c, assumed not to cross the x-axis. We know (see Exercise 8, Section 4) that $l(s) \le l(c)$. Let S and C be the surfaces generated by rotation of s and c about the x-axis. Show by example that $A(S)$ may be bigger than $A(C)$.

6. Let P be a parallelogram spanned by two vectors in $\mathcal{R}^3$. Prove that

$$A^2(P) = A_{yz}^2(P) + A_{zx}^2(P) + A_{xy}^2(P),$$

where $A_{yz}(P)$, $A_{zx}(P)$ and $A_{xy}(P)$ are the areas of the projections of P on the coordinate planes.

7. Prove that equivalent parametrizations assign the same area to a surface.

8. Prove that the integrand used in the n-dimensional surface-area formula is the area of the parallelotope spanned by the appropriate tangent vectors.

9. The **solid angle** determined by one nappe of a solid cone $\mathcal{C}$ in $\mathcal{R}^n$ with vertex at the origin is the area of the intersection of $\mathcal{C}$ with the unit sphere $|X| = 1$.
  (a) Show that the above definition leads to the usual definition of the angle between two lines in $\mathcal{R}^2$. [Suggestion: take $\mathcal{C}$ to be the region between the two lines; the intersection of $\mathcal{C}$ with $|X| = 1$ is an arc of a circle.]
  (b) Compute the solid angle determined by the solid cone

$$x^2 + y^2 \leq 2z^2, \qquad 0 \leq z. \qquad [Ans.\ \pi(2 - \sqrt{3}).]$$

6. IMPROPER INTEGRALS

The definition of the integral can be extended to functions that are unbounded and not necessarily zero outside some bounded set. We shall first consider some examples.

EXAMPLE 1. The function $f(x, y) = 1/x^2y^2$, defined for $x \geq 1$ and $y \geq 1$, has the graph shown in Figure 33. If B is the set of points (x, y) for which $x \geq 1$ and $y \geq 1$, it is natural to define $\int_B f\, dA$ in such a way that it can be called the volume under the graph of f. We can approximate this volume by computing the volume lying above bounded subrectangles of B. To be specific, let B_N be the rectangle with corners at $(1, 1)$ and (N, N)

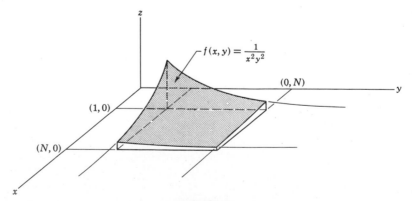

FIGURE 33

and with edges parallel to the edges of B. For $N > 1$ we have

$$\int_{B_N} f \, dA = \int_1^N dx \int_1^N \frac{1}{x^2 y^2} \, dy$$

$$= \left(\int_1^N \frac{dx}{x^2} \right)^2 = \left(1 - \frac{1}{N} \right)^2.$$

As N tends to infinity, the rectangles B_N eventually cover every point of B, and the regions above the B_N fill out the region under the graph of f. Then, by definition,

$$\int_B f \, dA = \lim_{N \to \infty} \int_{B_N} f \, dA = 1.$$

EXAMPLE 2. Let B be the disc $x^2 + y^2 \leq 1$ in $\Re^2$, and suppose

$$f(x, y) = -\log (x^2 + y^2), \qquad 0 < x^2 + y^2 \leq 1.$$

The graph of f is shown in Figure 34. Since f is unbounded near $(0, 0)$, we

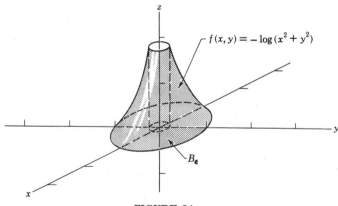

$$f(x, y) = -\log (x^2 + y^2)$$

FIGURE 34

cut out from B a disc centered at $(0, 0)$ and with radius ϵ. Call the part of B that is left B_ϵ. We have, using polar coordinates,

$$\int_{B_\epsilon} - \log (x^2 + y^2) \, dx \, dy = \int_0^{2\pi} d\theta \int_\epsilon^1 - (\log r^2) r \, dr$$

$$= -2\pi [r^2 \log r - \tfrac{1}{2} r^2]_\epsilon^1$$

$$= \pi + 2\pi \epsilon^2 \log \epsilon - \pi \epsilon^2.$$

Since $\lim_{\epsilon \to 0} (2\pi\epsilon^2 \log \epsilon - \pi\epsilon^2) = 0$, we get, by definition,

$$\int_B - \log (x^2 + y^2) \; dx \; dy = \lim_{\epsilon \to 0} \int_{B_\epsilon} - \log (x^2 + y^2) \; dx \; dy = \pi.$$

In the previous example the function $-\log (x^2 + y^2)$ becomes un-bounded in the disc $x^2 + y^2 \le 1$ only at the point $(0, 0)$. It is of course important to find all such points in attempting to integrate an unbounded function. In general we define an **infinite discontinuity point** for a function f to be a point X such that in any neighborhood of X, $|f|$ assumes arbitrarily large values.

EXAMPLE 3. Consider the function $g(x, y, z) = (x^2 + y^2 + z^2 - 1)^{-1/2}$ for (x, y, z) satisfying $1 < x^2 + y^2 + z^2 \le 2$. The domain of g is the region between the concentric spheres shown in Figure 35. Every point of the

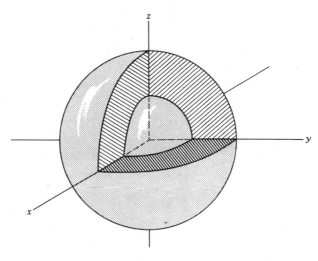

FIGURE 35

sphere $x^2 + y^2 + z^2 = 1$ is an infinite discontinuity point for g. In order to define the integral of g, we approximate its domain by shells B_ϵ de-termined by $1 + \epsilon \le x^2 + y^2 + z^2 \le 2$. These shells have the property that, although none of them contains an infinite discontinuity point, they fill out the entire domain of g as ϵ tends to zero. Introducing spherical coordinates, we obtain

$$\int_{B_\epsilon} (x^2 + y^2 + z^2 - 1)^{-1/2} \, dx \, dy \, dz$$

$$= \int_{1+\epsilon}^{2} dr \int_{0}^{2\pi} d\theta \int_{0}^{\pi} (r^2 - 1)^{-1/2} r^2 \sin \phi \, d\phi$$

$$= 4\pi \int_{1+\epsilon}^{2} (r^2 - 1)^{-1/2} r^2 \, dr$$

$$= 4\pi \left[\frac{1}{2} r \sqrt{r^2 - 1} + \frac{1}{2} \log (r + \sqrt{r^2 - 1}) \right]_{1+\epsilon}^{2}.$$

It follows immediately that

$$\lim_{\epsilon \to 0} \int_{B_\epsilon} (x^2 + y^2 + z^2 - 1)^{1/2} \, dx \, dy \, dz = 4\pi \sqrt{3} + 2\pi \log (2 + \sqrt{3}).$$

Before collecting the ideas illustrated above into a general definition, we make two requirements about the integrand f and the set B over which it is to be integrated.

(a) Let D be the set of points of B at which f is not continuous. The part of D lying in an arbitrary bounded rectangle is contained in finitely many pieces of smooth surface.

(b) The part of B lying in an arbitrary bounded rectangle has a boundary consisting of finitely many pieces of smooth surface.

Both conditions are satisfied in the three examples considered so far, and we shall assume that they hold throughout the rest of the section.

In the examples we have seen that the integral $\int_B f \, dV$ can sometimes be defined when either f or B is unbounded. The extended definition of the integral will be made in such a way that both phenomena can occur at once. We proceed as follows: An increasing family $\{B_N\}$ of subsets of B will be said to **converge to** B if every bounded subset of B on which f is bounded is contained in some one of the sets B_N. Notice that this notion of convergence depends not only on B but also on f. The index N can be chosen in any convenient way; it may, for example, tend to ∞ continuously or through integer values, or it may tend to some finite number. Throughout the rest of this section we shall assume that in any increasing family $\{B_N\}$ converging to B, each of the sets B_N satisfies condition (b).

The **integral of** f **over** B is by definition

$$\lim_N \int_{B_N} f \, dV = \int_B f \, dV,$$

provided that the limit is finite and is the same for every increasing family of bounded sets B_N converging to B. It is assumed that the B_N are chosen so that the ordinary Riemann integrals $\int_{B_N} f \, dV$ (as defined in Section 2) exist. The integral thus obtained is called the **improper Riemann integral** when it is necessary to distinguish it from the Riemann integral of a bounded function over a bounded set.

Although the requirement that the value of the integral be independent of the converging family of sets used to define it is a natural one, we shall see later that it is sometimes interesting to disregard it. Nevertheless, the next theorem shows that for positive functions the limit of $\int_{B_N} f \, dV$ is always independent of family of sets.

6.1 Theorem. Let f be non-negative on B and suppose that

$$\lim_N \int_{B_N} f \, dV$$

is finite for some particular increasing family of sets B_N converging to B. Then $\int_B f \, dV$ is defined and has the same value,

$$\lim_N \int_{C_N} f \, dV,$$

for every other family $\{C_N\}$ converging to B.

Proof. Since f is bounded on each B_N, we have for each N an index K such that

$$B_N \subset C_K.$$

Similarly there is an index M depending on K such that

$$C_K \subset B_M.$$

Then, because f is non-negative

$$\int_{B_N} f \, dV \le \int_{C_K} f \, dV \le \int_{B_M} f \, dV.$$

In addition

$$\int_{C_N} f \, dV \le \lim_N \int_{B_N} f \, dV$$

for all N. Because $\int_{C_N} f \, dV$ increases and is bounded above,

$$\lim_N \int_{C_N} f \, dV$$

exists. The double inequality shows that

$$\lim_N \int_{B_N} f \, dV = \lim_N \int_{C_N} f \, dV.$$

This completes the proof.

EXAMPLE 4. Let f be defined on the infinite strip S in $\mathfrak{R}^2$, shown in Figure 36, by $f(x, y) = y^{-1/2}e^{-x}$. Clearly f has an infinite discontinuity at

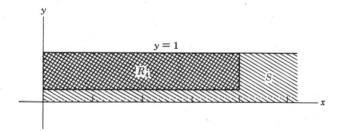

FIGURE 36

every point of the positive x-axis. We define R_N to be the rectangle in S bounded by the lines $x = N$ and $y = 1/N$, for $N > 1$. As N tends to infinity, R_N will converge to S. We have

$$\int_{R_N} f \, dA = \int_0^N dx \int_{1/N}^1 y^{-1/2}e^{-x} \, dy$$

$$= \left(\int_0^N e^{-x} \, dx \right) \left(\int_{1/N}^1 y^{-1/2} \, dy \right)$$

$$= (1 - e^{-N}) \left(2 - \frac{2}{\sqrt{N}} \right).$$

Then

$$\int_S y^{-1/2}e^{-x} \, dx \, dy = \lim_{N \to \infty} (1 - e^{-N}) \left(2 - \frac{2}{\sqrt{N}} \right) = 2.$$

EXAMPLE 5. The integral of $1/x^a$ over the positive x-axis, denoted by $\int_0^\infty x^{-a}\,dx$, fails to exist for any a. For consider, for $N > 0$,

$$\int_{1/N}^N x^{-a}\,dx = \begin{cases} \dfrac{N^{1-a} - 1/N^{1-a}}{1 - a}, & a \neq 1. \\[2ex] 2 \log N, & a = 1. \end{cases}$$

As N tends to infinity, we get infinity for a limit in every case. However, it is easy to verify that

$$\int_1^\infty x^{-a}\,dx = \frac{1}{a - 1}, \qquad \text{for } a > 1,$$

and

$$\int_0^1 x^{-a}\,dx = \frac{1}{1 - a}, \qquad \text{for } a < 1.$$

The integral

$$\int_{-1}^1 \frac{1}{x}\,dx$$

fails to exist if we require that its value be independent of the limit process by which it is computed. Indeed, if we integrate first over the intervals $[-1,\,-\delta]$ and $[\epsilon,\,1]$ with $0 < \delta < 1$ and $0 < \epsilon < 1$, we get

$$\int_{-1}^{-\delta} \frac{1}{x}\,dx + \int_\epsilon^1 \frac{1}{x}\,dx = \log |x| \Big]_{-1}^{-\delta} + \log x \Big]_\epsilon^1$$

$$= \log \frac{\delta}{\epsilon}.$$

As ϵ and δ tend to zero, $\log(\delta/\epsilon)$ can be made to tend to any given number. In particular, though, if we keep $\epsilon = \delta$, the limit is zero. For functions f having certain symmetries, it is sometimes significant to compute $\int_B f\,dV$ by a limit involving rather special sets B_N, even though some other family of sets may yield a different limit. When this is done and a limit is obtained, we speak of finding a **principal value** of the integral, and we write p.v. $\int_B f \, dV$ for the result. For the integral in the last part of Example 5 we would then write p.v. $\int_{-1}^{1} \frac{1}{x} \, dx = 0$.

EXAMPLE 6. Let (r, θ) be polar coordinates in $\mathfrak{R}^2$, and set $f(r, \theta) = (\sin \theta)/r^2$ over the disc D of radius 1 centered at the origin. Clearly f has an infinite discontinuity at the origin because, for instance, along the line $\theta = \pi/2$, f tends to ∞ and along the line $\theta = 3\pi/2$, f tends to $-\infty$. (See Figure 37 for the graph of f.) However, $\int_D f \, dA$ fails to exist in the ordinary

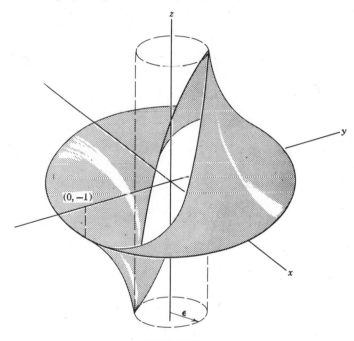

FIGURE 37

improper integral sense because the limit obtained from a sequence of regions in D will depend on the way in which the positive and negative values of f are balanced. The principal value of the integral can be determined by taking a limit over a family of annular regions. Let D_ϵ be the annulus $\epsilon \leq r \leq 1$. Then

$$\text{p.v.} \int_D f \, dV = \lim_{\epsilon \to 0} \int_{D_\epsilon} \frac{\sin \theta}{r^2} \, r \, dr \, d\theta$$

$$= \lim_{\epsilon \to 0} \int_0^{2\pi} \sin \theta \, d\theta \int_\epsilon^1 \frac{dr}{r} = 0.$$

The next theorem is a convenient test for the existence of an improper integral.

6.2 Theorem. Let f and g have the same infinite discontinuity points. If $|f| \leq g$ and $\int_B g \, dV$ exists, then so does $\int_B f \, dV$.

Proof. Let $\{B_N\}$ be an increasing family of sets converging to B. Since $f + |f| \leq 2|f| \leq 2g$, we have

$$\int_{B_N} (f + |f|) \, dV \leq 2 \int_{B_N} g \, dV \leq 2 \int_B g \, dV.$$

Then, because $f + |f| \geq 0$, $\int_{B_N} (f + |f|) \, dV$ increases as B_N increases, and we have

$$\lim_N \int_{B_N} (f + |f|) \, dV = l_1 \leq 2 \int_B g \, dV.$$

Similarly,

$$\lim_N \int_{B_N} |f| \, dV = l_2 \leq \int_B g \, dV.$$

Finally,

$$\lim_N \int_{B_N} f \, dV = \lim_N \left(\int_{B_N} (f + |f|) \, dV - \int_{B_N} |f| \, dV \right)$$

$$= \lim_N \int_{B_N} (f + |f|) \, dV - \lim_N \int_{B_N} |f| \, dV = l_1 - l_2.$$

Since the family B_N is arbitrary, $\int_B f \, dV$ is defined.

EXAMPLE 7. Let B be the disc $x^2 + y^2 \leq 1$ in $\mathcal{R}^2$, and let f be defined by

$$f(x, y) = \begin{cases} (x^2 + y^2)^{-1/2}, & \text{for } x \geq 0 \text{ and } x^2 + y^2 > 0. \\ (x^2 + y^2)^{1/2}, & \text{for } x < 0. \end{cases}$$

Since $\int_B (x^2 + y^2)^{-1/2} \, dx \, dy$ exists, and $|f(x, y)| \leq (x^2 + y^2)^{-1/2}$ for $0 < x^2 + y^2 \leq 1$, it follows from Theorem 6.2 that $\int_B f \, dx \, dy$ exists. The computation of the integral of f is left as an exercise.

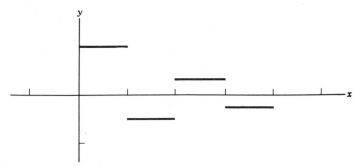

FIGURE 38

EXAMPLE 8. Let $j(x) = (-1)^{n-1}/n$ for $n - 1 \leq x < n$ and $n = 1, 2, 3, \ldots$. The graph of j is shown in Figure 38 as far out as $x = 4$. Then,

$$\lim_{n \to \infty} \int_0^n j(x) \, dx = \sum_{n=1}^{\infty} \frac{(-1)^{n-1}}{n} = \log 2,$$

and we can write

$$\int_0^{\infty} j(x) \, dx = \log 2,$$

if it is understood that the passage to the limit has been carried out in this special way. This example shares with the principal value examples the property that the value assigned to the integral depends on having taken a limit over some particular sequence of regions. Such an integral is called **conditionally convergent**. For another example see Exercise 8.

EXERCISES

1. In each part determine whether the integral is defined or not. If it is defined compute its value.

(a) $\displaystyle\int_0^{\infty} \frac{dx}{x^2 + 1}.$ $[Ans.\ \pi/2.]$

(b) $\displaystyle\int_{-\infty}^{\infty} \frac{dx}{x^2 - 1}.$

(c) $\displaystyle\int_0^1 \frac{dx}{\sqrt{1 - x^2}}.$

(d) $\displaystyle\int_{x^2+y^2\leq 1} \frac{dx\,dy}{\sqrt{x^2+y^2}}.$

(e) $\displaystyle\int_R \frac{(x-y)\,dx\,dy}{x^2+y^2}$ where R is the rectangle max $(\,|\,x\,|,\,|\,y\,|\,) \leq 1.$

(f) $\displaystyle\int_{x^2+y^2+z^2\geq 1} \frac{dx\,dy\,dz}{(x^2+y^2+z^2)^2}.$

(g) $\displaystyle\int_{x^2+y^2+z^2\geq 1} \frac{dx\,dy\,dz}{xyz}.$

(h) $\displaystyle\int_C e^{-x-y-z}\,dx\,dy\,dz$, where C is the infinite column

$$\text{max}\,(\,|\,x\,|,\,|\,y\,|\,) \leq 1, \qquad z \geq 0.$$

2. Prove that

$$\Gamma(n) = \int_0^\infty e^{-x}x^{n-1}\,dx = (n-1)!$$

for $n > 1$ an integer.

(b) Express $\displaystyle\int_T e^{-x}(x-y)^{-1/2}\,dx\,dy$ in terms of Γ, where T is the region

$x \geq 0,\, y \leq x.$

3. Let B be the ball $|\,X\,| \leq 1$ in $\mathfrak{R}^n$. For what values of a does $\displaystyle\int_B \frac{dV}{|\,X\,|^a}$ exist?

4. Compute (a) p.v. $\displaystyle\int_{-\infty}^\infty \frac{x\,dx}{x^2+1}$, (b) p.v. $\displaystyle\int_{-1}^1 \frac{x\,dx}{2x-1}.$

5. Compute the values of the function $g(y) = \displaystyle\int_{-1}^1 \frac{x\,dx}{x-y}$, taking a principal

value of the integral when necessary.

6. Compute the integral of the function f in Example 7 in the text, and com-

pute $\displaystyle\int_B (x^2+y^2)^{-1/2}\,dx\,dy.$ $[Ans.\ \tfrac{4}{3}\pi,\ 2\pi.]$

7. Show that the integral of the function j in Example 8 of the text depends
on the sequence of sets used to compute the limit. [*Suggestion.* Take each
B_N to be a disconnected set of intervals.]

8. Let $f(x, y) = \sin(x^2+y^2)$ over the quadrant Q defined by $x \geq 0,\, y \geq 0.$
Show that $\int_Q f\,dA$ converges conditionally. (Suggestion: To get a limit,
integrate over increasing squares. Then integrate over quarter discs.)

9. In what sense does each of the following integrals exist? The possibilities are ordinary Riemann integral, improper integral, conditionally convergent integral, or none of these.

(a) $\displaystyle\int_{\pi}^{\infty} \frac{\sin x}{x^2}\, dx.$

(b) $\displaystyle\int_{0}^{\infty} \frac{\sin x}{x}\, dx.$

(c) $\displaystyle\int_{0}^{\infty} \sin x\, dx.$

(d) $\displaystyle\int_{0}^{1} \sin \frac{1}{x}\, dx.$

10. The integral $\displaystyle\int_{0}^{\infty} f(x)\, dx$ is said to be **Abel summable** to the value k if

$$\lim_{\epsilon \to 0+} \int_{0}^{\infty} e^{-\epsilon x} f(x)\, dx = k.$$

Find the Abel value of (a) $\displaystyle\int_{0}^{\infty} \sin x\, dx,$ (b) $\displaystyle\int_{0}^{\infty} \cos x\, dx.$

11. (a) Compute $\displaystyle\int_{\mathcal{R}^2} e^{-x^2 - y^2}\, dx\, dy.$ (Use polar coordinates.)

(b) Use the result of part (a) to compute $\displaystyle\int_{-\infty}^{\infty} e^{-x^2}\, dx.$

(c) Compute $\displaystyle\int_{\mathcal{R}^n} \exp\left(-x_1^2 - \ldots - x_n^2\right) dV.$

12. (a) Show that the area bounded by the graph of $y = 1/x$, the x-axis, and the line $x = 1$ is infinite.

(b) Compute the volume swept out by rotating the region described in (a) about the x-axis.

13. Let f be positive and unbounded on an unbounded set B in $\mathcal{R}^2$. Consider the region C between the graph of f and B, and show that if

$$\int_{B} f\, dA \quad \text{and} \quad \int_{C} dV$$

both exist, then they are equal.

14. Show that if $\int_{B} |f|\, dV$ exists, then so does $\int_{B} f\, dV$. Without conditions (a) and (b) this is false. For example, let B be the unit interval $0 \le x \le 1$ and f the function

$$f(x) = \begin{cases} 1, & \text{if } x \text{ is rational.} \\ -1, & \text{if } x \text{ is irrational.} \end{cases}$$

15. Show that if the ordinary Riemann integral $\int_B f \, dV$ exists, then it exists as an improper integral (given conditions (a) and (b)) and the two integrals are equal.

16. The following inequalities are valid under the assumption that the integrals exist as ordinary Riemann integrals. In that case they are all immediate consequences of Theorems 2.7 and 2.8. Decide which of them hold for improper integrals and find the proof for each one that does hold.

(a) If f is non-negative and integrable over C and over a subset B then

$$\int_B f \, dV \le \int_C f \, dV.$$

(b) If f is non-negative and integrable on B then

$$\underline{f} \int_B dV \le \int_B f \, dV \le \bar{f} \int_B dV,$$

where $\underline{f}$ and $\bar{f}$ are the **infimum** and **supremum**, respectively, of f on B.

17. Prove that

$$\int_0^1 dy \int_1^\infty \left(e^{-xy} - 2e^{-2xy} \right) dx \ne \int_1^\infty dx \int_0^1 \left(e^{-xy} - 2e^{-2xy} \right) dy.$$

Appendix I

Theory of Determinants

1. PROPERTIES OF VOLUME AND OF ORIENTATION

The algebraic and geometric properties of vector spaces presented in Chapter 1 have all been abstracted from certain intuitive properties of one-, two-, and three-dimensional physical space. Now we want to find axioms for two more properties of ordinary space: volume and orientation. The reason for doing this is that the determinant of a matrix can be analyzed geometrically in such a way that it appears as an oriented volume.

We begin with n-dimensional volume, keeping in mind ordinary volume in three-dimensional space, area in two-dimensional space, and length in one-dimensional space. Among its most intuitive properties are these:

Volume is non-negative (Positivity).

When sets do not overlap, the volume of their union equals the sum of their volumes (Additivity).

When a set is translated or reflected, its volume is unchanged.

Subspaces of lower dimension have zero n-dimensional volume.

We shall proceed from the above geometric properties to establish informally some algebraic properties of volume that will serve us better as formal axioms. These algebraic properties will be conceptually less appealing than the geometric properties, but simpler to manipulate. Then later we can rederive the geometric properties as theorems.

Let us first consider the volume of a **parallelotope**, which by definition consists of all linear combinations $c_1 X_1 + \ldots + c_n X_n$, with coefficients c_k between 0 and 1, of n linearly independent vectors $X_1, \ldots, X_n$ in n-dimensional space. The X_k are called the **principal edges** of the parallelotope. The other edges we shall never have occasion to mention. In two dimensions a parallelotope is an ordinary parallelogram. In three dimensions it is a parallelepiped. But notice that our definition of parallelotope forces it to have one vertex at the origin. One can extend the definition of parallelotope by allowing $X_1, \ldots, X_n$ to be linearly dependent, yet keep the rest of the definition as is. Let us call such a set a **degenerate parallelotope**. Since it has dimension less than n, it has zero n-dimensional volume. However, a non-degenerate parallelotope always has positive volume.

We begin to look for algebraic properties by considering the pair of two-dimensional parallelograms in Figure 1. Clearly, we can cut each of these up into smaller parallelograms of the same size and shape as that exhibited in Figure 2. If area is defined for all parallelograms (not only for those that have a vertex at 0), then invariance of area under translation forces us to give the same area a to each of the five small parallelograms sketched in Figure 1. And then additivity of area forces us to assign areas $2a$ and $3a$, respectively, to the two big parallelograms in Figure 1. Because

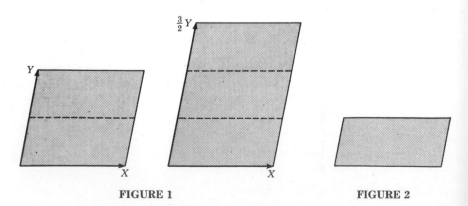

FIGURE 1   FIGURE 2

we can neglect sets of lower dimension, we do not have to worry about the edges of any parallelogram occurring in the above argument. Similar reasoning applies in comparing any two parallelograms with principal edges X, Y and X, cY, respectively, where c is an arbitrary positive rational number. If the former parallelogram has area A, the latter must have area cA. And by a continuity argument (using additivity and positivity of area), it is possible to get the same conclusion for arbitrary positive real c. To see what happens for negative c, it is enough to consider the case $c = -1$ exhibited in Figure 3. The parallelogram with principal edges

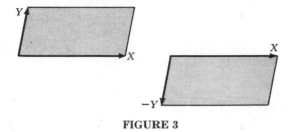

FIGURE 3

X, $-Y$ is simply a reflection of the parallelogram with principal edges X, Y. Hence the two parallelograms must have the same area. The case $c = 0$ in effect asks for the area of the degenerate parallelogram with principal edges X and O. This set is identical with the edge X alone. Because we neglect linear sets of lower dimension, it must have area zero.

All the above arguments generalize in an obvious way to n dimensions. Hence we state as one of the formal axioms for volume:

$\mathbf{V_1}$. If a parallelotope Q has the same principal edges as parallelotope P, except that the ith edge of Q is c times the ith edge of P, then the volume of Q is $|c|$ times the volume of P.

Again in two dimensions, consider the pair of parallelograms in Figure 4. We claim that these must have the same area. For, cut each of them in

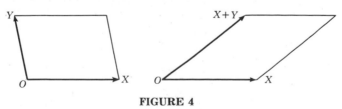

FIGURE 4

half as in Figure 5, and clearly triangles A and A' are identical. Furthermore, triangle B' is simply B translated by adding the vector X. If area is defined for all triangles, then additivity forces us to assign equal areas to

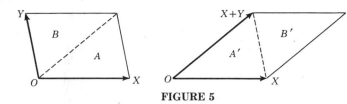

FIGURE 5

the parallelogram with edges X, Y and the parallelogram with edges X, $Y + X$. As before, we ignore edges, because they are linear sets of lower dimension. The same kind of argument may be used for a parallelotope in n-space. When you replace X_i by $X_i + Y_j$, you are in effect bisecting the parallelotope and translating one of the two halves across the other. As in two dimensions, where we considered the area of triangles, the argument is valid only if volume is defined for a more extensive class of sets than parallelotopes. One natural class of sets, extensive enough for our purpose, is the class of convex polyhedra, where by definition a **convex polyhedron** consists of all linear combinations $c_1X_1 + \ldots + c_rX_r$, with $c_k \geq 0$ and $\Sigma c_k = 1$, of vectors $X_1, \ldots, X_r$ (not requiring r to equal the dimension of the space). Hence, we state our second formal axiom for volume.

> V_2. Suppose a parallelotope Q has the same principal edges as parallelotope P, except that the ith edge of Q is the vector sum of the ith and jth edges of P, with $i \neq j$. Then P and Q must have the same volume.

Let us restate the algebraic axioms for volume in symbolic form. We regard **vol** as a function defined for every parallelotope (degenerate or not). Thus equivalently we can regard **vol** as a function of n vector variables $X_1, \ldots, X_n$, the edges of the parallelotope.

V_0.   **vol** $(X_1, \ldots, X_n) > 0$,   unless $X_1, \ldots, X_n$ are dependent.

V_1.   **vol** $(\ldots cX \ldots) = |c|$ **vol** $(\ldots X \ldots)$

V_2.   **vol** $(\ldots X + Y \ldots Y \ldots) =$ **vol** $(\ldots X \ldots Y + X \ldots)$

$$= \textbf{vol} \ (\ldots X \ldots Y \ldots).$$

Notice that the operations used in the last two axioms resemble the elementary operations used in Section 2 of Chapter 1 for solving systems of linear equations.

We shall next consider orientation. The 2-dimensional ordered basis (X, Y) displayed in Figure 6 is said to have **positive orientation**, because the angle θ is positive going from X to Y. The basis (X, Y) in Figure 7

FIGURE 6   FIGURE 7

has negative orientation. Of course, if you were to look at each of these bases by turning the page over and holding it up to the light, the positive orientation would become negative, and vice versa. But from either side of the paper you can at least say that the two bases have *opposite* orientations.

In three dimensions orientation is more complicated. The ordered basis (X, Y, Z) in Figure 8(a) has positive orientation, and the basis (X, Y, Z) in Figure 8(b) has negative orientation. It is possible to distinguish one

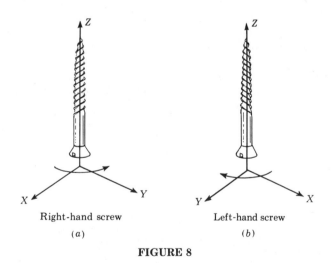

Right-hand screw   Left-hand screw

(a)   (b)

FIGURE 8

orientation from the other by comparing the action of right-hand and left-hand screws, as shown in the same figure. If in each case the screw is turned in the indicated direction (from X to Y), then the screw will travel in the direction of Z. The screw in 8(a) has a right-hand thread and the one in 8(b) has a left-hand thread. Thus the orientations of the respective bases are sometimes called right-hand or left-hand instead of positive or negative.

Notice also that one basis cannot be continuously transformed into the other without having some vector pass through the plane spanned by the others. In other words, the vectors of a basis maintain the *same* orientation if they are moved continuously in such a way that they remain independent. This principle still applies for an ordered basis of two vectors in the plane. Hence we shall take the following as fundamental for orientation in n dimensions.

Altering a single vector in an ordered basis changes the orientation of this basis if and only if the alteration moves the vector across the hyperplane spanned by the fixed vectors.

Recall that a hyperplane H can always be defined by some linear functional F, and consists precisely of those vectors X such that $FX = 0$ (see Section 13 of Chapter 1). Vectors X_1 and X_2 are on opposite sides of H if and only if FX_1 and FX_2 have opposite signs.

The most important thing about orientation in n dimensions is that it is possible to have just two choices for orientation. It is for this reason that it is possible to distinguish between orientations by two terms, say positive and negative, or, as will be convenient later, by $+1$ and -1. The fact that we can have just two orientations in higher dimensions is not at all obvious. However, it will follow from the definition of determinant that for each n-dimensional space there is a function, denoted **orn**, and defined for each ordered set of n vectors in the space, such that

$$O_0. \quad \textbf{orn} \ (X_1, \ldots, X_n) = \begin{cases} \pm 1 & \text{if } X_1, \ldots, X_n \text{ are independent} \\ 0 & \text{if } X_1, \ldots, X_n \text{ are dependent} \end{cases}$$

$$O_1. \quad \text{For } c \neq 0, \textbf{orn} \ (\ldots cX \ldots) = \frac{c}{|c|} \textbf{orn} \ (\ldots X \ldots).$$

$$O_2. \quad \textbf{orn} \ (\ldots X + Y \ldots Y \ldots) = \textbf{orn} \ (\ldots X \ldots Y + X \ldots)$$
$$= \textbf{orn} \ (\ldots X \ldots Y \ldots).$$

Notice the similarity of O_1 and O_2 to the corresponding properties that we have listed for volume. These two orientation properties are consequences of the general principle that orientation changes sign when a vector of a basis is moved across the hyperplane spanned by the others. The implication is geometrically obvious for O_1; the notation $c/|c|$ is simply a way of writing $+1$ or -1 according as $c > 0$ or $c < 0$. As for O_2, let H be the hyperplane spanned by the edges other than X (in particular, Y is one of these) and let F be a linear functional defining H. Then FX and $F(X + Y)$ have the same sign. In fact

$$F(X + Y) = FX + FY = FX + 0 = FX.$$

Thus X and $X + Y$ lie on the same side of the hyperplane H.

EXERCISES

Prove or disprove each of the statements in exercises 1, 2, and 3 for the function **v** defined as follows: For any two vectors X, Y in $\mathfrak{R}^2$,
$$\mathbf{v}(X, Y) = \begin{cases} 0, \text{ if } X \text{ and } Y \text{ are dependent,} \\ 1, \text{ if } X \text{ and } Y \text{ are independent.} \end{cases}$$

1. The function **v** satisfies axiom V_0

2. The function **v** satisfies axiom V_1

3. The function **v** satisfies axiom V_2.

4. If X, Y, Z are the principal edges of a parallelotope in 3-space, then the tips of these vectors constitute three of the eight vertices of this parallelotope. Name vectors that have their tips at the other five vertices.

5. State and solve the n-dimensional version of Exercise 4 above.

6. Give examples of two different sets X_1, Y_1, Z_1 and X_2, Y_2, Z_2 such that the degenerate parallelotopes they span (call them P_1 and P_2) are the same set of points.

7. Show that replacing each principal edge of an ordered parallelogram by its negative leaves the orientation unchanged. Show that replacing each principal edge of a parallelepiped (in 3-space) by its negative reverses the orientation. Generalize these observations to n dimensions.

8. Using the proof of theorem 2.6 (how to accomplish an interchange of rows by means of elementary additions and multiplications) in Section 2 of Chapter I, show that interchanging two principal edges of an ordered parallelotope always changes the orientation.

9. Among the $n!$ possible orderings of basis vectors $X_1 \ldots X_n$ show that exactly $n!/2$ of these orderings have positive orientation. [Use Exercise 8, and induction.]

10. Let $E_1 = (1, 0, 0)$, $E_2 = (0, 1, 0)$, $E_3 = (0, 0, 1)$ be the natural basis vectors in $\mathfrak{R}^3$. List all ordered bases containing E_1, E_2, E_3 and having the same orientation as (E_1, E_2, E_3). List all ordered bases having the opposite orientation.

2. PROPERTIES OF THE DETERMINANT

We have found axioms for **vol** and **orn**. By multiplying together orientation and volume, we create a function called the **determinant**. We lose nothing by exchanging two functions for one, since **orn** and **vol** can at any time be recovered as the $\pm$ sign and absolute value, respectively, of **det**. Hence we shall give axioms directly for a function **det**, defined for each ordered parallelotope (or each ordered set of n vectors) in a given n-dimensional vector space.

D_0. **det** $(X_1, \ldots, X_n)$ is real-valued, and not identically zero.

D_1. **det** $(\ldots cX \ldots) = c$ **det** $(\ldots X \ldots)$.

D_2. **det** $(\ldots X + Y \ldots Y \ldots) = $ **det** $(\ldots X \ldots Y + X \ldots)$

$$= \text{det} \ (\ldots X \ldots Y \ldots).$$

These axioms are immediately derivable from the ones for **orn** and **vol**. If we continue to think of **det** as **orn**·**vol**, then clearly **det** $(X_1, \ldots, X_n) = 0$ if and only if the parallelotope $X_1, \ldots, X_n$ is degenerate (that is, if and only if the vectors $X_1, \ldots, X_n$ are dependent). But since we are making a fresh start with axioms D_0, D_1, D_2, we will obtain this dependence property as a theorem, namely 2.6 below.

In Section 17 of Chapter 1, we have given an explicit formula for the determinant of an n-by-n matrix. If each column of ·the matrix is interpreted as a vector, then we have defined a certain real-valued function of n vectors $X_1, \ldots, X_n$. It would seem natural now to try to verify the axioms directly for this function. Although such a direct verification is feasible in the 2-by-2 case, it is tedious in higher-dimensional cases. It is more practical first to establish several generally useful algebraic properties of **det**. Then in Section 3 we will be able to argue inductively, using not only the axioms but also their consequences in dimension $n - 1$, to establish D_0, D_1, and D_2 in dimension n. If the columns of a square matrix are interpreted as vectors, the derived properties of **det** will become properties of the determinant of a matrix as listed in Chapter 1. In the present section, however, all our arguments will be conditional. Strictly speaking, each of the Theorems 2.1 through 2.6 that we are about to prove should be announced in the following style: "If **det** is a function with properties D_0, D_1, D_2, then $\ldots$."

2.1 Theorem. **det** $(\ldots 0 \ldots) = 0$.

Proof. Use D_1 with $c = 0$.

2.2 Theorem. **det** $(\ldots X \ldots X \ldots) = 0$.

Proof. By D_1, **det** $(\ldots X \ldots X \ldots) = -$**det** $(\ldots -X \ldots X \ldots)$, and by D_2 and Theorem 2.1,

det $(\ldots -X \ldots X \ldots) = $ **det** $(\ldots 0 \ldots X \ldots) = 0$.

2.3 Theorem.

$$\det (\ldots X + cY \ldots Y \ldots) = \det (\ldots X \ldots cX + Y \ldots)$$

$$= \det (\ldots X \ldots Y \ldots).$$

More generally, $\det (X_1, \ldots, X_n)$ is multiplied by c_i if some X_i is replaced by

$$\sum_{k=1}^{n} c_k X_k.$$

Proof. If $c = 0$, there is nothing to prove. Take $c \neq 0$. Then, using D_1 and D_2,

$$\det (\ldots X + cY \ldots Y \ldots) = -\frac{1}{c} \det (\ldots X + cY \ldots - cY \ldots)$$

$$= -\frac{1}{c} \det (\ldots X \ldots -cY \ldots)$$

$$= \det (\ldots X \ldots Y \ldots).$$

One computes $\det (\ldots X \ldots cX + Y \ldots)$, similarly. The second part of the theorem now follows by repeated application of the first half, and a single application of D_1.

If we hold $n - 1$ of the principal edges of a parallelotope fixed, and regard $\det$ as a function of a single variable edge,

$$X \longrightarrow \det (\ldots X \ldots),$$

then D_1 and 2.4 together assert that this function is a linear functional.

2.4 Theorem.

$$\det (\ldots X + Y \ldots) = \det (\ldots X \ldots) + \det (\ldots Y \ldots).$$

Proof. Consider first the case where the set of n vectors $\ldots X \ldots$ is linearly independent, and hence is a basis. Then Y equals some linear combination

$$cX + \sum_{k \neq i} c_k X_k.$$

And

$$X + Y = (1 + c)X + \sum_{k \neq i} c_k X_k.$$

So we have, using the general version of 2.3,

$\det (\ldots X + Y \ldots)$

$$= \det \left(\ldots (1 + c)X + \sum_{k \neq i} c_k X_k \ldots \right)$$

$$= \det (\ldots (1 + c)X \ldots)$$

$$= (1 + c) \det (\ldots X \ldots)$$

$$= \det (\ldots X \ldots) + c \det (\ldots X \ldots)$$

$$= \det (\ldots X \ldots) + \det (\ldots cX \ldots)$$

$$= \det (\ldots X \ldots) + \det \left(\ldots cX + \sum_{k \neq i} c_k X_k \ldots \right)$$

$$= \det (\ldots X \ldots) + \det (\ldots Y \ldots).$$

If $\ldots X \ldots$ is linearly dependent, but $\ldots Y \ldots$ is linearly independent, then we have essentially the same situation as above. Hence we need finally only consider the case where both sets are linearly dependent. In this case also, $\ldots X + Y \ldots$ is linearly dependent (see Exercise 1). To finish the argument, it is enough to show that every linearly dependent set $X_1, \ldots, X_n$ must have $\det (X_1, \ldots, X_n) = 0$. (For then every determinant in sight will be zero.) But if some X_i is a linear combination of the other X_k, apply the general version of 2.3 with $c_i = 0$. This completes the proof of 2.4.

2.5 Theorem. $\det (\ldots Y \ldots X \ldots) = -\det (\ldots X \ldots Y \ldots).$

Proof. Using 2.4,

$\det (\ldots X + Y \ldots X + Y \ldots) = \det (\ldots X \ldots X \ldots)$

$\qquad + \det (\ldots Y \ldots Y \ldots) + \det (\ldots X \ldots Y \ldots)$

$\qquad\qquad\qquad\qquad\qquad\qquad + \det (\ldots Y \ldots X \ldots).$

But by 2.2,

$\det (\ldots X \ldots X \ldots) = \det (\ldots Y \ldots Y \ldots)$

$\qquad\qquad = \det (\ldots X + Y \ldots X + Y \ldots) = 0.$

2.6 Theorem. $\det (Y_1, \ldots, Y_n) = 0$ if and only if $Y_1, \ldots, Y_n$ are linearly dependent.

Proof. If $Y_1, \ldots, Y_n$ are linearly dependent, then some Y_i can be written as

$$\sum_{k \neq i} c_k Y_k.$$

Hence, by 2.3, with $c_i = 0$, we get

$$\det (Y_1, \ldots, Y_n) = \det \left(\ldots \sum_{k \neq i} c_k Y_k \ldots \right) = 0.$$

Suppose next that $Y_1, \ldots, Y_n$ are linearly independent, and hence constitute a basis. Given any vectors $X_1, \ldots, X_n$, we can write each X as a linear combination of the Y's. Hence using D_1, 2.4 and 2.5, we find that $\det (X_1, \ldots, X_n)$ is a sum of terms each one of which is some multiple of $\det (Y_1, \ldots, Y_n)$. Thus if $\det (Y_1, \ldots, Y_n) = 0$ for this one basis $(Y_1, \ldots, Y_n)$, it follows that $\det (X_1, \ldots, X_n) = 0$ for all choices of vectors $X_1, \ldots, X_n$. This proves 2.6.

We can use the previous theorems to justify, for instance, the formula for the 2-by-2 determinant given in Chapter 1. Let

$$A = \begin{pmatrix} a_1 \\ a_2 \end{pmatrix} \quad \text{and} \quad B = \begin{pmatrix} b_1 \\ b_2 \end{pmatrix}$$

be vectors in $\mathfrak{R}^2$. Then

$$\begin{pmatrix} a_1 \\ a_2 \end{pmatrix} = a_1 E_1 + a_2 E_2 \quad \text{and} \quad \begin{pmatrix} b_1 \\ b_2 \end{pmatrix} = b_1 E_1 + b_2 E_2,$$

where E_1 and E_2 are the natural basis vectors in $\mathfrak{R}^2$. We have

$$\det (A, B) = \det (a_1 E_1 + a_2 E_2, b_1 E_1 + b_2 E_2).$$

From the linearity properties of $\det$ we get

$$\det (A, B) = a_1 b_1 \det (E_1, E_1) + a_2 b_2 \det (E_2, E_2)$$
$$+ a_1 b_2 \det (E_1, E_2) + a_2 b_1 \det (E_2, E_1).$$

Notice that $\det (E_i, E_j) = -\det (E_j, E_i)$. As a result

$$\det (A, B) = (a_1 b_2 - a_2 b_1) \det (E_1, E_2).$$

At this point we have a natural way to remove the factor $\det (E_1, E_2)$. Because the vectors E_1 and E_2 determine a square of area 1 in $\mathfrak{R}^2$ we can use the interpretation of the determinant as an oriented volume. Indeed, requiring that det $(E_1, E_2) = 1$ leads to the formula

$$\mathbf{det} \left(\begin{pmatrix} a_1 \\ a_2 \end{pmatrix}, \begin{pmatrix} b_1 \\ b_2 \end{pmatrix} \right) = a_1 b_2 - a_2 b_1.$$

As we have done in Chapter 1 we can ignore the inner parentheses and use this formula to define the determinant of a 2-by-2 matrix. Then it is straightforward to verify that the determinant thus defined has properties D_0, D_1 and D_2 as a function of the columns of the matrix.

EXERCISES

1. Prove that if each of the n-tuples $(\ldots X \ldots)$ and $(\ldots Y \ldots)$ is linearly dependent, then so is $(\ldots X + Y \ldots)$.

2. Show that if det is a function satisfying D_0, D_1, and D_2, then the product c det, where c is any nonzero real number, also satisfies them.

3. Show that if det and det$'$ are functions satisfying D_1 and D_2, then the sum det $+$ det$'$ also satisfies them. What about D_0?

3. UNIQUENESS AND EXISTENCE OF DETERMINANT FUNCTIONS

A determinant function on an n-dimensional space is a function det defined for each ordered set of n vectors such that the axioms D_0, D_1, D_2 are satisfied. Although we have already developed some of the properties of determinant functions, we have not yet proved that any exist. In this section we shall prove that it is possible to define a determinant function on any n-dimensional vector space. As for uniqueness, we shall show that, given any determinant function, every other determinant function on the same space is a numerical multiple of it.

3.1 Theorem. Suppose det is a determinant function on an n-dimensional space $\mathfrak{X}$. Then, if $a \neq 0$, a det is also a determinant function. Conversely, every determinant function on $\mathfrak{X}$ is such a multiple of det.

Proof. If det $(X_1, \ldots, X_n) \neq 0$, then obviously

$$(a \text{ det})(X_1, \ldots, X_n) = a(\text{det } (X_1, \ldots, X_n)) \neq 0.$$

To check D_1, we write

$$(a \text{ det})(\ldots cX \ldots) = a(\text{det } (\ldots cX \ldots))$$
$$= a(c \text{ det } (\ldots X \ldots))$$
$$= ca \text{ det } (\ldots X \ldots)$$
$$= c(a \text{ det})(\ldots X \ldots).$$

Verification of D_2 is similar. In order to prove the second part of the theorem, let **det′** be an arbitrary determinant function on $\mathfrak{X}$, and let $Y_1, \ldots, Y_n$ be a basis. Since, by Theorem 2.6, **det** $(Y_1, \ldots, Y_n) \neq 0$, we may set

$$a = \frac{\mathbf{det'}\ (Y_1, \ldots, Y_n)}{\mathbf{det}\ (Y_1, \ldots, Y_n)}.$$

Furthermore, $a \neq 0$. It is easy to verify that the function a **det** − **det′** satisfies D_1 and D_2. On the other hand,

$$(a\ \mathbf{det} - \mathbf{det'})\ (Y_1, \ldots, Y_n)$$

$$= a\ \mathbf{det}\ (Y_1, \ldots, Y_n) - \mathbf{det'}\ (Y_1, \ldots, Y_n)$$
$$= 0.$$

Since a **det** − **det′** assigns the value zero to a basis, we conclude from Theorem 2.6 that it is not a determinant function. Since we have checked that D_1 and D_2 hold, it must be D_0 that is not satisfied, and a **det** − **det′** is identically zero. Thus **det′** $= a$ **det**, and the proof is complete.

We turn now to the harder problem of existence. It follows from the preceding theorem that if there is one determinant function on $\mathfrak{X}$, then there are infinitely many. It therefore remains to prove

3.2 Theorem. On every n-dimensional vector space $\mathfrak{X}$, a determinant function exists.

Proof. By induction on n. If $n = 1$, we may pick a basis for $\mathfrak{X}$ consisting of a single vector X_1. Then every vector in $\mathfrak{X}$ is a unique multiple of X_1, and we can define

$$\mathbf{det}\ (aX_1) = a.$$

This function is not identically zero because it assigns the value 1 to X_1. D_1 obviously holds, and D_2 does not apply.

We next assume that $n \geq 2$. Consider a decomposition of $\mathfrak{X}$ into the direct sum of a subspace $\mathfrak{Y}$ having dimension 1 and a subspace $\mathfrak{Z}$ having dimension $n - 1$. This means that every vector X in $\mathfrak{X}$ can be written uniquely $X = Y + Z$ with Y in $\mathfrak{Y}$ and Z in $\mathfrak{Z}$. The induction hypothesis implies that there exists a determinant function **det′** on $\mathfrak{Y}$ and a determinant function **det″** on $\mathfrak{Z}$. The problem is to construct a determinant function for $\mathfrak{X}$ using

det′ and **det″**. The solution is as follows: For any $X_1, \ldots, X_n$ in $\mathfrak{X}$, let

$$X_i = Y_i + Z_i, \qquad i = 1, \ldots, n,$$

where Y_i is in $\mathcal{Y}$ and Z_i is in $\mathcal{Z}$. We define

$$\textbf{det}\ (X_1, \ldots, X_n) = \sum_{j=1}^{n} (-1)^{1+i}\ \textbf{det}′\ (Y_j)$$

$$\cdot \textbf{det}″\ (Z_1, \ldots, \hat{Z}_j, \ldots, Z_n). \qquad (1)$$

Here the notation $(Z_1, \ldots, \hat{Z}_j, \ldots, Z_n)$ stands for the ordered set of $n - 1$ vectors that remains after deleting Z_j from the set $Z_1, \ldots, Z_n$.

It remains to prove that the function **det** defined by equation (1) is actually a determinant function. Let us first prove that it is not identically zero. Pick a basis $W_1, \ldots, W_n$ for $\mathfrak{X}$ with W_1 in $\mathcal{Y}$, and $W_2, \ldots, W_n$ in $\mathcal{Z}$ and such that

$$\textbf{det}′\ (W_1) = \textbf{det}″\ (W_2, \ldots, W_n) = 1.$$

If, to apply formula (1), we write each $W_i = Y_i + Z_i$, then $Y_1 = W_1$ and $Z_1 = 0$, while for $i > 0$ we have $Y_i = 0$ and $Z_i = W_i$. Hence only the first term is different from zero in the sum in formula (1), and we get

$$\textbf{det}\ (W_1, \ldots, W_n) = \textbf{det}′\ (W_1)\ \textbf{det}″\ (W_2, \ldots, W_n) = 1.$$

Verification of D_1 is straightforward. Using D_1 in dimension $n - 1$, and the hypothesis of induction, we obtain

$$\textbf{det}\ (X_1, \ldots, cX_i, \ldots, X_n)$$

$$= \textbf{det}\ (Y_1 + Z_1, \ldots, cY_i + cZ_i, \ldots, Y_n + Z_n)$$

$$= \sum_{\substack{j=1 \\ j \ne i}}^{n} (-1)^{j+1}\ \textbf{det}′\ (Y_j)\ \textbf{det}″\ (Z_1, \ldots, \hat{Z}_j, \ldots, cZ_i, \ldots, Z_n)$$

$$+ (-1)^{i+1}\ \textbf{det}′\ (cY_i)\ \textbf{det}″\ (Z_1, \ldots, \hat{Z}_i, \ldots, Z_n)$$

$$= c \sum_{j=1}^{n} (-1)^{j+1}\ \textbf{det}′\ (Y_j)\ \textbf{det}″\ (Z_1, \ldots, \hat{Z}_j, \ldots, Z_n)$$

$$= c\ \textbf{det}\ (X_1, \ldots, X_n).$$

Verification of D_2 is analogous, but somewhat harder. For notational simplicity we shall content ourselves with proving the special case **det** $(X_1 + X_2, X_2, \ldots, X_n) = $ **det** $(X_1, X_2, \ldots, X_n)$.

Notice that we shall use in dimensions 1 and $n - 1$ not only the axiom D_1 but also the derived property Theorem 2.4.

det $(X_1 + X_2, X_2, \ldots, X_n)$

$$= \textbf{det } (Y_1 + Y_2 + Z_1 + Z_2, Y_2 + Z_2, \ldots, Y_n + Z_n)$$

$$= \textbf{det}' (Y_1 + Y_2) \textbf{ det}'' (Z_2, \ldots, Z_n)$$
$$- \textbf{det}' (Y_2) \textbf{ det}'' (Z_1 + Z_2, Z_3, \ldots, Z_n)$$

$$+ \sum_{j=3}^{n} (-1)^{1+j} \textbf{ det}' (Y_j) \textbf{ det}'' (Z_1 + Z_2, Z_2, \ldots, \hat{Z}_j, \ldots, Z_n).$$

By the additivity of **det**$'$, Theorem 2.4, the first of the above three terms is

det$'$ (Y_1) **det**$''$ $(Z_2, \ldots, Z_n)$ + **det**$'$ (Y_2) **det**$''$ $(Z_2, \ldots, Z_n)$.

The second is

$-$**det**$'$ (Y_2) **det**$''$ $(Z_1, Z_3, \ldots, Z_n)$ $-$ **det**$'$ (Y_2) **det**$''$ $(Z_2, \ldots, Z_n)$.

Applying D_2 (in dimension $n - 1$) to the third term, we get

$$\sum_{j=3}^{n} (-1)^{j+1} \textbf{ det}' (Y_j) \textbf{ det}'' (Z_1, Z_2, \ldots, \hat{Z}_j, \ldots, Z_n).$$

Hence, the total sum is

det $(X_1 + X_2, X_2, \ldots, X_n)$

$$= \sum_{j=1}^{n} (-1)^{1+j} \textbf{ det}' (Y_j) \textbf{ det}'' (Z_1, \ldots, \hat{Z}_j, \ldots, Z_n)$$

$$= \textbf{det } (X_1, \ldots, X_n).$$

This completes the proof of the existence theorem.

It is a corollary of 3.1 that the sum of any two determinant functions on $\mathfrak{X}$ is either a determinant function or the function identically zero. Hence, the results of this section can be neatly summarized as follows.

3.3 Theorem. On an n-dimensional space $\mathfrak{X}$, the determinant functions together with the zero function constitute a 1-dimensional vector space.

In the vector space $\mathfrak{R}^n$ of n-dimensional column vectors, we may define the **standard determinant function** to be the one that assigns the value 1 to the natural basis vectors

$$E_1 = \begin{pmatrix} 1 \\ 0 \\ \cdot \\ \cdot \\ \cdot \\ 0 \end{pmatrix}, \quad E_2 = \begin{pmatrix} 0 \\ 1 \\ \cdot \\ \cdot \\ \cdot \\ 0 \end{pmatrix}, \quad \ldots, \quad E_n = \begin{pmatrix} 0 \\ 0 \\ \cdot \\ \cdot \\ \cdot \\ 1 \end{pmatrix}.$$

3.4 Theorem. Let A be an n-by-n matrix whose columns we denote by $X_1, \ldots, X_n$. If the determinant of A is defined as in Section 17 of Chapter 1 and if **det** is the standard determinant function on $\mathfrak{R}^n$, then

$$\mathbf{det}\ (X_1, \ldots, X_n) = \det A.$$

Proof. By induction on n. For $n = 1$, the theorem is trivial, so we assume that $n \geq 2$. Let us write $\mathfrak{R}^n$ as the direct sum $\mathfrak{R}^n = \mathfrak{R} + \mathfrak{R}^{n-1}$ by decomposing each vector in $\mathfrak{R}^n$ as follows:

$$\begin{pmatrix} x_1 \\ x_2 \\ \cdot \\ \cdot \\ \cdot \\ x_n \end{pmatrix} = \begin{pmatrix} x_1 \\ 0 \\ \cdot \\ \cdot \\ \cdot \\ 0 \end{pmatrix} + \begin{pmatrix} 0 \\ x_2' \\ \cdot \\ \cdot \\ \cdot \\ x_n \end{pmatrix}.$$

We identify the first vector on the right with the number x_1 and the second vector with the column

$$\begin{pmatrix} x_2 \\ \cdot \\ \cdot \\ \cdot \\ x_n \end{pmatrix}$$

in $\mathfrak{R}^{n-1}$. Let **det'** and **det''** be the standard determinant functions on $\mathfrak{R}$ and $\mathfrak{R}^{n-1}$ respectively. We now use formula (1) in the proof of the existence theorem 3.2 to define **det** on $\mathfrak{R}^n$. Applying (1), we get

$$\mathbf{det}\ (X_1, \ldots, X_n)$$

$$= \sum_{j=1}^{n} (-1)^{1+j}\ \mathbf{det'}\ (a_{1j}) \cdot \mathbf{det''}\ (\bar{X}_1, \ldots, \hat{X}_j, \ldots, \bar{X}_n)$$

$$= \sum_{j=1}^{n} (-1)^{1+j} a_{1j}\ \mathbf{det''}\ (\bar{X}_1, \ldots, \hat{X}_j, \ldots, \bar{X}_n), \tag{2}$$

where each $\bar{X}_k$ is obtained from X_k by deleting the 1st coordinate a_{1k}. The preceding equation shows, first of all, that

$$\text{det } (E_1, \ldots, E_n) = 1.$$

Hence **det** is the standard determinant function on $\mathfrak{R}^n$. Next, by the induction hypothesis $\text{det}'' (\bar{X}_1, \ldots, \hat{X}_j, \ldots, X_n)$ equals the determinant (as defined in Section 17, Chapter 1) of the minor matrix A_{1j} obtained by deleting the 1st row and jth column of A. Hence, using (2) and the definition of **det** A in Section 17, Chapter 1, we get

$$\text{det } (X_1, \ldots, X_n) = \sum_{j=1}^{n} (-1)^{1+j} a_{1j} \text{ det } A_{1j} = \text{det } A.$$

This completes the proof.

EXERCISES

1. Given a determinant function **det** on an n-dimensional vector space $\mathfrak{X}$, define

$$\text{vol} = \left| \text{ det} \right|$$

$$\text{orn} = \frac{\text{det}}{\left| \text{ det} \right|},$$

and verify that these functions satisfy the axioms for volume and orientation in Section 1.

2. Prove that on an n-dimensional vector space there are precisely two orientation functions that satisfy the axioms O_0, O_1, O_2. How are these two functions related?

3. Give the details in the proof of Theorem 3.3 using 3.1 and 3.2.

4. DETERMINANTS OF LINEAR TRANSFORMATIONS AND MATRICES

Let **A** be a linear transformation of an n-dimensional vector space $\mathfrak{X}$ *into itself.* Choose a determinant function **det** on $\mathfrak{X}$, and define the function **d** by

$$\mathbf{d}(X_1, \ldots, X_n) = \text{det } (\mathbf{A}X_1, \ldots, \mathbf{A}X_n), \tag{1}$$

for all $X_1, \ldots, X_n$ in $\mathfrak{X}$. It is easy to check that **d** has the properties D_1 and D_2. Hence, if **d** is not identically zero, it is a determinant function, and so by Theorem 3.1 we have

$$\mathbf{d} = a \text{ det} \tag{2}$$

for some number $a \neq 0$. On the other hand, if **d** is the zero function, equation (2) still holds with $a = 0$. The number a is by definition the

determinant of the linear transformation A, which we shall denote by **det A.** Combining (1) and (2), we obtain the defining equation

$$\text{det } \mathbf{A} \text{ det } (X_1, \ldots, X_n) = \text{det } (\mathbf{A}X_1, \ldots, \mathbf{A}X_n). \tag{3}$$

It is important to know that the number $a = \text{det } \mathbf{A}$ depends only on **A** and not on the particular choice of the determinant function **det**. In fact, if we multiply the latter function by some number b, then the defining Equation (3) is simply multiplied on both sides by b, leaving **det A** unchanged. Hence the determinant of a linear transformation is a unique number, unlike the determinant functions on $\mathfrak{X}$, which are determined only up to a constant multiple.

Geometrically, the absolute value of **det A** is the amount by which **A** stretches volume. For the absolute value of any determinant function is a volume function satisfying the axioms V_0, V_1, V_2 of Section 1. Thus, setting **vol** $= |\text{ det }|$ in Equation (3), we get

$$\text{vol } (\mathbf{A}X_1, \ldots, \mathbf{A}X_n) = |\text{ det } \mathbf{A} |\text{ vol } (X_1, \ldots, X_n).$$

The parallelepiped spanned by $X_1, \ldots, X_n$ is therefore transformed by **A** into a parallelepiped having $|\text{ det } \mathbf{A} |$ times the volume of the original one.

If **det A** is positive, the transformation **A** leaves the orientation of every ordered basis unchanged. If the determinant is negative, the orientation is reversed. To see that this is so, observe that $\text{det}/|\text{ det }|$ is an orientation function having the properties O_0, O_1, O_2 described in Section 1. Setting **orn** $= \text{det}/|\text{ det }|$, we obtain from equation (3) that

$$\pm 1 = \frac{\text{det } \mathbf{A}}{|\text{ det } \mathbf{A} |} = \frac{\text{orn } (\mathbf{A}X_1, \ldots, \mathbf{A}X_n)}{\text{orn } (X_1, \ldots, X_n)},$$

provided **det A** $\neq 0$ and $X_1, \ldots, X_n$ are independent. It follows that **orn** $(\mathbf{A}X_1, \ldots, \mathbf{A}X_n)$ and **orn** $(X_1, \ldots, X_n)$ have the same or opposite signs according as **det A** is positive or negative.

Here are some properties of the determinant of a linear transformation.

4.1 Theorem. **det A** $\neq 0$ if and only if **A** is invertible.

Proof. Let $X_1, \ldots, X_n$ be a basis. If **A** is invertible, then $\mathbf{A}X_1, \ldots, \mathbf{A}X_n$ is also a basis, and

$$\text{det } \mathbf{A} \text{ det } (X_1, \ldots, X_n) = \text{det } (\mathbf{A}X_1, \ldots, \mathbf{A}X_n).$$

By 2.6 both **det** $(X_1, \ldots, X_n) \neq 0$ and **det** $(\mathbf{A}X_1, \ldots, \mathbf{A}X_n) \neq 0$. Hence also **det A** $\neq 0$. On the other hand, if **A** is not invertible, then $\mathbf{A}X_1, \ldots, \mathbf{A}X_n$ are linearly dependent. Hence, by 2.6, **det** $(\mathbf{A}X_1, \ldots, \mathbf{A}X_n) = 0$, and so **det A** $= 0$.

4.2 Theorem. det $(AB) = (\det A)(\det B)$.

Proof. Let $X_1, \ldots, X_n$ be a basis. Then,

$$\det (AB) \det (X_1, \ldots, X_n) = \det (ABX_1, \ldots, ABX_n)$$
$$= \det A \det (BX_1, \ldots, BX_n)$$
$$= (\det A)(\det B) \det (X_1, \ldots, X_n).$$

Since $\det (X_1, \ldots, X_n) \neq 0$, we can cancel.

4.3 Theorem. If I is the identity, then $\det I = 1$. More generally, $\det (cI) = c^n$, where n is the dimension of the vector space.

Proof. Let $X_1, \ldots, X_n$ be a basis. Then

$$\det (cI) \det (X_1, \ldots, X_n) = \det (cX_1, \ldots, cX_n)$$
$$= c^n \det (X_1, \ldots, X_n).$$

Again, $\det (X_1, \ldots, X_n) \neq 0$, and we may cancel.

4.4 Corollary. If A is invertible, then $\det A^{-1} = (\det A)^{-1}$.

Proof. $(\det A^{-1})(\det A) = \det (A^{-1}A) = \det I = 1$.

The next theorem connects the determinant of a linear transformation with the determinant of a matrix as it is defined in Section 17 of Chapter 1.

4.5 Theorem. The determinant of a linear transformation equals the determinant of any matrix that defines the transformation. More explicitly, if $\mathfrak{X} \overset{A}{\to} \mathfrak{X}$ is a linear transformation and Γ is any basis for $\mathfrak{X}$, then

$$\det A = \det \begin{pmatrix} A \\ \Gamma\Gamma \end{pmatrix}.$$

Proof. The function **det** which assigns to each set of vectors $X_1, \ldots, X_n$ in $\mathfrak{X}$ the determinant of the matrix whose columns are

$$\begin{pmatrix} X_1 \\ \Gamma \end{pmatrix}, \ldots, \begin{pmatrix} X_n \\ \Gamma \end{pmatrix}$$

is a determinant function. Let $\Gamma = (Y_1, \ldots, Y_n)$. Then,

$$\begin{pmatrix} Y_k \\ \Gamma \end{pmatrix} = E_k, \quad k = 1, \ldots, n,$$

so $\det (Y_1, \ldots, Y_n) = \det I = 1$.

From Equation (3), which defines the determinant of a linear transformation, we therefore get

$$\det \mathbf{A} = \det \, (\mathbf{A}Y_1, \ldots, \mathbf{A}Y_n).$$

However, the columns of $\begin{pmatrix} \mathbf{A} \\ \Gamma\Gamma \end{pmatrix}$ are precisely the vectors

$$\begin{pmatrix} \mathbf{A}Y_1 \\ \Gamma \end{pmatrix}, \ldots, \begin{pmatrix} \mathbf{A}Y_n \\ \Gamma \end{pmatrix}.$$

Hence,

$$\det \mathbf{A} = \det \, (AY_1, \ldots, AY_n) = \det \begin{pmatrix} \mathbf{A} \\ \Gamma\Gamma \end{pmatrix}.$$

and the proof is complete.

As a result of 4.5, the properties of the determinant of a linear transformation enumerated in Theorems 4.1 through 4.4 also hold for the determinant of a matrix.

The theory of determinants can also be developed from the theory of elementary operations as set forth in Sections 2 and 4 of Chapter 1. For let A be an n-by-n matrix. By elementary operations we can decide whether A is singular or invertible. If A is singular, then $\det A = 0$. If A is invertible, then A equals some product $Q_1 \ldots Q_s$ of elementary matrices. These are the inverses of the matrices that represent the elementary operations used to bring A into reduced form. (See Theorem 4.1, Section 4, Chapter 1.) By virtue of the product rule, Theorem 4.2, it follows that to compute $\det A$ we need only know how to compute $\det Q$, where Q is an elementary matrix.

4.6 Theorem. If Q is the matrix corresponding to an elementary multiplication by $c \neq 0$, then $\det Q = c$.

4.7 Theorem. If Q is the matrix corresponding to an elementary addition, then $\det Q = 1$.

Notice that we have not specified whether the elementary operations are being applied to rows or to columns. This is because the set of all matrices corresponding to elementary row operations is the same as the set of all matrices corresponding to elementary column operations. If Q is an elementary matrix, then QA is the result of applying a row operation to A, and AQ is the result of applying a column operation. The proofs of 4.6 and 4.7 follow directly from the form of an elementary matrix. If multiplication by Q multiplies the ith row by c, then

$$Q = \begin{pmatrix} 1 & 0 & & \cdot & \cdot & \cdot & & 0 \\ 0 & 1 & & & & & & \\ \cdot & & 1 & & & & & \\ \cdot & & & c & & & & \\ \cdot & & & & 1 & & & \cdot \\ \cdot & & & & & & \cdot & \\ 0 & \cdot & & \cdot & \cdot & \cdot & & 1 \end{pmatrix}$$

where the c occurs in the ith row and ith column. If forming QA adds the jth row of A to its ith row, then

$$Q = \begin{pmatrix} 1 & & \cdot & \cdot & \cdot & \\ \cdot & 1 & & 1 & \cdot & \cdot & \cdot \\ \cdot & & \cdot & & & \\ \cdot & & & 1 & & \\ & & & & 1 & \\ 0 & & \cdot & \cdot & \cdot & 1 \end{pmatrix}$$

where the 1 off the diagonal occurs in the ith row and jth column. It is easy to compute the determinants of these two matrices.

The following remark is obvious.

If Q is an elementary matrix, then $\det Q = \det Q^t$. We can apply this fact to prove the following generalization of it.

4.8 Theorem. For any n-by-n matrix A, $\det A^t = \det A$.

Proof. First, suppose that A has an inverse. We know from Theorem 4.1 of Chapter 1 that A can be written as a product of elementary matrices. Thus

$$A = Q_1 \cdot Q_2 \ldots Q_k.$$

But then

$$\det A^t = \det (Q_1 \ldots Q_k)^t$$

$$= \det Q_k^t \ldots Q_1^t$$

$$= \det Q_k^t \ldots \det Q_1^t.$$

We have observed that $\det Q^t = \det Q$ for an elementary matrix Q, so

$$\det A^t = \det Q_k \ldots \det Q_1$$

$$= \det Q_1 \ldots \det Q_k$$

$$= \det (Q_1 \ldots Q_k)$$

$$= \det A.$$

In case A fails to have an inverse we will show that A^t has no inverse, and hence by Theorem 4.1, that $\det A$ and $\det A^t$ are both zero. Suppose A^t had an inverse, call it B. Then $A^t B = I$. Transposing the matrices on each side, we get $B^t A = I$. But then A has an inverse, contradicting the assumption that it hasn't. This completes the proof.

5. DETERMINANTS IN EUCLIDEAN SPACE

Let $\mathfrak{X}$ be an n-dimensional vector space with an inner product $X \cdot Y$, making it a euclidean space. At the end of Section 16 of Chapter 1 we discussed linear transformations $\mathbf{A}$ that preserve the inner product, that is, such that $\mathbf{A}X \cdot \mathbf{A}Y = X \cdot Y$. Suppose that such a transformation has matrix A *with respect to an orthonormal basis*. Then we have observed that A is an orthogonal matrix and that, for any orthogonal matrix A, $A^{-1} = A^t$. As a related fact we have the following theorem.

5.1 Theorem. If A is an orthogonal matrix, then $\det A = \pm 1$.

Proof. We have $(\det A)^2 = (\det A)(\det A^t)$, because $\det A = \det A^t$. Then, since $A^t = A^{-1}$,

$$(\det A)^2 = (\det A)(\det A^{-1})$$

$$= \det (A A^{-1})$$

$$= \det I = 1.$$

The next theorem is important because it expresses the fact that, when a determinant function is normalized by making it 1 on some orthonormal basis, it will automatically assign the value 1 to every other orthonormal parallelotope with the same orientation. Of course, for those with the opposite orientation we will get -1. The reason for this is that two orthonormal bases are related by an orthogonal matrix, and that an orthogonal matrix has determinant ± 1.

5.2 Theorem. Let $X_1, \ldots, X_n$ be an orthonormal basis for $\mathfrak{X}$. If **det** is chosen so that $\mathbf{det}\,(X_1, \ldots, X_n) = 1$, then $\mathbf{det}\,(Y_1, \ldots, Y_n) = \pm 1$ for every other orthonormal basis $Y_1, \ldots, Y_n$.

Proof. Let the linear transformation **A** be defined by $\mathbf{A}X_j = Y_j$, $j = 1, \ldots, n$. The matrix $A = (a_{ij})$ of this transformation with respect to $X_1, \ldots, X_n$ is defined by

$$Y_j = \mathbf{A}X_j = \sum_{i=1}^{n} a_{ij}X_i, \qquad j = 1, \ldots, n.$$

By Theorem 16.1 of Chapter 1, A is an orthogonal matrix, and so $\det A = \pm 1$. By Theorem 4.5, $\mathbf{det}\,\mathbf{A} = \det A$. Hence, using the definition of the determinant of a linear transformation, we get

$$\mathbf{det}\,(Y_1, \ldots, Y_n) = \mathbf{det}\,(\mathbf{A}X_1, \ldots, \mathbf{A}X_n)$$
$$= \mathbf{det}\,\mathbf{A}\,\mathbf{det}\,(X_1, \ldots, X_n)$$
$$= \mathbf{det}\,\mathbf{A}$$
$$= \pm 1.$$

This completes the proof.

Appendix II

Proofs of Calculus Theorems

1. INTRODUCTION

The fundamental theorems of analysis are derived from the algebraic properties and also from the limit properties of $\mathfrak{R}^n$. In this book we have taken as assumptions two basic limit properties. The first and more fundamental concerns the notion of *supremum* and *infimum*.

The **supremum** of a set S of real numbers is a number s with the properties (a) if x is in S, then $x \leq s$; (b) if y is a number such that $x \leq y$ for all x in S, then $s \leq y$. The definition of the **infimum** of S is obtained by reversing the inequalities in the above two conditions. For many sets, the supremum is the same as the maximum element and the infimum is the same as the minimum element. On the other hand, the open interval $0 < x < 1$ has infimum and supremum equal 0 and 1, respectively, but the interval has neither a minimum nor maximum element. It can be proved from the definition of the real numbers that *every bounded subset of the real numbers has an infimum and a supremum.*

The second limit property is itself a consequence of the first. *If the function* $\Re^n \xrightarrow{f} \Re$ *is continuous and K is a closed bounded subset of the domain of f, then there exists a point* X_0 *in K such that*

$$fX \leq fX_0, \quad \text{for all } X \text{ in } K.$$

This theorem is frequently paraphrased by saying that a continuous function on a closed bounded set attains its maximum. The two functions f and g defined by

$$f(x) = \frac{1}{x}, \qquad 0 < x \leq 1,$$

$$g(x) = \begin{cases} 1, & 0 \leq x \leq 1, \\ \dfrac{1}{x - 1}, & 1 < x \leq 2, \end{cases}$$

illustrate the necessity of the two hypotheses of the theorem. Neither of these functions attains a maximum value on its domain. The trouble is that although f is continuous, its domain is not closed. On the other hand, the domain of g is closed and bounded, but g is not continuous.

Replacement of f by $-f$ shows that *a continuous function on a closed bounded set attains its minimum.*

2. EQUIVALENCE OF NORMS

Basic to calculus are the **limit definitions**: limit point, limit, continuity, interior point, open set, boundary, closed set, and differentiability. Each of these has been given directly or indirectly in terms of the euclidean norm on $\Re^n$, with respect to which the distance between two points $X = (x_1, \ldots, x_n)$ and $Y = (y_1, \ldots, y_n)$ is the number

$$|X - Y| = [(x_1 - y_1)^2 + \ldots + (x_n - y_n)^2]^{1/2}.$$

The same definitions can be made in an arbitrary vector space provided a norm is given. We recall that a norm on $\mathfrak{X}$ is a real-valued function $\| \ \|$ with domain equal to $\mathfrak{X}$ and with the three properties

Positivity: $\| X \| > 0,$ except that $\| 0 \| = 0.$

Homogeneity: $\| aX \| = | a | \| X \|.$

Triangle Inequality: $\| X + Y \| \leq \| X \| + \| Y \|.$

The purpose of this section is to prove that in a finite-dimensional vector space the limit definitions are independent of the choice of norm. That is, if X_0 is a limit point of a set S with respect to one norm, then it is a limit point of S with respect to every norm, and the same goes for the other definitions referred to above. It follows, in particular, that these basic limit concepts are in no way dependent upon a euclidean inner product.

For any two norms $\| \ \|_1$ and $\| \ \|_2$ on a vector space $\mathfrak{X}$, we define $\| \ \|_1$ to be **equivalent** to $\| \ \|_2$ if there exist positive real numbers k and K such that, for any X in $\mathfrak{X}$,

$$k \, \| \, X \, \|_1 \leq \| \, X \, \|_2 \leq K \, \| \, X \, \|_1. \tag{1}$$

It is easy to check that this is a true equivalence relation, that is, it satisfies the three requirements

Reflexivity: Every norm is equivalent to itself.

Symmetry: $\| \ \|_1$ is equivalent to $\| \ \|_2$ if and only if $\| \ \|_2$ is equivalent to $\| \ \|_1$.

Transitivity: If $\| \ \|_1$ is equivalent to $\| \ \|_2$ and if $\| \ \|_2$ is equivalent to $\| \ \|_3$, then $\| \ \|_1$ is equivalent to $\| \ \|_3$.

More important is the fact that equivalent norms result in the same definitions of limit point, limit, interior point, and differentiability. Continuity, open set, boundary, and closed set, which are defined in terms of the preceding concepts, are therefore also independent of a choice between equivalent norms.

To verify the above contention, let $\| \ \|_1$ and $\| \ \|_2$ be equivalent norms, and suppose that X_0 is a limit point of S with respect to $\| \ \|_1$. Then, for any $\epsilon_1 > 0$, there exists a point X in S such that $0 < \| \, X - X_0 \, \|_1 < \epsilon_1$. Thus, if $\epsilon_2 > 0$ is given arbitrarily, we may set $\epsilon_1 = \epsilon_2/K$ and obtain, by inequality (1),

$$0 < \| \, X - X_0 \, \|_2 \leq K \, \| \, X - X_0 \, \|_1 < K\epsilon_1 = \epsilon_2.$$

Hence, X_0 is a limit point of S with respect to $\| \ \|_2$. Suppose, next, that with respect to $\| \ \|_1$ we have

$$\lim_{X \to X_0} fX = Y_0.$$

Then, as we have just proved, X_0 is a limit point of the domain of f with respect to both norms. For any $\epsilon_1 > 0$, there exists $\delta_1 > 0$ such that if X is in the domain of f and $0 < \| \, X - X_0 \, \|_1 < \delta_1$, then $\| \, fX - Y_0 \, \|_1 < \epsilon_1$. Let $\epsilon_2 > 0$ be given arbitrarily, set $\epsilon_1 = \epsilon_2/K$, and then choose $\delta_2 = \delta_1 k$.

If $0 < \|X - X_0\|_2 < \delta_2$, it follows by inequality (1) that

$$0 < \|X - X_0\|_1 \leq \frac{1}{k}\|X - X_0\|_2 < \frac{\delta_2}{k} = \delta_1.$$

Hence,

$$\|fX - Y_0\|_2 \leq K\|fX - Y_0\|_1 < K\epsilon_1 = \epsilon_2,$$

and we conclude that $\lim fX = Y_0$ with respect to $\|\ \ \|_2$. The arguments for the definitions of interior point and differentiability are similar, and we omit the details.

With respect to a given norm on a vector space $\mathfrak{X}$, the ϵ-**ball with center** X_0 is the set of all X in $\mathfrak{X}$ such that $\|X - X_0\| < \epsilon$. In general, an ϵ-ball doesn't look very ball-like. For example, with respect to the box norm on $\mathfrak{R}^2$ every ϵ-ball is a parallelogram (see Figure 16 in Chapter 2, p. 184). It follows directly from the inequalities (1) that two norms are equivalent if and only if any ϵ-ball about X_0 with respect to one norm is contained in some δ-ball about X_0 with respect to the other norm, and vice versa (see Figure 1).

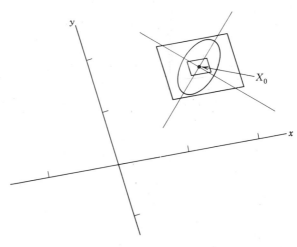

FIGURE 1

We now turn to the principal theorem:

2.1 Theorem. Any two norms on a finite-dimensional vector space $\mathfrak{X}$ are equivalent.

Proof. Let $\|\ \ \|$ be an arbitrary norm on $\mathfrak{X}$. Choose a basis $\{X_1, \ldots, X_n\}$ for $\mathfrak{X}$, and define a euclidean norm on $\mathfrak{X}$ by setting

$$|X| = \sqrt{x_1^2 + \ldots + x_n^2},$$

for any $X = x_1 X_1 + \ldots + x_n X_n$. We shall show that $\| \quad \|$ is equivalent to $| \quad |$, that is, there exist positive real numbers k and K such that $k \mid X \mid \leq \| X \| \leq K \mid X \mid$, for all X in $\mathfrak{X}$. By the transitivity property of the equivalence relation between norms, it then follows that any two norms on $\mathfrak{X}$ are equivalent.

For any $X = x_1 X_1 + \ldots + x_n X_n$, we have

$$\| X \| \leq \sum_{i=1}^{n} \mid x_i \mid \| X_i \| \leq \left(\sum_{i=1}^{n} \| X_i \| \right) \max_i \{\mid x_i \mid\}$$

$$\leq \left(\sum_{i=1}^{n} \| X_i \| \right) \sqrt{\sum_{i=1}^{n} x_i^2} = K \mid X \mid,$$

where $K = \sum_{i=1}^{n} \| X_i \| > 0$. We now prove that k exists. We contend that as a function of X the real-valued function $\| \quad \|$ is continuous with respect to the euclidean norm $| \quad |$. For if $\epsilon > 0$ is given, we pick $\delta = \epsilon / K$. Then, if $\mid X - X_0 \mid < \delta$,

$$\mid \| X \| - \| X_0 \| \mid \leq \| X - X_0 \| \leq K \mid X - X_0 \mid < \epsilon.$$

Let k be the minimum value of the function $\| \quad \|$ restricted to the euclidean unit sphere $\mid X \mid = 1$. Then, for any $X \neq 0$, it follows that $\| X / \mid X \mid \| \geq k$, and hence that

$$\| X \| \geq k \mid X \mid, \qquad \text{for any } X \text{ in } \mathfrak{X}.$$

This completes the proof of the equivalence of norms.

3. PROOF OF THE INVERSE FUNCTION THEOREM

The deepest mathematics in Chapter 2 is contained in the inverse and implicit function theorems, Theorems 8.2 and 10.3, respectively. The former, which we have not yet proved, served as the basis of our proof of the latter. The purpose of this section is to fill the gap in the argument. We begin with the following lemma.

3.1 Lemma. A linear transformation $\mathfrak{R}^n \overset{L}{\to} \mathfrak{R}^n$ is one-one if and only if there exists a positive real number m such that, for any X in $\mathfrak{R}^n$,

$$\mid LX \mid \geq m \mid X \mid.$$

Proof. If L is not one-one, there exists a nonzero vector X_0 such that $LX_0 = 0$. Then, for any positive real number m,

$$0 = \mid LX_0 \mid < m \mid X_0 \mid.$$

Conversely, suppose L is one-one. Then the inverse function is a linear transformation $\mathfrak{R}^n \xrightarrow{L^{-1}} \mathfrak{R}^n$. By Theorem 2.7 of Chapter 2, there exists a positive real number k such that

$$| L^{-1}Y | \leq k \, | \, Y \, | \qquad \text{for all } Y \text{ in } \mathfrak{R}^n.$$

Setting $m = 1/k$, we therefore obtain, for any X in $\mathfrak{R}^n$,

$$m \, | \, X \, | = m \, | \, L^{-1}LX \, | \leq mk \, | \, LX \, | = | \, LX \, |.$$

This completes the proof.

A function $\mathfrak{R}^n \xrightarrow{f} \mathfrak{R}^m$ is continuously differentiable at X_0 if the function that assigns to each X the differential $d_X f$ is continuous at X_0. Since continuity has been defined with respect to a norm, it is desirable when working with the notion of continuous differentiability to choose a norm on the space of differentials, that is, on the vector space $\mathfrak{L}$ of linear transformations $\mathfrak{R}^n \xrightarrow{L} \mathfrak{R}^m$. It was pointed out in Chapter 2, Section 2, and actually proved in Section 2 of Appendix II that one norm is as good as another. A convenient norm for $\mathfrak{L}$ is defined as follows: For every linear transformation $\mathfrak{R}^n \xrightarrow{L} \mathfrak{R}^m$, Theorem 2.7 of Chapter 2 assures the existence of a positive real number k with the property that

$$| LX | \leq k \, | \, X \, |, \qquad \text{for all } X \text{ in } R^n. \tag{1}$$

We define $\| L \|$ to be the *infimum* of all such numbers k. The reader should supply the simple proofs that

(a) The function $L \to \| L \|$ is a norm on $\mathfrak{L}$, that is, it satisfies Theorems 2.4, 2.5, and 2.6, and

(b) For any $\mathfrak{R}^n \xrightarrow{L} \mathfrak{R}^m$,

$$| LX | \leq \| L \| \, | \, X \, |, \qquad \text{for all } X \text{ in } \mathfrak{R}^n. \tag{2}$$

Notice that the proof that the function $L \to \| L \|$ is a norm makes no use of any distinguishing features of the euclidean norms on $\mathfrak{R}^n$ and $\mathfrak{R}^m$. An equivalent norm on $\mathfrak{L}$ can be defined in the same way with respect to any two norms on $\mathfrak{R}^n$ and $\mathfrak{R}^m$.

3.2 Lemma. Let $\mathfrak{R}^n \xrightarrow{f} \mathfrak{R}^n$ be a differentiable function that is continuously differentiable at X_0 and such that $d_{X_0} f$ is one-one. Then there exist positive real numbers δ and M such that if $| \, X - X_0 \, | < \delta$, then

$$| \, (d_X f) \, Y \, | \geq M \, | \, Y \, |, \qquad \text{for any } Y \text{ in } \mathfrak{R}^n.$$

Proof. By Lemma 3.1, there exists $m > 0$ such that

$$| \, (d_{X_0} f) \, Y \, | \geq m \, | \, Y \, |, \qquad \text{for any } Y \text{ in } \mathfrak{R}^n.$$

Since f is continuously differentiable at X_0, there exists $\delta > 0$ such that if $| \, X - X_0 \, | < \delta$, then $\| d_X f - d_{X_0} f \| < m/2$. Hence, by

Inequality (2), for any Y in $\mathfrak{R}^n$, we have

$$| (d_X f - d_{X_0} f) Y | \le \| d_X f - d_{X_0} f \| \, | Y | \le \frac{m}{2} | Y |.$$

It follows by the triangle inequality that

$$| (d_X f) Y | \ge | (d_{X_0} f) Y | - | (d_X f - d_{X_0} f) Y | \ge \frac{m}{2} | Y |.$$

The proof is completed by setting $M = m/2$.

It is a consequence of 3.1 and 3.2 that if a differentiable function $\mathfrak{R}^n \xrightarrow{f} \mathfrak{R}^n$ is continuously differentiable at X_0 and if $d_{X_0} f$ is one-one, then $d_X f$ is one-one in a neighborhood of X_0. The following is the key lemma in the proof of the inverse function theorem.

3.3 Lemma. Let $\mathfrak{R}^n \xrightarrow{f} \mathfrak{R}^n$ be a differentiable function that is continuously differentiable at X_0 and such that $d_{X_0} f$ is one-one. Then there exist positive real numbers δ and M such that $| fX' - fX | \ge M | X' - X |$ whenever $| X - X_0 | < \delta$ and $| X' - X_0 | < \delta$.

Proof. By Lemma 3.1, there exists $m > 0$ such that

$$| (d_{X_0} f) Y | \ge m | Y |, \qquad \text{for all } Y \text{ in } \mathfrak{R}^n. \tag{3}$$

Set $M = m/2\sqrt{n}$. Since f is continuously differentiable at X_0, there exists $\delta > 0$ such that if $| X - X_0 | < \delta$, then $\| d_X f - d_{X_0} f \| < M$. Let X and X' be any two vectors satisfying $| X - X_0 | < \delta$ and $| X' - X_0 | < \delta$. We set $Z = X' - X$. Then, for all t in the interval $0 \le t \le 1$,

$$| X + tZ - X_0 | = | tX' + (1 - t)X - X_0 |$$
$$= | t(X' - X_0) + (1 - t)(X - X_0) |$$
$$\le t | X' - X_0 | + (1 - t) | X - X_0 | < \delta,$$

that is, the δ-ball about X_0 is convex (see Figure 2). We conclude that $\| d_{X+tZ} f - d_{X_0} f \| < M$, and thence, by Inequality (2), that

$$| (d_{X+tZ} f - d_{X_0} f) Y | \le M | Y |,$$

$$\left\{ \begin{aligned} &\text{for any } Y \text{ in } \mathfrak{R}^n, \\ &0 \le t \le 1. \end{aligned} \right. \tag{4}$$

For each $k = 1, \ldots, n$, let $\mathfrak{R}^n \xrightarrow{\pi_k} \mathfrak{R}$ be the projection on the kth coordi-

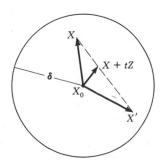

FIGURE 2

nate axis, that is, $\pi_k(x_1, \ldots, x_n) = x_k$. We define a set of real-valued functions $g_1, \ldots, g_n$ of a real variable by

$$g_k(t) = \pi_k f(X + tZ), \qquad \begin{cases} k = 1, \ldots, n, \\ 0 \leq t \leq 1. \end{cases}$$

Since every linear transformation, and in particular π_k, is its own differential, it follows from the chain rule that

$$g_k'(t) = \pi_k(d_{X+tZ} f)Z.$$

By the mean-value theorem, there exists t_k satisfying $0 < t_k < 1$ such that $g_k(1) - g_k(0) = g_k'(t_k)$. Hence,

$$\pi_k fX' - \pi_k fX = \pi_k(d_{X+t_kZ} f)Z.$$

Using the triangle inequality, we therefore obtain

$$|fX' - fX| \geq |\pi_k fX' - \pi_k fX|$$

$$\geq |\pi_k(d_{X_0} f)Z| - |\pi_k(d_{X+t_kZ} f - d_{X_0} f)Z|.$$

Now, for every $k = 1, \ldots, n$,

$$|\pi_k(d_{X+t_kZ} f - d_{X_0} f)Z| \leq |(d_{X+t_kZ} f - d_{X_0} f)Z|.$$

Since, the length of any vector in $\mathfrak{R}^n$ is less than or equal to $\sqrt{n}$ times the maximum of the absolute values of its coordinates, we have that, for at least one $k = 1, \ldots, n$,

$$|\pi_k(d_{X_0} f)Z| \geq \frac{1}{\sqrt{n}}|(d_{X_0} f)Z|.$$

Hence,

$$|fX' - fX| \geq \frac{1}{\sqrt{n}}|(d_{X_0} f)Z| - |(d_{X+t_kZ} f - d_{X_0} f)Z|.$$

Finally, therefore, by Inequalities (3) and (4), we obtain

$$|fX' - fX| \geq 2M|Z| - M|Z| = M|X' - X|,$$

and the proof is complete.

We are now ready to prove the inverse function theorem. The statement of this theorem that appears below is somewhat stronger than the one in the text (see Theorem 8.2, Chapter 2).

3.4 Inverse function theorem. Let $\mathfrak{R}^n \xrightarrow{f} \mathfrak{R}$ be a continuously differentiable function such that $d_{X_0} f$ is one-one. Then there is a neighborhood N of

X_0 such that f restricted to N has a continuously differentiable inverse f^{-1}. The image set fN is open. For any point X in N,

$$d_Y f^{-1} = (d_X f)^{-1}, \qquad \text{where } Y = fX.$$

Proof. By Lemmas 3.2 and 3.3, there exist positive real numbers δ and M such that, where N is the set of all X such that $|X - X_0| < \delta$, we have

$$|(d_X f) Y| \geq M |Y|, \qquad \text{for any } X \text{ in } N, \text{ and } Y \text{ in } \mathfrak{R}^n. \tag{5}$$

$$|fX' - fX| \geq M |X - X'|, \qquad \text{for any } X \text{ and } X' \text{ in } N. \tag{6}$$

It follows from relation (6) that if $X \neq X'$, then $fX \neq fX'$. Thus f restricted to N is one-one and consequently has an inverse f^{-1}. It remains to prove:

I. *The image set fN is open.* Let Y_1 be an arbitrary point in fN. We must show that every Y in $\mathfrak{R}^n$ sufficiently close to Y_1 also lies in fN. Let X_1 be the pre-image in N of Y_1, that is, $fX_1 = Y_1$. Since N is open, there exists $\delta_1 > 0$ such that the set B of all X such that $|X - X_1| \leq \delta_1$ is contained in N (see Figure 3). Notice that B

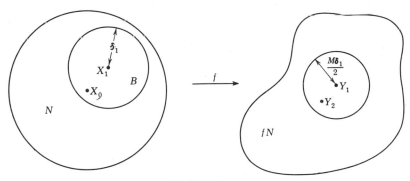

FIGURE 3

contains its boundary. We contend that the number $M\delta_1/2$ is an adequate measure of what is sufficiently close to Y_1. Hence let Y_2 be an arbitrary vector such that $|Y_2 - Y_1| < M\delta_1/2$. The proof of part I is completed by showing that there exists a vector X_2 in N (actually in B) such that $fX_2 = Y_2$. Let X_2 be a vector in B such that the distance between Y_2 and fX_2 is a minimum. Minimizing distance is the same as minimizing the square of distance. Hence, X_2 is a minimum point for the function g defined by

$$gX = |fX - Y_2|^2 = (fX - Y_2) \cdot (fX - Y_2), \qquad \text{for any } X \text{ in } B.$$

We claim that X_2 lies in the interior of B. For suppose otherwise; that is, suppose that $|X_2 - X_1| = \delta_1$. Then, by relation (6),

$$|fX_2 - Y_1| = |fX_2 - fX_1| \geq M|X_2 - X_1| = M\delta_1.$$

Hence, by the triangle inequality,

$$|fX_2 - Y_2| \geq |fX_2 - Y_1| - |Y_1 - Y_2| > \frac{M\delta_1}{2} > |Y_1 - Y_2|$$

$$= |fX_1 - Y_2|,$$

and this contradicts the minimality of $|fX_2 - Y_2|$. We conclude (see Theorem 1.1 of Chapter 3) that $d_{X_2}g = 0$. It follows by the chain rule and the expression for the differential of the square of the euclidean norm (see Exercise 14, Section 4, Chapter 2) that, for any Z in $\Re^n$,

$$0 = (d_{X_2}g)Z = 2(fX_2 - Y_2) \cdot (d_{X_2}f)Z. \tag{7}$$

We know, by relation (5) and Lemma 3.1, that $d_{X_2}f$ is one-one. Its range is therefore equal to $\Re^n$, and there therefore exists a vector Z such that $(d_{X_2}f)Z = fX_2 - Y_2$. Thus, by Equation (7),

$$0 = 2(fX_2 - Y_2) \cdot (fX_2 - Y_2),$$

and we obtain finally $fX_2 - Y_2 = 0$. This completes the proof that fN is open.

II. *For any X in N, the inverse of $d_X f$ satisfies the condition for being the differential of f^{-1} at $Y = fX$.* This amounts to proving

$$\lim_{fX' \to fX} \frac{X' - X - (d_X f)^{-1}(fX' - fX)}{|fX' - fX|} = 0.$$

Regarding X as a fixed vector in N, we set

$$S = \frac{X' - X - (d_X f)^{-1}(fX' - fX)}{|fX' - fX|},$$

$$R = \frac{fX' - fX - (d_X f)(X' - X)}{|X' - X|},$$

for X' in N and $X' \neq X$. Then,

$$S = -\frac{|X' - X|}{|fX' - fX|}(d_X f)^{-1}R.$$

From relation (5) we have $|fX' - fX| \geq M|X' - X|$. Hence, if $\lim_{X' \to X} S = 0$, it follows that $\lim_{fX' \to fX} S = 0$. Furthermore,

$$\frac{|X' - X|}{|fX' - fX|}$$

is bounded. Finally, since every linear transformation is continuous,

$$\lim_{X' \to X} (d_X f)^{-1} R = (d_X f)^{-1} \lim_{X' \to X} R = (d_X f)^{-1} 0 = 0.$$

We conclude that $\lim_{X' \to X} S = 0$, and the proof of part II is complete. We now know f^{-1} is differentiable, it only remains to prove that

III. f^{-1} *is continuously differentiable.* We must prove that, for any X_1 in N, if $Y_1 = fX_1$, then

$$\lim_{Y \to Y_1} d_Y f^{-1} = d_{Y_1} f^{-1}.$$

Since we have established that $d_Y f^{-1} = (d_X f)^{-1}$, it suffices to prove that

$$\lim_{X \to X_1} (d_X f)^{-1} = (d_{X_1} f)^{-1}.$$

For convenience, we abbreviate $d_X f = L_X$. By setting $Y = L_X^{-1} Z$ in inequality (5), we obtain

$$|L_X^{-1} Z| \leq \frac{1}{M} |Z|, \qquad \text{for any } X \text{ in } N, \text{ and } Z \text{ in } \mathfrak{R}^n. \tag{8}$$

Choose $\epsilon > 0$ arbitrarily, and, using the continuous differentiability of f at X_1, choose $\delta_1 > 0$ such that the set N_1 consisting of all X with $|X - X_1| < \delta_1$ is contained in N and such that if X is in N_1, then $\|L_X - L_{X_1}\| < \epsilon M^2$. Then, by relations (2) and (8), we have, for any X in N_1 and Z in $\mathfrak{R}^n$,

$$|(L_X^{-1} - L_{X_1}^{-1})Z| = |L_X^{-1}(L_X - L_{X_1})L_{X_1}^{-1} Z|$$

$$\leq \frac{1}{M} |(L_X - L_{X_1})L_{X_1}^{-1} Z|$$

$$\leq \epsilon M |L_{X_1}^{-1} Z| \leq \epsilon |Z|.$$

It follows that $\|L_X^{-1} - L_{X_1}^{-1}\| \leq \epsilon$, and the proof is complete.

It is worth remarking that the hypothesis that f be continuously differentiable at points other than X_0 is used in the above proof only to show that the differentiable inverse function f^{-1} is continuously differentiable on all of fN. If we alter the conditions of Theorem 3.4 to read that f is a differentiable function with continuous differentiability at X_0, then the only change in the conclusions of the theorem is that f^{-1} is a differentiable function and continuously differentiable at the one point $Y_0 = fX_0$.

4. EXISTENCE OF THE RIEMANN INTEGRAL

We shall prove the existence theorem for multiple integrals that is given in Theorem 2.1, Section 2, of Chapter 4. The statement of the theorem is as follows.

> **Theorem.** Let f be defined and bounded on a bounded set B in $\mathfrak{R}^n$, and let the boundary of B be contained in finitely many pieces of smooth surface. If f is continuous on B except perhaps on finitely many pieces of smooth surface, then f is integrable over B. The integral $\int_B f \, dV$ is independent of the values of f on any piece of smooth surface.

By a **piece of smooth surface** in $\mathfrak{R}^n$ is meant the image of a closed bounded set under a continuously differentiable function $\mathfrak{R}^m \xrightarrow{\phi} \mathfrak{R}^n$, $m < n$.

We turn first to the problem of showing why pieces of smooth surface are negligible when they lie in the domain of integration of a function. The box norm, denoted by double vertical bars $\| \ \|$, is used frequently in this section because of the convenience of having rectangular "spheres" in defining the integral. The proofs may, of course, be adapted to any norm.

4.1 Theorem. Let $\mathfrak{R}^m \xrightarrow{g} \mathfrak{R}^n$ be continuously differentiable. (We do not assume $m < n$.) Then, for every closed bounded subset K in the domain of g, there is a constant M such that, for all X and Y in K,

$$\| \, gY - gX \, \| \le M \, \| \, Y - X \, \|.$$

Proof. Denote by $K \times K$ the subset of $\mathfrak{R}^{2m}$ consisting of all $2m$-tuples (X, Y) such that X and Y are each in K. It is easy to see that $K \times K$ is closed and bounded in $\mathfrak{R}^{2m}$. Consider the function

$$F(X, Y) = \begin{cases} \dfrac{\| \, gY - gX - (d_X g)\,(Y - X) \, \|}{\| \, Y - X \, \|}, & \text{if } X \neq Y. \\ 0, & \text{if } X = Y. \end{cases}$$

We shall show that F is continuous. At points (X, Y) for which $X \neq Y$, F is continuous because both numerator and denominator are continuous and the denominator is not zero. On the other hand, if both X and Y tend to some point Z in the domain of g, then (X, Y) tends to (Z, Z), and we have to show that F tends to zero. We can apply the mean-value theorem, Theorem 6.2 of Chapter 2, to the coordinate functions g_k of g, $k = 1, \ldots, n$. We have, for each k,

$$g_k Y - g_k X = (d_{X_k} g_k)(Y - X),$$

for X and Y in a sufficiently small neighborhood of Z and for some X_k on the segment joining X and Y. Then

$$\| gY - gX - d_X g(Y - X) \|$$

$$= \max_{1 \leq k \leq n} | (d_{X_k} g_k)(Y - X) - (d_X g_k)(Y - X) |$$

$$= \max_{1 \leq k \leq n} \left| \sum_{j=1}^{m} \left(\frac{\partial g_k}{\partial x_j} X_k - \frac{\partial g_k}{\partial x_j} X \right)(y_j - x_j) \right|$$

$$\leq \max_{1 \leq k \leq n} \left| \sum_{j=1}^{m} \left(\frac{\partial g_k}{\partial x_j} X_k - \frac{\partial g_k}{\partial x_j} X \right) \right| \| Y - X \|.$$

Since the partial derivatives are continuous, and each X_k tends to Z as X and Y do, it follows that

$$\lim_{(X,Y) \to (Z,Z)} F(X, Y) = 0.$$

We conclude that F is continuous.

Since F is continuous on the closed bounded set $K \times K$, it attains its maximum value M', and so $F(X, Y) \leq M'$, for X and Y in K. Hence,

$$\| gY - gX - d_X g(Y - X) \| \leq M' \| Y - X \|,$$

and the inequality $\| A \| - \| B \| \leq \| A - B \|$ shows that

$$\| gY - gX \| \leq M' \| Y - X \| + \| d_X g(Y - X) \|, \tag{1}$$

for all X and Y in K. But we have

$$\| d_X g(Y - X) \| = \max_{1 \leq k \leq n} \left| \sum_{j=1}^{m} \left(\frac{\partial g_k}{\partial x_j} \right) X(y_j - x_j) \right|$$

$$\leq \max_{1 \leq k \leq n} \left| \sum_{j=1}^{m} \frac{\partial g_k}{\partial x_j} X \right| \| Y - X \|.$$

The continuity of the partial derivatives on K implies the existence of a constant M'' such that

$$\| d_X g(Y - X) \| \leq M'' \| Y - X \|.$$

This inequality together with (1) implies that

$$\| gY - gX \| \leq (M' + M'') \| Y - X \|, \qquad X, Y \text{ in } K,$$

which was to be shown.

4.2 Theorem. If S is a piece of smooth surface in $\mathfrak{R}^n$, then S can be covered by finitely many coordinate rectangles of arbitrarily small total content. The covering can be done in such a way that no point of S lies on the boundary of the union of the set of covering rectangles.

Proof. The case in which S is just a point is trivially true, so we assume $m \geq 1$. The piece of surface S is the image under a continuously differentiable function $\mathfrak{R}^m \xrightarrow{g} \mathfrak{R}^n$, $m < n$, of a closed bounded set K in $\mathfrak{R}^m$. We enclose K in a cube of side length s, and subdivide the cube into smaller cubes of side length s/N, where N is an integer bigger than 1. There are N^m of these little cubes. On each of the little cubes that contain any points of K we have by Theorem 4.1

$$\| gX - gY \| \leq M \| X - Y \| \leq M\frac{s}{N},$$

where M is a constant depending only on K and g. This means that the image under g of the part of K in each little cube is contained in a cube of side length $M(s/N)$. Then the surface S is contained in N^m cubes each of volume $(Ms/N)^n$. The total volume of the cubes containing S is at most $N^m(Ms/N)^n = (Ms)^n/N^{n-m}$. Since $n > m$, the total volume can be made arbitrarily small by making N large. By enlarging the side length of each covering rectangle to $(Ms + 1)/N$, the last condition of the theorem can be met.

As a corollary, we get the fact that *a piece of smooth surface has zero content.*

Our application of the next theorem will be restricted to real-valued functions, but the proof is no different for vector-valued functions.

4.3 Theorem. If f is a continuous function defined on a closed bounded set C, then f is uniformly continuous on C. That is, given any $\epsilon > 0$, there is a $\delta > 0$ such that whenever $| X - Y | < \delta$, then $|fX - fY| < \epsilon$.

Proof. Let $\epsilon > 0$ be given. For each X in C, let $\Delta_\epsilon(X)$ be the set of real numbers d, $0 < d \leq 1$, such that for Y and Z in C, $|fY - fZ| < \epsilon$ whenever $| Y - X | < d$ and $| Z - X | < d$. Since

$$|fY - fZ| \leq |fY - fX| + |fX - fY|,$$

the continuity of f at X implies that $\Delta_\epsilon(X)$ is not empty. Define

$$\delta_\epsilon(X) = supremum \text{ of } \Delta_\epsilon(X).$$

We shall first prove that δ_ϵ is a continuous function of X on C. Fix X and let X' be such that $| X - X' | < \frac{1}{2}\delta_\epsilon(X)$. Then the ball of radius $\delta_0 = \delta_\epsilon(X) - | X - X' |$ about X' is contained in the ball of radius $\delta_\epsilon(X)$ about X. This implies, by the definition of δ_ϵ, that $\delta_0 \leq \delta_\epsilon(X')$, or that

$$\delta_\epsilon(X) - \delta_\epsilon(X') \leq |X - X'|.$$

Notice that the last inequality depends only on having $|X - X'| < \delta_\epsilon(X)$. However, by the stronger inequality $|X - X'| < \frac{1}{2}\delta_\epsilon(X)$, the ball of radius $\delta_\epsilon(X')$ about X' contains X. Therefore the role of X can be interchanged with that of X' to give

$$\delta_\epsilon(X') - \delta_\epsilon(X) \leq |X - X'|.$$

Putting this together with the previously obtained inequality, we get

$$|\delta_\epsilon(X) - \delta_\epsilon(X')| \leq |X - X'|,$$

from which follows the continuity of δ_ϵ at X.

Let δ be the minimum value of the continuous function δ_ϵ on the closed bounded set C. Since δ_ϵ is positive, δ is also positive. It follows from the definitions of $\Delta_\epsilon(X)$ and of *supremum* that, for each X in C, the number $\delta_\epsilon(X)$ is a member of the set $\Delta_\epsilon(X)$. Finally, therefore, suppose that $|X - Y| < \delta$. Then

$$|X - Y| < \delta \leq \delta_\epsilon(X),$$

and so

$$|fX - fY| < \epsilon.$$

This completes the proof.

Now we can prove the existence theorem for integrals stated at the beginning of the section. Suppose that f and B are as described in the hypotheses. We must produce a number which we shall prove is the Riemann integral of f over B. Let f_B be the function f extended to be zero outside B. For an arbitrary grid G covering B, let R_k be the kth bounded rectangle of G, and let f_k be the *infimum* of f_B on R_k. Define

$$\underline{S}(G) = \sum_{k=1}^{N} f_k V(R_k).$$

Similarly, define

$$\bar{S}(G) = \sum_{k=1}^{N} \bar{f}_k V(R_k),$$

where $\bar{f}_k$ is the *supremum* of f_B on R_k. Then clearly

$$\underline{S}(G) \leq \sum_{k=1}^{N} (f_B X_k) V(R_k) \leq \bar{S}(G), \tag{2}$$

if the Riemann sum is an arbitrary one formed from the grid G. Furthermore, if G' is a grid consisting of a subdivision of the rectangles of a grid G, we have

$$\underline{S}(G) \leq \underline{S}(G') \leq \bar{S}(G') \leq \bar{S}(G).$$

In particular, if G and G'' are two grids, and G' contains all the rectangles of both of them, then

$$\underline{S}(G) \leq \underline{S}(G') \leq \bar{S}(G') \leq \bar{S}(G''). \tag{3}$$

We define

$$I_B f = supremum \text{ of } \underline{S}(G),$$

where the *supremum* is taken over all grids G covering B. We have from relation (3) that

$$\underline{S}(G) \leq I_B f \leq \bar{S}(G),$$

or

$$- \bar{S}(G) \leq -I_B f \leq -\underline{S}(G).$$

This inequality added to (2) gives

$$\left| \sum_{k=1}^{N} (f_B X_k) V(R_k) - I_B f \right| \leq \bar{S}(G) - \underline{S}(G),$$

in which the Riemann sum has been formed from the grid G.

Now all we have to do is show that $\bar{S}(G) - \underline{S}(G)$ can be made arbitrarily small if the mesh of G is made small enough. Then according to the definition of the integral we will have shown that the integral of f over B exists and is $I_B f$. Let ϵ be a positive number. By Theorem 4.2, we can cover the boundary of B, the smooth surfaces containing the discontinuity points of f, and any other smooth surface on which we would like to disregard the values of f, with finitely many open rectangles $R_1', \ldots, R_l'$, of total content less than ϵ. On the part of B not covered by these rectangles, f is continuous, so by Theorem 4.3 there is a $\delta > 0$ such that $\bar{f}_k - \underline{f}_k < \epsilon$ over any rectangle R_k belonging to a grid with mesh less than δ. By making the mesh still smaller, say less than δ', we can arrive at a mesh size such that the rectangles $R_1', \ldots, R_l'$ are always contained in finitely many rectangles $R_1'', \ldots, R_m''$ of any grid with mesh less than δ' and such that the total content of the latter rectangles is less than 2ϵ. Suppose that the remaining rectangles of such a grid G are $R_1, \ldots, R_n$, that $|f| < M$ on B, and that B is contained in a rectangle of volume N. Then

$$\bar{S}(G) - \underline{S}(G) = \sum_{k=1}^{m} (\bar{f}_k'' - \underline{f}_k'') V(R_k'') + \sum_{k=1}^{n} (\bar{f}_k - \underline{f}_k) V(R_k)$$

$$< (2M)(2\epsilon) + \epsilon N = \epsilon(4M + N).$$

Thus we have made

$$\left| \sum_{k=1}^{N} (f_B X_k) V(R_k) - I_B f \right| < \epsilon(4M + N),$$

for any grid of small enough mesh. Since ϵ can be made arbitrarily small the proof is complete.

5. THE CHANGE-OF-VARIABLE FORMULA FOR INTEGRALS

This section contains a proof of the change-of-variable theorem (Theorem 3.1) of Chapter 4.

Theorem. Let $\mathfrak{U}^n \xrightarrow{T} \mathfrak{R}^n$ be a continuously differentiable transformation. Let R be a set in $\mathfrak{U}^n$ having a boundary consisting of finitely many pieces of smooth surface. Suppose that R and its boundary are contained in the interior of the domain of T and that

(a) T is one-one on R.

(b) J, the Jacobian determinant of T, is different from zero on R, except perhaps on finitely many pieces of smooth surface

Then, if the function f is bounded and continuous on TR (the image of R under T)

$$\int_{TR} f \, dV = \int_{R} (f \circ T) \, |J| \, dV.$$

If f should be discontinuous on a smooth surface S contained in R, then the formula can be applied to R with S deleted. The subsequent inclusion of S and TS in the domains of integration will affect neither integral.

*Proof.** We first consider the special case in which f is the constant function 1, and T is linear. Then T can be written as the product of elementary linear transformations of two types: numerical multiplication of a coordinate,

$$M(x_1, \ldots, x_k, \ldots, x_n) = (x_1, \ldots, ax_k, \ldots, x_n), \tag{1}$$

and addition of one coordinate to another,

$$A(x_1, \ldots, x_k, \ldots, x_n) = (x_1, \ldots, x_k + x_j, \ldots, x_n). \tag{2}$$

* The proof we give is contained in one by J. Schwartz, "The Formula for Change of Variable in a Multiple Integral," *American Math. Monthly,* vol. 61, no. 2 (February, 1954).

By looking at the matrices of these transformations, it is easy to see that $\det M = a$ and $\det A = 1$. Once the special case of the theorem has been verified for each of these two types, it follows for arbitrary nonsingular linear transformations by successive application of the product rule for determinants. Let R_k be the projection of R on the subspace perpendicular to the kth coordinate axis. For each point $(x_1, \ldots, x_{k-1}, x_{k+1}, \ldots, x_n)$ in R_k, let I_k be the set of all x_k such that $(x_1, \ldots, x_n)$ is in R. For the linear transformation (1), we have by iterated integration

$$\int_R |J|\, dV = \int_{R_k} dV_{n-1} \int_{I_k} |a|\, dx_k.$$

If we denote by $|a|\, I_k$ the set of all numbers of the form $|a|\, x_k$, where x_k is in I_k, we obtain by 1-dimensional change of variable

$$\int_{R_k} dV_{n-1} \int_{I_k} |a|\, dx_k = \int_{R_k} dV_{n-1} \int_{|a|I_k} du_k$$

$$= \int_{MR} dV.$$

For the linear transformation (2), we denote by $I_k + x_j$ the set of all numbers $x_k + x_j$, where x_k is in I_k. Then iterated integration and 1-dimensional change of variable yield

$$\int_R |J|\, dV = \int_R dV = \int_{R_k} dV_{n-1} \int_{I_k} dx_k$$

$$= \int_{R_k} dV_{n-1} \int_{I_k + x_j} dx_k = \int_{AR} dV.$$

This completes the proof of the theorem for linear transformations T and constant functions f.

In proving the general theorem, we shall use the following norm for the matrix (l_{ij}) of a linear transformation L. Let

$$\| L \| = \max_{1 \le i \le n} \sum_{j=1}^{n} |l_{ij}|.$$

If we also use the box norm $\| X \|$ for vectors, then $\| LX \| \le \| L \|\, \| X \|$. Suppose now that C is a cube of side length $2s$ contained in R and with center P. We have by the mean-value theorem

$$T_k X - T_k P = d_{Y_k} T_k (X - P), \qquad X \text{ in } C, k = 1, \ldots, n,$$

where the T_k are the coordinate functions of T, and Y_k is some point on the segment joining X to P. Then

$$\| TX - TP \| \leq \max_{Y \text{ in } C} \| d_Y T \| \, \| X - P \|,$$

which implies that TC is contained in the cube defined by

$$\| Z - TP \| \leq s \, \{ \max_{Y \text{ in } C} \| d_Y T \| \}.$$

Because of this, we have

$$V(TC) \leq \{ \max_{Y \text{ in } C} \| d_Y T \| \}^n V(C). \tag{3}$$

Notice that if L is an arbitrary one-one linear transformation and S is a set bounded by finitely many smooth surfaces then $V(LS) = | \det L | \, V(S)$. This follows from the special case of the change-of-variable theorem that we have just proved for linear transformations. Now we take $S = TC$ and $L = (d_X T)^{-1}$. Then, applying (3) with T replaced by $(d_X T)^{-1} \circ T$, we get

$$| \det (d_X T)^{-1} | \, V(TC) = V((d_X T)^{-1} \circ TC)$$

$$\leq \{ \max_{Y \text{ in } C} \| (d_X T)^{-1} \circ d_Y T \| \}^n V(C),$$

or

$$V(TC) \leq | \det (d_X T) | \, \{ \max_{Y \text{ in } C} \| (d_X T)^{-1} \circ d_Y T \| \}^n V(C) \tag{4}$$

Let the cube C be subdivided into a finite set $C_1, \ldots, C_N$ of non-overlapping cubes with centers $X_1, \ldots, X_N$, and suppose that δ is the maximum side length of all of them. Apply (4) to each C_k, taking $X = X_k$ in each case. Addition gives

$$V(TC) \leq \sum_{k=1}^{N} | \det (d_{X_k} T) | \, \{ \max_{Y \text{ in } C_k} \| (d_{X_k} T)^{-1} \circ d_Y T \| \}^n V(C_k).$$

Since T is continuously differentiable, $d_Y T$ is a continuous function of Y, and $(d_{X_k} T)^{-1} \circ d_Y T$ approaches the identity as Y tends to X_k. Then there is a function $h(\delta)$, tending to zero with δ such that

$$\{ \max_{Y \text{ in } C_k} \| (d_{X_k} T)^{-1} \circ d_Y T \| \}^n \leq 1 + h(\delta).$$

This gives

$$V(TC) \leq [1 + h(\delta)] \sum_{k=1}^{N} | \det (d_{X_k} T) | \, V(C_k).$$

As δ approaches zero, the sum on the right approaches $\int_C |J| \, dV$, because det $(d_X T) = J(X)$. Then the last inequality becomes

$$\int_{TC} dV \le \int_C |J| \, dV. \tag{5}$$

Having proved this last inequality, we use it to prove the formula for more general sets than cubes. We shall assume $f \ge 0$. The general case follows by considering the positive and negative parts of f separately and adding the resulting formula for each part. Let G be a cubical grid covering R and having mesh δ. Let $C_1, \ldots, C_N$ be the cubes of G that are contained in R. If we let R_N be the part of R that is not contained in any of the cubes C_k, then $R = C_1 \cup \ldots \cup C_N \cup R_N$. Whenever Y_k is a point of C_k and $X_k = TY_k$, we shall write f_k for $(f \circ T) Y_k$ and fX_k. Then because of (5), we have

$$\sum_{k=1}^N f_k \int_{TC_k} dV \le \sum_{k=1}^N f_k \int_{C_k} |J| \, dV.$$

From this it follows that

$$D = \int_{TR} f \, dV - \int_R (f \circ T) |J| \, dV$$

$$\le \int_{TR} f \, dV - \sum_{k=1}^N f_k \int_{TC_k} dV + \sum_{k=1}^N f_k \int_{C_k} |J| \, dV$$

$$- \int_R (f \circ T) |J| \, dV.$$

Since $TR = TC_1 \cup \ldots \cup TC_k \cup TR_N$, we have

$$D \le \int_{TR_N} f \, dV + \sum_{k=1}^N \int_{TC_k} (f - f_k) \, dV$$

$$+ \sum_{k=1}^N \int_{C_k} (f_k - f \circ T) |J| \, dV - \int_{R_N} (f \circ T) |J| \, dV.$$

Because T is continuously differentiable it follows from Theorem 4.1 of this appendix that there is a constant B for which

$$\| TX - TY \| \le B \| X - Y \|, \qquad \text{for all } X \text{ and } Y \text{ in } R. \tag{6}$$

Now let ϵ be a positive number. Since f is uniformly continuous on TR (apply Theorem 4.3 of this appendix to TR together with its boundary) we can choose δ, the mesh of G, small enough that

$$| (f \circ T)Y - f_k | \leq \epsilon, \qquad \text{for } Y \text{ in } C_k, \, k = 1, \ldots, N.$$

By using (6) and if necessary taking δ still smaller, we can get

$$| fX - f_k | \leq \epsilon, \qquad \text{for } X \text{ in } TC_k, \, k = 1, \ldots, N.$$

Then

$$D \leq \int_{TR_N} f \, dV - \int_{R_N} (f \circ T) \mid J \mid dV + \epsilon \{ V(TR) + V(R) \}.$$

Since R is assumed to have a volume, there is a mesh such that $V(R_N) \leq \epsilon$. Again using (6) and if necessary decreasing the mesh again we can get $V(TR_N) \leq B^n \epsilon$. Then

$$D \leq \epsilon \{ MB^n + M + V(TR) + V(R) \},$$

where M is a number such that $f \leq M$ on TR and $(f \circ T) \mid J \mid \leq M$ on R. Since ϵ is arbitrary we must have $D \leq 0$, that is,

$$\int_{TR} f \, dV \leq \int_R (f \circ T) \mid J \mid dV.$$

If we apply this last inequality to the situation in which T is replaced by T^{-1}, we get

$$\int_R (f \circ T) \mid J \mid dV \leq \int_{TR} (f \circ T \circ T^{-1}) \mid J \circ T^{-1} \mid \mid J' \mid dV,$$

where J' is the Jacobian determinant of the transformation T^{-1}. But $(J \circ T^{-1})(J') = 1$, so

$$\int_{TR} f \, dV \leq \int_R (f \circ T) \mid J \mid dV \leq \int_{TR} f \, dV,$$

and the desired equality has been proved.

If J is zero on some piece of smooth surface S in R, then the above proof breaks down, because T^{-1} may fail to be continuously differentiable. However, by Theorem 4.2 of this appendix S can be enclosed in the interior of a union U of finitely many rectangles of arbitrarily small content v, and the image surface TS will be contained in an image region TU having content at most $B^n v$, where

B is the constant of relation (6). Then applying the change of variable formula to the region R with U deleted, we get

$$\left| \int_{TR} f \, dV - \int_{R} (f \circ T) \mid J \mid dV \right|$$

$$\leq \left| \int_{TU} f \, dV \right| + \left| \int_{U} (f \circ T) \mid J \mid dV \right|$$

$$\leq MB^n v + Mv,$$

where $\mid f \mid$ and $\mid f \circ T \mid \mid J \mid$ are both less than M. Letting v tend to zero, we get the final equality.

Index